Witherbys Seamanship International Ltd.

Ship Stability for Mates/Masters

Martin A. Rhodes (BSc. Hons)
Lecturer, Ship Stability,
Glasgow College of Nautical Studies

WITHERBYS PUBLISHING
Seamanship INTERNATIONAL

First published 2003 by Witherbys Seamanship International Ltd,
4, Dunlop Square, Deans Estate,
Livingston, West Lothian, EH54 8SB
E-mail: info@seamanship.com

ISBN 0-9534379-3-0

FOREWORD

It has been my privilege over recent years to be engaged in a wide variety of training activities for the development and enhancement of the professional skills of seafarers. The industry rarely witnesses such dramatic shifts in a cultural awareness, as we have seen in recent years, in recognition of seafarers professional skills. These skills are not only a foundation in a difficult industry, but must also be maintained throughout a seafarers working life.

Seamanship International has developed a series of professional educational products that fit the needs for this continual development. Indeed, those of us who have learnt the hard school of ship stability by traditional and well tested methods, will be refreshed by this training material which encompasses both traditional and basic concepts with a blend of current and relevant issues for the present day Deck Officer.

This ship stability book, I believe, will become a desk companion to many a ships officer and will be a must-have for any ships library. I commend Seamanship International in their approach, to that which is without doubt, one of the most hazardous and commercially critical subjects in the maritime business.

Capt. Simon Kembery. BSc.(Hons). FNI.
Group Training & Planning Manager
V.Ships

CONTENTS

INTRODUCTION

This book of the CD-ROM software of the same name is aimed at students studying for professional merchant navy deck officer certificates of competency. *Ship Stability for Mates/Masters* covers the syllabus requirements for the current *Scottish Qualifications Authority (SQA)* examinations (conducted on behalf of the *Maritime and Coastguard Agency (MCA)*) up to STCW Chief Mate/Master Reg. II/2 (Unlimited) standard. It also covers the content of *HND Ship Stability Units* being currently offered by UK colleges as part of the underpinning knowledge required for certification to Officer of the Watch (OOW) and Chief Mate levels (STCW 95*)*. Because this text is likely to be used by students not serving on UK registered ships, or who might be attending non-UK college courses, IMO regulation requirements are also quoted where appropriate in addition to the MCA requirements.

It has been my experience that many students, resulting from their lack of mathematical ability, often meet the subject of *Ship Stability* with apprehension. This is the main reason for the downfall of many students studying this subject. This book version of the CD-ROM software is designed to address this problem by covering the subject content in the simplest way I believe possible and at an assumed mathematical level that is appropriate for a learner studying independently. Solutions to worked examples are broken down into sequential logical steps, each step being explained in as simple a format I think possible. The solutions given set an example for the extent and type of presentation that should be adopted for examination purposes.

All examples used are designed to be of a type and standard that are likely to be encountered in real SQA examinations. It is this approach which gives this work an added advantage over some of the currently available and somewhat dated text books on the subject of *Ship Stability*, where a high level of mathematical ability is often assumed. It has often been the experience of many students to encounter worked examples in text books that are not sufficiently broken down to enforce proper understanding. Relevant formulae are derived where appropriate to enhance understanding.

Suggested approaches to studying this subject

Students often complain to me that the subject *Ship Stability* is one of the most difficult examination subjects in which to succeed, this is certainly my experience evidenced by student results in terms of both internal college assessments and external SQA examinations. If the syllabuses are considered, I feel that it is the sheer *volume* of topics that need to be learned, and not the mathematical complexity of any single topic area that presents the problems. In light of this I will make the following suggestions to help you succeed.

Approaches to study

1. Study starts on *day one* of the college course you are attending. At the end of each day read over the notes for the topics covered during that day, do not try to *learn* them, simply read them through and verify that you *understand* what is being said. Learning comes naturally after *reading* and *understanding*. If there are areas that are unclear, make a note of them and ask for clarification at the earliest opportunity. Reference to this text book might offer an alternative, more understandable explanation of any topic area that you are having difficulty with.

2. Always attempt questions provided on tutorial sheets as soon as possible after the relevant topic(s) have been taught. For calculation type questions always indicate each step and show all working for the questions; your answers will provide excellent reference material for revision purposes later on. Past SQA examination papers are an invaluable source of revision material.

3. Many questions require you to recall facts, particularly when t comes to questioning knowledge of current legislation. For example a question might ask:

State the stability information that must be provided to the master under the current Load Line regulations.

My approach to this would be to read Schedule 6 in MSN 1752(M) (where this is stated) a number of times. Each time that you do this, do *not* try to learn it, quite simply the more times that you read it the more of the information will be retained in your memory. It's like watching a film five or more times, eventually you will remember the whole story!

4. In class, if the lecturer says something that you do not understand then *ask!* Don't ever feel embarrassed or stupid, if you don't understand what the lecturer is talking about, you can guarantee that perhaps half the others in the class don't understand either!

5. Try not to study on your own all the time. It helps if you find a suitable 'study partner' so that you both benefit from the improved understanding of different topic areas that each of you will have. *A problem shared is a problem halved!*

6. Don't over do it! Aim to study at no more than half-hour intervals at a time and find an activity that you can do for 15-30 minutes in between study periods (for example, plan to watch a few favorite TV programs to ensure suitable short study breaks in the evenings.) Failing this, you will end up making careless mistakes in calculations, getting more and more frustrated and making progressively slower progress.

7. If you are studying in the evening, do not go straight to bed afterwards. Your mind will still be 'going round and round' - thinking too much about your studies and problems. Do something else, maybe take a walk or get exercise. Choose something that will relax you, and make you think of other things. Even go to the pub for a pint to unwind (*one* pint that is, not one dozen!)

8. Stay healthy: get enough sleep and eat sensibly. Take regular exercise; you need exercise to work well.

9. Always think positive, don't think about the future and the possibility of failing. I have always believed that exams are there to be failed by some, if everybody were to pass them; there would be no point in having them! I have failed exams myself in the past, so what! I simply took them again and passed with higher marks than I would have ever anticipated passing with first time around – problem solved!

10. Simply do your best; you cannot do more than that!

Approaches to passing exams

As long as you have done sufficient study preparation, you should be feeling confident; so now it is simply a case of going for it!

1. The night before relaxation is the key. No last minute cramming. Sort out the things that you need to take with you to the exam. Sort out the clothes you are going to wear. Don't forget your watch. Double-check the time and the venue. Try to have an early night.

2. Eat breakfast/lunch, even though food might be the last thing on your mind on the morning of the examination. Food 'feeds the brain' and increases mental awareness.

3. Allow extra time for traveling. Unexpected things can happen so allow an extra 15-30 minutes or so just in case.

4. Get your mind in focus. Once in the exam room organize your pens and pencils and get yourself comfortable. Take some really deep breaths and stay calm. Look at the others around you; it helps you to remember that everybody else in the room with you is in the same boat!

5. Keep your energy levels high. The SQA examination lasts for three hours. *Take short breaks.* Put your pen down and flex your hand a few times to avoid getting cramp of pain while writing. *Feed your brain* – mental activity requires your brain to have a sufficient supply of glucose – this is why it is very important to eat before the exam. Take sweets in that you can suck *quietly*.

6. It is very important to manage your time effectively during the exam. By using your time correctly you can increase your chances of achieving high marks. Spending too much time on one question means that marks available from other questions maybe reduced or lost totally. Place your watch on the table so that you are always aware of what time is still remaining. Allocate a certain amount of time to a particular question. Avoid continuing on for anything in excess of five minutes more than the allocated time because you will start to eat into the time available to answer the other questions. If a question is not completed, leave it, progress on to the other questions and return to this answer when you have time remaining at the end or as you recall other relevant detail.

7. The SQA examination involves a three hour paper with six questions, usually three calculation type questions and three descriptive or theory type questions. If you have done sufficient revision you will have plenty of time to answer all the questions, quite often a question can be answered fully in twenty minutes, leaving a spare ten minutes per question for checking over your work at the end.

8. When you hear the words *'You may begin'* – STOP! Do not charge straight into answering the questions, read each question carefully and make brief notes on how to approach the questions on scrap paper provided (or in the last page of the examination booklet, you can cross these out at the end). Choose an easy question to start with, it will boost your confidence at the beginning of the exam, the time when you will be most nervous and this will help put you at ease.

9. Many students concentrate on obtaining full marks for the calculations and then hope that they scrape enough marks together from the descriptive questions. You must answer *all questions* and in some examinations it is a requirement that you achieve a minimum percentage of marks for *each question* (say 30%). In such cases, you could still fail despite having achieved the overall pass mark!

10. Always show all working and intermediate steps in calculations. Even though you might get the answer wrong, if the method is correct you will be awarded marks, in the event of a clerical error you will probably only lose a few marks. You will always get marks for parts of the question you have done correctly, this is why it is vital that all working be clearly shown.

11. When doing calculation questions fold the exam paper so that you can only see the question you are doing. I have seen so many assessment papers that have failed because the student took data from the wrong question!

12. It is really important that you thoroughly read the question before you start to write your answer. Read it through a couple of times and underline key words so that you are totally clear of what is being asked.

13. Answer the question correctly. You will be wasting valuable examination time if you include irrelevant information, which would be better spent on other questions. It is much better to aim for quality rather than quantity. You will not automatically get extra marks because you have written a ten-page essay rather than a five–page one. If the question is ambiguous make sure that you include a note as to how you have interpreted the meaning of the question.

14. Use short sentences. A good length of sentence is between 10–20 words. Clarify each of your main points. Avoid the use of fancy words or jargon. In general opt for plain English. However, do use the standard terminology used for the subject.

15. Legibility and neatness. Provided that your handwriting is reasonably neat, it is unlikely that handwriting will be a problem and that you will lose marks because your writing is unclear. Whilst you cannot totally ignore legibility and neatness, it is the content of what you are writing that is much more important than the way it looks. You must pay attention to the layout of your answers. Always use a ruler for diagrams and plenty of colours to make them more understandable. However, if your writing is untidy you must make efforts to improve it well before the exam date; if the marker cannot read your script you will get no marks!

16. Always start a new question on a new page and clearly indicate your final answers to all calculations.

17. It is quite normal to occasionally have difficulty in remembering one or two pieces of information. In such cases leave plenty of page space at the end of your answer, move on to another question and add to the question you are having difficulty with as the information comes to mind later on in the exam.

18. Never leave the examination room before the allocated time; use any additional time at the end to read through your answers and especially, to recheck calculations.

19. You must use a *non-programmable* calculator in the examination; it is usual practice for calculators to be checked before the examination.

20. Always assume that the marker *knows nothing about the subject!* Your answers should be written in such a way that anybody can reasonably understand what you are saying. *NEVER use the words 'etc.'* or *'and so on';* this is evidence of laziness and you will be penalised if you do not state all the detail required.

21. Post-exam review. There is no point in criticising yourself for things that you might have done wrong. You can review your performance with a view to coming up with constructive ideas that will help you to improve your performance if you have to resit the examination at a later date. You never know, you might have done better than you think!

I hope these points will help you.

Tell us what you think!
You, the reader of this book are our most important critic. I value any opinion or criticisms you might have on the presentation and content of this book. You may contact me via *Seamanship International Ltd.* to offer any opinions or suggestions for improvement; they will be gratefully received. Although great care has been taken in the writing and production of this publication, neither myself, nor *Seamanship International Ltd.* can accept responsibility for any errors, omissions or consequences which might result.

Good luck with your studies,

Martin A. Rhodes

SECTION 1 - BASIC PRINCIPLES

INTRODUCTION

This section introduces the laws governing flotation and will help in the understanding of why ships float. It will form the basic level of understanding necessary to complete this learning program.

Learning Objectives

On completion of this section the learner will achieve the following:

1. Understand the terms *Density*, *Mass* and *Volume* and be able to complete simple calculations relating to these terms.
2. Understand the laws governing flotation.
3. Understand the change in draught/freeboard that will occur when a box-shaped vessel moves between water of different densities.
4. Applies (2) and (3) to calculations based on the flotation of box-shaped vessels.

1.1 DENSITY, MASS AND VOLUME

1.1.1 Density

The *density* of any given substance is its *mass per unit volume.*

This can be expressed as:

$$\textbf{DENSITY} = \frac{\textbf{MASS}}{\textbf{VOLUME}}$$

For ship stability purposes the units commonly used are:

mass:	*tonnes (t)*
volume:	*cubic metres (m^3)*
density:	*tonnes per cubic metre (t/m^3)*

Rearranging the above formula gives:

$$\textbf{VOLUME} = \frac{\textbf{MASS}}{\textbf{DENSITY}}$$

and:

$$\textbf{MASS} = \textbf{VOLUME} \times \textbf{DENSITY}$$

Example 1

A piece of steel measures 0.1 m × 2.2 m × 6.0 m and has a density of 7.80 t/m³. Calculate its mass.

Solution

$$Mass = Volume \times Density$$
$$Mass = (0.1 \times 2.2 \times 6.0) \times 7.80$$
$$Mass = \textbf{10.296 tonnes}$$

Example 2

A block of aluminium measures 0.8 m × 0.6 m × 0.3 m and has a mass of 0.389 tonnes. Calculate the density of the aluminium.

Solution

$$Mass = Volume \times Density$$

Therefore:

$$Density = \frac{Mass}{Volume}$$

$$Density = \frac{0.389}{(0.8 \times 0.6 \times 0.3)} = \frac{0.389}{0.144} = \textbf{2.701 t/m}^3$$

Example 3

A rectangular ballast tank is 12 m long, 8 m wide and has a depth of 4 m. Calculate the mass of salt water ballast, density 1.025 t/m³, that can be loaded into the tank.

Solution

$$Mass = Volume \times Density$$
$$Mass = (12 \times 8 \times 4) \times 1.025$$
$$Mass = \textbf{393.6 tonnes}$$

Example 4

A fuel oil tank has length 4.2 m, breadth 3.4 m and a depth of 6.0 m. If 50 tonnes of fuel oil (density 0.84 t/m³) is loaded what will be the sounding (level) of oil in the tank?

Solution

$$Mass = Volume \times Density$$
$$50 = (4.2 \times 3.4 \times sounding) \times 0.84$$

$$Sounding = \frac{50}{4.2 \times 3.4 \times 0.84} = \textbf{4.168 m}$$

1.1.2 Relative Density (RD)

Quite often the *Relative Density (RD)* of a substance is quoted instead of *Density*. This is simply a *ratio* of the density of the substance in question to that of *Fresh Water*.

The density of fresh water is 1.000 t/m^3.

In the previous example the *density* of the oil was 0.84 t/m^3. The *relative density* of the oil was 0.84; in other words, the density of the oil is 0.84 times that of fresh water!

1.1.3 Density of water in which a ship typically floats

A ship is presumed to always float in water that lies in the following density range:

Fresh water (FW):	*1.000 t/m^3*	*(RD 1.000)*	*to*
Salt water (SW):	*1.025 t/m^3*	*(RD 1.025)*	

Water that lies between these two extremes is termed *Dock Water (DW).*

If a question states that a ship is floating in salt water (SW) then it can be always assumed that the water density is 1.025 t/m^3.

Similarly, if in fresh water (FW) then a density of 1.000 t/m^3 can be assumed.

1.2 THE LAWS OF FLOTATION

1.2.1 Archimedes' principle

This states that *when a body is wholly or partially immersed in a liquid, it experiences an upthrust (apparent loss of mass - termed Buoyancy force (Bf)), equal to the mass of liquid displaced.*

Consider a block of steel measuring 2 m $\times$ 2 m $\times$ 2 m that has a density of 7.84 t/m^3.

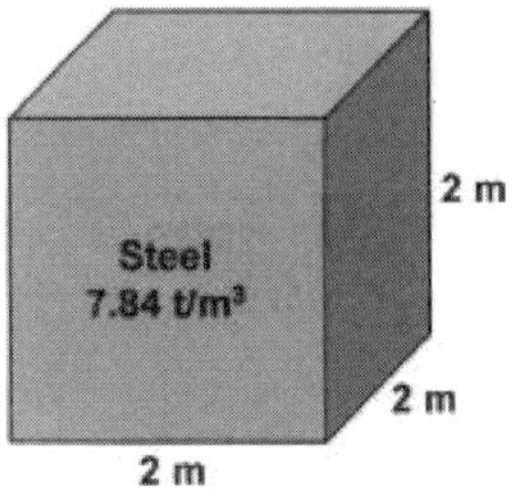

Fig. 1.1

Example 5 (a)

If the block were to be suspended by a ship's crane that has a very accurate load gauge, what mass would register on the gauge if the block were suspended over the ship's side in air?

Solution (a)

The block is suspended in air!

Since: Mass = Volume × Density;

Mass of the block = (2m × 2m × 2m) × 7.84 t/m^3 = ***62.72 t***

The crane driver now lowers the block so that it becomes *half submerged* in the dock water that has a density of 1.020 t/m^3.

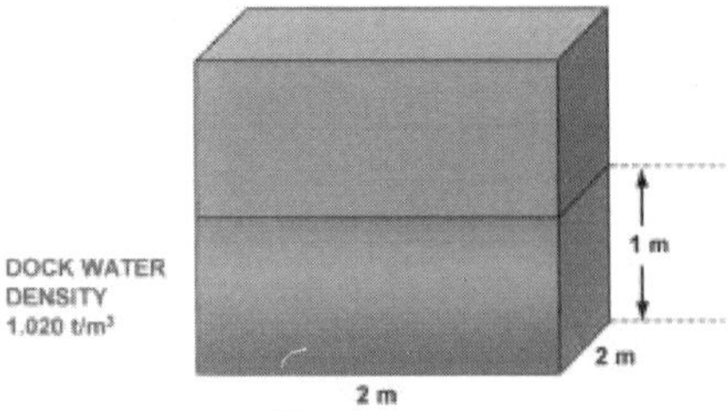

Fig 1.2

Example 5 (b)

What mass will the gauge now indicate?

Solution (b)

The block is now displacing a volume of water where: Volume of water displaced = (2m × 2m × 1m) = 4m^3

∴ *Mass of water displaced = Volume × Density of the dock water;*

= 4 m^3 × 1.020 t/m^3

= 4.08 t which represents the upthrust due to buoyancy force (Bf) created by the displaced water.

∴

Mass of block	*62.72 t*
Upthrust due to Bf	*4.08 t*
Gauge reading	***58.64 t***

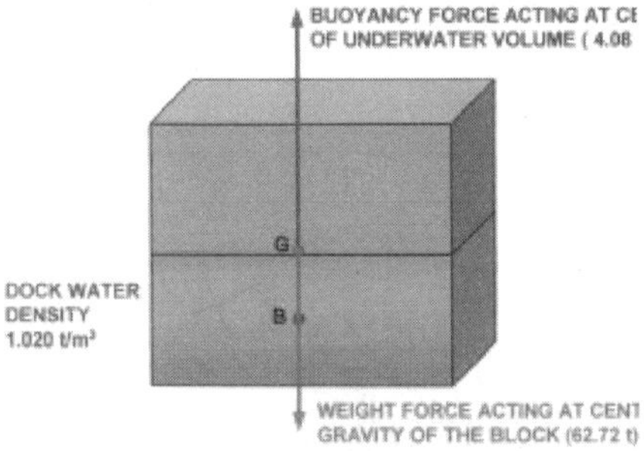

Fig. 1.3

Example 5 (c)

What mass will the gauge indicate if the crane driver now lowers the block so that it is completely submerged in the dock water?

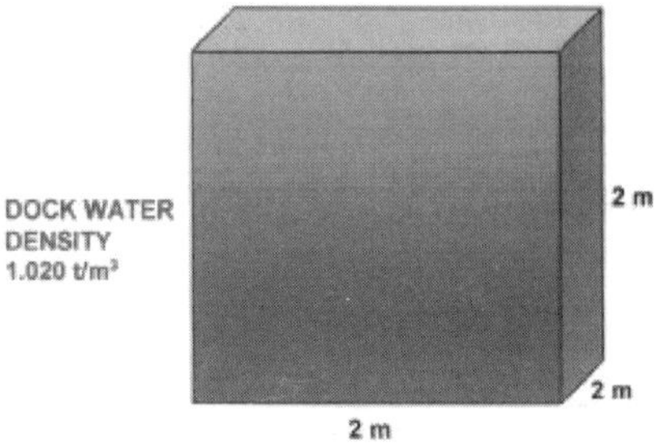

Fig. 1.4

Solution (c)

The block is now displacing a volume of water where:

Volume of water displaced = (2m × 2m × 2m)= 8m^3

Mass of water displaced = Volume × Density of the dock water;
= 8 m^3 × 1.020 t/m^3
= 8.16 t which represents the upthrust of the buoyancy force (Bf) created by the displaced water.

∴		
	Mass of block	*62.72 t*
	Upthrust due to Bf	*8.16 t*
	Gauge reading	***54.56 t***

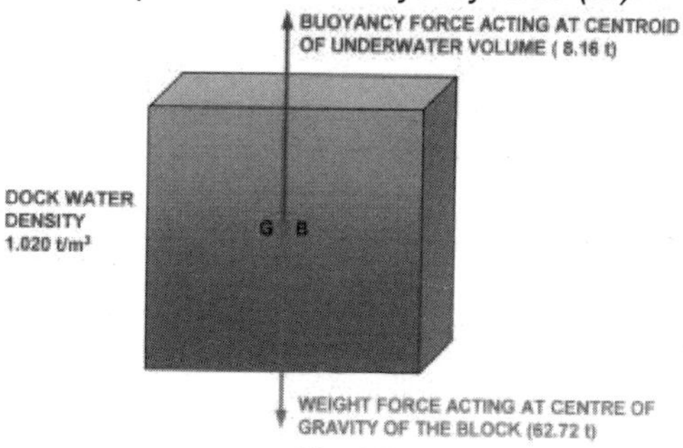

Fig.1.5

1.2.2 Law of flotation

This states that *every floating body displaces it's own mass of the liquid in which it floats.*

The *displacement* of a ship (or any floating object) is defined as *the number of tonnes of water it displaces*. It is usual to consider a ship displacing salt water of density 1.025 t/m^3, however, fresh water values of displacement (1.000 t/m^3) are often quoted in ship's hydrostatic data.

The *volume of displacement* is the *underwater volume of a ship* afloat i.e. the volume *below* the waterline.

To calculate the displacement (W) of a ship the following needs to be known:
The volume of displacement (V)
The density of the water in which it floats (ρ)

Since: MASS = VOLUME $\times$ DENSITY

the mass, or *displacement*, of a ship is calculated by:

DISPLACEMENT = VOLUME OF DISPLACEMENT $\times$ WATER DENSITY

i.e. $\mathbf{W = V \times \rho}$

1.2.3 Draught and Freeboard

Consider the ship shown.

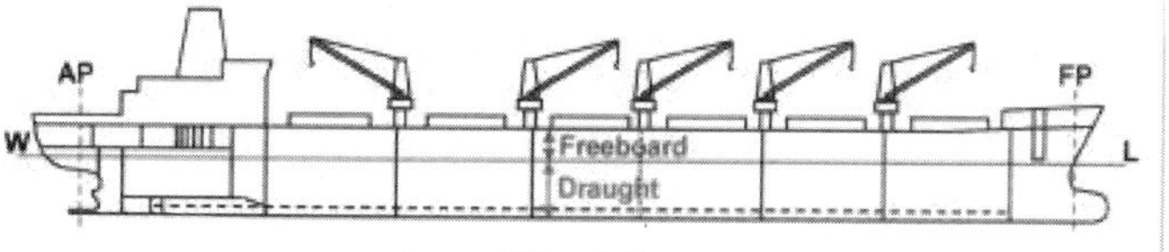

Fig. 1.6

Draught is the distance from the keel to the waterline (WL), as measured at the forward and aft ends of the ship. (More precisely the draught readings are taken as those read at the *Forward* and *Aft Perpendiculars* - these terms are defined in *Section 12)*. It is expressed in *metres*. If the draughts forward and aft are the same then the ship is said to be on an *even keel* (as shown).

Freeboard is the distance between the waterline (WL) and the top of the uppermost continuous deck. It is usually expressed in *millimetres* and is measured *amidships.*

Hull Depth = Draught + Freeboard

1.2.4 Reserve Buoyancy

This is the *volume of the enclosed spaces above the waterline.* Because reserve buoyancy is a very important factor in determining a ship's seaworthiness *minimum* freeboards are assigned to a ship to ensure that there is adequate reserve buoyancy at all times.

1.3 SIMPLE BOX-SHAPED VESSEL CALCULATIONS

1.3.1 To calculate the displacement of a box-shaped vessel

Consider the vessel shown

MASS = VOLUME × DENSITY

i.e. **DISPLACEMENT = VOLUME OF DISPLACEMENT × WATER DENSITY**

where: **VOLUME OF DISPLACEMENT = LENGTH × BREADTH × DRAUGHT**

$(V = L \times B \times d)$

Therefore:

$$\mathbf{DISPL._{BOX} = (L \times B \times d) \times \rho}$$

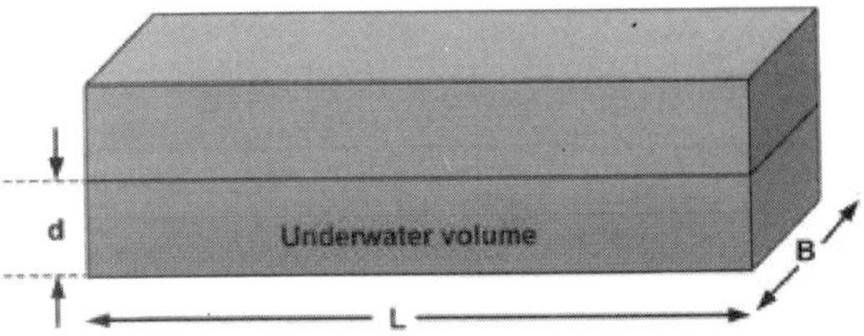

Fig.1.7

Example 6 (a)

Calculate the displacement of a box-shaped vessel that has length 80 m, breadth 16 m and floats at a draught of 4.2 m in salt water (density 1.025 t/m³).

Solution (a)

$DISPL._{BOX} = (L \times B \times d) \times \rho$

$\therefore \quad DISPL._{BOX} = (80 \times 16 \times 4.2) \times 1.025$

$\therefore \quad DISPL._{BOX} = \mathbf{5510.4\ t}$

Consider what happens to the box-shaped vessel in the previous example, if it is now towed into water of a lesser density, say 1.006 t/m³.

If the formula: **DISPLACEMENT = VOLUME OF DISPLACEMENT × WATER DENSITY**

is considered, the water density has *decreased*. Since the displacement has *not* changed, then the *volume of displacement* must *increase* in order that the displacement remains constant.

Therefore, the box-shaped vessel will *sink* a little i.e. the *draught increases*.

Example 6 (b)

What will the draught of the box-shaped vessel be now if it is floating in water of density 1.006 t/m³?

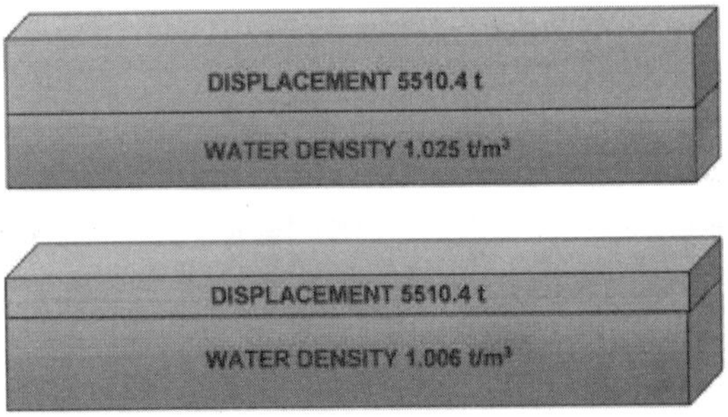

Fig. 1.8

Solution (b)

$DISPL._{BOX} = (L \times B \times d) \times \rho$

$5510.4 = (80 \times 16 \times d) \times 1.006$

$5510.4 = 1287.68\ d$

$\therefore \quad \dfrac{5510.4}{1287.68} = d = \mathbf{4.279\ m}$

Note that the increase in draught is:

4.279 m -
4.200 m
0.079 m (7.9 cms or 79 mm)

1.3.2 Summary

If a ship moves into water of *lesser density,* the draught will *increase.*
If a ship moves into water of *greater density,* the draught will *decrease.*

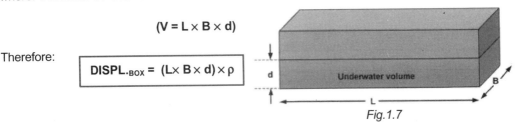

SECTION 2 - FORM COEFFICIENTS

INTRODUCTION

Form coefficients are *ratios* that numerically compare the ship's underwater form to that of regular shapes having the same major dimensions as the ship.

They are primarily used at the design stage, prior to construction, to predict factors such as resistance to forward motion that the ship will experience during operation. Such information is then used to estimate the ship's power requirements for the desired service speed.

Block coefficient is a ratio that is considered in the calculation and assignment of a ship's freeboard.

Learning Objectives

On completion of this section the learner will achieve the following:

1. Understand the term *Coefficient of fineness of the water-plane area* (C_W).
2. Understand the term *Block coefficient* (C_B).
3. Understand the term *Midships coefficient* (C_M).
4. Understand the term *Longitudinal prismatic coefficient* (C_P).
5. Complete simple calculations on (1) to (4) above.

2.1 COEFFICIENT OF FINENESS OF THE WATERPLANE AREA (C_W)

Is defined as the *ratio of the ship's water-plane area (WPA) to the area of a rectangle having the same length (L) and breadth (B) of the ship at the waterline in question.*

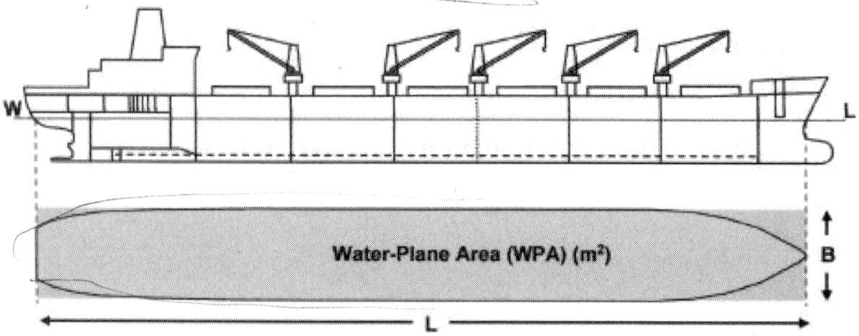

Fig. 2.1

$$\mathbf{Cw = \frac{WPA}{L \times B}}$$

Since the ship's WPA is less in area than the rectangle formed around it, *the value of C_W must always be less than 1.00.*

<u>*Example 1*</u>

A ship has a length and breadth at the waterline of 40.1 m and 8.6 m respectively. If the water-plane area is 280 m² calculate the coefficient of fineness of the water-plane area (C_W).

<u>*Solution*</u>

$$Cw = \frac{WPA}{L \times B} = \frac{280}{40.1 \times 8.2} = \mathbf{0.812}$$

Note that the answer has no units; it is simply a comparison of one area to another!

2.2 BLOCK COEFFICIENT (C_B)

The block coefficient (C_B) of a ship is the *ratio of the underwater volume of a ship to the volume of the circumscribing block.*

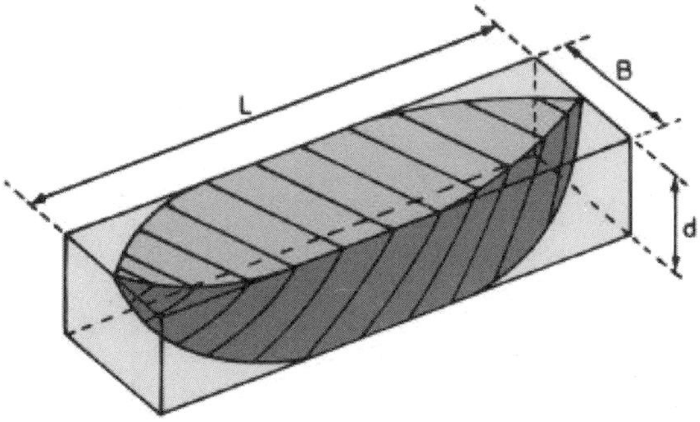

Fig. 2.2

$$C_B = \frac{\text{Volume of displacement}}{L \times B \times d}$$

Therefore:

$$\text{Displacement}_{SHIP} = (L \times B \times d \times C_B) \times \rho$$

Since the ship's volume of displacement is less than the volume of displacement of the surrounding block, *the value of C_B must always be less than 1.00.*

Example 2

A ship floats at a draught of 3.20 m and has a waterline length and breadth of 46.3 m and 15.5 m respectively. Calculate the block coefficient (C_B) if its volume of displacement is 1800 m^3.

Solution

$$C_B = \frac{\text{Volume of displacement}}{L \times B \times d} = \frac{1800}{46.3 \times 15.5 \times 3.2}$$

$$C_B = \mathbf{0.784}$$

Example 3

A ship has length 200 m and breadth 18 m at the waterline. If the ship floats at an even keel draught of 7.56 m in water RD 1.012 and the block coefficient is 0.824 calculate the displacement.

Solution

Displacement = Volume of displacement × Density

∴ *Displacement = (Length × Breadth × draught × C_B) × Density*

∴ *Displacement = (200 × 18 × 7.56 × 0.824) × 1.012 = **22695 t***

2.3 MIDSHIPS AREA COEFFICIENT (C_M)

The midships coefficient (C_M) of a ship at any draught is the ratio of the underwater transverse area of the midships section to the product of the breadth and draught (the surrounding rectangle).

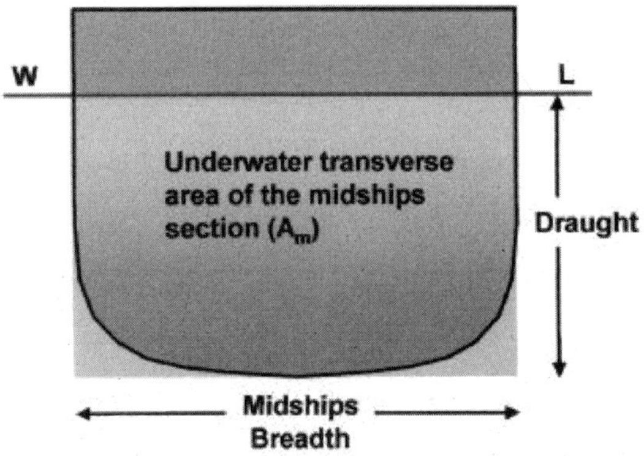

Fig. 2.3

$$C_M = \frac{\text{Underwater transverse area of midships section } (A_m)}{\text{Breadth} \times \text{Draught}}$$

$$C_M = \frac{A_M}{B \times d}$$

Similarly, *the value of C_M must always be less than 1.00.*

This coefficient may be used to determine the *prismatic coefficient (C_P).*

Example 4

A ship floats at a draught of 4.40 m and has a waterline breadth of 12.70 m. Calculate the underwater transverse area of the midships section if C_M is 0.922.

Solution

$$C_M = \frac{Am}{B \times d}$$

$$0.922 = \frac{Am}{12.70 \times 4.40}$$

$$0.922 = \frac{Am}{55.88}$$

$$0.922 \times 55.88 = Am = \mathbf{51.521\ m^2}$$

2.4 LONGITUDINAL PRISMATIC COEFFICIENT (C_P)

The longitudinal prismatic coefficient (C_P) of a ship at any draught is the *ratio of the underwater volume of the ship to the volume of the prism formed by the product of the transverse area of the midships section and the waterline length.*

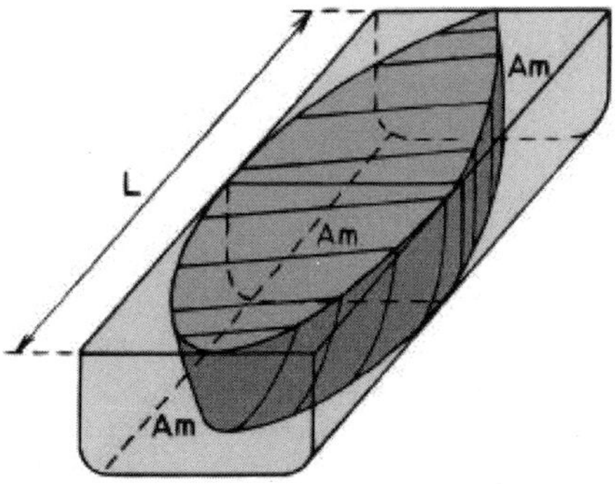

Fig. 2.4

$$C_P = \frac{\text{Volume of displacement of ship}}{\text{Volume of prism}}$$

$$C_P = \frac{\text{Volume of displacement of ship}}{\text{Waterline length} \times \text{Area of midship section (Am)}}$$

This coefficient gives an indication of how much the ship's form changes at the ends. Similarly, *the value of C_P must always be less than 1.00.*

Example 5

A ship has the following details:

Draught 3.63 m;
Waterline length 48.38 m;
Waterline breadth 9.42 m;
Cm 0.946;
Cp 0.778.

Calculate the volume of displacement.

Solution

The formulae are:

$$Cm = \frac{Am}{B \times d} \qquad Cp = \frac{\text{Volume of displacement}}{L \times Am}$$

Starting with:

$$Cm = \frac{Am}{B \times d} \qquad 0.946 = \frac{Am}{9.42 \times 3.63}$$

$$Am = 0.946 \times 9.42 \times 3.63 \quad = \quad 32.348\ m^2 \quad \text{and;}$$

$$Cp = \frac{\text{Vol. of displacement}}{L \times Am} \qquad 0.778 = \frac{\text{Vol. of displacement}}{48.38 \times 32.348}$$

$$\text{Vol. of displacement} = 0.778 \times 48.38 \times 32.348 = \mathbf{1217.6\ m^3}$$

It should be noted that for most courses only knowledge of the *Coefficient of fineness of the water-plane area (C_W)* and the *Block coefficient (C_B)* is required.

SECTION 3 -TONNES PER CENTIMETRE IMMERSION (TPC)

INTRODUCTION

TPC is the first of the ship's hydrostatic data that is supplied to a ship that will be considered in detail. It allows a means of calculating the change in draught that will occur when loading or discharging weights.

Learning Objectives

On completion of this section the learner will achieve the following:

1. Understand the term *Tonnes per centimetre immersion.*
2. Derive the formula for TPC.
3. Understand the factors that affect the value of TPC.
4. Use Displacement and TPC values from tabulated hydrostatic particulars to perform simple calculations involving draught changes when cargo is loaded or discharged.

3.1 TONNES PER CENTIMETRE IMMERSION (TPC)

The *TPC* for any given draught *is the weight that must be loaded or discharged to change the ship's mean draught by one centimetre.*

Consider the ship shown floating in salt water (RD 1.025) with a water-plane area (WPA) at the waterline as shown.

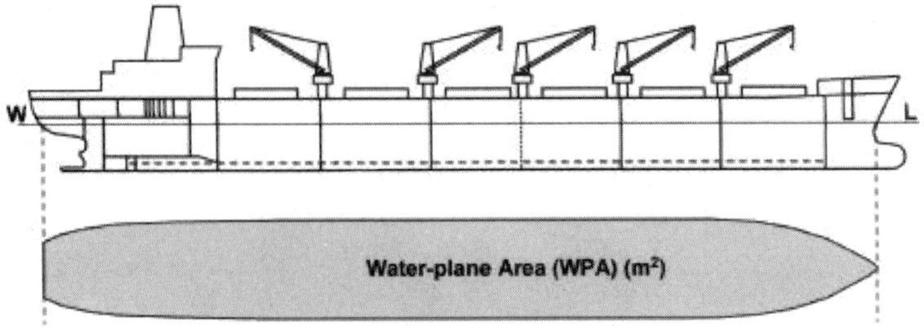

Fig. 3.1

A weight of 30 tonnes is loaded on deck so that the mean draught increases by 1 cm.

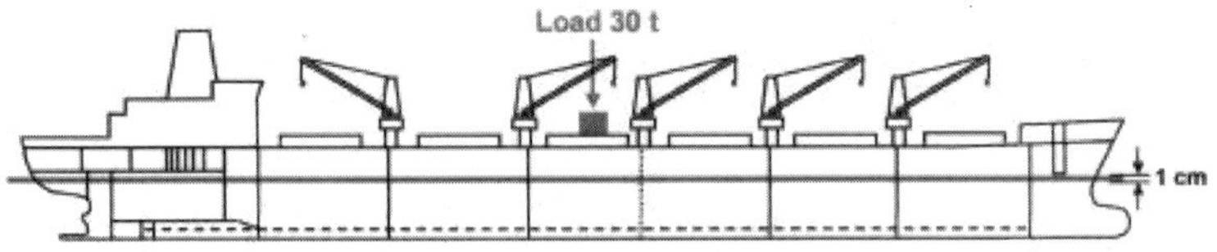

Fig. 3.2

Since the ship's displacement is equal to the mass of water displaced *(Law of Flotation)* it follows that the *mass of the additional 'slice' of displaced water is equal to the added weight of 30 tonnes.*

In this instance, 30 tonnes represents the value of the *Tonnes per Centimetre Immersion (TPC)* for the ship at the initial draught before the weight was loaded.

3.2 TPC FORMULA

Consider the previous situation.

Since: Mass = Volume $\times$ Density

then:
Mass of additional slice of water = Volume of the additional slice of water $\times$ Density.
If the WPA is assumed to not significantly change between the two waterlines, then:
Volume of the slice = WPA (m^2) $\times$ 1 cm;

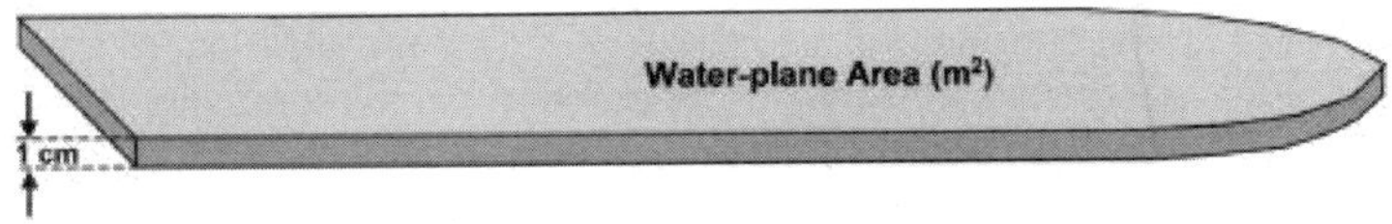

Fig. 3.3

We cannot multiply m^2 by *cms*, therefore:

$$\text{Volume of slice} = \text{WPA } (m^2) \times \frac{1}{100} \text{ (m)};$$

$$\therefore \quad \text{Added displacement (t)} = \text{WPA } (m^2) \times \frac{1}{100} \text{ (m)} \times \text{density } (t/m^3);$$

Therefore, the formula for TPC is:

$$\boxed{\mathbf{TPC = \frac{WPA}{100} \times \rho}}$$

Example 1
Calculate the TPC for a ship with a water-plane area of 1500 m^2 when it is floating in:

(a) fresh water;
(b) dock water of RD 1.005;
(c) salt water.

Solution

$$TPC = \frac{WPA}{100} \times \rho$$

(a) $TPC = \frac{1500}{100} \times 1.000 = \mathbf{15.000}$

(b) $TPC = \frac{1500}{100} \times 1.005 = \mathbf{15.075}$

(c) $TPC = \frac{1500}{100} \times 1.025 = \mathbf{15.375}$

3.3 FACTORS AFFECTING TPC

Consideration of the TPC formula: $TPC = \frac{WPA}{100} \times \rho$

shows that:

* *TPC increases with WPA and for a normal ship-shape the WPA will increase with draught.*
* *TPC increases with density.*

Two values of TPC are often quoted in ship's hydrostatic data, TPC_{SW} and TPC_{FW}. However, hydrostatic data for *M. V. Almar is given for saltwater only.*

Consider the hydrostatic particulars for *M.V. Almar* on *page 12* of the stability data book.

If the ship were floating at a draught of 5.00 m in *salt water* (RD 1.025) the displacement of the ship would be 15120 tonnes. To sink the ship by exactly 1 cm, 31.96 tonnes would have to be loaded.

Consider the situation if the ship were to float at the same draught of 5.00 m but in fresh water (RD 1.000).

Would the displacement and TPC values be the same as they were in salt water?

Consider the following diagrams showing the ship floating at the *same draught* but in *different water densities*.

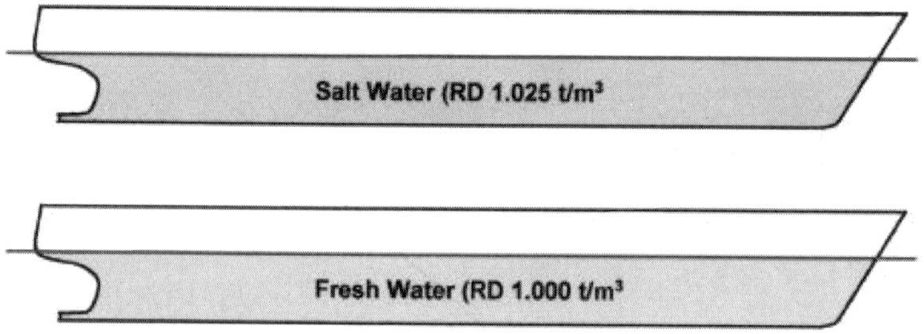

Fig. 3.4

DISPLACEMENT = VOLUME OF DISPLACEMENT × WATER DENSITY

For both situations the *volume of displacement* is the same!

It follows that the displacement of the ship when at a draught of 5.00 m in *salt water* must be *greater* than the displacement of the ship when at the *same draught in fresh water* (since salt water is denser than fresh water!).

Consider now the TPC value for both situations.

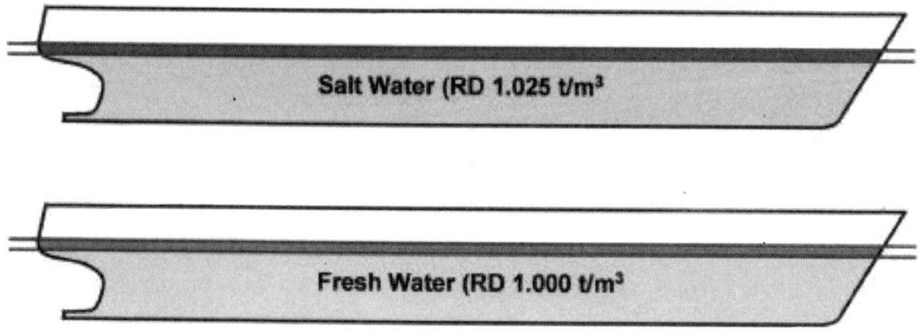

Fig. 3.5

By similar reasoning a *1 cm slice of salt water* will have a *greater mass* than a *1 cm slice of fresh water*. Therefore, for the same draught of 5.00 m the *TPC in salt water will be greater than the TPC in fresh water.*

Determination of the equivalent fresh water values of displacement and TPC for fresh water is very simple.

The hydrostatic data gives the following saltwater values for a draught of 5.00 m:

Displacement:	*15120 tonnes*
TPC:	*31.96 tonnes*

Displacement in fresh water (RD 1.000) $= 15120 \times \frac{1.000}{1.025} = 14751$ *tonnes.*

TPC in fresh water (RD 1.000) $= 31.96 \times \frac{1.000}{1.025} = 31.18$ *tonnes.*

<u>*Example 2*</u>

Using the hydrostatic particulars determine the displacement and TPC values for the ship when floating at a draught of 6.30 m in:

(a) *salt water (RD 1.025);*
(b) *fresh water (RD 1.000);*
(c) *dock water (RD 1.012).*

<u>*Solution*</u>

(a) *The hydrostatic data gives the following salt water values for a draught of 5.00 m:*

Displacement:	***19310 tonnes***
TPC:	***32.46 tonnes***

(b) *Displacement in fresh water (RD 1.000)*

$$= 19310 \times \frac{1.000}{1.025} = \mathbf{18839\ tonnes.}$$

TPC in fresh water (RD 1.000)

$$= 32.46 \times \frac{1.000}{1.025} = \mathbf{31.67\ tonnes.}$$

(c) *Displacement in dock water (RD 1.012)*

$$= 19310 \times \frac{1.012}{1.025} = \mathbf{19065\ tonnes.}$$

TPC in dock water (RD 1.012)

$$= 32.46 \times \frac{1.012}{1.025} = \mathbf{32.05\ tonnes.}$$

<u>*Note*</u>

It is usual to work to the same number of decimal places as the values given in the tables.

3.4 LOAD/DISCHARGE PROBLEMS

If given a TPC value for a particular draught, then the change in draught that will occur as a result of loading or discharging weights, termed either *sinkage* or *rise* as appropriate, may be calculated using:

$$\textbf{Sinkage/Rise (cms)} = \frac{\mathbf{w}}{\mathbf{TPC}}$$

where *w* represents the total weight that is loaded or discharged. Having calculated the sinkage/rise of the ship, this is then applied to the initial draught.

Use of the above formula may be also used to determine the weight to load or discharge to achieve a required draught where:

$$\mathbf{w = Sinkage/Rise \times TPC}$$

<u>*Example 3*</u>
M.V. Almar has an initial mean draught of 4.40 m in salt water and is required to complete loading with a draught of 6.70 m. Using the hydrostatic particulars calculate the amount of cargo that must be loaded.

Two methods may be used as follows:

<u>*Method 1*</u>
1. *Read off the $DISPL_{SW}$ values for both the initial and required final draught.*
2. *Subtract the smaller from the larger.*
3. *Result equals the amount to load.*

<u>*Method 2*</u>
1. *Read off the TPC_{SW} values for both the initial and required final draughts.*
2. *Calculate the mean TPC_{SW} value.*
3. *Calculate the required change in draught; in this case sinkage.*
4. *Use the formula:* $\text{Sinkage/Rise (cms)} = \frac{w}{TPC}$ *to find 'w', the amount to load.*

<u>*Solution*</u>

<u>*Method 1*</u>

Initial draught 4.40 m	$DISPL_{SW}$ *13200 t*
Required draught 6.70 m	$DISPL_{SW}$ *20610 t*
Cargo to load	***7410 t***

<u>*Method 2*</u>

Initial draught 4.40 m	TPC_{SW} *31.78 t*
Required draught 6.70 m	TPC_{SW} *32.66 t*

$$\text{Mean } TPC_{SW} = \frac{31.78 + 32.66}{2} = 32.22\text{ t}$$

$$\text{Sinkage (cms)} = 6.70\text{ m} - 4.40\text{ m} = 2.30\text{ m} = 230\text{ cms}$$

$$\text{Sinkage (cms)} = \frac{w}{TPC_{SW}}$$

$$\text{Cargo to load (w)} = \text{Sinkage} \times \text{Mean } TPC_{SW}$$

$$= 230 \times 32.22 = \mathbf{7410.6\ t}$$

The answers differ slightly for two reasons:

1. In using the mean value of TPC it is assumed that the TPC value changes *linearly* between the range of draughts concerned. This is not so, as the underwater form of a ship does not (usually) change uniformly with draught.

2. Displacement values taken from the hydrostatic data in using *method 1* will be rounded to the nearest whole tonne.

If the change in draught is only small it is usual to use the TPC value for the initial waterline instead of the mean TPC value as shown in the examples. Obviously the greater the amount of cargo loaded or discharged; the greater will be the error!

Example 4
M.V. Almar has an initial mean draught of 5.80 m in salt water and loads 11300 t of cargo. Using the hydrostatic particulars calculate the final displacement and mean draught.

Solution

Method 1

Initial draught 5.80 m	$DISPL_{SW}$	*17690 t*
Cargo loaded		*11300 t*
FINAL DISPL.		*28990 t*

Enter data with final displacement gives a final mean draught of 9.200 m.

Method 2

Initial draught 5.80 m	$DISPL_{SW}$	*17690 t*	TPC_{SW} *32.26 t*
Cargo loaded		*11300 t*	
FINAL DISPL.		*28990 t*	TPC_{SW} *34.43 t*

$$\text{Mean } TPC_{SW} = \frac{32.26 + 34.43}{2} = 33.345\ t$$

$$\text{Sinkage (cms)} = \frac{w}{TPC_{SW\ MEAN}}$$

$$\text{Sinkage (cms)} = \frac{11300}{33.345} = 338.9\ \text{cms} = 3.389\ m$$

Initial draught	*5.800 m*
Sinkage	*3.389 m*
FINAL DRAUGHT	***9.189 m***

It should be evident from *Example 4* that direct use of the *Displacement* and *TPC* values given in the hydrostatic data results in a more accurate answer *(Method 1)*. Using the formula method leads to unnecessary working and results in a less accurate answer.

Example 5
M.V. Almar arrives in port with a mean draught of 5.30 m in dock water RD 1.016. How much cargo may be loaded to ensure that the maximum draught on completion is 5.70 m in the dock water?

Solution

Method 1

Initial draught 5.30 m $\quad$ $DISPL_{SW}$ *16080 t*

$$DISPL_{DW} = 16080 \times \frac{1.016}{1.025} = 15939\ t$$

Final draught 5.70 m $\quad$ $DISPL_{SW}$ *17370 t*

$$DISPL_{DW} = 17370 \times \frac{1.016}{1.025} = 17217\ t$$

Initial $DISPL_{DW}$	16080 t
Final $DISPL_{DW}$	17217 t
Cargo to load	**1278 t**

Method 2

Initial draught 5.30 m $\quad$ TPC_{SW} *32.07 t*

$$TPC_{DW} = 32.07 \times \frac{1.016}{1.025} = 31.79\ t$$

Final draught 5.70 m $\quad$ TPC_{SW} *32.22 t*

$$TPC_{DW} = 32.22 \times \frac{1.016}{1.025} = 31.94\ t$$

$$\text{Mean } TPC_{DW} = \frac{31.79 + 31.94}{2} = 31.865\ t$$

Sinkage (cms) = 5.70 m - 5.30 m = 0.40 m = 40 cms

$$\text{Sinkage (cms)} = \frac{w}{\text{Mean } TPC_{DW}}$$

Cargo to load (w) = Sinkage × Mean TPC_{DW}

$$= 40 \times 31.865 = \mathbf{1274.6\ t}$$

It should be evident from the previous example that:

* *The displacement for the correct density must be used in the calculation.*

* *The TPC for the density of water in which the ship is loading in should be used in the calculation.*

It is usual to calculate the amount to load on the basis of the required *salt water draught* since seasonal load lines assigned to the ship apply to the ship at sea in *salt water.*

SECTION 4 - LOAD LINES

INTRODUCTION

Most ships will be assigned a *minimum freeboard* and a corresponding set of load lines. These will be permanently marked on each side of the ship (certain classes of ship are exempt from these requirements).

Load lines assigned to a ship correspond to ocean areas or 'zones'. Oceans around the world are divided into these zones in terms of both geographical location and time of year (season). By ensuring that the appropriate seasonal load line mark is not submerged at sea in salt water (RD 1.025) the ship will always have the necessary reserve buoyancy to ensure seaworthiness.

To ensure that the appropriate load line is never submerged at sea, it is essential that the learner has a thorough knowledge of the load line markings, their spacing and dimensions. The ability to perform calculations to determine the maximum amount to load is also important, especially to the ship owner, as the absolute maximum cargo in terms of weight should be carried whenever possible. It is also essential that the ship is never 'overloaded', as contravention of the conditions of load line assignment will arise, resulting in the ship being unseaworthy with respect to legislative requirements.

Learning Objectives

On completion of this section the learner will achieve the following:

1. Know the dimensions of a set of load lines as would be assigned to a ship.
2. Understand the term *Fresh Water Allowance (FWA)* and derive the formula for *FWA.*
3. Understand the term *Dock Water Allowance (DWA).*
4. Perform calculations relating to the loading of a ship to the appropriate load line mark.

4.1 LOAD LINE DIMENSIONS

The load lines as they would appear on the *starboard* side of a ship are shown.

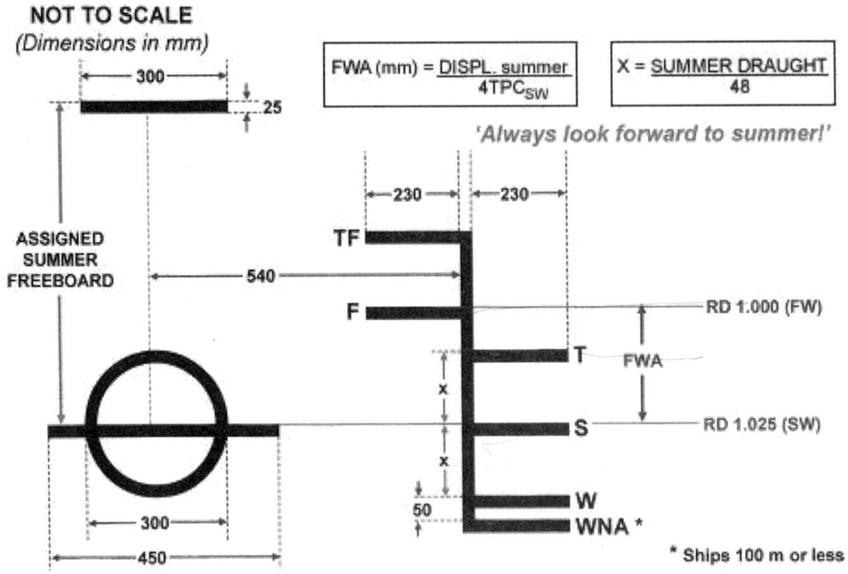

Fig. 4.1

The following points should be carefully noted:

1. The notations assigned to the load lines are as follows:

   S: Summer
   W: Winter
   T: Tropical
   WNA: Winter North Atlantic
   F: Fresh
   TF: Tropical Fresh

   Each load line indicates the *minimum freeboard* that applies to the seasonal zone and/or area as stipulated in the *International Convention on Load Lines, 1966.*
   (Refer to Annex II: Zones, Areas and Seasonal Periods)

2. The ship will be loaded to the appropriate load line when the waterline is level with the *top edge* of the mark concerned when floating in *salt water (RD 1.025).*

3. The spacings between the load lines are measured from the *top edge* of one line to the *top edge* of the other.

4. The *assigned (Summer) freeboard* is measured from the *top edge* of the *Plimsoll line* (which corresponds to the top edge of the Summer line) to the *top edge* of the *deck line.*
5. The 'WNA' load line mark is only assigned to ships that are *100 metres or less in length.* Ships over 100 m will load to the 'W' mark as appropriate.

6. With the exception of *'FWA'* and *'X'*, *all* dimensions are the same for *all* ships, regardless of size of ship.

7. Load lines should be *clearly* and *permanently* marked on the ship's side; dark on light background or vice-versa.

4.2 FRESH WATER ALLOWANCE (FWA)

Fresh Water Allowance (FWA) is the number of millimetres by which the mean draught changes when a ship passes from salt water to fresh water, or vice-versa, when the ship is loaded to the Summer displacement.

The FWA is found by the formula:

$$\textbf{FWA (mm)} = \frac{\textbf{DISPL. Summer}}{\textbf{4TPC}_{SW}}$$

TPC_{SW} is the salt-water TPC value for the summer load draught.

4.2.1 The 'ship as a hydrometer'

If the load line marks are considered, the *top of the Summer mark* and the *top of the Fresh mark* act as the limits of a scale of density that would appear on a hydrometer (an instrument for measuring liquid density).

The ship behaves as a very large hydrometer!

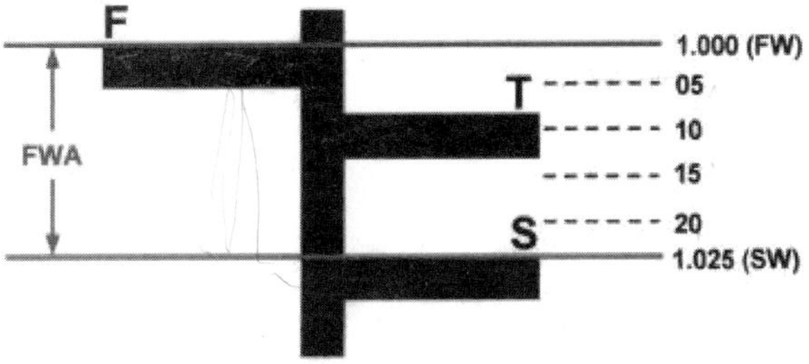

Fig.4.2

If the ship were loaded to the *Summer displacement* in *salt water (RD 1.025)* then the water line would be level with the top edge of the Summer (S) load line. If now towed into *fresh water (RD 1.000)* the ship would sink by the *fresh water allowance* such that the water line would now be level with the top edge of the Fresh (F) load line.

Obviously the reverse would happen if moving from FW to SW!

4.2.2 Derivation of the FWA formula

The displacement of a ship may be calculated by:

$$\text{Displacement}_{SHIP} = L \times B \times d \times C_B \times \rho$$

Consider the ship shown loaded to the *Summer draught* floating in:
(i) salt water;
(ii) fresh water.

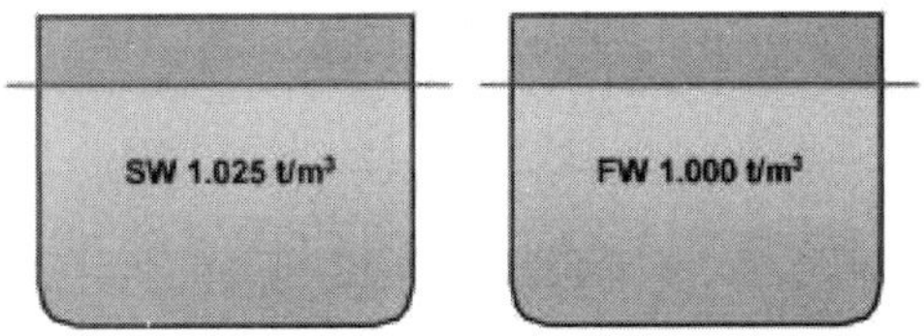

Fig.4.3

The displacements will be different but the volumes of displacement will be the same. If a ship is floating at a draught in FW, to find the equivalent SW displacement for the same draught:

$$DISPL_{SW} = DISPL_{FW} \times 1.025$$

Therefore, for the ship shown: $DISPL_{FW} \times 1.025 = DISPL_{FW} + (WPA \times FWA \times 1.000\ t/m^3)$

where FWA is expressed in *metres*.

$$DISPL_{FW} \times 1.025 = DISPL_{FW} + (WPA \times FWA)$$
$$1.025DISPL_{FW} = DISPL_{FW} + (WPA \times FWA)$$
$$1.025DISPL_{FW} - DISPL_{FW} = (WPA \times FWA)$$
$$0.025DISPL_{FW} = (WPA \times FWA) \quad \text{(i)}$$

Consider now the formula for TPC, where the TPC_{SW} is the weight required to sink the ship whilst at the summer displacement by 1 cm:

$$TPC_{SW} = \frac{WPA}{100} \times 1.025$$

Rearranging this gives:

$$WPA = \frac{TPC_{SW} \times 100}{1.025} \quad (ii)$$

where the WPA is that for the *Summer load draught waterline*.

Substituting equation (ii) into equation (i):

$$0.025DISPL_{FW} = \frac{100 \times TPC_{SW} \times FWA}{1.025}$$

$$FWA\ (m) = \frac{0.025 \times DISPL_{FW} \times 1.025}{100 \times TPC_{SW}}$$

To express FWA in *mm* then:

$$\frac{FWA}{1000} = \frac{0.025 \times DISPL_{FW} \times 1.025}{100 \times TPC_{SW}}$$

Rearranging gives:

$$FWA\ (mm) = \frac{0.025 \times DISPL_{SW} \times 1000}{100 \times TPC_{SW}}$$

Therefore:

$$FWA\ (mm) = \frac{0.25 \times DISPL_{SW}}{TPC_{SW}}$$

Thus:

$$\mathbf{FWA\ (mm) = \frac{DISPL.\ Summer}{4TPC_{SW}}}$$

Example 1

A ship floats in SW at the Summer displacement of 1680 tonnes. If the TPC_{SW} is 5.18, how much will the draught change by if the ship is towed to a berth where the density of the water is 1.000 t/m^3?

Solution

In moving from SW to FW the ship will experience sinkage by an amount equal to the FWA.

$$FWA\ (mm) = \frac{DISPL.\ Summer}{4TPC_{SW}}$$

$$FWA = \frac{1680}{4 \times 5.18} = \mathbf{81.1\ mm}$$

The draught will increase by 81.1 mm!

4.3 DOCK WATER ALLOWANCE (DWA)

The Dock Water Allowance (DWA) of a ship is the number of millimetres by which the mean draught changes when a ship passes from salt water to dock water, or vice-versa, when the ship is loaded to the Summer displacement.

Consider the load line marks shown. The top of the *Summer* mark and the top of the *Fresh* mark both act as the limits of a scale of density, indicating the position of the *salt water* and *fresh water* waterlines respectively for a ship loaded to the *Summer displacement.* If such a ship was to be floating in water of an intermediate density, termed *Dock Water*, the change in draught when going from *salt water* to *dock water* can be easily determined.

Consider the scale marked on the section of load line shown.

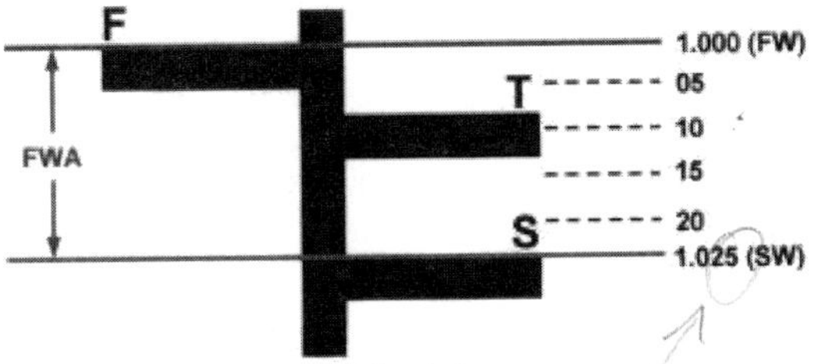

Fig.4.4

If the ship were to go from SW to dock water of RD 1.010, the draught would change by the DWA. The amount of the DWA is simply a fraction of the FWA as shown, in this case 3/5ths or 15/25ths of the FWA value.

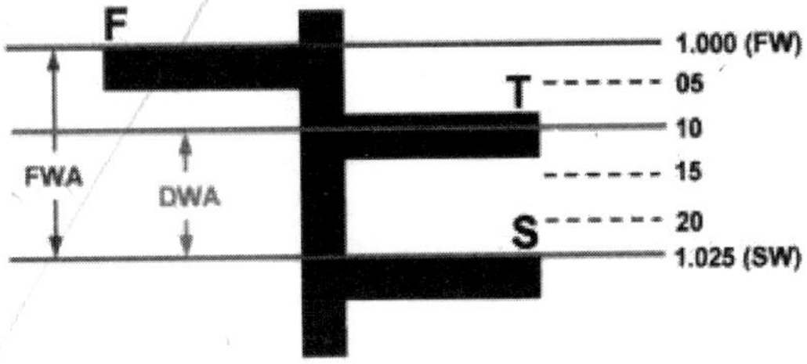

Fig. 4.5

The DWA, as a fraction of the FWA, is found by the formula:

$$\textbf{DWA (mm)} = \textbf{FWA} \times \frac{(1025 - \text{RD dock water})}{25}$$

Note The densities are multiplied by 1000 to simplify the working.

Example 2
A ship has a FWA of 200 mm. Calculate the change in draught that will occur if the ship proceeds from SW to a berth where the RD of the dock water is 1.018.

Solution

$$DWA\ (mm) = FWA \times \frac{(1025 - RD\ dock\ water)}{25}$$

Therefore: $DWA\ (mm) = 200 \times \frac{(1025 - 1018)}{25}$

DWA = ***56 mm***

The draught will increase by 56 mm!

The DWA formula is easily modified to calculate the change in draught that would occur if the ship were to proceed from dock water of one density to dock water of another.

$$\textbf{DWA (mm)} = \textbf{FWA} \times \frac{(RD_{DW1} \sim RD_{DW2})}{25}$$

(~ means difference between; take smaller value from greater value.)

Example 3
A ship is loaded to its summer displacement and is to proceed down river from a berth where the dock water RD is 1.004 to another berth where the dock water RD is 1.016. If the FWA is 260 mm, calculate the change in draught that will occur and state whether it is an increase or a decrease.

Solution

$DWA\ (mm) = FWA \times \frac{(RD_{DW1} \sim RD_{DW2})}{25}$ Therefore: $DWA\ (mm) = 260 \times \frac{(1016 - 1004)}{25}$

DWA = ***124.8 mm***

The draught will decrease by 125 mm since the ship is moving into more dense water!

Note Answers need only be to the nearest mm!

4.4 LOAD LINE CALCULATIONS

4.4.1 The need for applying DWA/FWA to ensure maximum cargo is loaded

When loading a ship it is desirable to load as much cargo as possible. If the ship is loading in water that is *less dense* than salt water, such as dock water, then allowance should be made for the ship *rising* out of the water on reaching the sea, salt water density being *greater* than that of the dock water.

Consider the following situation:

A ship is loading in the Summer zone in dock water RD 1.012. It can legally load so that the salt-water waterline is level with the top edge of the Summer Load Line.

Consider the situation where the officer in charge of loading, loads cargo until the dock water waterline becomes level with the top edge of the Summer load line!

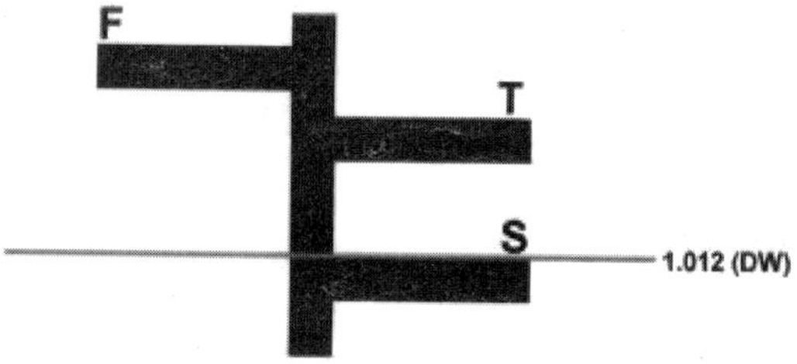

Fig. 4.6

When the ship proceeds to sea, on reaching salt water (RD 1.025) the ship will rise and be light of the Summer marks as shown.

MORE CARGO COULD HAVE BEEN LOADED SINCE THE SHIP IS LIGHT OF THE SUMMER LOAD LINE MARK!

To avoid this situation, but to also ensure that too much cargo is never loaded, the amount to safely load can be readily calculated.

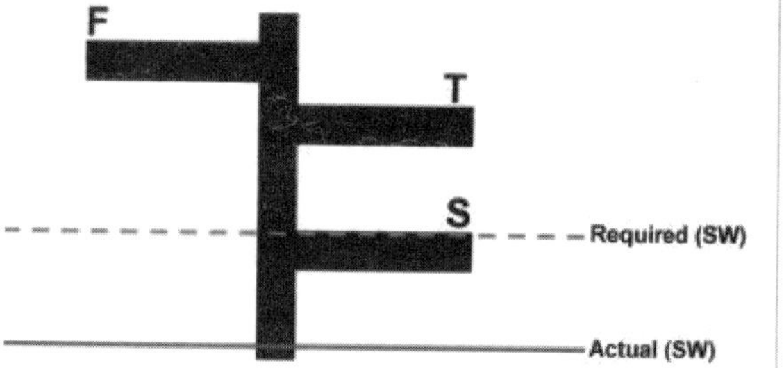

Fig. 4.7

The aim of the problem is to ensure that on proceeding to sea the ship rises to the desired seasonal load line mark. This is achieved by considering the 'Fresh Water Allowance' or 'Dock Water Allowance' as appropriate in the calculation.

4.4.2 Procedure for conducting Load Line calculations

The following examples illustrate the method to be used to determine the maximum amount of cargo to load when the ship is floating in dock water. It is important that the calculation procedure is followed exactly, particularly in *step 2* of the next example.

<u>Example 4</u>

A ship has a Summer load draught of 5.80 m, FWA 140 mm and TPC of 21.82. The ship is loading at a berth in dock water RD 1.007 and the present draught is 5.74 m. Calculate the maximum amount of cargo that can still be loaded for the ship to be at the Summer load line mark on reaching the sea allowing for 26 tonnes of fuel still to be loaded prior to sailing.

<u>Solution</u>

1. *Calculate DWA (to the nearest mm).*

$$DWA\ (mm) = 140 \times \frac{(1025 - 1007)}{25} = 100.8\ mm \approx 101\ mm$$

2. *Calculate the 'permitted sinkage' in dock water. Always start with the required load line draught and work as follows:*

Required Summer draught	*(1.025)*	*5.800 m*
DWA		*+ 0.101 m*
Required draught	*(1.007)*	*5.901 m*
Initial draught	*(1.007)*	*5.740 m*
Permitted sinkage	*(1.007)*	*0.161 m*

3. *Calculate the maximum amount that can still be loaded in dock water, ignoring any allowances for fuel or other items.*

Permitted sinkage (cms) = $\frac{w}{TPC}$

Therefore: *w = Permitted sinkage (cms) × TPC*

$$w = 16.1 \times 21.82 \times \frac{1.007}{1.025} = 345.1 \text{ tonnes}$$

Note that TPC must be corrected for the density of the dock water!

4. *Make allowance now for items other than cargo that must be loaded*

*Total that can be loaded **	*345.1 tonnes*
Fuel still to load	*26.0 tonnes*
Maximum cargo to load	***319.1 tonnes***

Note Had the given TPC not been converted for the density of the dock water, the total that could be loaded would have worked out as: w = 16.1 × 21.82 = 351.3 tonnes; resulting in the ship being **OVERLOADED BY 6.2 TONNES!*

Example 5

A ship is floating in dock water RD 1.002 at a draught of 4.30 m. How much more cargo must be loaded to ensure that the ship will be at the Winter load line mark given that the Winter draught corresponding to the winter displacement is 4.32 m and the TPC is 21.60 and the FWA is 100 mm.

Note that the TPC value given will always be the one that corresponds to salt water for the waterline that is being loaded to.

Solution

1. *Calculate DWA.*
DWA (mm) = 100 × $\frac{(1025 - 1002)}{25}$ *= 92 mm*

2. *Calculate the 'permitted sinkage' in dock water.*

Required Winter draught	*(1.025)*	*4.320 m*
DWA		*+ 0.092 m*
Required draught	*(1.002)*	*4.412 m*
Initial draught	*(1.002)*	*4.300 m*
Permitted sinkage	*(1.002)*	*0.112 m*

3. *Calculate the maximum amount that can still be loaded in dock water.*
Permitted sinkage (cms) = $\frac{w}{TPC}$
Therefore: *w = Permitted sinkage (cms) × TPC*

$$w = 11.2 \times 21.60 \times \frac{1.002}{1.025} = 236.5 \text{ tonnes}$$

*Total that can be loaded **236.5 tonnes.***

Sometimes a question may be a little more difficult whereby knowledge of the load line dimensions is essential. *It is recommended that a sketch be drawn to fully understand what is being asked!* Consider the next example.

Example 6

A ship is floating in dock water RD 1.006. The waterline to port is 12 cm below the lower edge of the 'S' mark and on the starboard side is 4 cm above the upper edge of the 'W' mark. If the Summer displacement is 21620 tonnes (corresponding to a draught in salt water of 6.86 m, TPC 18.6), how much cargo remains to be loaded to ensure that the ship will be at the Winter mark in salt water.

Solution

1. *Identify the load lines that are mentioned in the question ('S' and 'W' in this case); sketch them (port or starboard, it does not matter) and enter all known dimensions, calculating them as necessary.*

   Thickness of the lines:25 mm (2.5 cms; 0.025 m)

   Distance between Winter and Summer load lines (X):

   $$X = \frac{\text{Summer draught}}{48} = \frac{6.86}{48} = 0.143 \text{ m}$$

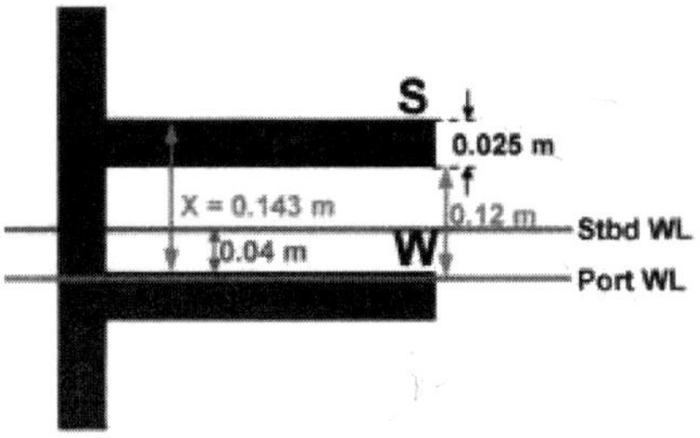

Fig. 4.8

2. *Starting with a known draught (Summer) calculate the draught on each side by applying the distances in the sketch.*

	PORT		STBD
Summer draught	*6.860*		*6.860*
Line thickness	*-0.025*	*'X'*	*- 0.143*
	-0.120		*+ 0.040*
Draught each side	*6.715 m*		*6.757 m*

3. *Calculate initial mean draught.*

   Initial mean draught (RD 1.006) $= \frac{6.715 + 6.757}{2} = 6.736$ *m*

4. *Calculate DWA (in this case FWA must first be calculated).*

   $$FWA \text{ (mm)} = \frac{\text{DISPL. Summer}}{4TPC_{SW}} = \frac{21620}{4 \times 18.6} = 290.6 \text{ mm}$$

   $$DWA \text{ (mm)} = 290.6 \times \frac{(1025 - 1006)}{25} = 220.8 \text{ mm} \approx 221 \text{ mm}$$

5. *Calculate the required Winter draught.*

Summer draught	*6.860 m*
'X'	*0.143 m*
Required Winter draught	*6.717 m*

6. *Calculate the 'permitted sinkage' in dock water.*

Required Winter draught	*(1.025)*	*6.717 m*
DWA		*+ 0.221 m*
Required draught	*(1.006)*	*6.938 m*
Initial draught	*(1.006)*	*6.736 m*
Permitted sinkage	*(1.006)*	*0.202 m*

7. *Calculate the maximum amount that can still be loaded in dock water.*

$$\text{Permitted sinkage (cms)} = \frac{w}{TPC}$$

Therefore: $w = \text{Permitted sinkage (cms)} \times TPC$

$$w = 20.2 \times 18.6 \times \frac{1.006}{1.025} = \mathbf{368.8\ tonnes}$$

SECTION 5 - CENTRE OF GRAVITY (G) AND CENTRE OF BUOYANCY (B)

INTRODUCTION

Consider a ship heeled over by some external force, such as the wind.

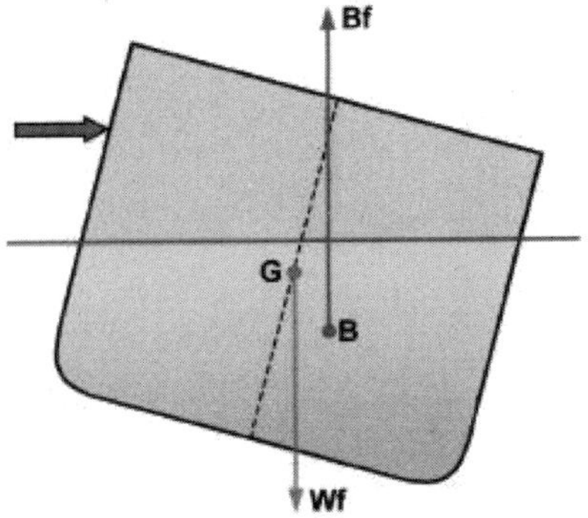

Fig. 5.1

G represents the *centre of gravity* of the ship and B the *centre of buoyancy*. These are the points of application of the weight force (Wf), acting vertically downwards, and the buoyancy force (Bf) acting vertically upwards. Ship stability is concerned with the relative positions of G and B as the ship is heeled.

Consider what will happen to the ship once the external heeling force is removed.

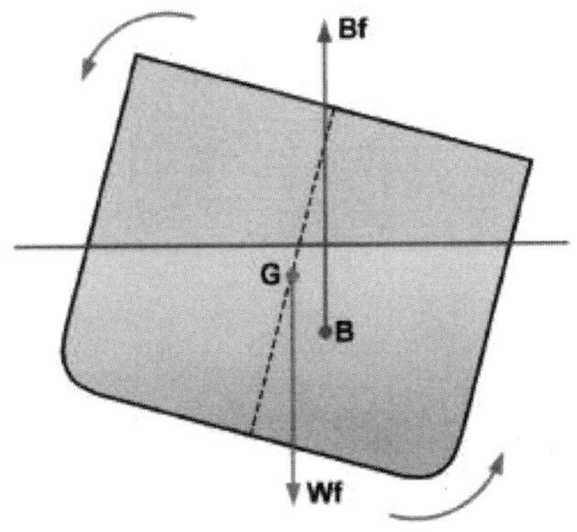

Fig. 5.2

If the lines of action of Wf and Bf are considered, they will act to return the ship to the upright condition.

This section concerns the *vertical* position of the ship's centre of gravity (G) and how its position changes when weights are shifted, loaded and discharged.

The factors influencing the position of the centre of buoyancy will also be discussed.

Learning Objectives

On completion of this section the learner will achieve the following:

1. Understand the term *Centre of Gravity (G).*
2. Understand the effect on G of *shifting* a single weight vertically up/down.
3. Understand the effect of *loading* a single weight in a position vertically above/below G.
4. Understand the effect of *discharging* a single weight from a position vertically above/below G.
5. Calculate the effect on G when shifting, loading or discharging *multiple* weights.
6. Understand the term *Centre of Buoyancy (B)* and identify the factors that influence it's position.
7. Perform calculations based on (2) to (5) above.

5.1 CENTRE OF GRAVITY (G)

'Centre of gravity' (G) of a ship may be defined as being the point where the total weight force (Wf) of the ship is considered to act vertically downwards.

Provided weights within the ship are properly secured, the position of G is assumed to not move as the ship heels. (Obviously if the ship heels excessively lashings may give way causing cargo to shift!)

Weight force (Wf) always acts vertically downwards!

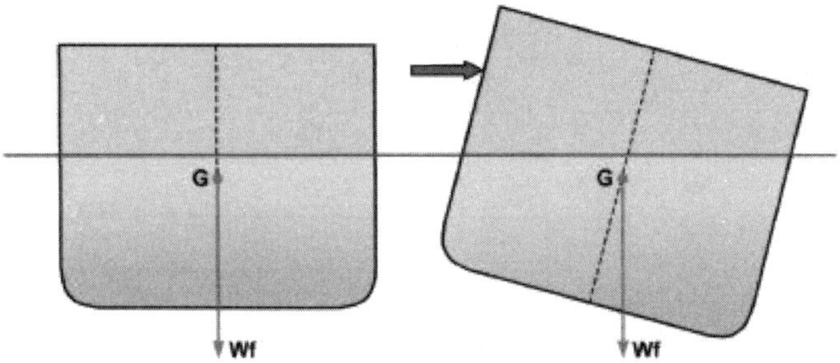

Fig. 5.3

When weights are *shifted* on board, *loaded* or *discharged* G will move. Whenever G is caused to move the *'shift of G'* must be calculated.

The position of the centre of gravity within the ship is the most influential factor in determining its stability. The officer in charge of loading the ship must be fully conversant with the way that G moves when shifting, loading and discharging weights.

The vertical position of G is expressed in terms of *'metres above the keel' (KG).*

The vertical position of the centre of gravity of a weight on board is also expressed in terms of *'metres above the keel' (Kg).*

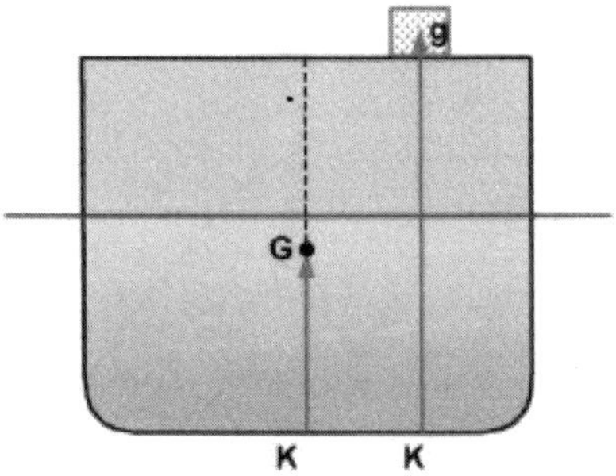

Fig. 5.4

5.2 SINGLE WEIGHT PROBLEMS

5.2.1 *Effect of shifting a weight already on board*

Whenever a weight already on board is shifted G will move *parallel to and in the same direction as the shift of the centre of gravity of the weight (g).*

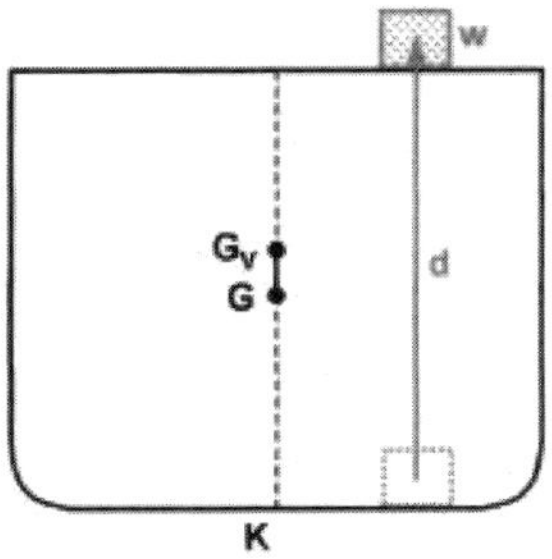

Fig. 5.5

The shift of G is calculated by the formula:

$$GG_V = \frac{w \times d}{W}$$

where: ***'w'*** is the weight shifted.
'd' is the distance through which the weight is shifted.
'W' is the ship's displacement, which includes the weight being shifted.

In this instant GG_V is a shift of G *upwards* i.e. *KG increases*.

Example 1

A ship displaces 5000 t and has an initial KG of 4.5 m. Calculate the final KG if a weight of 20 t is moved vertically upwards from the lower hold (Kg 2.0 m) to the upper deck (Kg 6.5 m).

Solution

$$GG_V = \frac{w \times d}{W} = \frac{20 \times (6.5 - 2.0)}{5000} = 0.018\ m$$

Initial KG	*4.500 m*
GGv up	*0.018 m*
FINAL KG	***4.518 m***

5.2.2 *Effect of loading a weight*

Whenever a weight is loaded G will move *directly towards the centre of gravity of the loaded weight (g).* Consider the ship shown where a weight is loaded onto the deck on one side. G moves to G_1.

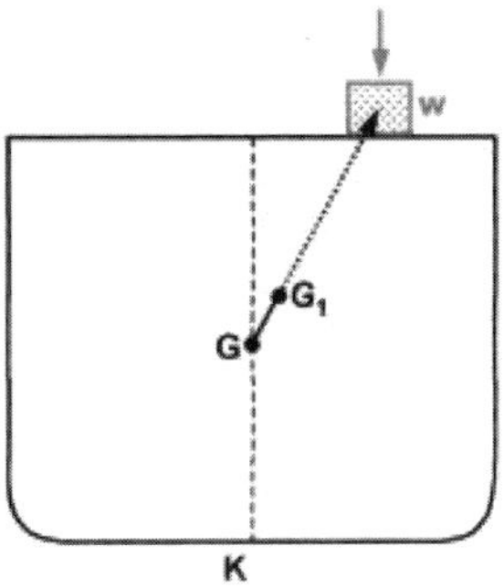

Fig. 5.6

For calculation purposes the movement of G to G_1 is considered to have two components:

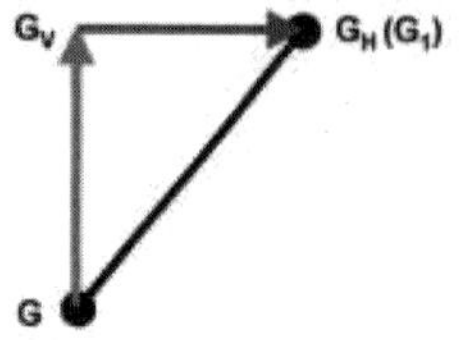

Fig. 5.7

GG_V: a vertical component; and *GG_H: a horizontal component.*

At this stage it is only the *vertical* component of the shift of G that is to be considered since only this component will affect KG.

(The horizontal component is considered in Section 11 - List.)
In this case, the KG of the ship will *increase.*

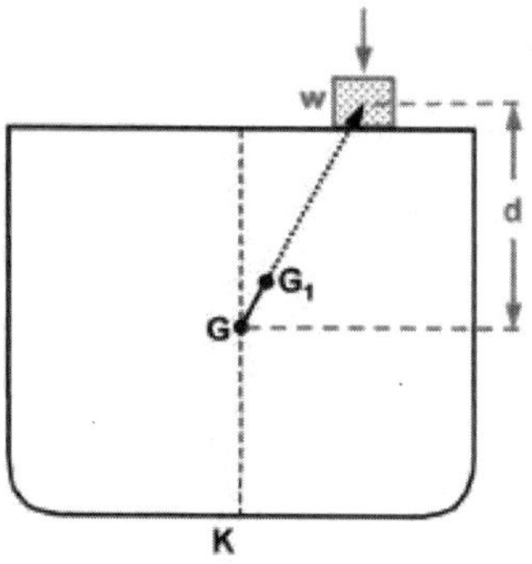

Fig. 5.8

The vertical component of the shift of G is calculated by the formula:

$$\mathbf{GGv = \frac{w \times d}{W + w}}$$

where: **'w'** is the weight loaded.
'd' is the *vertical* distance between G of the ship and g of the loaded weight.
'W' is the ship's *initial* displacement.

<u>NOTE</u> A common mistake in using this formula is to use the initial KG of the ship instead of d! Also note that the displacement increases because a weight is loaded, hence: 'W + w' in the formula!

<u>Example 2</u>
A ship displaces 12500 t and has an initial KG of 6.5 m. Calculate the final KG if 1000 t of cargo is loaded into the lower hold at Kg 3.0 m.

<u>Solution</u>

$$GGv = \frac{w \times d}{W + w} = \frac{1000 \times (6.5 - 3.0)}{12500 + 1000} = 0.259\ m$$

Initial KG	*6.500 m*
GGv down	*0.259 m*
FINAL KG	***6.241 m***

<u>Example 3</u>
A ship displaces 17200 t and has an initial KG of 8.4 m. Calculate the final KG if 1400 t of cargo is loaded onto the main deck at Kg 10.5 m.

<u>Solution</u>

$$GGv = \frac{w \times d}{W + w} = \frac{1400 \times (10.5 - 8.4)}{17200 + 1400} = 0.158\ m$$

Initial KG	*8.400 m*
GGv up	*0.158 m*
FINAL KG	***8.558 m***

5.2.3 *Effect of discharging a weight*

Whenever a weight is discharged, G will move *directly away from the centre of gravity of the discharged weight (g).*

Consider the ship shown where a weight is discharged from the upper deck. G moves to G_1.

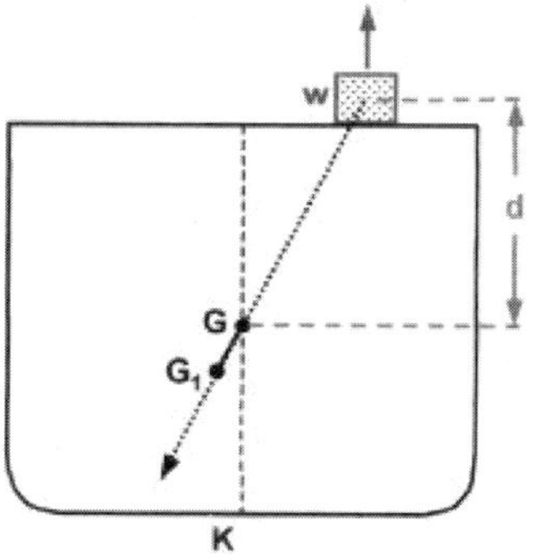

Fig.5.9

In this case the KG of the ship will *decrease*

The vertical component of the shift of G is calculated by the formula: $$\mathbf{GG_V = \frac{w \times d}{W - w}}$$

where: ***'w'*** is the weight discharged.
'd' is the *vertical* distance between G of the ship and g of the discharged weight.
'W' is the ship's *initial* displacement.

<u>Example 4</u>

A ship has a displacement of 13400 t and an initial KG of 4.22 m. 320 t of deck cargo is discharged from a position Kg 7.14 m. Calculate the final KG of the ship.

<u>Solution</u>

$$GGv = \frac{w \times d}{W - w} = \frac{320 \times (7.14 - 4.22)}{13400 - 320} = 0.071 \text{ m down}$$

Initial KG	*4.220 m*
GGv	*0.071 m*
FINAL KG	***4.149 m***

<u>Example 5</u>

A ship displaces 18000 t and has an initial KG of 5.30 m. Calculate the final KG if 10000 t of cargo is discharged from the lower hold (Kg 3.0 m).

<u>Solution</u>

$$GG_1 = \frac{w \times d}{W - w} = \frac{10000 \times (5.3 - 3.0)}{18000 - 10000} = 2.875 \text{ m}$$

Initial KG	*5.300 m*
GGv ~~up~~ DOWN	*2.875 m*
FINAL KG	***~~8.175~~ m***

5.3 MULTIPLE WEIGHT PROBLEMS

It would be very tedious to do a calculation for every single weight that is shifted, loaded on or discharged from the ship.

In practice *'moments about the keel'* are taken to determine the final KG of the ship, where:

MOMENTS (t-m) = WEIGHT (t) × DISTANCE (m)

If a ship is considered, then: **MOMENTS (t-m) = DISPLACEMENT (t) × KG (m)**

Therefore: **KG (m) = $\frac{\textbf{MOMENTS (t-m)}}{\textbf{DISPLACEMENT (t)}}$**

When a number of weights are shifted, loaded or discharged, the moments for each weight are calculated. These are summed up and simply divided by the final displacement of the ship to give the final KG.

A tabular approach is adopted and the method is easily illustrated by way of an example. One important point to note is that the first weight to be entered into the table is that of the ship's *initial displacement* along with the ship's *initial KG*.

Example 6
A ship displaces 10000 t and has a KG of 4.5 m.

The following cargo is worked: *Load:* *120 t at Kg 6.0 m;*
730 t at Kg 3.2 m.
Discharge: *68 t from Kg 2.0 m;*
100 t from Kg 6.2 m.
Shift: *86 t from Kg 2.2 m to Kg 6.0 m.*

Calculate the final KG.

Consider the table shown. Each weight is multiplied by its KG to give a moments value. The sign of this value (+ or -) depends on whether the weight is loaded or discharged. In the case of the weight that is shifted, this is simply treated as two separate weights: one that is discharged; and another of same weight that is loaded!

	WEIGHT (t)	KG (m)	MOMENTS (t-m)
Ship (+)	10000	4.50	45000.00
Load (+)	120	6.00	720.00
Load (+)	730	3.20	2336.00
Discharge (-)	-68	2.00	-136.00
Discharge (-)	-100	6.20	-620.00
* Discharge (-)	-86	2.20	-189.20
*Load (+)	86	6.00	516.00
FINAL	**10682**	**4.459**	**47626.80**

The final KG (4.459 m) is simply found using the formula: $KG\ (m) = \frac{MOMENTS\ (t\text{-}m)}{DISPLACEMENT\ (t)}$

i.e. $\frac{47626.80}{106882.00}$ = ***4.459 m***

Note Answers should be given to 3 decimal places. This method may be used for single weight problems also, with the advantage being that the direction of movement of G (either up or down) need not be considered. A final KG is 'automatically' calculated!
To prove this you should rework the previous single weight examples.

A prerequisite for any KG calculation to be correct is that the ship's *Lightweight Displacement* and *KG* values be accurate. This is the subject of *Section 19 - Inclining Experiment.*

5.4 CENTRE OF BUOYANCY (B)

'Centre of Buoyancy' of a ship is defined as being at the geometric centre of the underwater volume of the ship at a particular instant and is the point through which the total buoyancy force (Bf) is considered to act vertically upwards.

Its position will constantly move as the ship moves at sea.

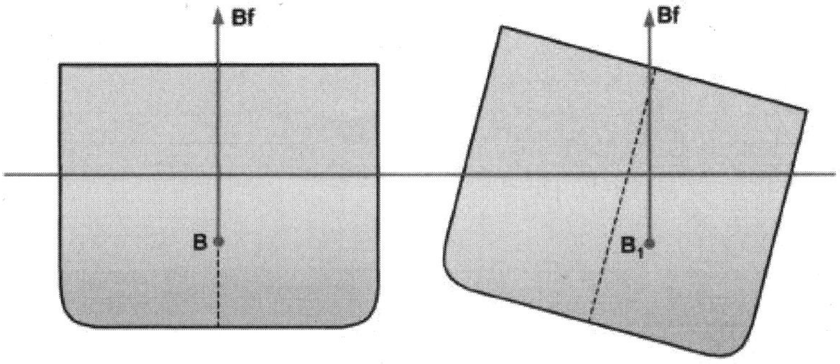

Fig. 5.10

Although the centre of gravity (G) is assumed to remain in the same place as the ship heels (provided weights do not shift within the ship), *the centre of buoyancy constantly moves as the ship pitches, rolls and heaves*.

As the displacement (and draught) of the ship changes, so will the position of the centre of buoyancy when the ship is upright.

The vertical position of the centre of buoyancy is termed the KB, being the vertical distance from the keel (K) to the centre of buoyancy (B).

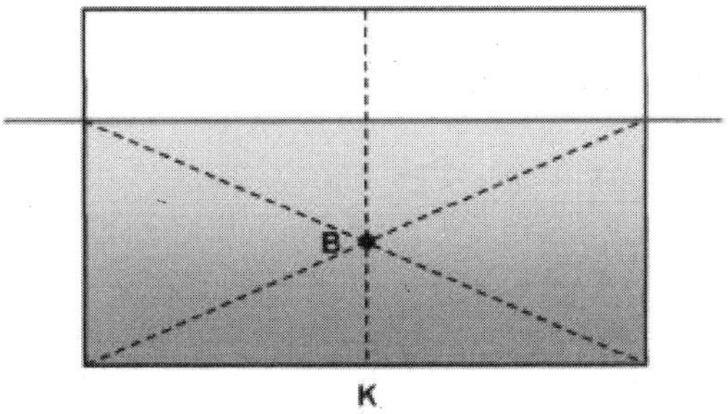

Fig. 5.11

For a box-shaped vessel on even keel KB is *half the draught.*

SECTION 6 - INTRODUCTION TO TRANSVERSE STATICAL STABILITY

INTRODUCTION

Having discussed the positions of the centre of gravity and the centre of buoyancy in the previous section, it is now appropriate to introduce how their relative positions affect the stability of a ship as it is heeled.

In this section the stability of a ship is introduced in terms of how it may be quantified within small angles of heel. It introduces the *'Curve of Statical Stability'* or *'GZ Curve'* as a means of representing the stability of a ship in a graphical format.

Learning Objectives

On completion of this section the learner will achieve the following:

1. Understand the term *'Transverse Statical Stability'.*
2. Understand the term *'Righting Lever'* and how righting levers are presented as a *'Curve of Statical Stability'* (GZ Curve) for different angles of heel.
3. Understand the term *'Righting Moment'.*
4. Understand the term *'Initial Transverse Metacentre'* and it's relevance to the initial stability of a ship when heeled within small angles.
5. Understand the term *'Metacentric Height'* and it's relevance to current IMO minimum stability criteria.
6. Calculate the *'Moment of Transverse Statical Stability'* for a ship at a specified angle of heel.

6.1 TRANSVERSE STATICAL STABILITY

'Transverse statical stability' is a term used to describe the ability of a ship to return to the upright when it has been forcibly heeled by an external force and is momentarily at rest when floating in still water.

The words: *external force;*
momentarily at rest; and;
still water are very important.

A simple way of considering the above statement is to imagine someone with a model boat floating in a bath of *still water*. The model is held in a heeled position, representing the *external force*, and then let go. If a snapshot photograph is taken the instant that the person lets go of the model, then the positions of the centre of gravity and centre of buoyancy may be considered at the same instant, hence the term *momentarily at rest*. This idea should be borne in mind when considering transverse statical stability.

When a ship is heeled at sea by wind and waves the situation might be different to our imagined still water situation. This is one of the limitations of evaluating ship stability for still water conditions only to be applied in the dynamic environment in which the ship actually operates!

It is the relative positions of the centre of gravity (G) and the centre of buoyancy (B) as the ship is heeled to a particular angle that determines how stable a ship is.

Consider the ship shown. When upright, in *still water,* lines of action of both the weight force (Wf) and buoyancy force (Bf) acting through the points G and B respectively are shown. If the ship is heeled by an *external force* to some angle the relative positions of G and B change causing the lines of action of Wf and Bf to become horizontally separated.

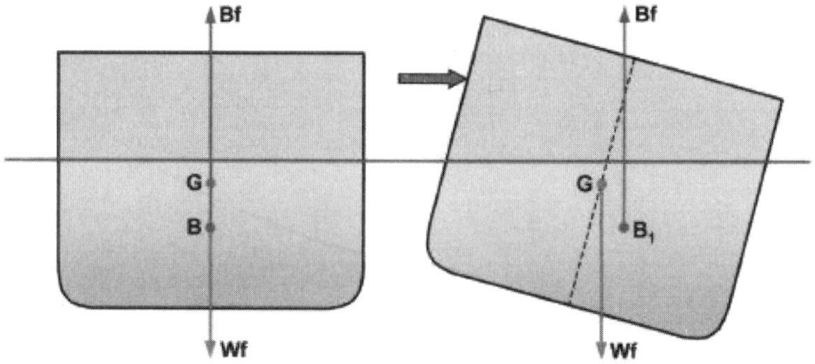

Fig. 6.1

If the external force is removed it is evident that the ship will return to the upright as a result of the forces acting through G and B_1.

6.2 RIGHTING LEVER (GZ)

Righting lever (GZ) is defined as the horizontal distance, measured in metres, between the centre of gravity (G) and the vertical line of action of the buoyancy force (Bf) acting through the centre of buoyancy (B_1) when the ship is heeled.

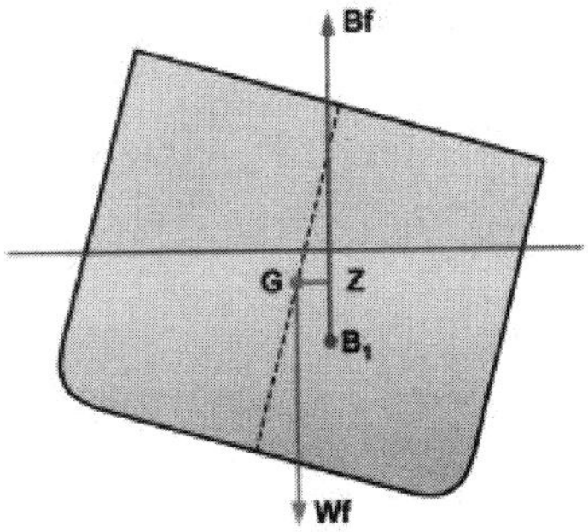

Fig. 6.2

Righting lever (GZ) increases to some maximum value and then decreases as the ship progressively heels further.

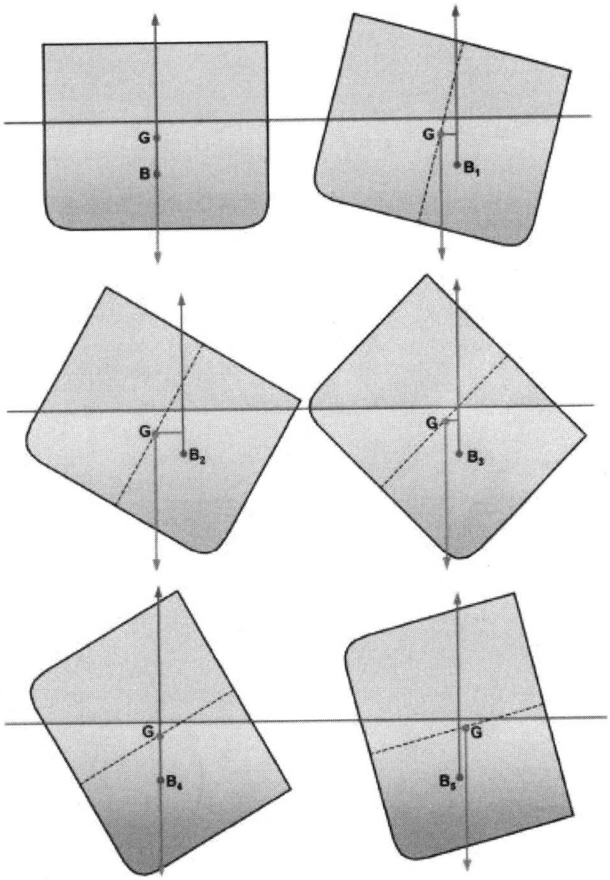

Fig. 6.3

The righting levers for specified angles of heel are represented on a Curve of Statical Stability, *commonly known as a* GZ Curve *as shown.*

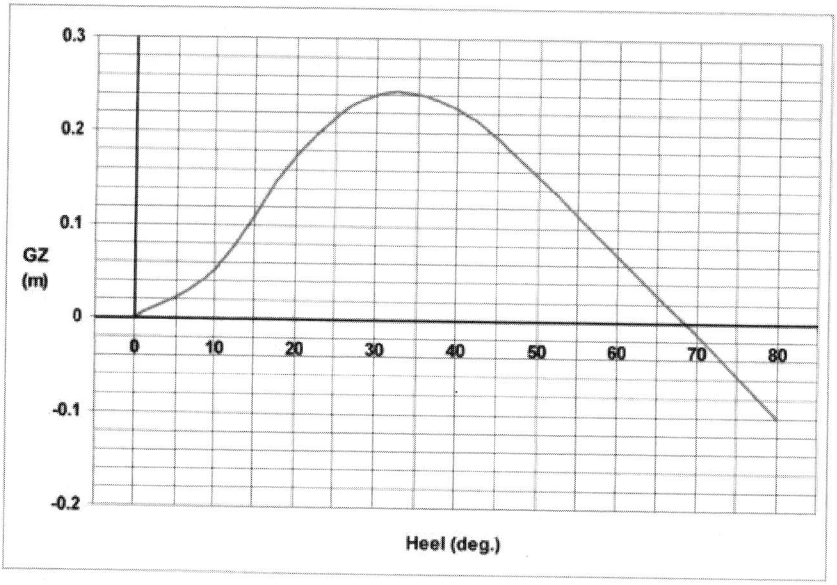

Fig. 6.4

The procedure for producing such a curve is discussed in *Section 10.*

6.3 MOMENT OF STATICAL STABILITY (RIGHTING MOMENT)

The *moment of statical stability*, commonly referred to as the *righting moment,* at any given angle of heel is found by:

RIGHTING MOMENT (t-m) = GZ (m) × DISPLACEMENT (t)

which results from the buoyancy force (Bf) (being equal to the ship's displacement (Wf)), acting on the end of the lever GZ, which pivots about G.

The righting moment at any angle of heel represents the *instantaneous 'value' of the ship's ability to return to the upright, expressed in tonnes-metres, when the ship is in 'still water' conditions and is momentarily at rest i.e. acceleration forces as the ship rolls are ignored.*

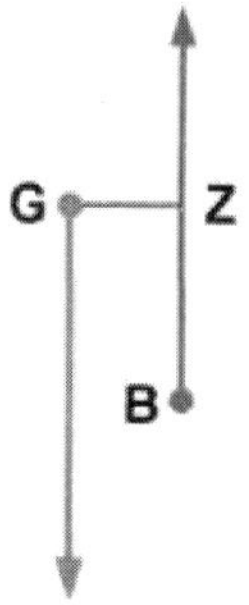

Fig. 6.5

Example 1

Calculate the moment of statical stability (righting moment) for a ship with a displacement of 12000 tonnes if the righting lever (GZ) is 0.46 m when heeled over.

Solution

RIGHTING MOMENT = GZ × DISPLACEMENT
RM = 0.46 × 12000
RM = ***5520 t-m***

6.4 INITIAL TRANSVERSE METACENTRE (M)

Is defined as the point of intersection of successive lines of action of buoyancy force (Bf) when the ship is in the initial upright condition and subsequently heeled conditions.

It is assumed to be at a *fixed position* when the ship is heeled within *small angles* only.

Consider the ship shown.

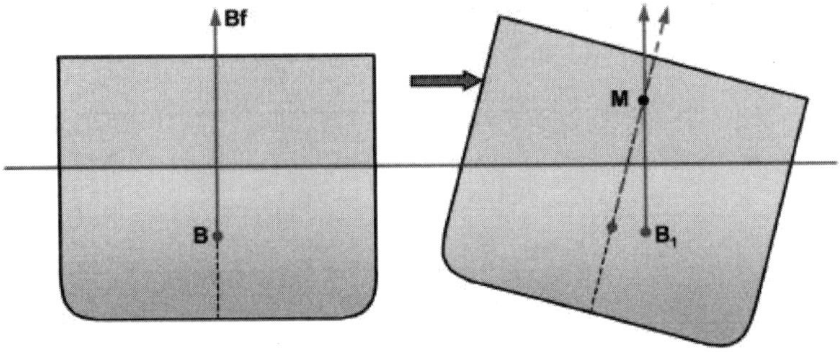

Fig. 6.6

When the ship heels beyond small angles the point of intersection has to move, hence the term *Initial Transverse Metacentre*.

It's position is expressed as a height above the keel in metres and is termed KM.

The value of KM is tabulated in ship's hydrostatic data and its position varies with draught.

The Initial Transverse Metacentre is investigated further in *Section 8*.

6.5 METACENTRIC HEIGHT (GM)

This is the vertical distance between the ship's centre of gravity (G) and the initial transverse metacentre (M).

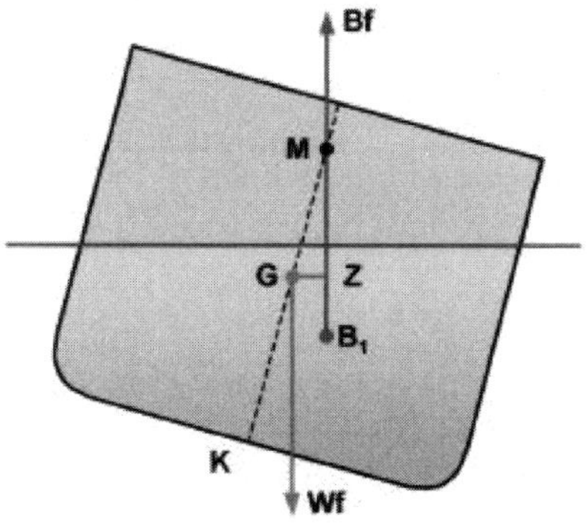

Fig. 6.7

The GM is very important in determining the *initial stability* of the ship i.e. the stability of the ship at small angles of heel.

If the centre of gravity (G) of the ship shown was higher, the righting lever (GZ) would be smaller and the ship would be less stable (since the righting moment would be smaller!).

If the centre of gravity (G) of the ship shown was lower, the righting lever (GZ) would be larger and the ship would be more stable (since the righting moment would be larger!).

Consider the vertical positions of the centre of gravity (G) and the initial transverse metacentre (M) for the ship shown in *Figure 6.7.*

M is *above* G.

KM - KG = GM

where GM is a *positive value.*

Whenever M is *above* G the ship will be in a *stable condition*, in other words, the ship will have *positive stability*. It is the aim of the officer in charge of loading the ship to ensure that this is the case at all times.

In the normal loaded condition the initial metacentric height (GM) should not be less than 0.15 m. (Code on Intact Stability for All Types of Ships Covered by IMO Instruments (IMO) - Chapter 3 Section 3.1.2.4.)

6.6 CALCULATING THE MOMENT OF STATICAL STABILITY AT *SMALL* ANGLES OF HEEL

In triangle GZM: $\sin\theta = \frac{OPP}{HYP} = \frac{GZ}{GM}$

Therefore: **$GZ = GM \times \sin\theta$**

Having found GZ:

RIGHTING MOMENT = GZ × DISPLACEMENT

Note The above formula for GZ can only be used for *small* angles of heel.

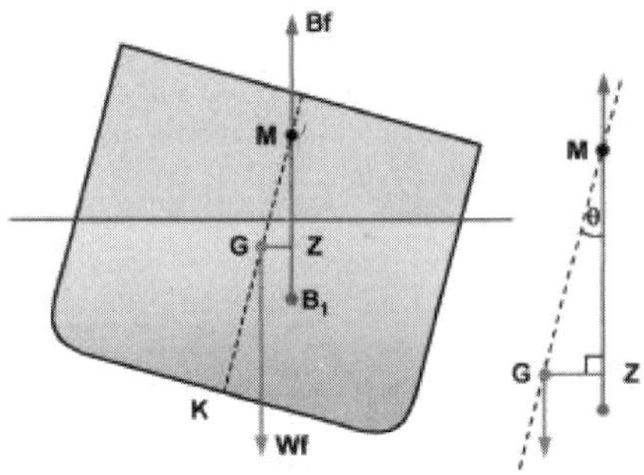

Fig. 6.8

Example 2

A ship has a displacement of 9420 tonnes and a KM of 9.22 m. In its present loaded condition the KG is 7.46 m.

Calculate the moment of statical stability available if the ship is heeled to:

(a) 2 deg.

(b) 4 deg.

(c) 8 deg.

Solution

KM	*9.22 m*
KG	*7.46 m*
GM	*1.76 m*

(a)

$GZ = GM \times \sin\theta$

$GZ = 1.76 \times \sin 2^\circ = 0.06142$ m

RM = GZ × DISPLACEMENT.

RM = 0.06142 × 9420 = **578.6 t-m**

(b)

$GZ = GM \times \sin\theta$

$GZ = 1.76 \times \sin 4^\circ = 0.12277$ m

RM = GZ × DISPLACEMENT

RM = 0.12277 × 9420 = **1156.5 t-m**

(c)

$GZ = GM \times \sin\theta$

$GZ = 1.76 \times \sin 8^\circ = 0.24494$ m

RM = GZ × DISPLACEMENT

RM = 0.24494 × 9420 = **2307.4 t-m**

Example 3

A ship has a displacement of 8900 tonnes, a corresponding KM of 9.400 m and a KG of 7.620 m.

(a) Calculate the moment of statical stability when the ship is heeled to 5 degrees.

(b) A weight of 200 tonnes is shifted from the lower hold (Kg 4.26 m) to the upper deck (Kg 12.60 m).
Calculate the moment of statical stability that will now exist if the ship is again heeled to 5 degrees.

Solution

(a)

KM	*9.400 m*
KG	*7.620 m*
GM	*1.780 m*

GZ = GM × Sin θ; *GZ = 1.780 × Sin 5° = 0.15514 m*
RM = GZ × DISPLACEMENT; *RM = 0.15514 × 8900 =* ***1380.7 t-m***

(b) *Take moments about the keel:*

	WEIGHT (t)	KG (m)	MOMENTS (t-m)
Initial displ.	8900	7.62	67818.0
Discharge	-200	4.26	-852.0
Load	200	12.60	2520.0
FINAL	**8900.0**	**7.807**	**69486.0**

KM	9.400
FINAL KG	7.807
FINAL GM	**1.593**

GZ = GM × Sin θ; *GZ = 1.593 × Sin 5° = 0.13884 m*
RM = GZ × DISPLACEMENT; *RM = 0.13884 × 8900 =* ***1235.7 t-m***

Available righting moment has reduced as a result of the increased KG!

In this section the transverse statical stability of a *stable* ship at *small* angles of heel has been discussed.

A *small angle of heel* is often considered to be any inclination of the ship up to approximately 10°. A more accurate definition of a *small angle* of heel for a particular ship is the subject of discussion for *Section 16 - The Wall Sided Formula.*

SECTION 7 - CONDITIONS OF STABILITY

INTRODUCTION

In the previous section, *transverse statical stability* was discussed in terms of a ship that was in a *stable* condition only. It is essential to discuss the behaviour of a ship when it may become *unstable*.

A ship may become unstable if the centre of gravity (G) is allowed to rise too high. There are a number of possible causes of this, principle ones being the loading of too much weight high up in the ship and the effect of free surfaces in slack tanks.

This section simply discusses stability and instability in terms of the relative positions of G, B and M.

Learning Objectives

1. Understand the term *'stable condition'.*
2. Understand the term *'neutral condition'.*
3. Understand the terms *'unstable condition'* and *'angle of loll'.*

7.1 STABLE CONDITION

A ship is in a *stable* condition of stability if, when heeled by an external force in still water to a small angle of inclination, *it returns to the upright when the force is removed.*

Consider a ship that is floating upright in still water, with the positions of G and B as shown, where the initial transverse metacentre (M) is above G.

i.e. KM - KG = GM; which has a *positive* value.

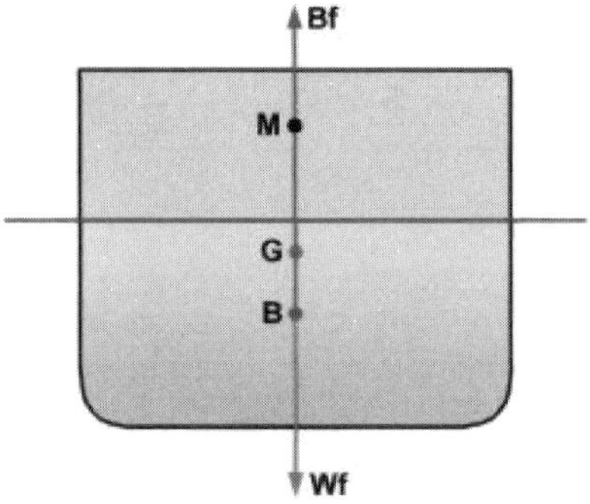

Fig. 7.1

The ship is now heeled by an external force to a *small angle* of inclination.

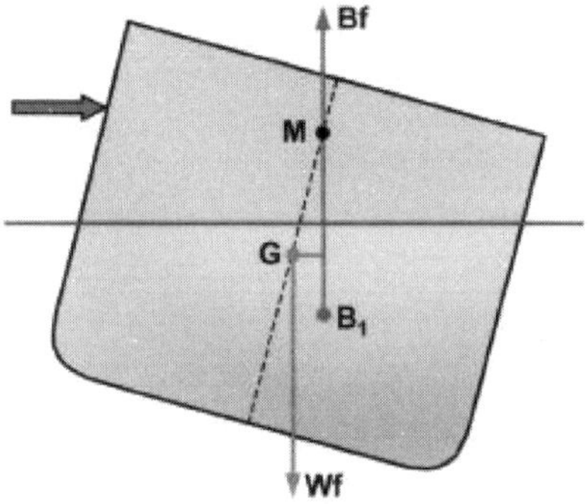

Fig. 7.2

Consider the lines of action of weight force (Wf), acting downward from G, and buoyancy force (Bf), acting upwards from B_1 through the initial transverse metacentre (M). The ship will want to return to the upright condition when the external force is removed.

In this stable condition the righting lever GZ is acting to right the ship.
G is below M; initial GM is positive.

7.2 NEUTRAL CONDITION

A ship is in a *neutral* condition of stability if, when heeled by an external force in still water to a small angle of inclination, *it comes to rest at an indeterminate angle of heel within small angles of inclination.*

Consider a ship that is floating upright in still water with G and B as shown. The initial transverse metacentre (M) is at the same height as G.

i.e. KM - KG = 0; *GM = 0*

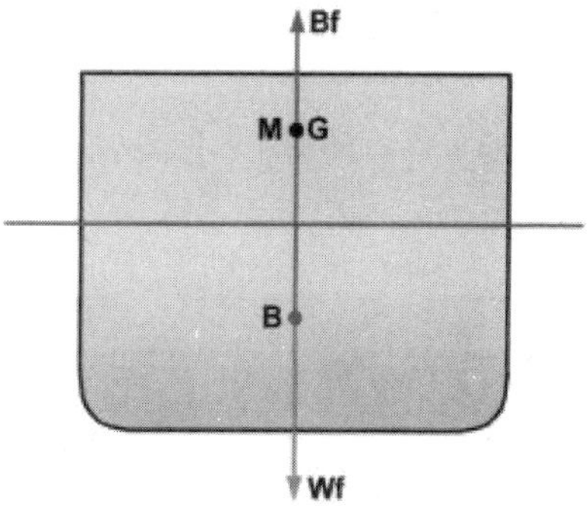

Fig. 7.3

The ship is now heeled by an external force to a *small angle* of inclination.

Since the ship has *no GM*, the lines of action of Wf and Bf remain in the *same vertical*; there is *no horizontal separation* between them when the ship is heeled within *small angles* of inclination. Thus, righting lever GZ will not exist.

In this neutral condition the righting lever GZ will not exist. G is at the same height as M; the ship has zero GM. The ship will settle at an indeterminate angle of heel within small angles when acted upon by successive external forces.

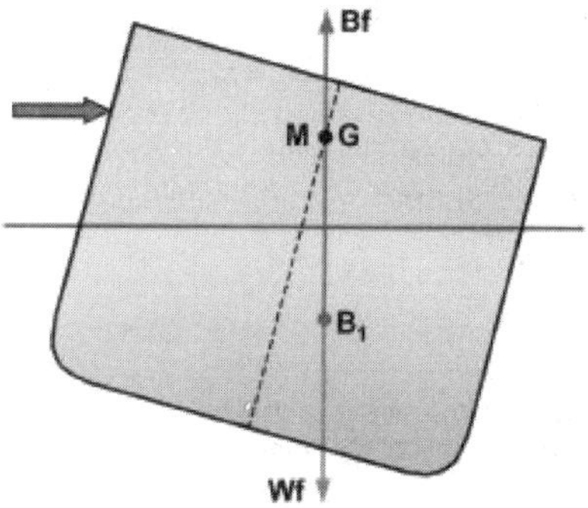

Fig. 7.4

If the ship is heeled *beyond* small angles the centre of buoyancy (B) will move *outboard* of the centre of gravity (G). This causes a positive righting lever, GZ, to take effect to return the ship back to some indeterminate small angle of heel once the external force is removed.

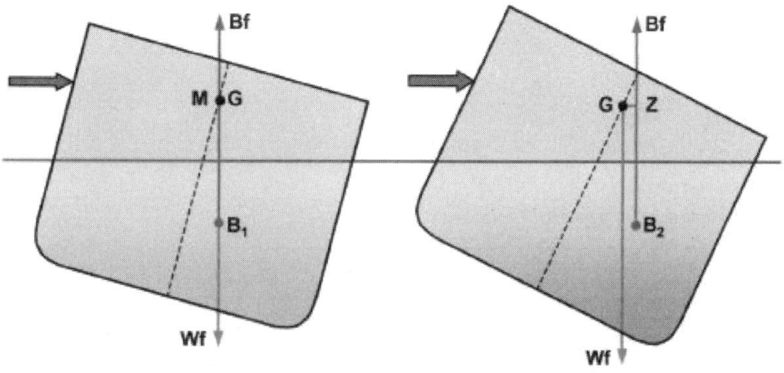

Fig. 7.5

Note

When heeled beyond the initial small angles of inclination the initial transverse metacentre (M) no longer applies - hence the term *initial*. At these larger angles of heel M can be assumed to be at some indeterminate position on the line of action of buoyancy force (Bf) at any instant - it just depends where the point of intersection of the lines of action of buoyancy force are at that particular instant as the ship is in the process of heeling!

7.3 UNSTABLE CONDITION AND ANGLE OF LOLL

A ship is in an *unstable* condition if, when heeled by an external force in still water to a small angle, *it continues to heel further when the external force is removed.*

Consider a ship that is floating upright in still water with G and B as shown. The initial transverse metacentre (M) is below G.

i.e. KM - KG = GM; which has a *negative* value.

The ship now heels to a small angle of inclination.

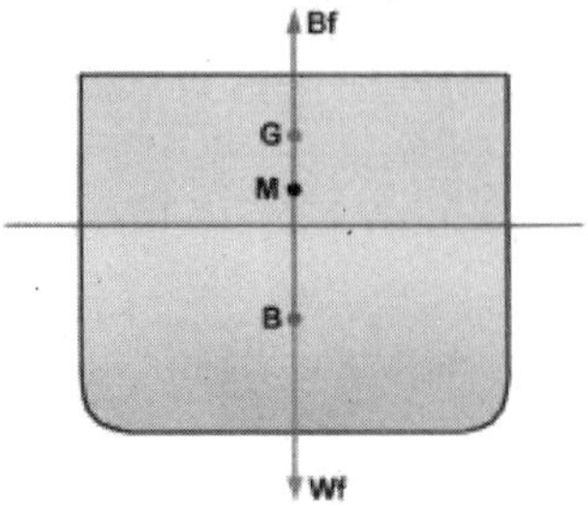

Fig. 7.6

Consider the lines of action of Wf and Bf. They are acting in such a way to cause the ship to heel further over. *GZ is a capsizing lever!*

The question that now comes to mind is: *Will the ship capsize?*

Possibly! As the ship continues to heel, the centre of buoyancy (B) will move outward as the underwater volume of the ship changes shape.

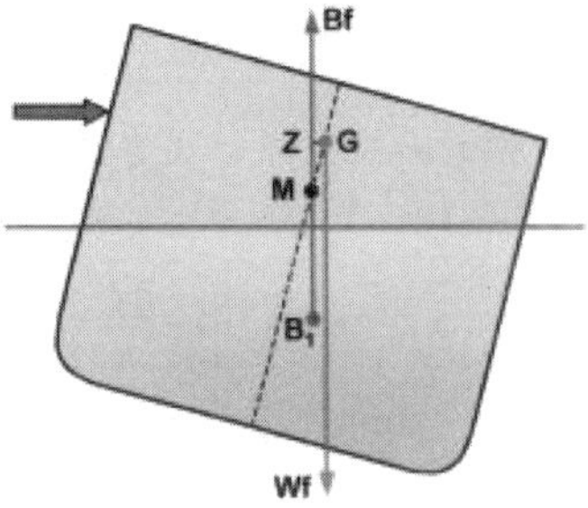

Fig. 7.7

Provided that the centre of buoyancy can move sufficiently outboard to attain a new position vertically below G then the capsizing lever will disappear and the ship will come to rest at an *angle of loll. If the centre of gravity were very high then the ship would possibly capsize.*

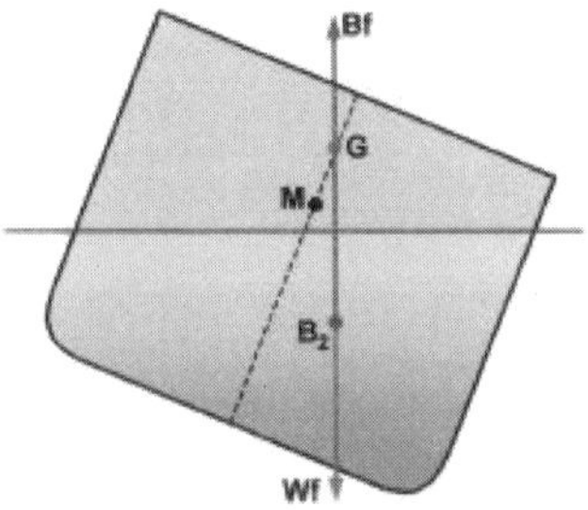

Fig. 7.8

If the ship is heeled *beyond* the angle of loll the centre of buoyancy (B) will move outboard of the centre of gravity (G). This causes a positive righting lever (GZ) that will act to *return the ship back to the angle of loll.*

<u>Note</u> A ship lying at an angle of loll is in a potentially dangerous situation. If wind and/or waves were to cause the ship to roll through the vertical it would, in theory, come to rest at the same angle of loll on the other side. However, the momentum of the ship as it rolls over may be sufficient to cause it to capsize. In any event, cargo shift would be likely which would cause the situation to worsen further.

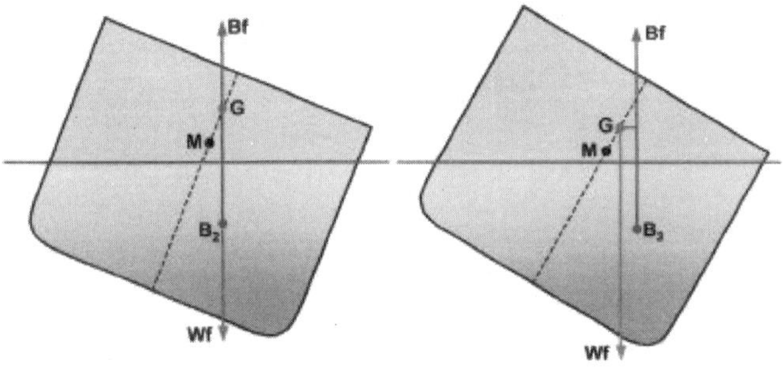

Fig. 7.9

The effects of 'free liquid surfaces' in slack tanks are a principal cause of instability in ships. *Section 9* considers free surface effect in detail. Whenever instability is suspected the procedures in *Section 15* must be strictly followed.

SECTION 8 - INITIAL TRANSVERSE METACENTRE

INTRODUCTION

When designing a ship the factors that influence the height of the initial transverse metacentre (KM) are of prime importance. It follows that the greater the KM value, then the greater will be the GM for any given KG. It is important to appreciate that *KG alone* is not the influencing factor on the ship's initial condition of stability. It will be seen in this section that KM changes with draught/displacement; this means that a particular KG value may give adequate initial stability with respect to GM at one draught but not at another.

In this section, the learner will calculate KM values for box-shaped vessels whereby it will be seen at first hand the factors that influence KM.

Metacentric diagrams are introduced as a means of graphical representation of the ship's initial stability.

Learning Objectives

On completion of this section, the learner will achieve the following:

1. Understand more comprehensively the term *Initial Transverse Metacentre*.
2. Calculate KM values for a box-shaped vessel and produce a *metacentric diagram*.
3. Use a metacentric diagram to determine the condition of stability of a ship at various draughts for a given assumed KG.
4. Use a metacentric diagram to determine the required final KG to ensure that a ship completes loading with a required GM.
5. Understand the factors affecting KM.

8.1 INITIAL TRANSVERSE METACENTRE EXPLAINED

The initial transverse metacentre is the *point of intersection of the lines of action of buoyancy force (Bf) when the ship is in the initial upright condition and subsequently heeled conditions, within small angles of heel.*

Consider the ship shown, heeled to some small angle of inclination.

It can be seen that a wedge of buoyancy has been transferred from the high side to the heeled side (bb_1). The resultant movement of B to B_1 at this instant is one that is *parallel to* and in the *same direction* as the *shift of the centroid of the transferred volume of buoyancy*.

BB_1 could be calculated using the formula:

$$BB_1 = \frac{v \times bb_1}{V}$$

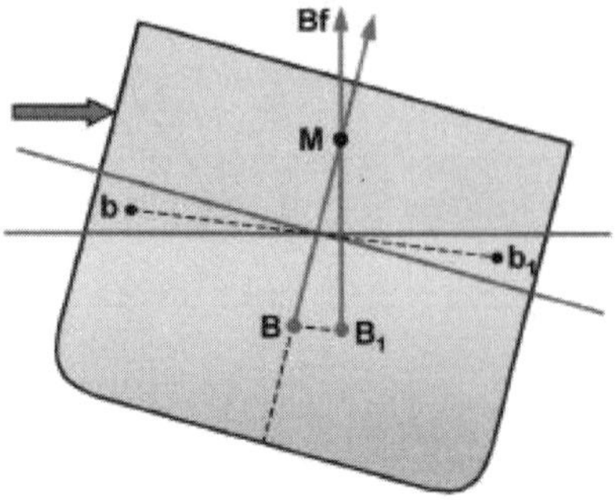

Fig. 8.1

where:

- ***v*** is the volume of the transferred wedge;
- ***bb_1*** is the distance through which it's centroid has moved, and;
- ***V*** is the volume of displacement of the ship.

(Note that this formula is similar to the shift of a single weight formula!)

8.1.1 Metacentric Radius

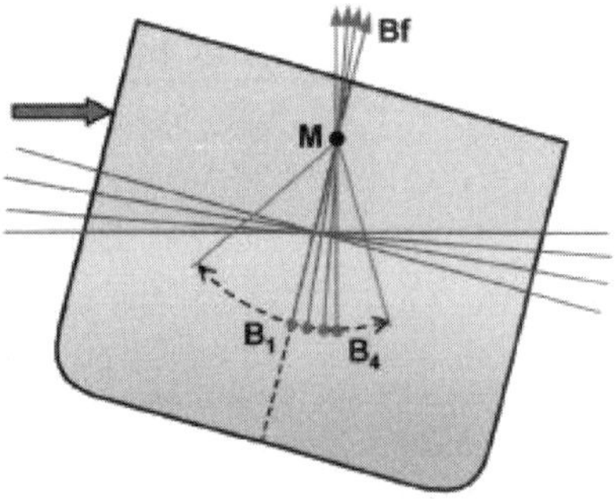

Fig. 8.2

If B is plotted for several *small angles* of heel, it may be assumed that it follows the arc of a circle centred at M.

BM is termed the *metacentric radius*.

8.1.2 Calculating KM for box-shaped vessels

It is convenient to consider the KM for a box-shaped vessel because the maths is simple, however, the same principles will apply for ship shapes. KM is calculated by the formula:

$$KM = KB + BM$$

For a box-shaped vessel on an even keel:

$$KB = \frac{\text{draught}}{2}$$

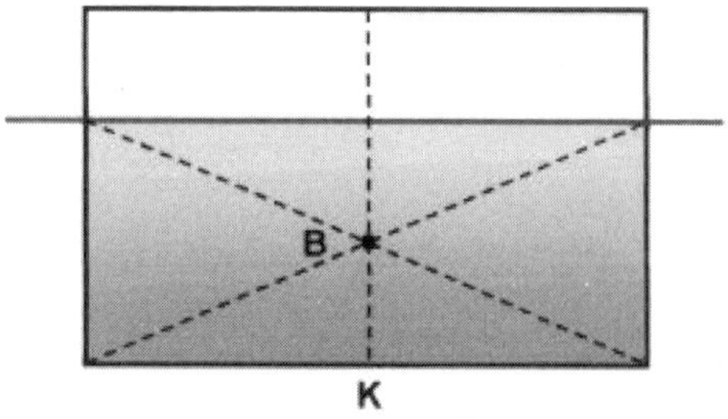

Fig. 8.3

BM is calculated by: $$\mathbf{BM = \frac{I}{V}}$$

where I is the *moment of inertia (second moment of area)* of the water-plane area (WPA) about a longitudinal axis of rotation passing through the centre of the water-plane area; and V is the *volume of displacement* of the vessel.

8.1.2.1 Moment of inertia (second moment of area) of the water-plane area

Consider the water-plane area of a box-shaped vessel shown.

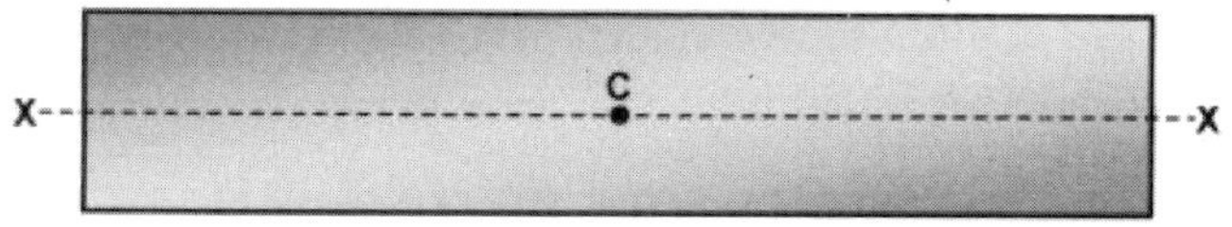

Fig. 8.4

C is the geometric centre of the water-plane area and **XX** is the longitudinal axis about which it is to be rotated.

(In reality, it is the ship that will rotate about this axis as it heels, however it is convenient to think of the water-plane area rotating about the same axis instead!)

For a box-shaped vessel: $$\mathbf{I = \frac{LB^3}{12}}$$

where L and B are the *length* and *breadth* of the water-plane area respectively. *I* is in units of metres^4 (m^4).

At this level it is not necessary to understand the derivation of this formula, leave that to the men in white coats!

Since: $$\mathbf{BM = \frac{I}{V}}$$

it follows that: $$\mathbf{BM_{BOX} = \frac{LB^3}{12V}}$$

Therefore: $$\mathbf{BM_{BOX} = \frac{LB^3}{12LBd}}$$

thus: $$\mathbf{BM_{BOX} = \frac{B^2}{12d}}$$

A simplistic, but convenient, way of considering the effect of the moment of inertia of the water-plane area is to consider that it gives a ship *resistance to heeling!*

Therefore, the *larger the water-plane area*, the *less easily a ship will heel.*

If the formula for BM is considered:

it is *the breadth of the water-plane area that is most influential.* It is generally accepted that the *broader* a ship is, the *more stable* it will be.

To summarise: $$\mathbf{KM = KB + BM}$$

and for a box-shaped vessel: $$\mathbf{KM_{BOX} = \frac{d}{2} + \frac{B^2}{12d}}$$

8.2 METACENTRIC DIAGRAMS

A *metacentric diagram* is a graph showing how the value of KM changes with draught.

8.2.1 Producing a metacentric diagram

Follow the procedure in the following example.

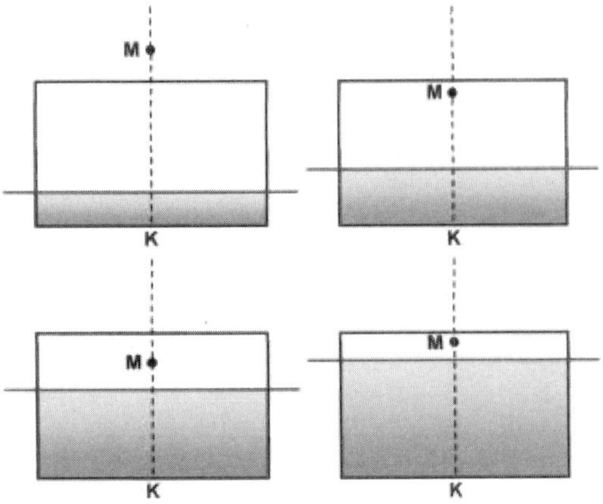

Fig. 8.5

Example 1

(a) Prove that the KM of a box-shaped vessel changes with draught as shown below for the range of draughts 1.00m to 15.00m given that length is 100m and breadth is 20m.

Solution

(a) The values for KM are shown having been calculated using:

KM = KB + BM where:

KB = $\frac{draught}{2}$; *and* *BM =* $\frac{B^2}{12d}$

From the values calculated it is seen that as draught increases, KM reduces to a minimum value and then starts to increase again.

Draught (m)	KB (m)	BM (m)	KM (m)
1	0.50	33.33	33.83
2	1.00	16.67	17.67
3	1.50	11.11	12.61
4	2.00	8.33	10.33
5	2.50	6.67	9.17
6	3.00	5.56	8.56
7	3.50	4.76	8.26
8	4.00	4.17	8.17
9	4.50	3.70	8.20
10	5.00	3.33	8.33
11	5.50	3.03	8.53
12	6.00	2.78	8.78
13	6.50	2.56	9.06
14	7.00	2.38	9.38
15	7.50	2.22	9.72

KM decreasing (draughts 1 to 8)

KM (draughts 8 to 15)

(b) If the KG were 9.00 m determine the following:
(i) the range of draughts
(ii) at which the vessel will be unstable;
(iii) the righting moment when the vessel is heeled to an angle of 5° if the upright draught is 3.00 m in salt water (RD 1.025).

Solution

Plot the values of KM with the X-axis labelled 'draught' and the Y-axis labelled 'KM' and 'KG'. Plot an assumed value of KG = 9.00 m on the graph (This will be a straight line!).

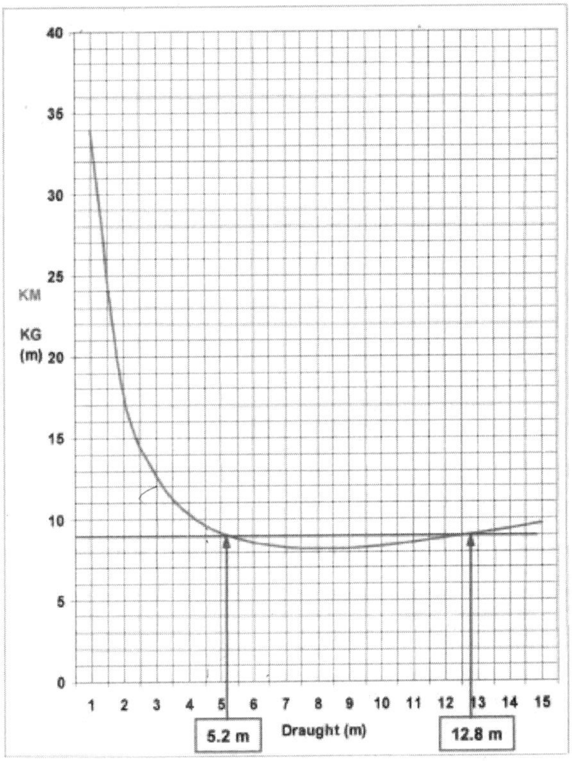

(i) *For the vessel to be unstable the KG must be greater than the KM at the draught concerned. This occurs between the draughts **5.2 m** and **12.8 m.***

(ii) *At a draught of 3.00 m KM was calculated to be 12.61m.*

KM 12.61 m
KG 9.00 m
GM 3.61 m

$DISPLACEMENT_{BOX} = L \times B \times d \times density$
$DISPLACEMENT_{BOX} = 100 \times 20 \times 3.00 \times 1.025$
$DISPLACEMENT_{BOX} = 6150$ tonnes
$GZ = GM \times \sin\theta$
$GZ = 3.61 \times \sin 5°$
$GZ = 0.31463....$metres

Therefore: *Righting moment = GZ × Displacement*
Righting Moment = 0.31463..... × 6150
*Righting moment = **1935 t-m***

8.2.2 To determine the final KG required to complete loading with a required GM

The box-shaped vessel for which the metacentric diagram was drawn had a length of 100 m and a breadth of 20 m. Consider the following example using the same metacentric diagram:

Example 2
It is intended to load the vessel to a maximum permissible draught in salt water of 4.5 m.
(a) *What is the maximum displacement of the vessel?*

Solution (a)

$DISPLACEMENT_{BOX} = (L \times B \times d) \times \rho$

$DISPLACEMENT_{BOX} = (100 \times 20 \times 4.5) \times 1.025$

$DISPLACEMENT_{BOX} = \mathbf{9225\ t}$

(b) *The required GM on completion of loading is 1.20 m. What is the maximum permissible KG?*

Solution (b)

From the graph the KM for a draught of 4.5 m is approximately 9.5 m.

	KM	9.5 m
Required:	GM	1.2 m
Maximum:	KG	**8.3 m**

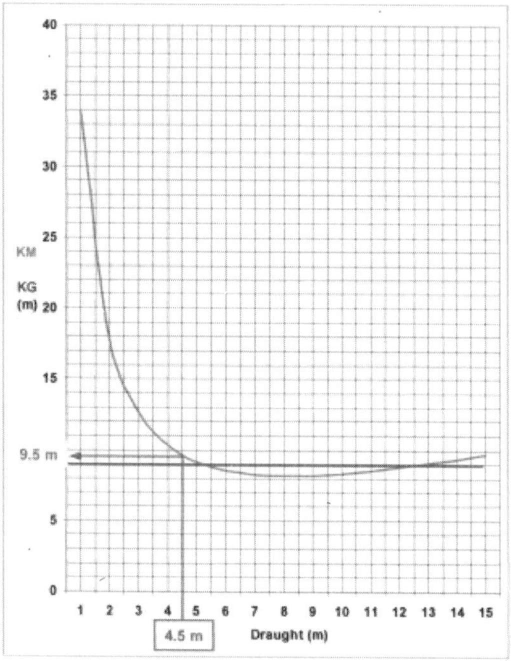

(c) *The vessel is currently loaded to displacement of 8465 t and has a KG of 8.40 m. What is the maximum Kg at which to load the final 760 t of cargo to ensure that the final GM requirement of 1.20 m is achieved?*

Solution (c)

In (b) it was determined that the maximum KG required was 8.3 m.

Take moments about the keel in the normal way but let 'x' equal the Kg at which to load the final 250 t.

In the formula: $KG\ (m) = \dfrac{MOMENTS\ (t\text{-}m)}{DISPLACEMENT\ (t)}$

the final KG is already known as 8.3 m!

$KG\ (m) = \dfrac{MOMENTS\ (t\text{-}m)}{DISPLACEMENT\ (t)}$

	WEIGHT (t)	KG (m)	MOMENTS (t-m)
Initial displ.	8465	8.4	71106
Load	760	x	760x
FINAL	**9225**		**71106 + 760x**

$8.3 = \dfrac{(71106 + 760x)}{9225}$

Solving 'x' will give the answer!

$8.3 \times 9225 = 71106 + 760x$

$76567.5 = 71106 + 760x$

$76567.5 - 71106 = 760x$

$5461.5 = 760x$ *Therefore:* $\dfrac{5461.5}{760} = x = \mathbf{7.186\ m}$

The maximum Kg at which to load the final 760 t weight is 7.186 m to ensure that the final KG does not exceed 8.3 m, thus ensuring that the final GM is at least 1.2 m.

Had the value of KM been calculated using the formula instead of taking it from the graph a more accurate answer would have resulted.
In practice the metacentric diagram for a ship (if available) will have to be used as presented in the stability data book, since the KM for a ship shape is not readily determined.

Note A question might ask for the *maximum weight that can be loaded at a specified Kg to ensure that a final KG value is not exceeded*. In this case the same method as in *Answer (c)* would be used except that *'x' equals the amount of cargo to load* at the specified Kg instead.

8.3 FACTORS AFFECTING KM

8.3.1 Beam

Consider two ships of different beam each heeled to the same angle of inclination as shown.

In the narrow ship a *small* wedge of buoyancy is transferred from the high side to the low side (bb_1) causing B to move to B_1.

Initial transverse metacentre is at M_1.

In the broader ship, a *larger* wedge of buoyancy is transferred from the high side to the low side (bb_1) causing B to move further out to B_1. Initial transverse metacentre is higher at M_2.

If the formula:

$$BB_1 = \frac{v \times bb_1}{V}$$

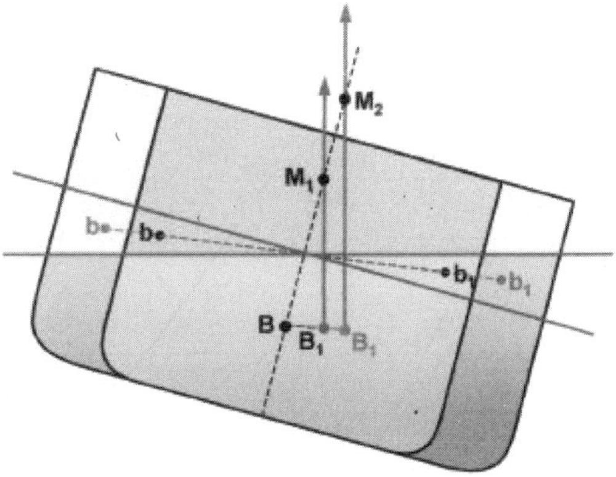

Fig. 8.6

is considered the larger the volume of the transferred wedge of buoyancy and the greater the distance through which the centroid of the wedge is caused to shift, the greater will be the outward movement of B as the ship is heeled.

Thus: *KM increases as beam increases resulting in broader ships being more stable.*

8.3.2 Draught

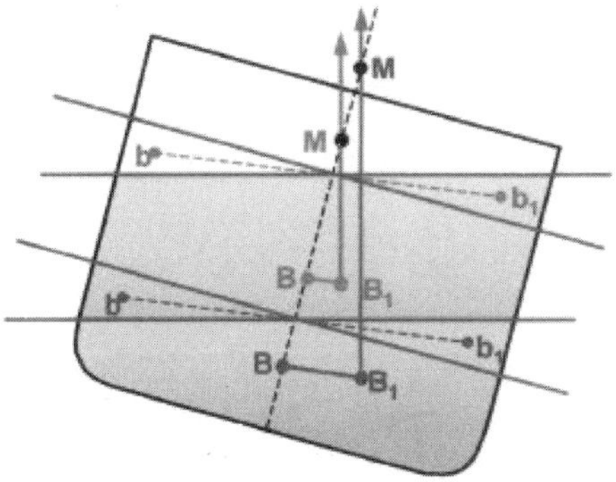

Fig. 8.7

Consider the formula:

$$BB_1 = \frac{v \times bb_1}{V}$$

At the *load draught (displacement)* the volume of the transferred wedge of buoyancy (v) represents a *smaller part* of the *total volume of displacement* of the ship (V) than it would at the *light draught (displacement).*

Thus: *KM decreases as draught increases for the normal range of operational draughts of a ship.*

SECTION 9 - FREE SURFACE EFFECT

INTRODUCTION

Most cases of instability in ships are the result of free surface effects. This occurs when tanks within the ship are only partially full, or slack. When a ship heels, liquid within a partially filled tank will move to the low side. It will be seen in this section that this adversely affects the transverse statical stability of a ship. It is essential that the learner fully understand the effect of slack tanks on transverse statical stability and the necessity to maintain to a minimum the number of slack tanks at any one time as appropriate.

Learning Objectives

On completion of this section the learner will achieve the following:

1. Understand the effect of a free liquid surfaces on the transverse statical stability of a ship.
2. Calculate the effect of *Free Surface* in a rectangular shaped tank and determine the effective (fluid) KG and GM of a ship.
3. Calculate *Free Surface Moments (t-m)* for a rectangular tank and take account of the free surface by including them in the KG moments table.
4. Understand the methods of representation of free surface data used in ship's tank sounding/ullage tables and use such data in typical calculations.
5. Understand the factors that influence free surface effect.

9.1 FREE SURFACE EFFECT AND THE LOSS OF TRANSVERSE STATICAL STABILITY

Consider the ship shown with a partially filled tank. Imagine the liquid in the tank is *frozen* and the ship is heeled to a small angle.

In the heeled condition GZ is the righting lever. Because the liquid is frozen it acts as a static weight and does not move.

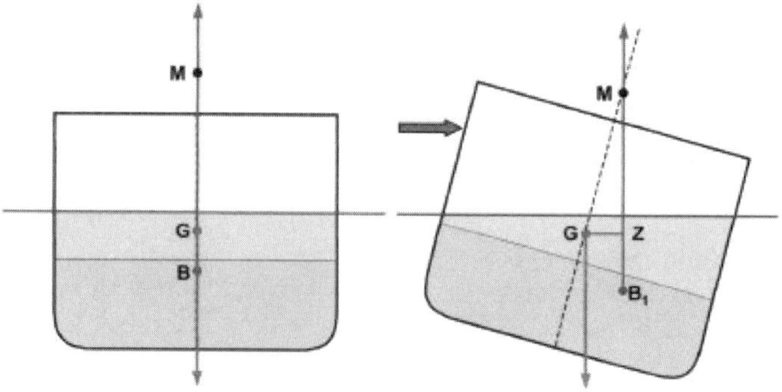

Fig. 9.1

Consider what will happen if the liquid in the tank thaws out and is then free to move as the ship heels, as would normally be the case.

In the initial upright condition everything appears as normal.

But note what happens as the ship is again heeled by an external force to the same *small* angle of inclination.

A wedge of the liquid is transferred to the low side of the ship (gg_1).

Since weight has shifted G moves *parallel* and in the *same direction* as the shift of the weight (GG_1).

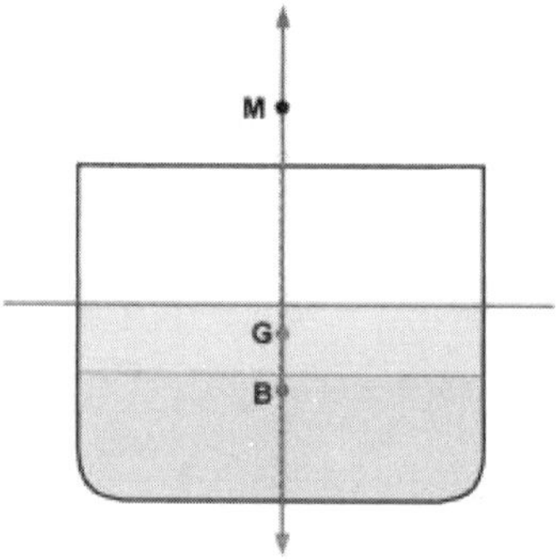

Fig. 9.2

This causes the righting lever to be reduced from GZ to G_1Z_1.

The righting lever G_1Z_1, is the same as the GZ that would have existed had *G been raised to G_V*.

GG_V represents the *virtual rise of G* that results from the free surface effect of the slack tank.

(G does *not* actually rise, but the movement of the liquid in the tank has the same effect on GZ values as if G had actually been caused to rise - hence the term *'virtual rise of G'!*)

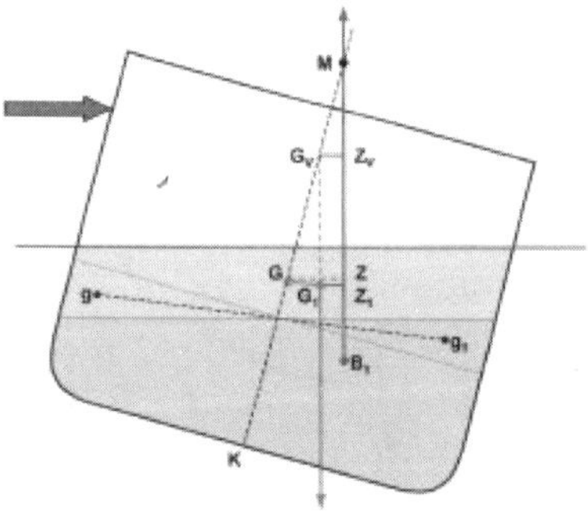

Fig. 9.3

Thus: *GM* is termed the *solid GM* ;
G_VM is termed the *effective* or *fluid GM*.

When calculating the GM of a ship it is important that the effects of free surfaces in slack tanks are considered. The loss of GZ will be greater as the number of slack tanks increases, i.e. the cumulative effect of all slack tanks must be accounted for.

IT IS ALWAYS THE FLUID GM THAT MUST BE DETERMINED TO TAKE ACCOUNT OF THE REDUCTION IN GZ VALUES THAT ARISES FROM LIQUID MOVEMENT WITHIN THE SHIP AS IT IS HEELED.

When the ship returns to the upright condition the centre of gravity (G_1) will move back to it's original position at G as the liquid in the tank finds its own level.

Remember; G does not actually move up to G_V.

9.2 FREE SURFACE DATA

For a *rectangular* shaped tank, the calculation of the effects of free surface is straightforward. However, not all tanks are this convenient regular shape and data relating to tanks of all shapes on board are included in the ship's *Tank Sounding Data* tables. This data can be provided in a number of ways, the person on board conducting the ships stability calculations must be familiar with the data supplied.

9.2.1 Calculating the effect of free surface in a rectangular shaped tank

For a tank that has a rectangular free surface the *virtual rise of G* in metres can be calculated by:

$$\mathbf{GG_V = \frac{lb^3}{12V} \times \frac{dt}{ds}}$$

ρ tank
ρ ship.

where: ***GG***$_V$ is the virtual rise of G in metres;
l is the tank length;
b is the tank breadth;
dt is the density of the liquid in the tank;
ds is the density of the water in which the ship floats (1.025 t/m^3);
and; ***V*** is the volume of displacement of the ship.

Since: DISPLACEMENT = VOLUME OF DISPLACEMENT × DENSITY

i.e. $W = V \times ds$

it follows that:

$$\mathbf{GG_V = \frac{lb^3}{12W} \times dt}$$

ρ

<u>*Example 1*</u>

A ship has an initial displacement of 10500 t and KG 7.60 m. A rectangular cargo oil tank of length 30 m and breadth 20 m is partially filled with 9600 t of oil (RD 0.86). If the Kg of the oil is 8.00 m, calculate the effective GM if the KM for the final displacement is 8.80 m.

Solution

1. *Taking moments about the keel, calculate the new solid KG.*

	WEIGHT (t)	KG (m)	MOMENTS (t-m)
Initial displ.	10500	7.60	79800
Cargo oil	9600	8.00	76800
FINAL	**20100**	**7.791**	**156600**

2. *Calculate the effect of free surface.*

$$GG_V = \frac{lb^3}{12W} \times dt \quad = \frac{30 \times 20^3}{12 \times 20100} \times 0.86 = 0.856\ m$$

(The final displacement must be used!)

3. *Calculate the solid GM and then apply the free surface correction to obtain the fluid GM.*

KM	8.800
SOLID KG	7.791
SOLID GM	1.009
FSE (GGv)	0.856
FLUID GM	**0.153**

9.2.2 *Free surface moments*

The *moment of inertia (I)*, often termed the *second moment of area,* of the free liquid surface of a rectangular tank may be determined by:

$$I = \frac{lb^3}{12} \ (m^4)$$

If the value of I is multiplied by the liquid density then a value of *'Free Surface Moments' (FSM's)* (t-m) is obtained.

$$\text{FSM's (t-m)} = \frac{lb^3}{12} \times dt$$

Consider the previous free surface effect formula: $GG_V = \frac{lb^3}{12W} \times dt$

Therefore: $GG_V = \frac{\text{FSM's}}{\text{Displacement}}$

Since: $\text{Final KG} = \frac{\text{Sum of moments}}{\text{Displacement}}$

it is evident from the above that the greater the value of the free surface moments, the greater the value of the effective KG and the greater the loss of GM (GG_V).

In calculating the effective GM it is usual to make allowances for free surfaces by incorporating the FSM's in the KG table where they must always be ADDED.

Consider the previous example.

Example 2

A ship has an initial displacement of 10500 t and KG 7.60 m. A rectangular cargo oil tank of length 30 m and breadth 20 m is partially filled with 9600 t of oil (RD 0.86). If the Kg of the oil is 8.00 m calculate the effective GM if the KM for the final displacement is 8.80 m.

Solution

1. *Calculate the FSM's using:*

$$\text{FSM's (t-m)} = \frac{lb^3}{12} \times dt$$

$$\text{FSM's (t-m)} = \frac{30 \times 20^3}{12} \times 0.86 = 17200 \text{ t-m}$$

2. *Taking moments about the keel, also adding the FSM's in the 'moments' column', calculate the fluid KG.*

	WEIGHT (t)	KG (m)	MOMENTS (t-m)
Initial displ.	10500	7.60	79800
Cargo oil	9600	8.00	76800
FSM's			17200
FINAL	**20100**	**8.647**	**173800**

3. *Apply the fluid KG value to the final KM to obtain the final fluid GM.*

KM	8.800
FLUID KG	8.647
FLUID GM	**0.153**

9.2.3 *Representation of free surface data in tank sounding/ullage tables*

In tank sounding or ullage tables free surface data for use in calculating the ship's effective KG and GM can be represented using alternative methods.

9.2.3.1 *Method 1 - Free surface moments for an assumed density value*

Consider the extract from a tank sounding table shown paying particular attention to the column headings.

Tank:	2CO.Stbd		Cargo Oil Density:		0.740
Sounding (cms)	**Weight (tonnes)**	**LCG (m foap)**	**TCG (m)**	**VCG (m)**	**FSM's (t-m)**
0	0.00	78.145	0.063s	1.503	0.0
25	13.00	78.29	2.963s	1.656	269.6
50	30.83	78.345	3.242s	1.785	300.3
75	49.31	78.366	3.365s	1.914	333.3
100	68.44	78.379	3.457s	2.044	368.2
125	87.92	78.389	3.525s	2.174	370.9
150	107.46	78.398	3.569s	2.302	373.7
175	127.05	78.406	3.602s	2.430	376.5
200	146.70	78.414	3.628s	2.557	379.3
225	166.41	78.421	3.648s	2.684	382.1

The table is for a cargo oil tank in a tanker - No. 2 Cargo Oil tank Starboard.

Free Surface Moments (FSM's) in tonnes-metres are tabulated for an *assumed liquid density* of 0.740 t/m^3.

Weight of liquid in the tank is tabulated against sounding for an *assumed liquid density* of 0.740 t/m^3.

VCG (Vertical Centre of Gravity or Kg) indicates the vertical position of the oil within the ship in terms of *metres above the keel* for the appropriate sounding.

<u>Example 3</u>

A ship displaces 5400 t and has a KG of 7.860 m. No. 2 Cargo Oil tank Stbd. is filled to a sounding of 150 cms with cargo oil RD 0.740. Calculate the final effective KG and GM if the KM for the final condition is 8.000 m. (Use the sounding table extract given.)

Tank:	2CO.Stbd		Cargo Oil Density:		0.740
Sounding (cms)	**Weight (tonnes)**	**LCG (m foap)**	**TCG (m)**	**VCG (m)**	**FSM's (t-m)**
0	0.00	78.145	0.063s	1.503	0.0
25	13.00	78.29	2.963s	1.656	269.6
50	30.83	78.345	3.242s	1.785	300.3
75	49.31	78.366	3.365s	1.914	333.3
100	68.44	78.379	3.457s	2.044	368.2
125	87.92	78.389	3.525s	2.174	370.9
150	107.46	78.398	3.569s	2.302	373.7
175	127.05	78.406	3.602s	2.430	376.5
200	146.70	78.414	3.628s	2.557	379.3
225	166.41	78.421	3.648s	2.684	382.1

Solution

Obtain cargo data from table.

Tank:	2CO.Stbd	Cargo Oil Density:	0.740

Sounding (cms)	Weight (tonnes)	LCG (m foap)	TCG (m)	VCG (m)	FSM's (t-m)
0	0.00	78.145	0.063s	1.503	0.0
25	13.00	78.29	2.963s	1.656	269.6
50	30.83	78.345	3.242s	1.785	300.3
75	49.31	78.366	3.365s	1.914	333.3
100	68.44	78.379	3.457s	2.044	368.2
125	87.92	78.389	3.525s	2.174	370.9
150	107.46	78.398	3.569s	2.302	373.7
175	127.05	78.406	3.602s	2.430	376.5
200	146.70	78.414	3.628s	2.557	379.3
225	166.41	78.421	3.648s	2.684	382.1

Calculate the final effective KG and hence the final effective GM.

	WEIGHT (t)	KG (m)	MOMENTS (t-m)
Initial displ.	5400.00	7.860	42444.0
Cargo oil	107.46	2.302	247.4
FSM's			373.7
FINAL	**5507.46**	**7.819**	**43065.1**

KM	8.000
FLUID KG	7.819
FLUID GM	**0.181**

For intermediate soundings, interpolation would be necessary to extract the values.

The previous example was straightforward, whereby the tank was loaded with liquid of the *same tabulated density*.

However, if liquid of a *different density* to that assumed by the tables had been run into the tank *the tabulated values of both weight and FSM's would be in error!*

Therefore, tabulated values must be corrected for the appropriate density.

(Both mass (weight) and the value of the FSM's are directly proportional to density.)

Consider the previous example again. This time *salt-water ballast (RD 1.025)* is loaded into the tank to the same level as before.

Example 4

A ship displaces 5400 t and has a KG of 7.860 m. No. 2 Cargo Oil tank Stbd. is filled to a sounding of 150 cms with salt water ballast RD 1.025. Calculate the final effective KG and GM if the KM for the final condition is 8.000 m. (Use the sounding table extract given.)

Tank:	2CO.Stbd	Cargo Oil Density:	0.740

Sounding (cms)	Weight (tonnes)	LCG (m foap)	TCG (m)	VCG (m)	FSM's (t-m)
0	0.00	78.145	0.063s	1.503	0.0
25	13.00	78.29	2.963s	1.656	269.6
50	30.83	78.345	3.242s	1.785	300.3
75	49.31	78.366	3.365s	1.914	333.3
100	68.44	78.379	3.457s	2.044	368.2
125	87.92	78.389	3.525s	2.174	370.9
150	107.46	78.398	3.569s	2.302	373.7
175	127.05	78.406	3.602s	2.430	376.5
200	146.70	78.414	3.628s	2.557	379.3
225	166.41	78.421	3.648s	2.684	382.1

Solution
Obtain cargo data from table as given.

Tank:	2CO.Stbd	Cargo Oil Density:	0.740

Sounding (cms)	Weight (tonnes)	LCG (m foap)	TCG (m)	VCG (m)	FSM's (t-m)
0	0.00	78.145	0.063s	1.503	0.0
25	13.00	78.29	2.963s	1.656	269.6
50	30.83	78.345	3.242s	1.785	300.3
75	49.31	78.366	3.365s	1.914	333.3
100	68.44	78.379	3.457s	2.044	368.2
125	87.92	78.389	3.525s	2.174	370.9
150	107.46	78.398	3.569s	2.302	373.7
175	127.05	78.406	3.602s	2.430	376.5
200	146.70	78.414	3.628s	2.557	379.3
225	166.41	78.421	3.648s	2.684	382.1

Actual mass of salt water ballast loaded is found by:

$$107.46 \times \frac{1.025}{0.740} = 148.85 \text{ tonnes}$$

Actual FSM's for the salt water ballast loaded is found by:

$$373.7 \times \frac{1.025}{0.740} = 517.625 \text{ tonnes-metres}$$

The Kg of the liquid is as before - not being affected by density!

Calculate the final effective KG and hence the final effective GM exactly as before.

	WEIGHT (t)	KG (m)	MOMENTS (t-m)
Initial displ.	5400.00	7.860	42444.0
SW ballast	148.85	2.302	342.7
FSM's			517.6
FINAL	**5548.85**	**7.804**	**43304.3**

KM	8.000
FLUID KG	7.804
FLUID GM	**0.196**

9.2.3.2 Method 2 - Moments of inertia (m^4) are tabulated

Consider the alternative extract from a tank-sounding table for the same tank shown.

Tank:	2CO.Stbd	

Sounding (cms)	Vol (cu. m)	LCG (m foap)	TCG (m)	VCG (m)	I (m4)
0	0.00	78.145	0.063s	1.503	0.0
25	17.57	78.29	2.963s	1.656	364.3
50	41.66	78.345	3.242s	1.785	405.8
75	66.64	78.366	3.365s	1.914	450.4
100	92.49	78.379	3.457s	2.044	497.6
125	118.81	78.389	3.525s	2.174	501.2
150	145.22	78.398	3.569s	2.302	505.0
175	171.69	78.406	3.602s	2.430	508.8
200	198.24	78.414	3.628s	2.557	512.6
225	224.88	78.421	3.648s	2.684	516.4

Moments of Inertia (I) in metres^4 (m^4) are tabulated.
Volume of liquid in the tank in cubic metres (m^3) is tabulated.

Density of the liquid is *not* considered.
To obtain the weight (mass) of the liquid and the Free Surface Moments which are to be incorporated into the KG moments table both *volume* and *I values as tabulated must be multiplied by the density of the liquid in the tank.*

<u>Example 5</u>
A ship displaces 5400 t and has a KG of 7.860 m. No. 2 Cargo Oil tank Stbd. is filled to a sounding of 150 cms with cargo oil RD 0.740. Calculate the final effective KG and GM if the KM for the final condition is 8.000 m. (Use the sounding table extract given.)

<u>Solution</u>
Obtain cargo data from table.

Tank:	**2CO.Stbd**				
Sounding (cms)	**Vol (cu. m)**	**LCG (m foap)**	**TCG (m)**	**VCG (m)**	**I (m4)**
0	0.00	78.145	0.063s	1.503	0.0
25	17.57	78.29	2.963s	1.656	364.3
50	41.66	78.345	3.242s	1.785	405.8
75	66.64	78.366	3.365s	1.914	450.4
100	92.49	78.379	3.457s	2.044	497.6
125	118.81	78.389	3.525s	2.174	501.2
150	145.22	78.398	3.569s	2.302	505.0
175	171.69	78.406	3.602s	2.430	508.8
200	198.24	78.414	3.628s	2.557	512.6
225	224.88	78.421	3.648s	2.684	516.4

× density gives t-m

Calculate the mass of oil in the tank. Mass = Volume × Density;Mass = 145.22 × 0.740 = 107.46 t

Calculate the FSM's for the oil. FSM's = I × Density; FSM's = 505.0 × 0.740 = 373.7 t-m

Calculate the final effective KG and hence the final effective GM as before.

	WEIGHT (t)	**KG (m)**	**MOMENTS (t-m)**
Initial displ.	5400.00	7.860	42444.0
Cargo oil	107.46	2.302	247.4
FSM's			373.7
FINAL	**5507.46**	**7.819**	**43065.1**

KM	8.000
FLUID KG	7.819
FLUID GM	**0.181**

9.2.3.3 Summary

You will not have a choice as to which of the two methods to use, it simply depends on the format of the tank sounding tables that are supplied to the ship.

Consider the significant errors in the calculation of GM that will occur if:

Tabulated FSM's for an assumed liquid density are not corrected for the actual density of the liquid in the tank!
Volume is not converted to mass!

Tabulated I values are not multiplied by the density of the liquid in the tank!

ALWAYS CHECK!

Tank sounding data for *M.V. Almar* are tabulated using assumed density values (Method 1).

9.3 FACTORS INFLUENCING FREE SURFACE EFFECT

Consider the free surface formula for loss of GM (GG_v): $\boxed{GG_V\,(m) = \frac{lb^3}{12W} \times dt}$

It is clear that the *breadth* of the tank is the most important factor.

9.3.1 Tank breadth

If a tank is subdivided, the loss of GM can be greatly reduced.
This can be demonstrated by way of the following *three* worked examples.

Example 6

A ship has a displacement of 12000 t and initial KG of 7.84 m.
A rectangular double bottom tank has the following dimensions; length 20 m, breadth 15 m and is filled with salt water ballast (RD 1.025) to a sounding of 2.00 m.
If the KM for the final condition is 8.00 m, calculate the final effective GM.

Solution

1. *Calculate the mass and Kg of the ballast water.*
   Mass = Volume × Density;
   Mass = (l × b × sounding) × density;
   Mass = (20 × 15 × 2) × 1.025 = 615.0 t

   Since it is a double bottom tank the Kg of the ballast water will be half the sounding:
   Kg = 0.5 × 2.0 = 1.00 m

2. *Calculate the FSM's for the rectangular free liquid surface:*

   $$FSM\text{'s (t-m)} = \frac{lb^3}{12} \times dt$$

   $$FSM\text{'s (t-m)} = \frac{20 \times 15^3}{12} \times 1.025 = 5765.6 \text{ t-m}$$

   Taking moments about the keel calculate the final KG and hence the final KM:

	WEIGHT (t)	KG (m)	MOMENTS (t-m)
Initial displ.	12000.00	7.840	94080.0
SW ballast	615.00	1.000	615.0
FSM's			5765.6
FINAL	**12615.00**	**7.964**	**100460.6**

KM	8.000
FLUID KG	7.964
FLUID GM	**0.036**

To satisfy the IMO intact stability requirements the minimum GM requirement for a ship is *0.15m*. This ship clearly does not satisfy that requirement!

Consider the same example but this time the tank will be *equally subdivided into two tanks.*

Example 7

A ship has a displacement of 12000 t and initial KG of 7.84 m.

A rectangular double bottom tank is equally subdivided has the following dimensions; length 20 m and breadth 15 m and is filled with salt water ballast (RD 1.025) to a sounding of 2.00 m.

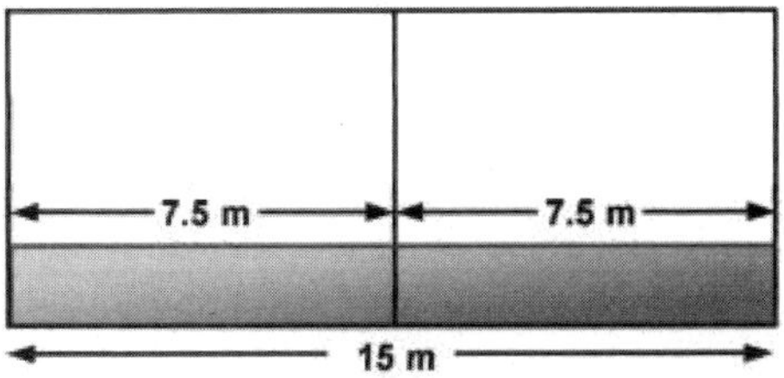

Fig. 9.4

If the KM for the final condition is 8.00 m calculate the final effective GM.
It can be seen that there are now *two* tanks each having a breadth of 7.5 m.

Solution

1. *Calculate the mass and Kg of the ballast water.*

   Mass = Volume × Density;
   Mass = (l × b × sounding) × density;
   Mass = (20 × 15 × 2) × 1.025 = 615.0 t

   Alternatively:
   Mass per tank = Volume × Density;
   Mass per tank = (l × b × sounding) × density;
   Mass = (20 × 7.5 × 2) × 1.025 = 307.5 t
   Total mass = 307.5 × 2 tanks = 615.0 t

   Since it is a double bottom tank the Kg of the ballast water will be half the sounding:
   Kg = 0.5 × 2.0 = 1.00 m

2. *Calculate the FSM's per tank for the rectangular free liquid surface:*

   $$FSM\text{'s (t-m)} = \frac{lb^3}{12} \times dt$$

   $$FSM\text{'s (t-m)} = \frac{20 \times 7.5^3}{12} \times 1.025 = 720.7 \text{ t-m}$$

   Total FSM's = 720.7 × 2 tanks = 1441.4 t-m

3. *Taking moments about the keel, calculate the final KG and hence the final GM:*

	WEIGHT (t)	KG (m)	MOMENTS (t-m)
Initial displ.	12000.00	7.840	94080.0
SW ballast	615.00	1.000	615.0
FSM's			1441.4
FINAL	**12615.00**	**7.621**	**96136.4**

KM	8.000
FLUID KG	7.621
FLUID GM	**0.379**

Subdividing the tank has resulted in the *final GM being much improved.*

This is a direct result of the reduced free surface moments.
For the undivided tank the total FSM's where 5765.6 t-m.
For the subdivided tank the total FSM's where 1441.4 t-m.
FREE SURFACE MOMENTS HAVE BEEN REDUCED TO ONE QUARTER OF THEIR ORIGINAL VALUE!

i.e. $\frac{5765.6}{4} = 1441.4$ t-m

Consider the same example but this time the tank will be *equally subdivided into three tanks.*

Example 8
A ship has a displacement of 12000 t and initial KG of 7.84 m. A rectangular double bottom tank, which is equally subdivided into three compartments, has length 20 m and overall breadth 15 m and is filled with salt water ballast (RD 1.025) to a sounding of 2.00 m.

If the KM for the final condition is 8.00 m, calculate the final effective GM.

It can be seen that there are now *three* tanks each having a breadth of 5.0 m.

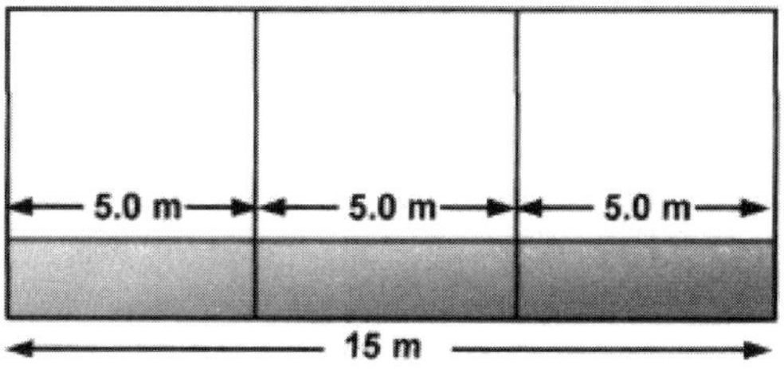

Fig. 9.5

1. *Calculate the mass and Kg of the ballast water.*

Mass = Volume × Density;
Mass = (l × b × sounding) × density;
Mass = (20 × 15 × 2) × 1.025 = 615.0 t

Alternatively:
Mass per tank = Volume × Density;
Mass per tank = (l × b × sounding) × density;
Mass = (20 × 5.0 × 2) × 1.025 = 205.0 t

Total mass = 205.0 × 3 tanks = 615.0 t

Kg = 0.5 × 2.0 = 1.00 m

2. *Calculate the FSM's per tank for the rectangular free liquid surface:*

$$FSM\text{'s (t-m)} = \frac{lb^3}{12} \times dt$$

$$FSM\text{'s (t-m)} = \frac{20 \times 5.0^3}{12} \times 1.025 = 213.542 \text{ t-m}$$

Total FSM's = 213.542 × 3 tanks = 640.625 t-m

3. *Taking moments about the keel calculate the final KG and hence the final KM:*

	WEIGHT (t)	KG (m)	MOMENTS (t-m)
Initial displ.	12000.00	7.840	94080.0
SW ballast	615.00	1.000	615.0
FSM's			640.6
FINAL	**12615.00**	**7.557**	**95335.6**

KM	8.000
FLUID KG	7.557
FLUID GM	**0.443**

As a result of subdividing the tank into three it is evident that the *final GM is further improved.*

This is a direct result of the reduced free surface moments.

For the undivided tank the total FSM's where 5765.6 t-m.
For the tank equally subdivided into three compartments the total FSM's where 640.6 t-m.

FREE SURFACE MOMENTS HAVE BEEN REDUCED TO ONE NINTH OF THEIR ORIGINAL VALUE!

i.e. $\frac{5765.6}{9} = 640.6$ t-m

The following conclusions may be drawn from the previous examples on subdivided tanks.

Equally subdividing a tank has the following effects on free surface:

(a) *No subdivision*

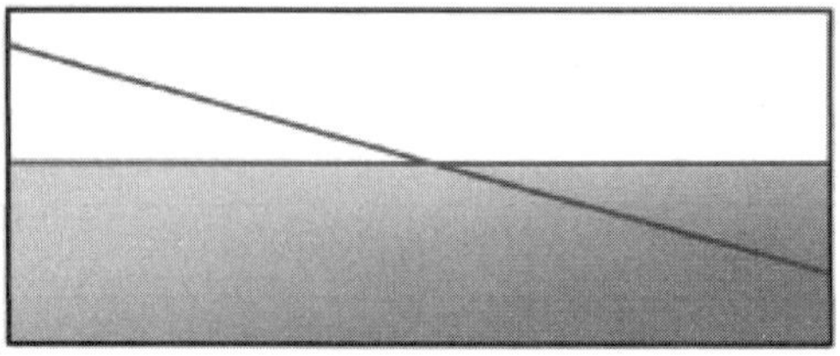

Fig. 9.6

(b) *A single subdivision*

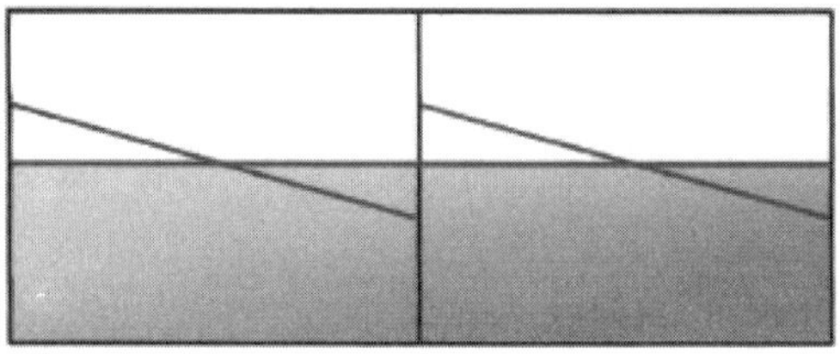

Fig 9.7

A single subdivision will reduce the free surface moments (and loss of GM) to *one quarter* of the original value.

(c) *Two subdivisions (creating three compartments)*

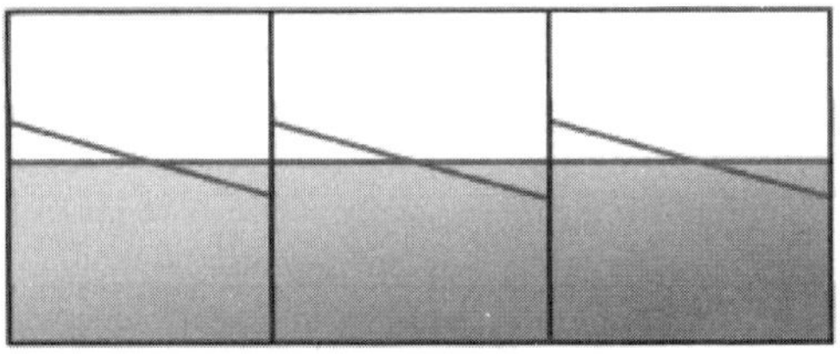

Fig. 9.8

Two subdivisions reduce the free surface moments (and loss of GM) to *one ninth* of the original value.

It follows that the original free surface moments (and loss of GM) will reduce by the factor of:

$$\frac{1}{n^2}$$

where ***n*** is the number of *equal sized* compartments into which the tank is subdivided.

Therefore, subdividing a tank into *four equal subdivisions* will reduce the FSM's to one sixteenth i.e.

$$\frac{1}{4^2} = \frac{1}{16}$$

and so on.......

It is usual to subdivide tanks into three compartments at most. The benefit of any further subdivision which would improve effective GM by a decreasing amount each time would be greatly offset by the additional steel weight and piping arrangements required. An exception might be in the case of a product or chemical carrier where such ships are designed to carry a wide range of cargoes at any one time in relatively smaller quantities.

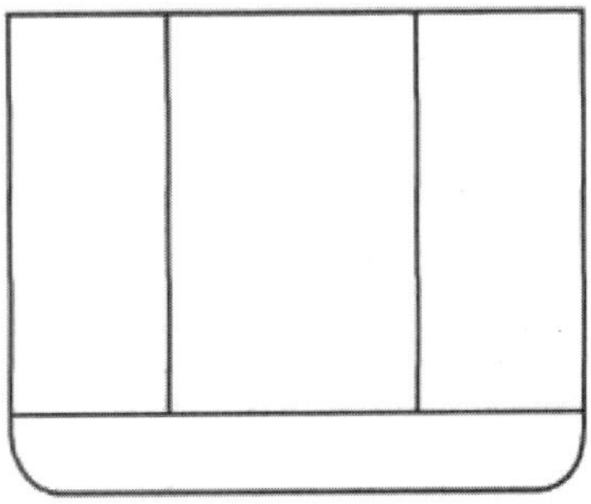

Typical oil tanker tank arrangement

Fig. 9.9

9.3.2 Tank length

Free surface moments (and loss of GM) are directly proportional to the length of the tank i.e. if the tank length is doubled so will be the value of the free surface moments (and loss of GM).

9.3.3 Density

Free surface moments (and loss of GM) are directly proportional to the density of the liquid in the tank as discussed in *9.2.3.1,* the greater the density of the liquid in the tank, the greater the FSM's and subsequent loss of GM.

9.3.4 Ship displacement

Free surface moments (and loss of GM) are inversely proportional to the displacement of the ship. For a given tank, the loss of GM will be smaller as the displacement increases and vice-versa. It should be noted that the actual free surface moments for any tank are *not* affected by the ship's displacement (since ship displacement is not included in the formula for their calculation anyway!).

9.4 IMPORTANT POINTS TO NOTE REGARDING FREE SURFACE MOMENTS

These are summarised as follows:

1. For a tank to be considered subdivided, it must be fitted with an *oil-tight* or *water-tight* longitudinal bulkhead ensuring that there is no possibility of liquid transfer. This means that any valves connecting the subdivided tanks must be capable of being fully closed.

2. A *wash plate* is fitted to prevent damage to internal tank plating that may be caused by wave action *within* the tank. *It does not reduce free surface effect!*

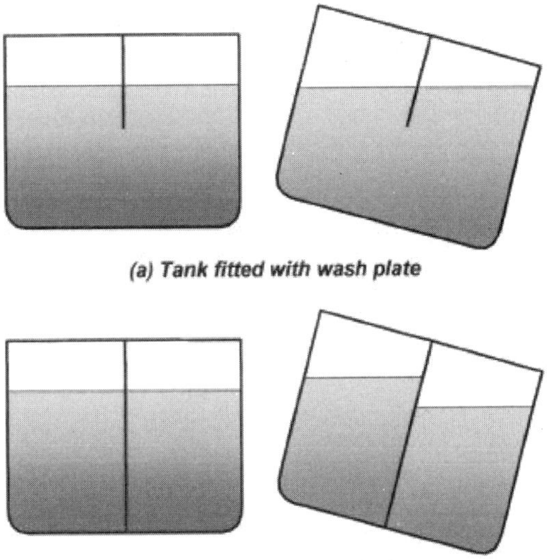

(a) Tank fitted with wash plate

(b) Tank fitted with longitudinal bulkhead

Fig. 9.10

3. If two similar rectangular tanks are filled to different levels, the *free surface moments for each will be the same.* (Consider the formula for FSM's if you are unsure!)

4. If a tank is *empty* or *pressed-up,* free surface moments will not exist in that tank.

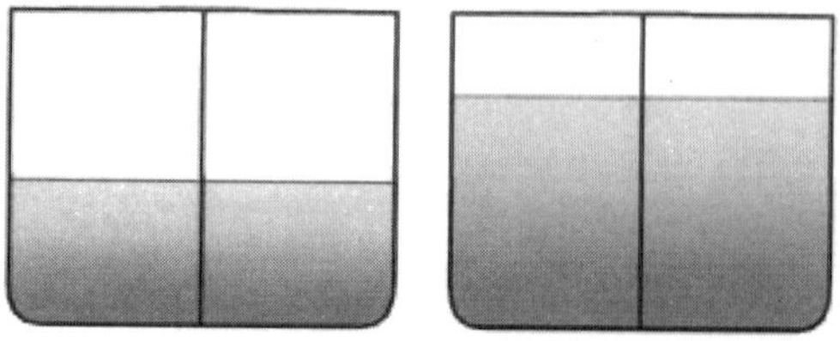

Fig. 9.11

5. When calculating the effective KG/GM, the free surface moments of *all* slack tanks must be incorporated into the KG moments table. (Loss of GM due to free surface will be that which results from the cumulative effects of all the slack tanks on board.)

SECTION 10 - CURVES OF STATICAL STABILITY (GZ CURVES)

INTRODUCTION

The *curve of statical stability*, or *GZ curve* as it is most commonly referred to, is a graphical representation of the ship's *transverse statical stability*.

Transverse statical stability is the term used to describe the ability of a ship to return to the upright, when it has been forcibly heeled by an external force and is momentarily at rest when floating in still water.

$$\text{RIGHTING MOMENT (t-m)} = \text{GZ (m)} \times \text{DISPLACEMENT (t)}$$

At any angle of heel, it is the *horizontal* disposition of G and B that determines the GZ value.

As a ship progressively heels over the *righting lever*, GZ, increases to some maximum value and then decreases until at some angle of heel it becomes negative i.e. it becomes a *capsizing lever.*

Calculating the value of GZ, at specified angles of heel for a ship's particular condition of loading, will allow a *curve of statical stability*, or *GZ curve*, to be produced.

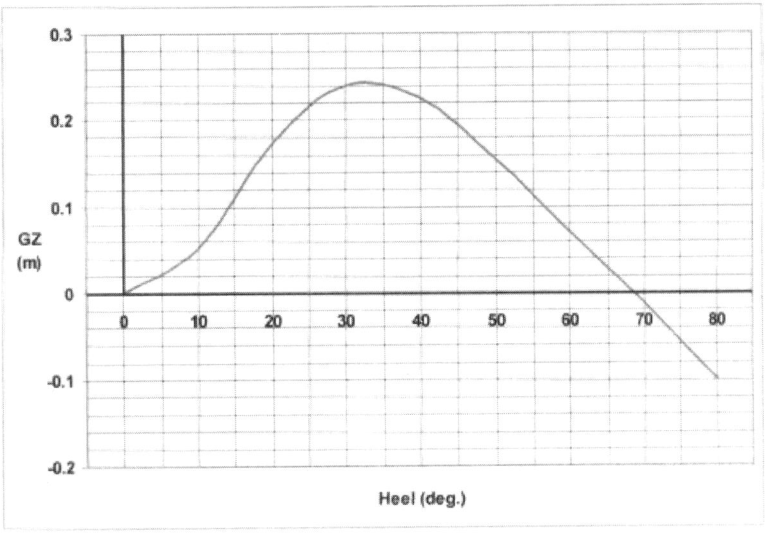

Fig. 10.1

The greater the values of GZ, the greater will be the *area* under the curve. Minimum standards with respect to the area under the curve (and other criteria) are specified in the *'Code on intact stability (IMO)'* and these are incorporated in the government legislation of most countries that adopt the IMO conventions.

Assessing compliance of a ship's loaded condition is considered in *Section 14*. It is the aim of this section to review the method of actually producing a curve of statical stability and to be able to extract basic information from it.

Learning Objectives

On completion of this section, the learner will achieve the following:

1. Understand the term *KN* and how *KN values* may be used to obtain GZ values for specified angles of heel.
2. Know the procedure for producing a curve of statical stability.
3. Identify the basic features of a curve of statical stability.
4. Understand the terms *Stiff* and *Tender* with respect to the curve of statical stability.

\LCULATING GZ VALUES

KN values

eels the centre of buoyancy (B) constantly
\nsverse position being dependent on:

- *the volume of displacement (and draught) of the ship;*
- *the angle of heel at any instant.*

The GZ value is predominantly dependent on the ship's KG. Because of the many possible positions of G, it is convenient to consider the GZ that would exist if G *were at the keel*, termed *KN*, and to make a correction for the actual height of G above the keel.

If the figure is considered:

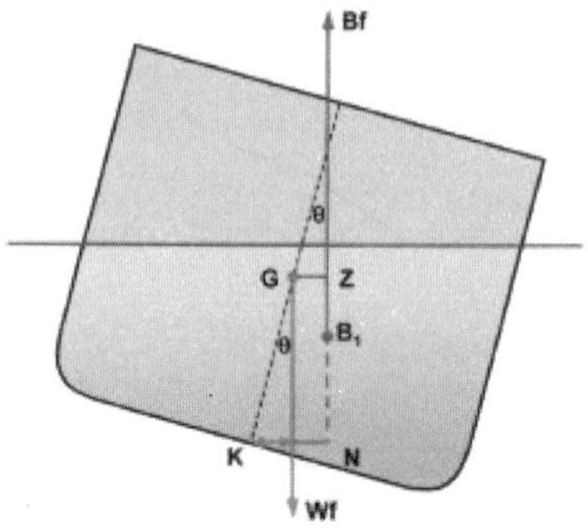

Correction to KN to obtain GZ value.

Fig. 10.2

$\text{Sine } \theta = \dfrac{\text{OPP}}{\text{HYP}}$ ∴ $\text{Sine } \theta = \dfrac{\text{Correction to KN}}{\text{KG}}$

Therefore: Correction to KN = KG × Sine θ

and: **GZ = KN - (KG Sine θ)**

Cross curves of stability (KN curves) are provided by the shipbuilder to allow GZ values to be determined for any value of displacement and KG. Alternatively, KN values may be tabulated.

It is usual that KN values are given for angles of heel at 10° or 15° intervals.

The KN values for *MV Almar* are given in tabulated format on page 16 of the stability data book.

For calculation purposes in this section, the tabulated KN values for MV Almar will be used. In some cases, interpolation of values may be necessary.

10.1.2 Procedure for calculating GZ values

Example 1

M.V. Almar completes loading with a displacement of 29000 t and a KG corrected for free surfaces of 8.92 m. Calculate the GZ values and GM if the KM for the loaded displacement is 9.46 m. (Use tabulated KN values for M.V. Almar.)

Solution

Using the formula: GZ = KN - (KG Sine θ) calculate the GZ values for the loaded condition.

Heel	10	20	30	40	60	80
KN	1.65	3.31	4.93	6.30	7.86	8.07
KG*Sin Heel	1.55	3.05	4.46	5.73	7.72	8.78
GZ	**0.10**	**0.26**	**0.47**	**0.57**	**0.14**	**-0.71**

KM	9.460
KG	8.920
GM	**0.540**

The GM calculated is that allowing for free surfaces since the question gave a fluid KG.

Fluid KG must always be used to calculate GZ values.

When KN values are *tabulated,* interpolation for displacement values other than those stated should be done, but it should be borne in mind that the rate of change of KN is not linear. If the KN values for *M.V. Almar* were plotted, they would be *curves - not straight lines!* However, any errors caused by interpolation of KN table values are likely to be negligible.

10.2 PROCEDURE FOR CONSTRUCTING THE CURVE OF STATICAL STABILITY

The following steps should always be undertaken when producing a curve of statical stability.

1. Determine the ship's displacement and effective KG for the condition being considered (effective KG being that taking into account free liquid surfaces in tanks).

2. From the hydrostatic data find the value of KM for the ship's displacement.

3. Find GM_{FLUID} using: $$GM = KM - KG_{FLUID}$$

4. Enter KN tables (or curves) and obtain KN value in metres for each angle of heel given.

5. Using: $$GZ = KN - (KG \text{ Sine } \theta)$$

   determine the GZ values for the angles of heel given.

6. Plot the GZ values.

7. Before joining all the points on the curve construct a vertical at 57.3° and from the base upwards mark off the value of the effective GM (using the GZ scale). From this point draw a straight line to the origin of the curve to be drawn. This will indicate the *initial trend* of the curve at *small angles of heel* and will assist in sketching the actual curve between the origin and the first plotted GZ value.

   (GZ and GM are closely related at small angles of heel.)

The curve for the GZ values calculated in *Example 1* is shown. Note the construction using the initial GM value of 0.54 m.

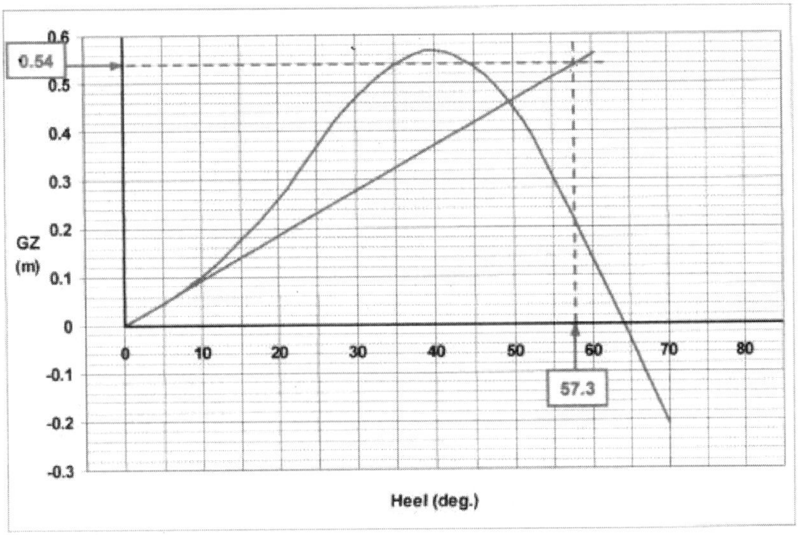

Fig. 10.3

10.3 BASIC INFORMATION AVAILABLE FROM THE CURVE OF STATICAL STABILITY

Consider the curve in the previous example. The following information can be extracted from it:

(a) *The GZ value for any angle of heel.*
This can be used to calculate the moment of statical stability for the ship at that particular angle of heel if the formula: RIGHTING MOMENT (t-m) = GZ (m) $\times$ DISPLACEMENT (t) is applied.

(b) *The maximum GZ and the angle of heel at which it occurs.*

(c) *The range of positive stability and the angle of vanishing stability (AVS).*

(d) *The approximate angle of deck edge immersion (θ_{DEI}).*

Figure 10.4 shows the ship heeled to the point where deck edge immersion takes place.

The angle at which this occurs is identified on the curve as the point where the *curve trend changes from increasing steepness to decreasing steepness.*

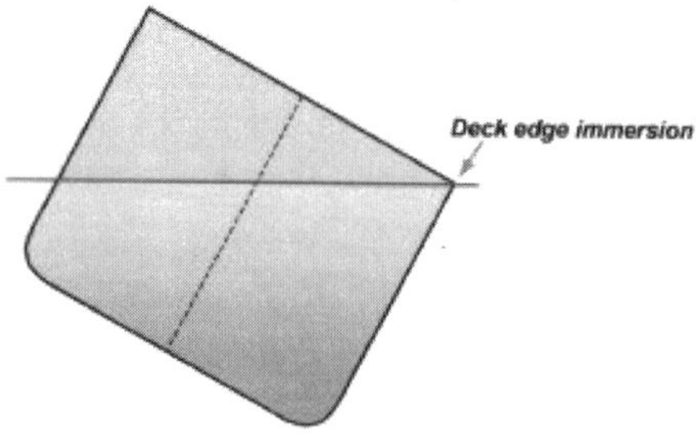

Fig. 10.4

This is known as the *point of inflexion* of the curve. It is often dfficult to estimate its position but it helps to identify the point of inflexion if a series of vertical lines are drawn on the curve. If each *slice* is taken in turn it may be considered if the trend is one of the following:

increasing steepness;
decreasing steepness;
or; *neither.*

It is only an approximation and open to interpretation!

Consider the curve constructed in the previous example, the aforementioned information is illustrated.

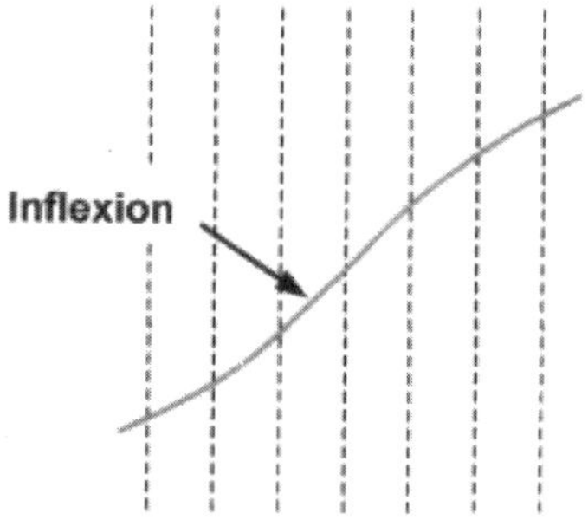

Fig. 10.5

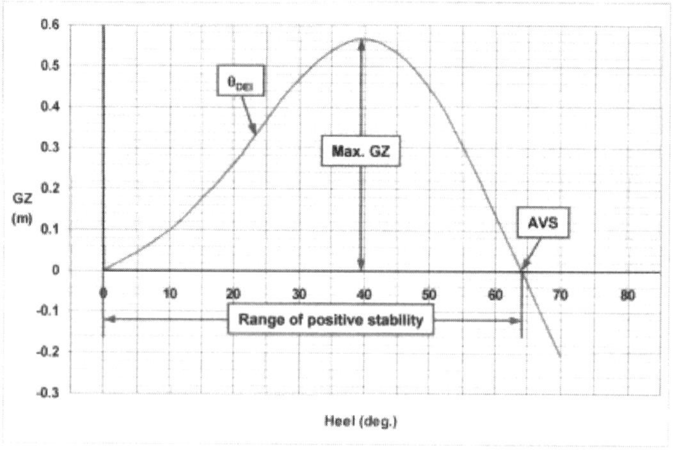

Fig. 10.6

From the curve:

The maximum GZ value is 0.57 m and occurs at an approximate angle of heel of 39°.

The range of stability is from 0° to 64° (the angle of vanishing stability being 64°).

The angle at which deck edge immersion takes place is approximately 23°.

10.4 CURVES OF STATICAL STABILITY FOR STIFF AND TENDER SHIPS

10.4.1 Stiff ships

A *stiff* ship is one with a *very large GM* caused by KG being too small. This occurs if too much weight is placed low down within the ship. The ship will be *excessively stable*, righting moments will be so large as to cause the ship to return to the upright very quickly when heeled. Roll period will be short.

A very large GM should be avoided for the following reasons:

- *The ship will return to the upright very quickly whereby the motion will be jerky causing excessive strain on cargo lashings and possible cargo shift.*
- *Loose gear will be thrown about.*
- *It is uncomfortable for crew and injury may result from the ship's quick motion.*
- *Structural damage to the ship may occur due to racking.*

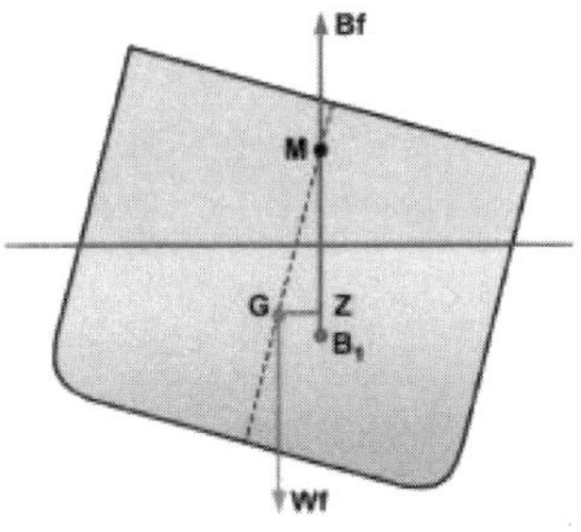

Fig. 10.7

10.4.2 Tender ships

A *tender* ship is one with a *very small GM* caused by KG being too large. This occurs if too much weight is placed high up within the ship. The ship will have *insufficient stability*, righting moments will be very small when heeled causing the ship to be sluggish and slow to return to the upright. Roll period will be long. (A tender ship is still a *stable* ship i.e. M is above G.)

A very small GM should be avoided for the following reasons:

Because of the small righting moments the ship will only offer limited resistance to being rolled, causing the ship to be rolled to larger angles of heel. This will increase the risk of water being shipped on deck.

The ship will be slow to return to the upright and will tend to remain at the extent of the roll for a comparatively long time. This will create greater and more prolonged strain on cargo lashings and increase the risk of cargo shift.

Rolling to excessive angles of heel is also uncomfortable for the crew and injury may result.

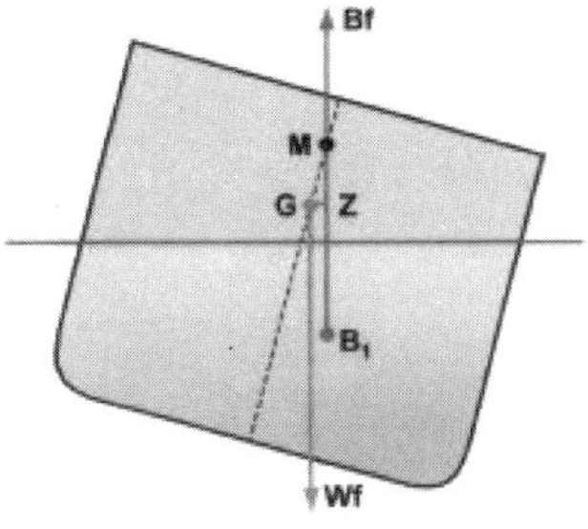

Fig. 10.8

As a guide, a GM of between 4-8% of the ships breadth is desirable. Container ships that have containers stowed on deck may probably be more suited to a GM value on the tender side of these limits to minimise the stresses on deck container lashings.

Typical curves of statical stability for both a stiff and tender ship are shown.

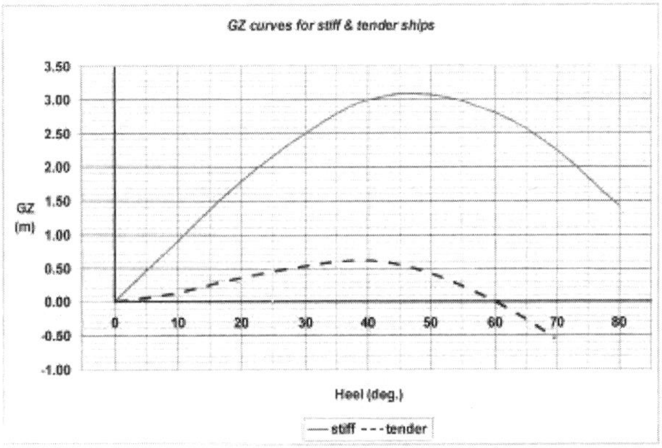

Fig. 10.9

SECTION 11 - LIST

INTRODUCTION

So far stability has only been considered for a ship that is upright, whereby G is on the centre line and the ship floats upright in still water. It is necessary to consider the position of G in the *transverse* sense as well as the vertical.

There is a distinction to be made between the terms *list* and *heel*, this often being overlooked or ignored completely.

List is the term used to describe a ship that is inclined due to the distribution of weights within it.

Heel is the term used to describe a ship that has been forcibly inclined by external forces (wind, waves etc.).

Learning Objectives

On completion of this section, the learner will achieve the following:

1. Calculate the list caused by a transverse shift of a single weight using the basic 'list triangle' for a ship that is initially upright.
2. Calculate the list caused by a transverse and vertical shift of a single weight for a ship that is initially upright.
3. Calculate the list caused by a single weight being loaded or discharged.
4. Calculate the weight to shift to bring a listed ship upright.
5. Calculate the final list when loading and/or discharging multiple weights for a ship that is initially upright.
6. Calculate the final list when loading and/or discharging multiple weights for a ship that is initially listed.
7. Calculate the weights to load each side of the centre line to ensure that the ship completes upright.
8. Understands the effect of free surface on list.

11.1 CALCULATING LIST CAUSED BY A TRANSVERSE SHIFT OF WEIGHT (THE LIST TRIANGLE)

Consider a ship floating upright, G and B on the centre line with a weight 'w' on one side.

The weight 'w' is shifted transversely across the deck.

Remember the rule:

If a weight already on board is shifted, G will move parallel to and in the same direction as the shift of the centre of gravity of the weight.

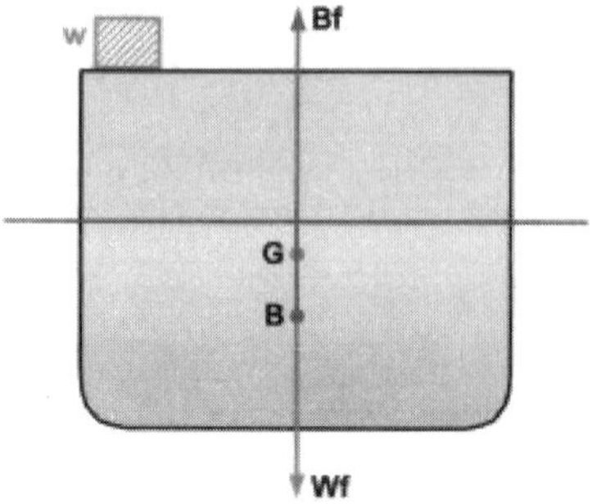

Fig. 11.1

G moves off the centre line to G_H and the ship lists over, coming to rest with the centre of buoyancy, B_1, vertically below the centre of gravity, now G_H.

The distance that G moves off the centre line, GG_H, is calculated using the formula:

$$GG_H = \frac{w \times d}{W}$$

where: ***'w'*** is the weight shifted;
'd' is the distance through which the weight is shifted, and;
'W' is the displacement of the ship (which includes the weight).

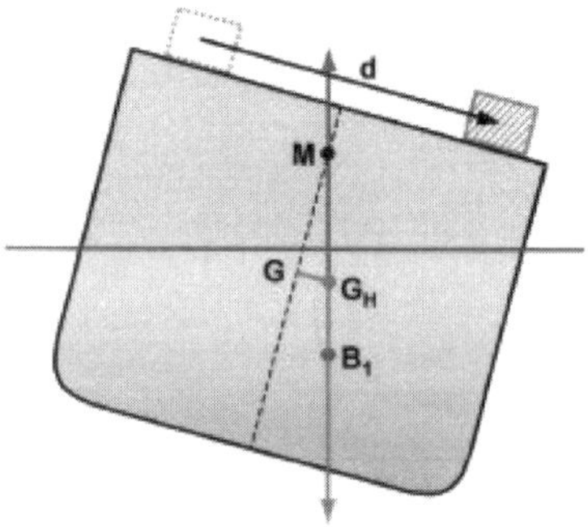

Fig. 11.2

The angle at the metacentre in the right-angled triangle GG_HM is the *list* (termed θ).

$$\text{Tan } \theta_{LIST} = \frac{OPP}{ADJ} = \frac{GG_H}{GM}$$

Therefore:

$$\textbf{Tan } \theta_{LIST} = \frac{GG_H}{GM}$$

For the above formula to be valid *the list must be restricted to a small angle*, i.e. the initial transverse metacentre is assumed to be in a fixed position within small angles of inclination only.

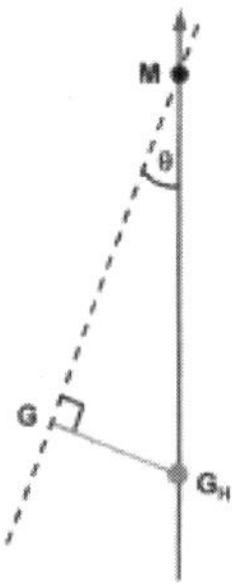

Fig. 11.3

Example 1

A ship initially upright displaces 12000 t and has KG 6.7 m and KM 7.3 m. A weight of 60 t already on board is shifted 14 m horizontally across the deck. Calculate the resulting angle of list.

Solution

KM	*7.3 m*
KG	*6.7 m*
GM	*0.6 m*

$$GG_H = \frac{w \times d}{W} \qquad GG_H = \frac{60 \times 14}{12000} = 0.070 \text{ m}$$

$$\text{Tan } \theta_{LIST} = \frac{GG_H}{GM} = \frac{0.070}{0.600} = 0.11667$$

List = 6.7°

11.2 CALCULATING LIST CAUSED BY A TRANSVERSE AND VERTICAL SHIFT OF WEIGHT – SHIP INITIALLY UPRIGHT

If a weight is shifted both *vertically* and *horizontally (Figure 11.4)* then the movement of G to G_1 is considered to have two components:

GG_V; a vertical component;
GG_H; a horizontal component.

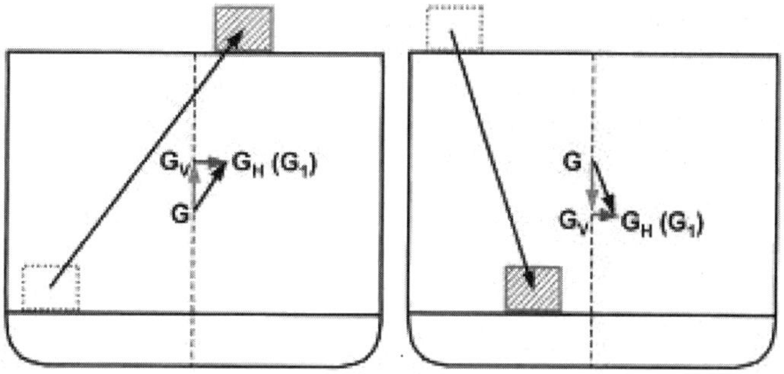

Fig. 11.4

The procedure for calculating the resultant list is as follows:

1. Calculate GG_V using: $GG_V = \frac{w \times d}{W}$
   '*d*' being the *vertical* distance through which the weight is shifted.

2. Apply GG_V to the ship's initial KG to find the final KG.
3. Calculate the final GM using: GM = KM - KG
4. Calculate GG_H using: $GG_H = \frac{w \times d}{W}$
   '*d*' being the *horizontal* distance through which the weight is shifted.
5. Using the formula: $\tan \theta_{LIST} = \frac{GG_H}{GM_{FINAL}}$ calculate the list.

Follow Example 2. It may help your understanding of the working if you do a sketch.

<u>Example 2</u>

A ship, initially upright, has a displacement of 12200 t, KG 6.36 m and KM 7.62 m. A weight of 40 t is in the lower hold in a position Kg 2.20 m, 4.00 m to port of the centre line.
Calculate the final list if the weight is shifted to a new position on deck, Kg 11.4 m, 2.6 m to starboard of the centre line.

<u>Solution</u>

1. $GG_V = \frac{w \times d}{W} = \frac{40 \times (11.4 - 2.2)}{12200} = 0.030\ m$

2.

Initial KG	*6.360 m*
GGv (up)	*0.030 m*
Final KG	*6.390 m*

3.

KM	*7.620 m*
Final KG	*6.390 m*
Final GM	*1.230 m*

4. $GG_H = \frac{w \times d}{W} = \frac{40 \times (4.0 + 2.6)}{12200} = 0.022\ m$

5. $\tan \theta_{LIST} = \frac{GG_H}{GM_{FINAL}} = \frac{0.022}{1.230} = 0.01789$

List = 1.0° Stbd

11.3 CALCULATING THE LIST DUE TO A SINGLE WEIGHT BEING LOADED OR DISCHARGED

If a weight is loaded or discharged then both the *vertical* and *horizontal* components of the shift of G must be considered and the *final GM* must be used to calculate the final list.

Remember the rules:
If a weight is loaded G will move directly towards the centre of gravity of the loaded weight.
If a weight is discharged G will move directly away from the centre of gravity of the discharged weight.

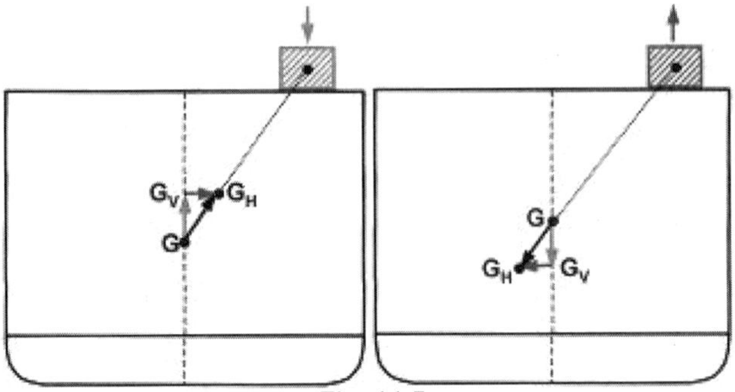

Fig. 11.5

The procedure for single weight load/discharge problems is as follows:

1. Calculate GG_V using: $GG_V = \frac{w \times d}{W \pm w}$

   'd' being the *vertical* distance between G of the ship and g of the loaded/discharged weight.

2. Apply GG_V to the ship's initial KG to find the final KG.

3. Calculate the final GM using: GM = KM - KG

4. Calculate GG_H using: $GG_H = \frac{w \times d}{W \pm w}$

   'd' being the *horizontal* distance between G of the ship and g of the loaded/discharged weight.

5. Using the formula: $\tan \theta_{LIST} = \frac{GG_H}{GM}$ calculate the list.

Follow Examples 3 and 4, one for a weight being loaded, the other for a weight being discharged. It may help your understanding of the working if you do a sketch for each case.

Example 3

A ship initially upright displaces 6400 t and has KG 4.6 m and KM 6.5 m. A weight of 80 t is loaded on deck at Kg 10.2 m, 6.2 m off the centre line to starboard. Calculate the final list. Assume KM remains constant.

Solution

$GG_V = \frac{w \times d}{W + w}$ $\quad GG_V = \frac{80 \times (10.2 - 4.6)}{6400 + 80} = 0.069\ m$

Initial KG	*4.600 m*	*KM*	*6.500 m*
GGv (up)	*0.069 m*	*Final KG*	*4.669 m*
Final KG	*4.669 m*	*Final GM*	*1.831 m*

$GG_H = \frac{w \times d}{W + w}$ $\quad GG_H = \frac{80 \times 6.2}{6400 + 80} = 0.077\ m$

$\tan \theta_{LIST} = \frac{GG_H}{GM_{FINAL}} = \frac{0.077}{1.831} = 0.04205$ **List = 2.4° Stbd.**

Example 4

A ship initially upright displaces 14480 t and has a KG 8.82 m and KM 10.96 m. A weight of 240 t is discharged from a position in the lower hold Kg 3.6 m, 2.8 m off the centre line to port. Calculate the final list. Assume KM remains constant.

Solution

$$GG_V = \frac{w \times d}{W - w} \qquad GG_V = \frac{240 \times (8.82 - 3.6)}{14480 - 240} = 0.088\ m$$

Initial KG	*8.820 m*	*KM*	*10.960 m*
GGv (up)	*0.088 m*	*Final KG*	*8.908 m*
Final KG	*8.908 m*	*Final GM*	*2.052 m*

$$GG_H = \frac{w \times d}{W - w} \qquad GG_H = \frac{240 \times 2.8}{14480 - 240} = 0.047\ m$$

$$\tan \theta_{LIST} = \frac{GG_H}{GM_{FINAL}} = \frac{0.047}{2.052} = 0.02290$$

List = 1.3° Stbd.

11.4 SHIFTING A WEIGHT ALREADY ON BOARD TO BRING A LISTED SHIP UPRIGHT

For a ship to be *upright*: *PORT MOMENTS = STARBOARD MOMENTS* where G must be on the centre line.

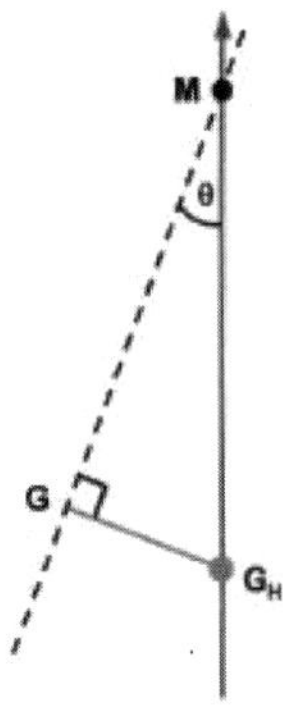

Fig.11.6

A ship that is listed will have G off the centre line by a distance GG_H as shown.

Consider the formula for a shift of weight: $GG_H = \frac{w \times d}{W}$

Rearranging this gives: $GG_H \times W = w \times d$

($GG_H \times W$) represents the listing moments that the ship initially has.
($w \times d$) represents the moments required to equal ($GG_H \times W$) if the ship is to complete upright.

Consider the following example

Example 5
A ship has a displacement of 12000 t and is initially listed 2° to starboard. If the KG of the ship is 11.60 m and the KM is 12.00 m, how much ballast water must be transferred from a starboard side ballast tank to a port side ballast tank through a distance of 16.00 m?

Solution
To complete upright: Port Moments = Starboard moments

Ship is initially listed to starboard.

KM	*12.00 m*
KG	*11.60 m*
GM	*0.40 m*

$\tan \theta_{LIST} = \frac{GG_H}{GM}$ $\tan 2° = \frac{GG_H}{0.40}$

$GG_H = \tan 2° \times 0.40 = 0.014$ m

G is off the centre line to starboard by 0.014 m.

Required port moments to counteract list ($w \times d$) must equal initial starboard listing moments ($GG_H \times W$).

$GG_H \times W = w \times d$
$0.014 \times 12000 = w \times 16.00$
$168 = 16w$
$w =$ ***10.5 tonnes to transfer***

11.5 MULTIPLE WEIGHT PROBLEMS – SHIP INITIALLY UPRIGHT

In practice list problems are solved by taking *moments about the keel* to determine final KG and then final GM; and then taking *moments about the centre line* to determine GG_H.

The procedure is as follows:

1. Take moments about the keel to determine the final KG:

$$\text{Final KG} = \frac{\text{Sum of moments about keel (t-m)}}{\text{Final Displacement (t)}}$$

2. Calculate the final GM: $GM = KM - KG$

3. Take moments about the centre line to calculate the final distance that G is off the centre line, GG_H: $$GG_H = \frac{\text{Sum of moments about centre line (t-m)}}{\text{Final Displacement (t)}}$$

4. Calculate the list: $$\tan\theta_{LIST} = \frac{GG_H}{GM_{FINAL}}$$

Follow the working in the next example.

Example 6
A ship displaces 8000 tonnes, KG 7.60 m and is initially upright.

The following cargo is worked:

Load: 300 t at Kg 0.60 m, 6.1 m to port of CL;
250 t at Kg 6.10 m, 7.6 m to stbd of CL;
Disch: 50 t from Kg 1.20 m, 4.6 m to port of CL;
500 t from Kg 12.60 m, 4.6 m to stbd of CL.

Calculate the final angle of list on completion of cargo if the KM for the final displacement is 9.36m.

Solution
Take moments about the keel to determine the final KG and GM.

	WEIGHT (t)	KG (m)	MOMENTS (t-m)
Initial displ.	8000	7.60	60800.00
Load	300	0.60	180.00
Load	250	6.10	1525.00
Discharge	-50	1.20	-60.00
Discharge	-500	12.60	-6300.00
FINAL	**8000**	**7.018**	**56145.00**

KM	9.360
KG	7.018
GM	**2.342**

Take moments about the centre line to determine GG_H

Weight	Dist off CL	Port moments (t-m)	Stbd moments (t-m)
8000	0.00	0.0	0.0
300	6.10	1830.0	
250	7.60		1900.0
50	4.60		230.0
500	4.60	2300.0	
		4130.0	2130.0
		2130.0	
		2000.0	

$$GG_H = \frac{\text{Net listing moments}}{\text{Final displacement}} = \frac{2000}{8000} = 0.250\text{m}$$

Calculate the final list.

$$\tan\theta_{LIST} = \frac{GG_H}{GM_{FINAL}} = \frac{0.250}{2.342} = 0.10675$$

Final list = 6.1° Port

11.6 MULTIPLE WEIGHT PROBLEMS – SHIP INITIALLY LISTED

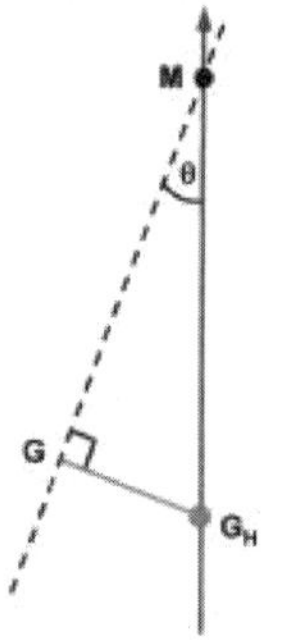

Fig. 11.7

If a ship is initially listed G must be off the centre line as shown:

Since: $\tan \theta_{LIST} = \dfrac{GG_H}{GM}$

then: $GG_H = \tan \theta_{LIST} \times GM$

where GG_H is the initial listing lever to be incorporated into the moments table for the ship. Consider the following example.

Example 7

A ship has a displacement of 15000 t, KG 8.6 m, KM 9.4 and is listed 6° to starboard. Cargo is worked as follows:

Load 150 t at Kg 7.6 m, 5.0 m to port of CL;
Load 305 t at Kg 8.0 m, on the CL;
Load 95 t at Kg 8.0 m, 4.2 m to starboard of CL.

Calculate the final angle of list.
(Assume KM remains constant)

Solution

Calculate initial GM.

KM	*9.400 m*
Initial KG	*8.600 m*
Initial GM	*0.800 m*

Calculate GG_H using: $GG_H = \tan \theta_{LIST} \times GM$
$GG_H = \tan 6° \times 0.800 = 0.084$ m.

Take moments about the keel to determine the final KG and GM.

	WEIGHT (t)	KG (m)	MOMENTS (t-m)
Initial displ.	15000	8.60	129000.0
Load	150	7.60	1140.0
Load	305	8.00	2440.0
Load	95	8.00	760.0
FINAL	**15550**	**8.575**	**133340.0**

KM	9.400
KG	8.575
GM	**0.825**

Take moments about the centre line to calculate final GG_H.

Weight	Dist off CL	Port moments (t-m)	Stbd moments (t-m)
15000	0.084		1260.0
150	5.000	750.0	
305	0.000	0.0	0.0
95	4.200		399.0
		750.0	1659.0
			750.0
			909.0

$GG_H = \dfrac{\text{Net listing moments}}{\text{Final displacement}} = \dfrac{909}{15550} = 0.058$m

Calculate the final list.

$\tan \theta_{LIST} = \dfrac{GG_H}{GM_{FINAL}} = \dfrac{0.058}{0.825} = 0.07030$

Final list = 4.0° Stud.

11.7 LOADING WEIGHTS ABOUT THE CENTRE LINE TO COMPLETE UPRIGHT

A common question arises where the ship is near completion of loading and the remaining cargo has to be distributed between two compartments that are either side of the centre line in such a way that the ship completes upright.

To complete upright: *Port moments must equal starboard moments!*

There are two methods of approach to this type of problem as shown in the next example.

Example 8 (Method 1)
From the following details calculate the final GM and the amount of cargo to load in each space so that the ship will complete loading upright:

Initial displacement 18000 t, KG 8.80 m, KM 9.40 m and listed 3° to starboard.
400 tonnes of cargo remains to be loaded where space is available in a tween deck Kg 10.5 m, 7.0 m to port of CL and 10.0 m to starboard of CL.
(Assume KM remains constant).

Solution
Calculate initial GM.

KM	*9.400*
Initial KG	*8.800*
Initial GM	*0.600*

Calculate GG_H using: $GG_H = \text{Tan}\ \theta_{LIST} \times GM$

$GG_H = \text{Tan}\ 3° \times 0.600 = 0.031$ m.

Take moments about the keel to determine the final KG and GM (note that all 400 t of cargo is loaded at Kg 10.5 m so treat as a single weight!).

	WEIGHT (t)	KG (m)	MOMENTS (t-m)
Initial displ.	18000	8.80	158400.0
Load	400	10.50	4200.0
FINAL	**18400**	**8.837**	**162600.0**

KM	9.400
KG	8.837
GM	**0.563**

Taking moments about the centre line load all 400 t in the port side.

Weight	Dist off CL	Port moments (t-m)	Stbd moments (t-m)
18000	0.031		558.0
400	7.000	2800.0	
		2800.0	558.0
		558.0	
		2242.0	

If all 400 t were loaded into the port side space the ship would complete with an excess of 2242 t-m moments to port. Therefore some of this 400 t must now be shifted to the space on the starboard side (a distance of 17.0 m).

$2242 = w \times d$

$2242 = w \times (7.0 + 10.0)$

$2242 = 17w$

$w = \frac{2242}{17} = 131.9$ *t to shift from port to starboard*

To complete upright:

Load *400.0 –*
131.9
268.1 t port ***Load 131.9 t Starboard***

Solution (Method 2)
Calculate initial GM.

KM	*9.400*
Initial KG	*8.800*
Initial GM	*0.600*

Calculate GG_H using: $GG_H = \tan \theta_{LIST} \times GM$

$GG_H = \tan 3° \times 0.600 = 0.031$ m.

Take moments about the keel to determine the final KG and GM (note that all 400 t of cargo is loaded at Kg 10.5 m so treat as a single weight!).

	WEIGHT (t)	KG (m)	MOMENTS (t-m)
Initial displ.	18000	8.80	158400.0
Load	400	10.50	4200.0
FINAL	**18400**	**8.837**	**162600.0**

KM	9.400
KG	8.837
GM	**0.563**

Taking moments about the centre line: Let x = cargo to load to port; (400 – x) = cargo to load to starboard.

Weight	Dist off CL	Port moments (t-m)	Stbd moments (t-m)
18000	0.031		558.0
x	7.000	7x	
(400 - x)	10.000		(4000 - 10x)
		7x	558 + (4000 - 10x)

To complete upright:

Port moments must equal starboard moments.

Therefore:

$7x = 558 + (4000 - 10x)$

$7x = 558 + 4000 - 10x$

$7x + 10x = 558 + 4000$

$17x = 4558$

$x = \frac{4558}{17}$

x = ***268.1 t to port***

400 – 268.1 = ***131.9 t to starboard***

11.8 LIST AND FREE SURFACE EFFECT

Consider *figure 11.8.*

The basic list triangle is GG_HM. GM is the ***solid*** metacentric height, the GM that would exist if the ship had no slack tanks.

GG_H is the distance that G is off the centre line.

GG_V is the virtual rise of G due to tank free surfaces. Since GM is reduced to G_VM (the ***Fluid GM***) it can be seen that the angle of list has increased for the same distance that G is off the centre line (GG_H).

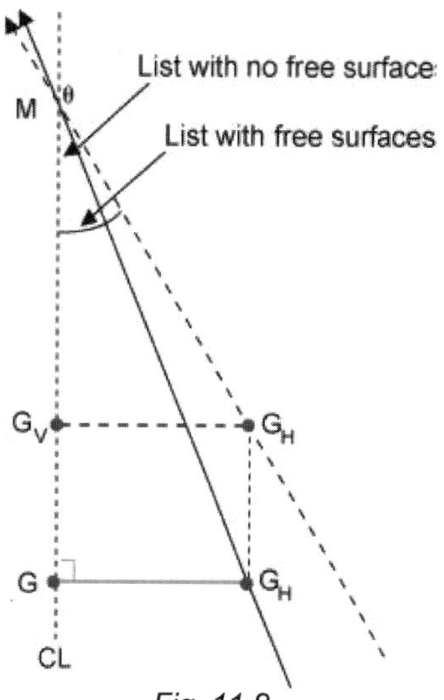

Fig. 11.8

The greater the free surface moments/free surface effect; the greater will be the list for the same listing moments.

Example 9

A ship displaces 13200 t, KG 10.2 m and is initially upright. Ballast water RD 1.025 is run into a rectangular DB tank length 24 m, breadth 10 m to a sounding of 4.00 m. If the Kg of the ballast water is 2.00 m and it's transverse centre of gravity (TCG) is 5.00 m to starboard of the centre line calculate the final angle of list:

(a) assuming no free surface moments;

(b) accounting for free surface moments.

Assume KM for the final displacement is 11.64 m.

Solution

mass of ballast water loaded = 24 × 10 × 4 × 1.025 = 984 t

(a) (assuming no FSM's)

	WEIGHT (t)	KG (m)	MOMENTS (t-m)
Initial displ.	13200	10.20	134640.0
Load	984	2.00	1968.0
FINAL	**14184**	**9.631**	**136608.0**

KM	11.640
KG	9.631
GM	**2.009**

Taking moments about the keel to determine final KG and GM.

Taking moments about the centre line calculate GG_H.

Weight	Dist off CL	Port moments (t-m)	Stbd moments (t-m)
13200	0.000	0.0	0.0
984	5.000		4920.0
		0.0	4920.0

$$GG_H = \frac{\text{Net listing moments}}{\text{Final displacement}} = \frac{4920}{14184} = 0.347 \text{ m}$$

Calculate the final list.

$$\tan \theta_{LIST} = \frac{GG_H}{GM_{FINAL}} = \frac{0.347}{2.009} = 0.17272$$

Final list = 9.8° Stbd.

(b) (including FSM's)

$$FSM\text{'s} = \frac{lb^3 \times dt}{12} = \frac{24 \times 10^3 \times 1.025}{12} = 2050 \text{ t-m}$$

Taking moments about the keel to determine final KG and GM.

	WEIGHT (t)	KG (m)	MOMENTS (t-m)
Initial displ.	13200	10.20	134640.0
Load	984	2.00	1968.0
FSM's			2050.0
FINAL	**14184**	**9.776**	**138658.0**

KM	11.640
KG	9.776
GM	**1.864**

The value of GG_H is not affected by free surface moments.

Calculate the final list.

$$Tan\theta_{LIST} = \frac{GG_H}{GM_{FINAL}} = \frac{0.347}{1.864} = 0.18616 \quad \textbf{List = 10.5° stbd.}$$

When calculating list free surface effects should always be accounted for, as they will always cause an ***increase*** in the list of the ship!

Example 10

A ship displacing 7790 t, KG 7.57 m, KM 8.12 m is floating upright. A double bottom tank of rectangular cross section is divided into two equal parts, each 16 m long, 6.9 m wide and 1.6 m deep. In the upright condition the port side is full of diesel oil (RD 0.88) and the starboard side is empty. Calculate the resulting angle of list when half of this oil is transferred to the starboard side of the tank.

Solution

Assume that the bottom of the double bottom tank is at the keel.

Mass of oil transferred =
$16 \times 6.9 \times 0.8 \times 0.88 = 77.7$ *tonnes*

Oil is moved down from Kg 1.2m to Kg 0.4m.

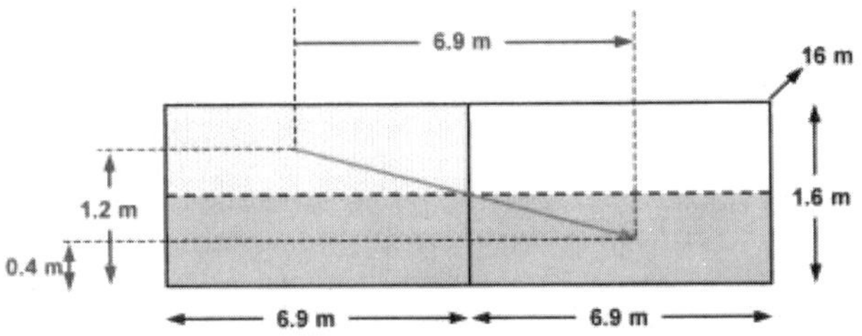

Fig. 11.9

$$FSM's = \frac{lb^3}{12} \times dt \times 2 \text{ tanks}$$

$$FSM's = \frac{16 \times 6.9^3}{12} \times 0.88 = 770.9 \text{ t-m}$$

Taking moments about the keel calculate the final KG and hence final GM.

	WEIGHT (t)	KG (m)	MOMENTS (t-m)
Initial displ.	7790.0	7.57	58970.30
Disch.	-77.7	1.20	-93.24
Load	77.7	0.40	31.08
FSM's			770.90
FINAL	**7790.0**	**7.661**	**59679.04**

KM	8.120
KG	7.661
GM	**0.459**

Oil is transferred to starboard through a distance of 6.9 m.

$$GG_H = \frac{w \times d}{W} = \frac{77.7 \times 6.9}{7790.} = 0.069 \text{ m}$$

Calculate the final list.

$$Tan\theta_{LIST} = \frac{GG_H}{GM_{FINAL}} = \frac{0.069}{0.459} = 0.15033 \quad \textbf{List = 8.5° stbd.}$$

SECTION 12 – INTRODUCTION TO TRIM

INTRODUCTION

Trim is the difference between the draughts forward and aft. When the forward and aft draughts are the same the ship is said to be on an *even keel*. Trim is an important consideration when loading and/or ballasting the ship. A small trim by the stern is desirable as most ships are expected to handle better in a seaway in this condition.

A trim by the head should be avoided for the following reasons:

* *the rudder will be immersed less making the ship difficult to steer.*
* *more water is likely to be shipped forward.*
* *reduced propeller immersion will lessen propulsion efficiency.*
* *if the ship is pitching (especially in the light condition) the propeller will tend to 'race'. This accompanied with increased vibration may cause propeller shaft damage.*
* *rudder efficiency will be intermittent as the ship pitches.*
* *ballast suctions are sited at the aft end of tanks, a head trim will make these impossible to empty completely.*

Excessive trim by the stern should also be avoided because:

* *the large wind area forward and too deep immersion of the stern will make the ship difficult to steer.*
* *pitching may be excessive in heavy weather causing excessive panting and pounding (this will be evident regardless of trim if the forward draught is too small).*
* *a large blind area will exist forward, especially with an aft bridge, hindering pilotage and reducing lookout effectiveness.*

Trim is especially important when dry-docking a ship. If trimmed too much by the stern excessive loss of stability and structural damage might occur (Section 21). Other considerations will include deepest draught limitations for both port entry and departure and the available water on a berth.

This section serves as an introduction to solving trim problems.
In *Section 3 - Tonnes per Centimetre Immersion (TPC)* it was emphasised that *mean hydrostatic values* of *TPC* should be used for the range of draughts concerned when loading and discharging weights. The same principles apply when conducting trim calculations, however, *as this is an introductory section to the topic it will be assumed at the outset that the hydrostatic particulars given in each example remain constant for the range of draughts concerned.*
In *Section 20 - Trim Using Hydrostatic Data*, the use of mean values will apply for calculations when appropriate.

Learning Objectives

On completion of this section the learner will achieve the following:

1. Understand the terms *Forward Perpendicular (FP), After Perpendicular (AP), Length between Perpendiculars (LBP), Length Overall (LOA)* and *Amidships.*
2. Interpret draught markings and read draughts.
3. Understand the term *Trim.*
4. Understand the term *Change of Trim.*
5. Understand the term *Moment to Change Trim by one Centimetre (MCTC)* and calculate the change of trim that occurs when a weight on board a ship is shifted.
6. Derives a formula for the calculation of *MCTC.*
7. Understand the term *Longitudinal Centre of Flotation (LCF).*
8. Calculate the final draughts when a weight on board a ship is shifted by consideration of the position of the LCF.
9. Calculate the final draughts when a single weight is loaded or discharged.
10. Calculate the final draughts when multiple weights are loaded and discharged.
11. Calculate the weight to shift to reduce the trim by a specified amount.
12. Calculate the weight to load to bring a ship to an even keel.
13. Calculate the weight to transfer to reduce the deepest draught by a specified amount.

12.1 TERMS RELATING TO SHIP LENGTH

The following terms relating to ship length should be understood.

12.1.1 Forward Perpendicular (FP)

This is the vertical line of reference that intersects the Summer Load waterline at the forward edge of the stem when the ship is on an even keel.

12.1.2 After Perpendicular (AP)

This is the vertical line of reference that coincides with the after edge of the stern post, or, if no stern post, then the turning axis of the rudder.

12.1.3 Length between perpendiculars (LBP)

Is the horizontal distance between the forward and after perpendiculars. It is this length that is considered when conducting trim calculations.

12.1.4 Length overall (LOA)

Is the horizontal distance between the after most part and forward most part of the ship.

12.1.5 Amidships

Is the mid point between the forward and aft perpendiculars. It is ***not*** the mid point in the length of the ship.

Consider *Figure 12.1.*

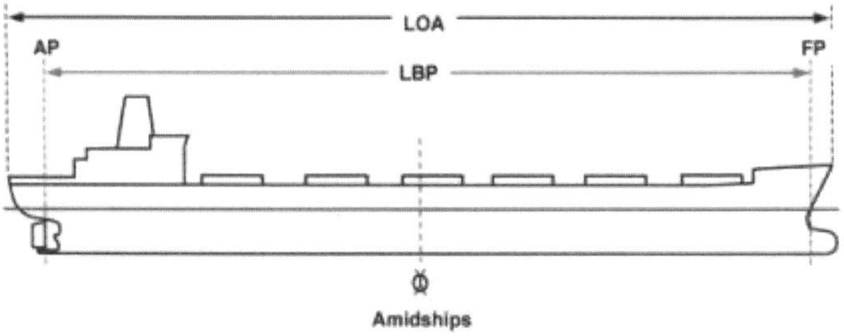

Fig. 12.1

12.2 DRAUGHT MARKS AND READING THE DRAUGHT

The draught marks on a ship should be marked at the *Forward* and *Aft Perpendiculars* on both sides. The numerals are 10 centimetres in height and are spaced 10 centimetres apart as shown.

The draught is read as shown in *Figure 12.3* using the ***lower edge*** of the numerals. Intermediate values have to be estimated. If the water is quite choppy then great accuracy will not be possible.

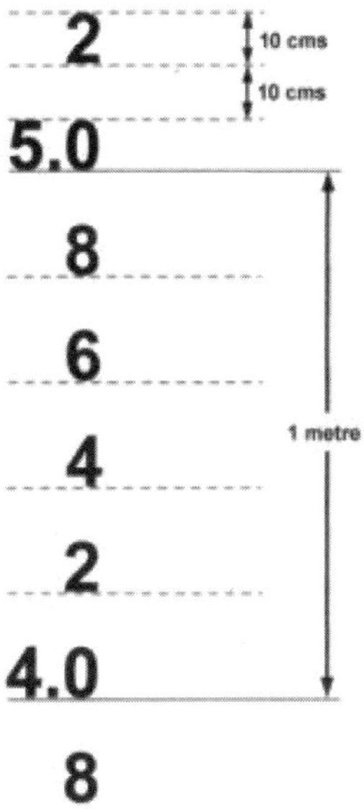

Fig. 12.2

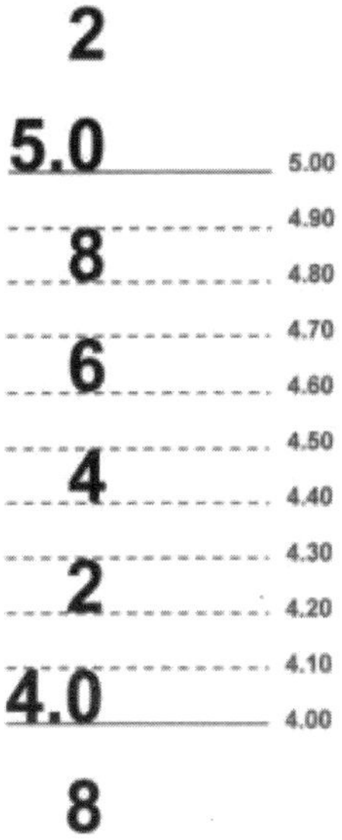

Fig. 12.3

<u>*Example 1*</u>
What is the draught reading for each of the waterlines shown in Figure 12.4?

<u>*Solution*</u>

(a) *2.80 m*
(b) *2.50 m*
(c) *Approximately 2.37 m*
(d) *Approximately 1.82 m*

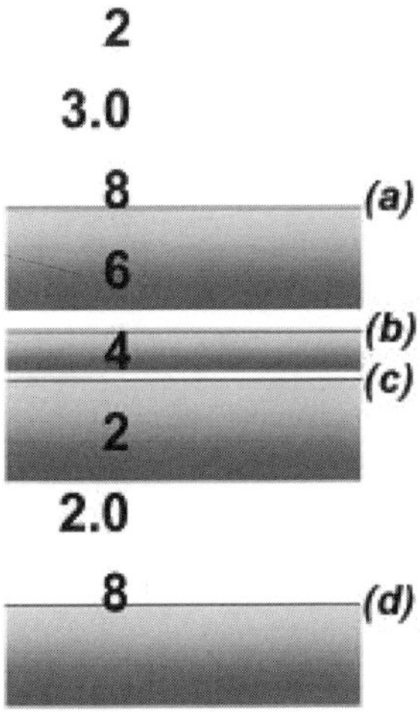

Fig. 12.4

Ideally the draughts should be read on both sides of the ship and the mean draught forward and the mean draught aft determined. For obvious reasons this is rarely done so before the draughts are read the ship should be brought to the upright condition to eliminate errors.

At the outset it was stated that the draught marks should be in line with the forward and after perpendiculars but this will never be so. At the after end the curvature of the stern may make the draught marks difficult to see. At the forward perpendicular there is nothing to mark them on! Therefore it is usual to set them a suitable distance forward and aft of the respective perpendiculars whereby the readings obtained will have to be corrected to the perpendiculars.

12.3 TRIM

Trim is the difference in centimetres or metres between the forward and aft draughts, as measured at the forward and aft perpendiculars.

Consider the ship shown in *Figure 12.5* with draughts Fwd. 2.20 m and Aft 2.68 m.

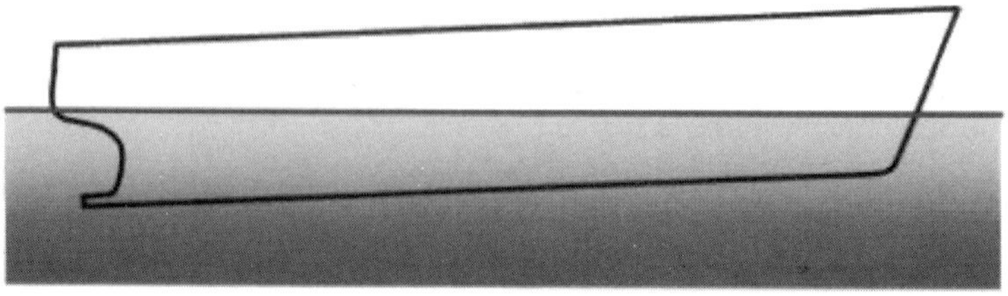

Fig. 12.5

The trim of the ship is: *2.68 -*
2.20
0.48 m by the stern, or; ***48 cms by the stern.***

The same ship is now floating with draughts Fwd 2.70 m and Aft 2.32 m.

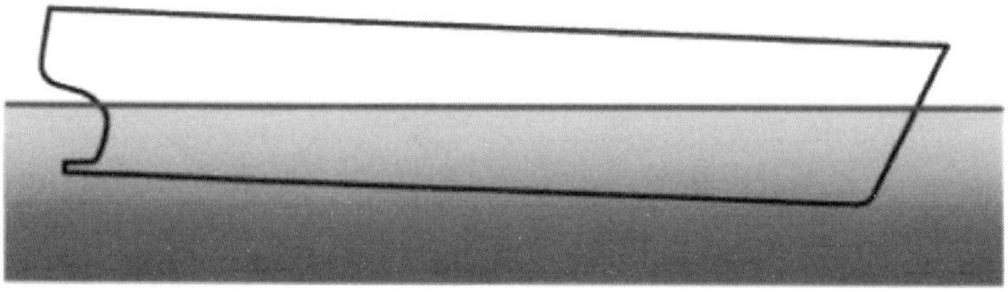

Fig. 12.6

The trim of the ship is: *2.70 -*
2.32
0.38 m by the head, or; ***38 cms by the head.***

12.4 CHANGE OF TRIM

If a weight is shifted longitudinally the ship will experience a *change of trim*.
Consider the following examples.

Example 2
A ship floats at draughts Fwd 6.000 m and Aft 6.200 m. A weight is then shifted forward. The final draughts are Fwd 6.080 m and Aft 6.120 m.
What change of trim has occurred?

Solution
Calculate the initial trim:

Aft	*6.200 m*
Fwd	*6.000 m*
Initial trim	*0.200 m by the stern*

Calculate the final trim:

Aft	*6.120 m*
Fwd	*6.080 m*
Final trim	*0.040 m by the stern*

Calculate the change of trim (COT):

Initial trim	*0.200 m by the stern*
Final trim	*0.040 m by the stern*
COT	*0.160 m by the HEAD*

The trim by the stern has reduced by 0.160 m.

Example 3
A ship floats at draughts Fwd 5.000 m and Aft 4.640 m. A weight is then shifted aft. The final draughts are Fwd 4.680 m and Aft 4.960 m.
What change of trim has occurred?

Solution
Calculate the initial trim:

Aft	*4.640 m*
Fwd	*5.000 m*
Initial trim	*0.360 m by the head*

Calculate the final trim:

Aft	*4.960 m*
Fwd	*4.680 m*
Final trim	*0.280 m by the stern*

Calculate the change of trim (COT):

Initial trim	*0.360 m by the head*
Final trim	*0.280 m by the stern*
COT	*0.640 m by the STERN*

The ship, initially trimmed by the head, completes trimmed by the stern.

Let us consider more closely what happens when a weight is shifted longitudinally. The ship shown is on an even keel with a weight on deck.

'G' is the longitudinal centre of gravity (LCG).
'B' is the longitudinal centre of buoyancy (LCB).

The weight is shifted aft along the deck through distance ***'d'*** metres. In accordance with the formula:

$$GG_1 = \frac{w \times d}{W}$$

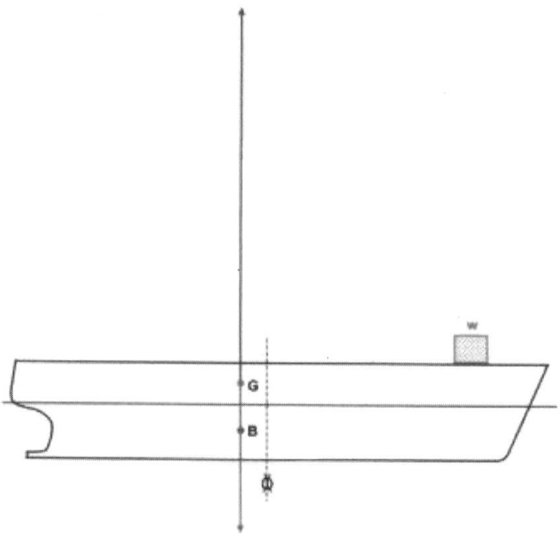

Fig. 12.7

G will move aft to G_1 (parallel to and in the same direction as the shift of the weight).

G and B become horizontally separated creating a trimming lever. This causes the ship to trim by the stern until B attains a new position vertically below the new longitudinal centre of gravity, G_1.

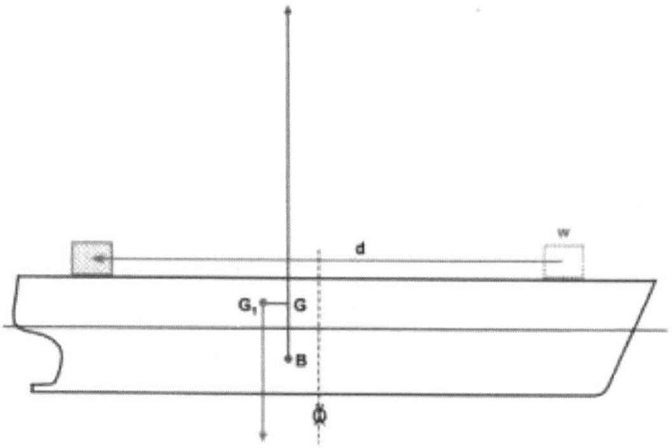

Fig.12.8

M_L is the *longitudinal metacentre*, GM_L being the *longitudinal metacentric height.*

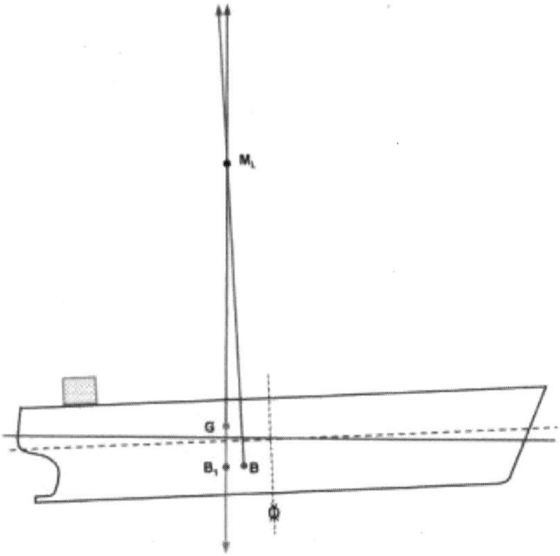

Fig.12.9

12.5 MOMENT TO CHANGE TRIM BY ONE CENTIMETRE (MCTC)

This is the *trimming moment* required to change the ships trim by exactly one centimetre.

It is tabulated in the ships hydrostatic particulars and is used to determine the change of trim that takes place when weights are shifted, loaded or discharged.

Consider the ship previously shown *Figures 12.7-12.9* where a weight was shifted aft along the deck. The change of trim can be calculated by the formula:

$$\textbf{COT (cms)} = \frac{\textbf{Trimming moment}}{\textbf{MCTC}}$$

where the trimming moment is: **w × d**

'w' being the weight shifted, and
'd' being the distance through which the weight is shifted longitudinally.

Thus:

$$\boxed{\textbf{COT (cms)} = \frac{\textbf{w} \times \textbf{d}}{\textbf{MCTC}}}$$

Example 4
A weight of 150 tonnes is moved aft by distance of 20 m. If the MCTC for the current draught is 250 t-m determine the final trim of the ship if the initial trim was 0.20 m by the stern.

Solution

$$COT\ (cms) = \frac{w \times d}{MCTC} = \frac{150 \times 20}{250} = 12\ cms$$

COT = 0.120 m

Initial trim:	*0.200 m by the stern*
COT:	*0.120 m further by the stern*
Final trim	***0.320 m** by STERN*

12.6 FORMULA FOR CALCULATING MCTC

In practice the MCTC value will always be found for the draught in question in the ship's hydrostatic particulars. However, in examinations it may have to be calculated and the formula for calculating MCTC is:

$$\mathbf{MCTC = \frac{W \times GM_L}{100LBP}}$$

where:
'W' is the ship's displacement;
'GM_L' is the longitudinal metacentric height, &;
'LBP' is the length between perpendiculars.

The derivation of this formula is as follows.

The ship in *Figure 12.10* is on an even keel with a weight on deck.

The weight is shifted aft along the deck through distance 'd' metres. In accordance with the formula:

$$GG1 = \frac{w \times d}{W}$$

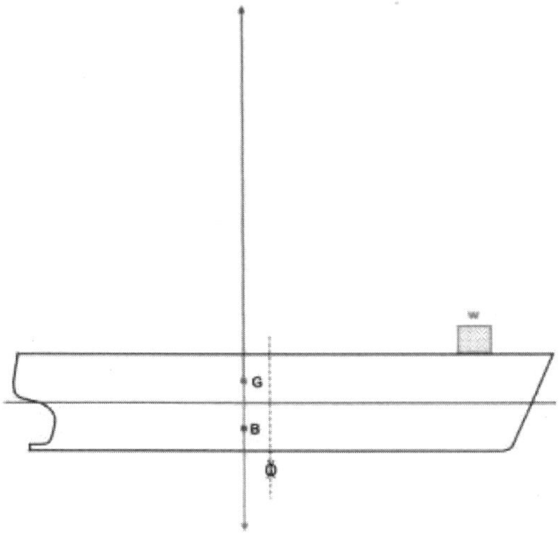

Fig. 12.10

G will move aft to G_1 (parallel to and in the same direction as the shift of the weight).

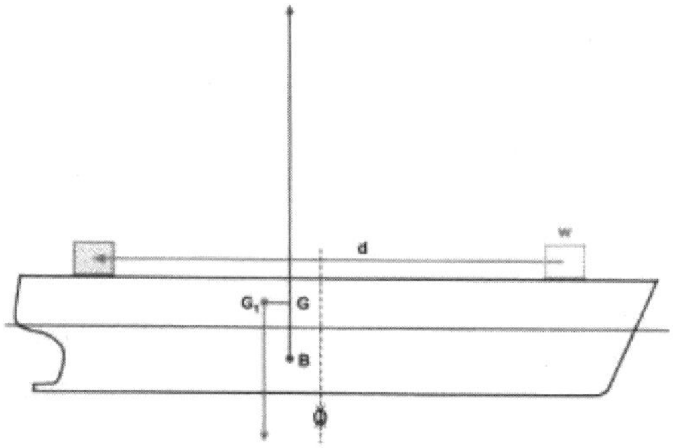

Fig. 12.11

G and B become horizontally separated creating a trimming lever. This causes the ship to trim by the stern until B attains a new position vertically below the new longitudinal centre of gravity, G_1 *(Figure 12.12)*.

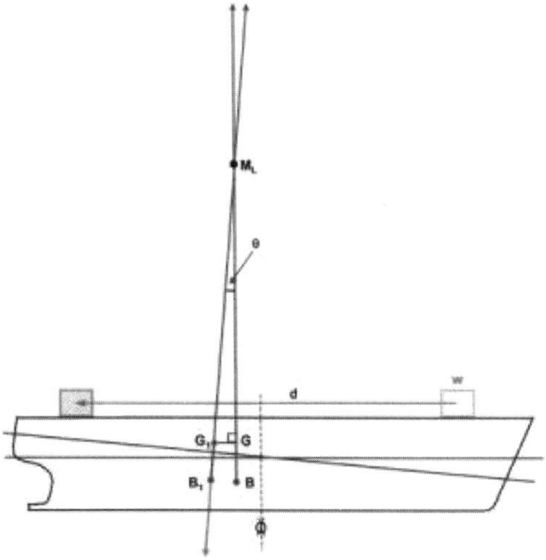

Fig. 12.12

GG_1M_L is a right angled triangle where:

$\text{Tan } \theta = \frac{OPP}{ADJ}$ therefore: $$\mathbf{Tan\ \theta = \frac{GG_1}{GM_L}}$$

Since: $\mathbf{GG_1 = \frac{w \times d}{W}}$ and; $\mathbf{Tan\ \theta = \frac{GG_1}{GM_L}}$

then: $$\mathbf{Tan\ \theta = \frac{w \times d}{W \times GM_L}}$$

Also, in *Figure 12.13*: $$\mathbf{Tan\ \theta = \frac{TRIM\ (m)}{LBP\ (m)}}$$

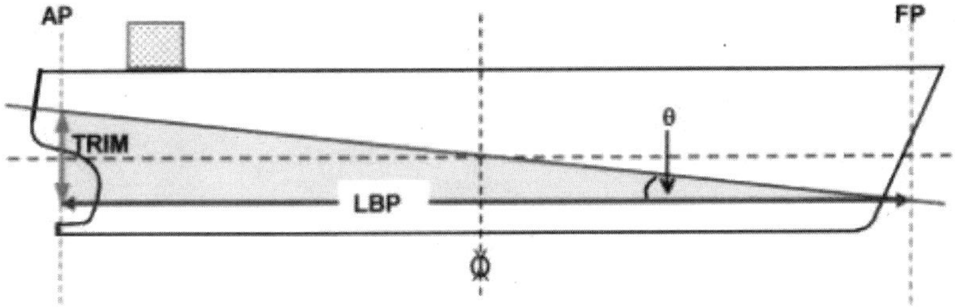

Fig. 12.13

If the change of trim due to the weight shifted is exactly *1 cm,* then:

$\mathbf{Tan\ \theta = \frac{0.01\ (m)}{LBP\ (m)}}$ which equals: $$\mathbf{Tan\theta = \frac{1}{100LBP}} \quad \mathbf{(1)}$$

Since:

$\mathbf{Tan\ \theta = \frac{w \times d}{W \times GM_L}}$ equals: $$\mathbf{Tan\ \theta = \frac{MCTC}{W \times GM_L}} \quad \mathbf{(2)}$$

(because (w × d) is the moment to change the trim by exactly 1 cm.)

Bringing formulae **(1)** and **(2)** together gives:

$$\mathbf{\frac{1}{100LBP} = \frac{MCTC}{W \times GM_L}}$$

Rearranging this gives:

$$\mathbf{MCTC = \frac{W \times GM_L}{100LBP}}$$

12.7 LONGITUDINAL CENTRE OF FLOTATION (LCF or F)

This is at the geometric centre of the ship's water plane area and is the point about which the ship will trim.

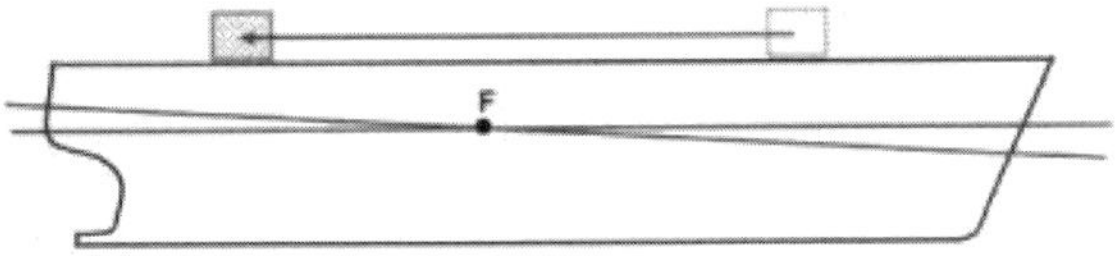

Fig. 12.14

Consider the ship where a weight is shifted longitudinally.

It can be seen that the LCF is in the same position in the ship's length as the point where the *initial and final waterlines intersect*.

It may be helpful to think of the ship as a child's see-saw that has its pivot point situated at the LCF.

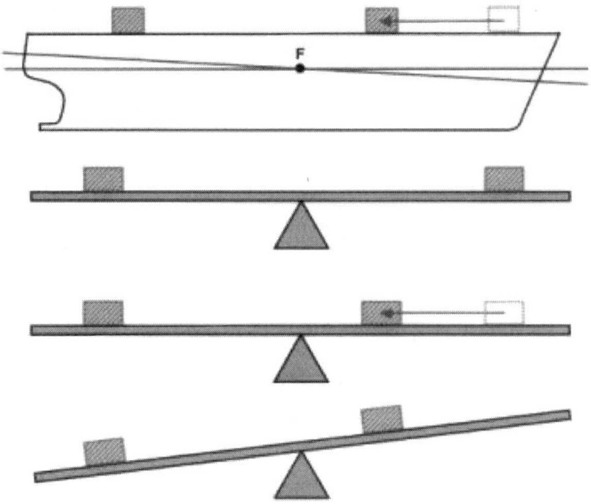

Fig. 12.15

Because the water plane area changes shape and size with draught the position of the LCF will also change with draught.

The position of the LCF is normally quoted in hydrostatic data as being so many *metres forward of the after perpendicular (foap).*

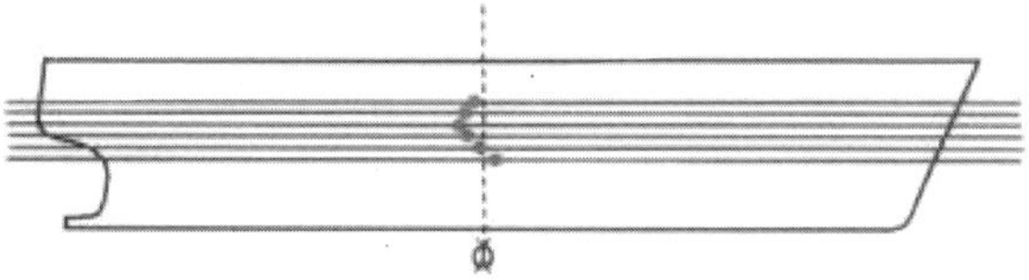

Fig. 12.16

The position of the LCF is important because if a ship experiences a change of trim, some of that change of trim must be applied to the aft draught and the remainder applied to the forward draught as can be seen.

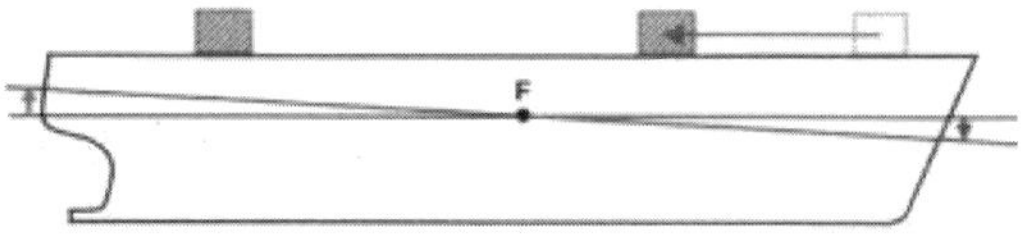

Fig. 12.17

In this case:

Aft draught *increases*; Forward draught *decreases*.

12.8 CALCULATING THE FINAL DRAUGHTS WHEN A WEIGHT IS SHIFTED

The position of the LCF determines how the change of trim (COT) will be apportioned between the forward and aft draughts.

12.8.1 Ship with LCF amidships

Consider a ship with a weight on deck as shown.

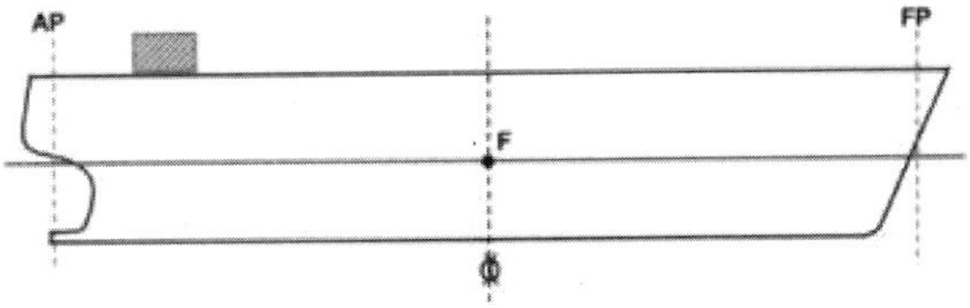

Fig. 12.18

The weight is shifted forward causing the ship to change trim by the head where:

$$\text{COT (cms)} = \frac{w \times d}{\text{MCTC}}.$$

The change of trim has to be shared between the forward and aft draughts where:

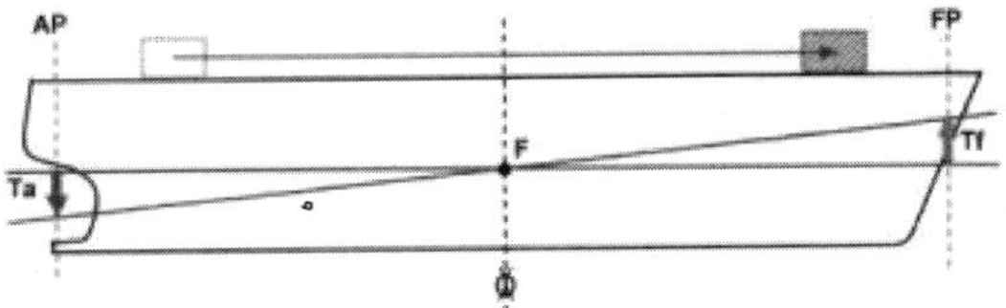

Fig. 12.19

'Ta' is change in draught aft due to trim, and;
'Tf' is the change in draught forward due to trim.

If the LCF is *amidships* the change of trim (COT) will be apportioned *equally* to the draughts forward and aft such that: $\mathbf{Ta = \frac{COT}{2}}$ and; $\mathbf{Tf = \frac{COT}{2}}$

Consider the following example.

Example 5
A ship floats at draughts F 6.50 m and A 6.80 m. Determine the final draughts if 25 tonnes is moved 45 m forward given that MCTC is 112.5 t-m and the LCF is amidships.

Solution
Calculate the change of trim (COT) $\quad COT = \frac{w \times d}{MCTC} = \frac{25 \times 45}{112.5} = 10$ *cms by the head*

Apportion the COT equally to the forward and aft draughts

$Ta = \frac{10}{2} = 5$ *cms* *(Aft draught will reduce by 5 cms)*

$Tf = \frac{10}{2} = 5$ *cms* *(Forward draught will increase by 5 cms)*

Ta = -0.050 m Tf = +0.050 m

Calculate the final draughts

Initial draughts	*F 6.500*	*A 6.800*
Trim	*+ 0.050*	*- 0.050*
FINAL	*F 6.550 m*	*A 6.750 m*

12.8.2 Ship with LCF not amidships

Consider a ship with a weight on deck. The LCF is aft of amidships.

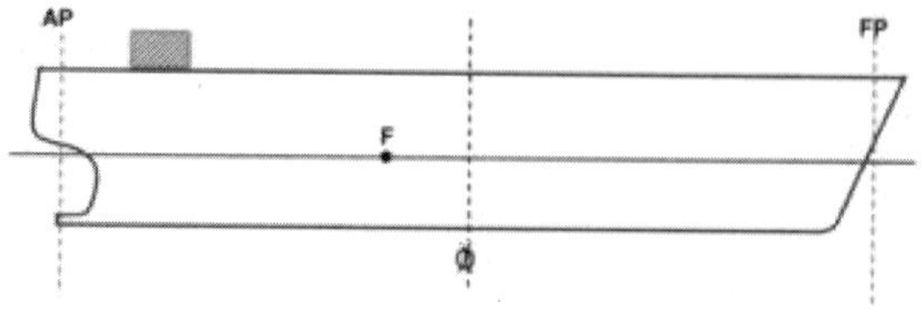

Fig. 12.20

The weight is shifted forward causing the ship to change trim by the head where:

$$\text{COT (cms)} = \frac{w \times d}{\text{MCTC}}$$

In this case it can be seen that the changes in draught forward and aft are *not* the same.

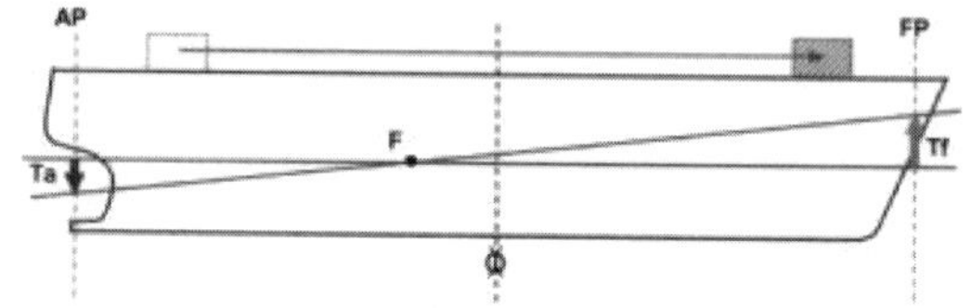

Fig. 12.21

The change of trim (COT) will have to be *apportioned* to the forward and aft draughts according to the position of the LCF within the ship's length.

'a' is length of ship *aft* of the LCF.

'f' is length of ship *forward* of the LCF.

$$\text{COT} = \text{Ta} + \text{Tf}$$

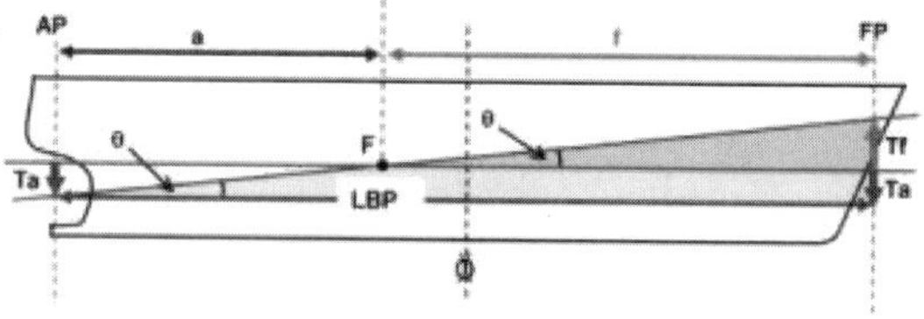

Fig. 12.22

Consider the similar triangles where:

$$\tan\theta = \frac{\text{OPP}}{\text{ADJ}}$$

$\tan\theta = \frac{\text{Tf}}{\text{f}}$ and; $\tan\theta = \frac{\text{COT}}{\text{LBP}}$

Therefore: $\frac{\text{Tf}}{\text{f}} = \frac{\text{COT}}{\text{LBP}}$

Rearranging this gives: $\boxed{\textbf{Tf} = \frac{\textbf{f}}{\textbf{LBP}} \times \textbf{COT}}$ and it follows that: $\boxed{\textbf{Ta} = \frac{\textbf{a}}{\textbf{LBP}} \times \textbf{COT}}$

<u>Example 6</u>

A ship has initial draughts F 10.25 m and A 10.15 m. A weight of 95 tonnes is moved aft through a distance of 42 m. Calculate the final draughts given that LBP is 100 m, LCF is 48 m foap and MCTC is 285 t-m.

<u>Solution</u>

Calculate the change of trim (COT) $\quad \text{COT} = \frac{w \times d}{\text{MCTC}} = \frac{95 \times 42}{285} = 14$ *cms by the <u>stern</u>*

Apportion the COT according to the LCF position

$\text{Ta} = \frac{48}{100} \times 14 = 6.7 \text{ cms} \qquad \text{Tf} = \frac{52}{100} \times 14 = 7.3 \text{ cms}$

(Alternatively: Tf = COT - Ta; Tf = 14.0 - 6.7 = 7.3 cms)

Weight is moved aft so the ship will trim by the STERN.

Ta = +0.067 m Tf = -0.073 m

Calculate the final draughts

Initial draughts	*F 10.250*	*A 10.150*
Trim	*- 0. 073*	*+ 0.067*
FINAL	*F 10.177 m*	*A 10.217 m*

12.9 THE EFFECT OF LOADING AND DISCHARGING WEIGHTS

If weights are loaded or discharged the effect of bodily sinkage or rise must also be considered.

$$\textbf{Sinkage/Rise cms} = \frac{w}{TPC}$$

The following procedure should be followed when *loading* a weight:

1. Load the weight at the LCF position and calculate the sinkage using the TPC value given. *(If a weight is loaded at the LCF the ship will sink uniformly, there will be no change of trim!)*
2. Calculate the COT by moving the weight from the LCF position to its actual loaded position.
3. Find Ta/Tf by apportioning the COT according to the position of the LCF.
4. Apply both the sinkage and Ta/Tf to the initial draughts to determine the final draughts.

Consider the following example.

Example 7
A ship 100 m in length floats at draughts F 7.00 m and A 6.80 m. Calculate the final draughts if 150 t is loaded 20 m foap given that TPC is 15 and MCTC is 150 t-m and LCF is 45 m foap.

TIP: Always draw a sketch to help you picture what is happening!

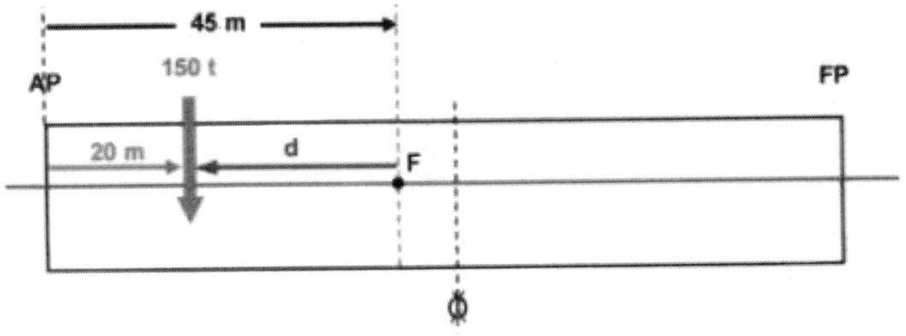

Fig. 12.23

Solution
Calculate the sinkage $\quad Sinkage = \frac{w}{TPC} = \frac{150}{15} = 10 \text{ cms} = 0.100 \text{ m}$

Calculate the change of trim (COT)

*('**d**' is the distance that the weight is loaded from the LCF)*

$$COT = \frac{w \times d}{MCTC} = \frac{150 \times (45 - 20)}{150} = 25.0 \text{ cms}$$

$$Ta = \frac{45}{100} \times 25.0 = 11.3 \text{ cms} = 0.113 \text{ m}$$

$$Tf = COT - Ta; Tf = 25.0 - 11.3 = 13.7 \text{ cms} = 0.137 \text{ m}$$

Weight is loaded aft of the LCF so the ship will trim by the STERN.

Calculate the final draughts

Initial draughts	*F 7.000*	*A 6.800*
Sinkage	*+ 0.100*	*+ 0.100*
	7.100	*6.900*
Trim	*- 0.137*	*+ 0.113*
FINAL	*F 6.963 m*	*A 7.013 m*

The same procedure applies when *discharging* a weight:

1. Discharge the weight from the LCF position and calculate the rise of the ship using the TPC value given.
2. Calculate the COT by considering the effect of moving the weight from its original position to the LCF.
3. Find Ta/Tf by apportioning the COT according to the position of the LCF.
4. Apply both the rise and Ta/Tf to the initial draughts to determine the final draughts.

Consider the following example.

Example 8

A with LBP 160 m floats at draughts F 3.22 m and A 3.10 m. Calculate the final draughts if 208 t is discharged from a position 118 m foap given that TPC is 32, MCTC is 306 t-m and LCF is 88 m foap.

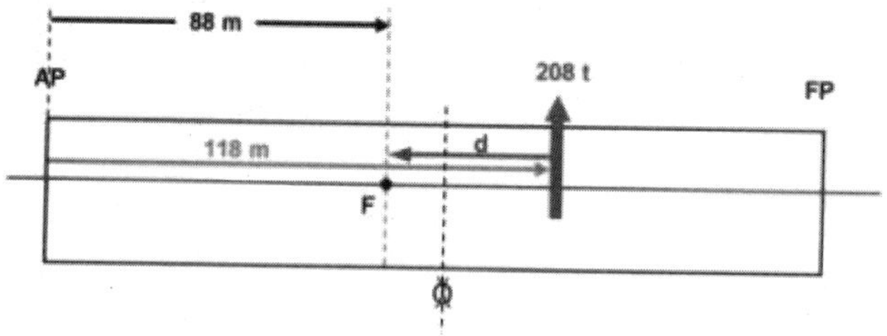

Fig. 12.24

Solution

Calculate the rise

$$\text{Rise} = \frac{w}{TPC} = \frac{208}{32} = 6.5 \text{ cms} = 0.065 \text{ m}$$

Calculate the change of trim (COT)

*(**'d'** is the distance that the weight is discharged from the LCF)*

$$COT = \frac{w \times d}{MCTC} = \frac{208 \times (118 - 88)}{306} = 20.4 \text{ cms}$$

$$Ta = \frac{88}{160} \times 20.4 = 11.2 \text{ cms} = 0.112 \text{ m}$$

$$Tf = COT - Ta = 20.4 - 11.2 = 9.2 \text{ cms} = 0.092 \text{ m}$$

Weight is discharged from forward of the LCF so the ship will trim by the STERN.

Calculate the final draughts

Initial draughts	*F 3.220*	*A 3.100*
Rise	*- 0.065*	*- 0.065*
	3.155	*3.035*
Trim	*- 0.092*	*+ 0.112*
FINAL	*F 3.063 m*	*A 3.147 m*

12.10 MULTIPLE WEIGHT PROBLEMS

Problems involving multiple weights require a tabular approach to be adopted where *moments are taken about the LCF.*

Consider the following example:

Example 9
A ship 120 m in length floats at draughts F 6.24 m and A 6.36 m. LCF is 54 m foap, TPC 14.2 and MCTC 116 t-m.

The following cargo is worked:

Load	*120 t*	*lcg 10.0 m foap;*
Load	*68 t*	*lcg 86 m foap;*
Discharge	*36 t*	*lcg 22 m foap;*
Discharge	*48 t*	*lcg 60 m foap.*

Calculate the final draughts.

Solution
In column (1) the weights loaded and discharged are summed to find the net weight loaded or discharged.
In column (2) the weights are listed as positive values, regardless of whether the weight is being loaded or discharged.
In column (3) the distance that each weight is loaded or discharged from the LCF is listed.
Trimming moments are calculated (Column 2 being multiplied by column 3) and entered in column (4) or (5) depending on whether they are head or stern moments.

(It is here that mistakes are commonly made whereby the moments are often applied the wrong way!)

Determine the net trimming moments - in this case 2240 t-m by the stern.

1 Weight (t)		2 Weight (t)	3 Dist from LCF (m)	4 Head moments (t-m)	5 Stern moments (t-m)
120		120	44		5280
68		68	32	2176	
-36		36	32	1152	
-48		48	6		288
104	load			3328	5568
					3328
					2240

Calculate the sinkage/rise of the ship

$$Sinkage\ (cms) = \frac{w}{TPC} = \frac{104}{14.2} = 7.3\ cms = 0.073\ m$$

Calculate the change of trim (COT)

$$COT = \frac{Trimming\ moments}{MCTC} = \frac{2240}{116} = 19.3\ cms\ by\ the\ \underline{stern}$$

$$Ta = \frac{54}{120} \times 19.3 = 8.7\ cms = 0.087\ m$$

$$Tf = COT - Ta = 19.3 - 8.7 = 10.6\ cms = 0.106\ m$$

Calculate the final draughts

Initial draughts	*F 6.240*	*A 6.360*
Sinkage	*+ 0.073*	*+ 0.073*
	6.313	*6.433*
Trim	*- 0.106*	*+ 0.087*
FINAL	*F 6.207 m*	*A 6.520 m*

There are many different types of questions that might be asked. Most problems are straightforward provided that you understand the information being given and can recognise the formula to which it belongs.

The next few sub-sections deal with frequently asked questions that are not quite as straightforward as those so far encountered.

It will be useful if you keep a copy of the formulae commonly used in this section in front of you: These are:

$$\text{Sinkage/Rise (cms)} = \frac{w}{TPC}$$

$$\text{COT (cms)} = \frac{w \times d}{MCTC} = \frac{\text{Trimming moment}}{MCTC}$$

$$Ta = \frac{a}{LBP} \times COT$$

$$Tf = COT - Ta$$

12.11 WEIGHT TO SHIFT TO REDUCE THE TRIM BY A SPECIFIED AMOUNT

Consider the following example.

Example 10

A ship LBP 152 m is floating at draughts F 4.60 m A 5.46 m. How much ballast water must be transferred from the aft peak tank (lcg 2 m foap) to the fore peak tank (lcg 150 m) in order to reduce the trim by the stern to 0.50 m if the MCTC is 156 t-m.

Solution

Calculate the initial trim

A	*5.46*
F	*4.60*
Initial trim	*0.86 m by the stern*

Calculate the change of trim required

Initial trim	*0.86 m by the stern*
Required trim	*0.50 m by the stern*
COT required	*0.36 m by the HEAD = 36 cms*

$$COT\ (cms) = \frac{w \times d}{MCTC} \qquad 36 = \frac{w \times (150 - 2)}{156}$$

$$\frac{36 \times 156}{148} = w \qquad w = \mathbf{37.9\ tonnes\ to\ transfer}$$

12.12 WEIGHT TO LOAD TO BRING A SHIP TO AN EVEN KEEL

Consider the following example.

Example 11

(a) *A ship floats with draughts F 6.32 m A 7.42 m. How much ballast water must be taken into a forward tank (lcg 168 m foap) in order to bring the ship to an even keel.*
LBP 184 m, TPC 33, MCTC 260 t-m and LCF 92 m foap.

(b) *Calculate the final draughts*

Solution

(a) *Calculate the initial trim*

A	*7.42*
F	*6.32*
Initial trim	*1.10 m by the stern*

Calculate the change of trim required

Initial trim	*1.10 m by the stern*
Required trim	*0.00 m even keel*
COT required	*1.10 m by the HEAD = 110 cms*

$$COT\ (cms) = \frac{w \times d}{MCTC} \qquad 110 = \frac{w \times (168 - 92)}{260}$$

$$\frac{110 \times 260}{76} = w$$ w = **376.3 tonnes to load**

(Remember that 'd' in the formula is the distance from the LCF that the weight is being loaded)

(b) *To calculate the final draughts*

Calculate the sinkage

$$Sinkage\ (cms) = \frac{w}{TPC} \qquad Sinkage = \frac{376.3}{33} = 11.4\ cms = 0.114\ m$$

The change of trim required is known to be 110 cms by the head.

Apportion this COT according to the position of the LCF

$$\text{Since LCF is amidships } Ta = Tf = \frac{COT}{2} = \frac{110}{2} = +/- 55\ cms$$

Calculate the final draughts

Initial	*F 6.320*	*A 7.420*
Sinkage	*+ 0.114*	*+ 0.114*
	6.434	*7.534*
Trim	*+ 0.550*	*- 0.550*
FINAL	*6.984 m*	*6.984 m (even keel)*

12.13 WEIGHT TO TRANSFER TO REDUCE THE DEEPEST DRAUGHT BY A SPECIFIED AMOUNT

Consider the following example.

Example 12

(a) *A ship has to cross a bar where the maximum depth of water is 9.5 m. The present draughts are F 7.55 m A 9.00 m. What is the minimum amount of ballast to transfer forward through a distance of 62 m in order to cross the bar with an under-keel clearance of 0.80 m. LBP 136 m, MCTC 248 t-m and LCF 65.6 m foap.*

(b) *Calculate the final draughts.*

Solution

(a)

Water depth available	*9.50*
Clearance required	*0.80*
Max. draught allowed	*8.70*
Deepest draught (aft)	*9.00*
Reduction required aft	*0.30 = 30 cms*

The reduction in draught aft will be achieved by a change of trim by the head.

Ta is the reduction in draught aft due to trim, which must be 30 cms.

Calculate the COT required

$$Ta = \frac{a}{LBP} \times COT \qquad 30 = \frac{65.6}{136} \times COT$$

$$COT = \frac{30 \times 136}{65.6} = 62.2 \text{ cms}$$

Calculate the weight to transfer

$$COT\ (cms) = \frac{w \times d}{MCTC} \qquad 62.2 = \frac{w \times 62}{248}$$

$$\frac{62.2 \times 248}{62} = w \qquad w = \textbf{248.8 tonnes to transfer}$$

(b) $Tf = COT - Ta$ $Tf = 62.2 - 30.0 = 32.2$ cms

Calculate the final draughts

Initial	*F 7.550*	*A 9.000*
Trim	*+ 0.322*	*- 0.300*
FINAL	*F 7.822 m*	*A 8.700 m*

Note

There are many ways of questioning your knowledge of trim, they have not all been covered in this section.

Always read the question carefully and highlight those elements in the trim formulae that are given. There will always be one formula with only one unknown and this is where you should start the problem. A sketch should be drawn when necessary to aid your understanding of what is being asked, this is helpful as it will help to prevent applying moments the wrong way. Balance your ruler on your finger and try to imagine the see-saw situation if it helps! Mistakes will be made but practice is the only way to overcome these.

Now attempt the tutorial questions, some will be recognised as being similar to those covered in this section, others may have to be given some further thought. If in doubt study the solutions carefully to identify any mistakes - that is what they are there for!

SECTION 13 – SUSPENDED WEIGHTS

INTRODUCTION

When a weight is suspended from a ship's crane or derrick it's effective centre of gravity will be *at the point of suspension* of the weight, being at the derrick or crane head. As soon as the weight is picked up, either from the quay or from somewhere on board, there will be an immediate transfer of the weight to the derrick (or crane) head with a resulting upward vertical movement of the ship's centre of gravity, G. This causes a corresponding reduction in metacentric height, GM. If the weight being lifted is substantial, as in the case of a heavy lift, the considerable upward movement of G cannot be ignored, requiring the *maximum permissible KG* or *minimum permissible GM* prior to lifting the weight, to be calculated to ensure that the ship remains stable during the lifting operation.

When the weight is plumbed over the side a larger than normal list will also occur and certain precautions will have to be taken to ensure that the maximum list is restricted to an acceptable limit.

Learning Objectives

On completion of this section the learner will achieve the following:

1. Understand the effect on KG of lifting a weight using ship's gear.
2. Calculate the *vertical* and *horizontal* components of the movement of the ship's centre of gravity (G) during a lifting operation and use these to determine the maximum angle of list that will occur.
3. Calculate the maximum permissible KG required prior to loading or discharging a weight to ensure that a certain list limit is not exceeded during the operation.
4. As (3) but with two weights.

13.1 EFFECT ON KG OF LIFTING A WEIGHT USING SHIP'S GEAR

Consider the situation where a weight *already on board* is to be lifted from a position in the lower hold using the ship's own derrick. Initial KG is shown.

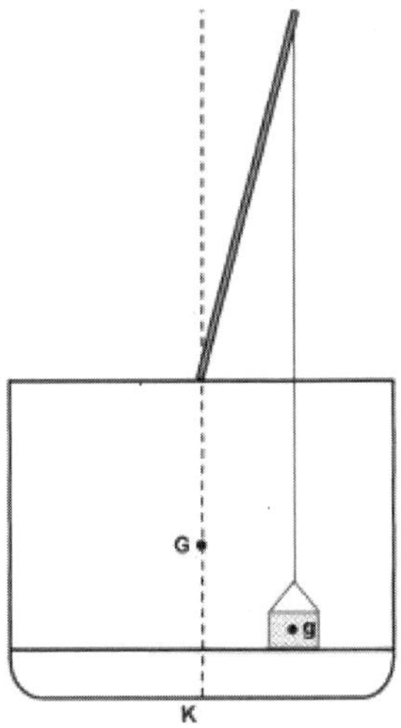

Fig. 1

As soon as the weight is lifted clear of the tank top the centre of gravity of the weight moves vertically up to its point of suspension at g_1. This results in a corresponding vertical movement of G to G_V, causing an *increase* in KG.

$$GG_V = \frac{w \times d}{W}$$

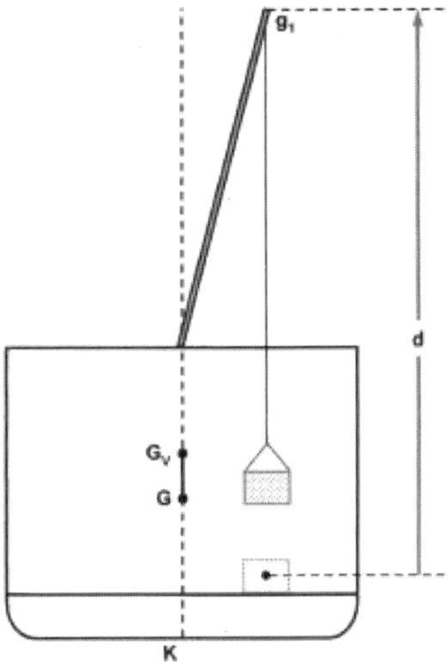

Fig. 2

where ***'d'*** is the distance through which the weight is effectively shifted upwards from it's initial stowage position to the derrick head.

<u>*Example 1*</u>
A ship has a displacement of 10516 t, KG 8.20 m and KM 9.00 m. A weight of 86 t in the lower hold, Kg 3.40 m, is lifted by the ship's heavy lift derrick, the head of which is 22.00 m above the keel.
(a) Calculate the GM when the weight is suspended.
(b) Calculate the final GM when the weight is restowed in the tween deck at Kg 8.50 m.

<u>*Solution*</u>
(a) $GG_V = \frac{w \times d}{W} = \frac{86 \times (22.00 - 3.40)}{10516} = 0.152\ m$

Initial KG	*8.200 m*
GG_V	*<u>0.152 m</u>*
KG when weight suspended	*8.352 m*
KM	*<u>9.000 m</u>*
GM when weight suspended	*<u>0.648 m</u>*

This is the minimum GM during the lifting operation.

(b) *To calculate the final GM when the weight has been shifted treat as a normal single weight problem - simply shift the weight from it's initial stowage position (Kg 3.40 m) to it's final stowage position (Kg 8.50 m) i.e. ignore the derrick.*

$$GG_V = \frac{w \times d}{W} = \frac{86 \times (8.50 - 3.40)}{10516} = 0.042\ m$$

Initial KG	*8.200 m*
GG_V	*0.042 m*
Final KG	*8.242 m*
KM	*9.000 m*
FINAL GM	*0.758 m*

The previous example was very simple as there was no horizontal shift of G involved as would be the case when loading or discharging a weight.

When loading or discharging weights using ship's lifting gear the following must be considered:

1. *the increase in KG/decrease in GM when the weight is suspended at the derrick/crane head;*
2. *the maximum angle of list that will occur when the derrick or crane is plumbed over the ship's side.*

13.2 LOADING A WEIGHT USING SHIP'S LIFTING GEAR

Consider the movement of the ship's centre of gravity (G) when a weight is lifted off the quay on one side of the ship and stowed in the lower hold on the centre line. (For the purpose of this explanation the ship is *not* shown to list.)

1. Derrick plumbed over the weight.

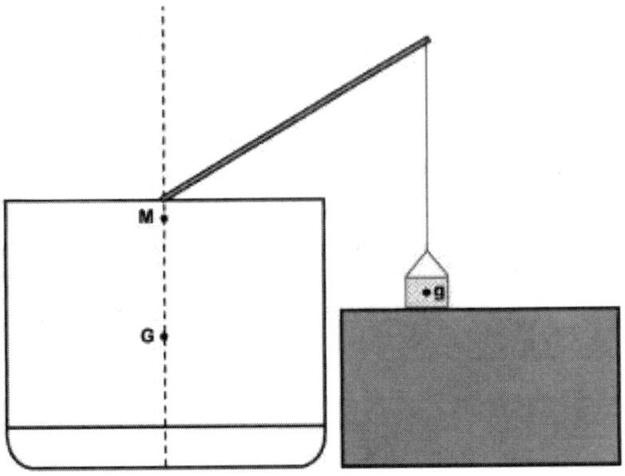

Fig. 13.3

2. Derrick picks the weight up off the quay.

G moves to G_1, directly towards the centre of gravity of the loaded weight - the point of suspension (g_1).

The movement GG_1 has two components:

GG_V: which causes an increase in KG/decrease in GM.

GG_H: which causes the ship to list.

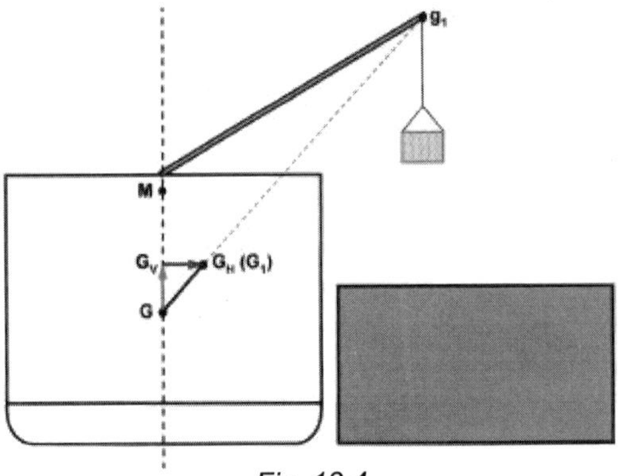

Fig. 13.4

It is at this stage that the *maximum list* would occur which coincides with the moment when the *GM has its minimum value*. Consider the list triangle *(Figure 13.5)*:

$$\text{Tan } \theta_{MAX.\ LIST} = \frac{GG_H}{GM_{MIN}}$$

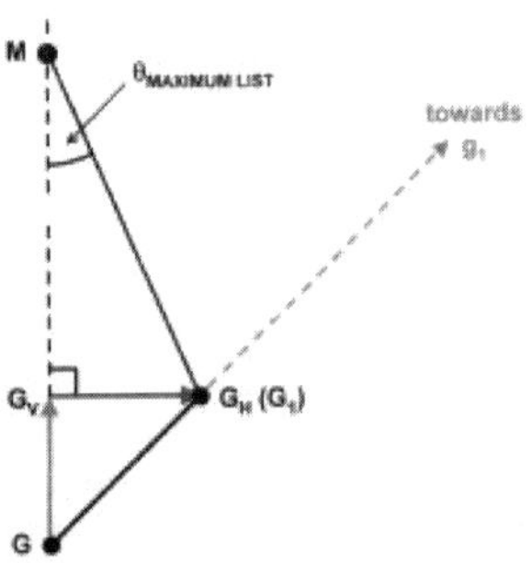

Fig. 13.5

3. Derrick swings inboard to plumb stowage position on the centre line.

G_1 moves to G_2 as the weight is swung inboard from g_1 to g_2. Ship becomes upright.

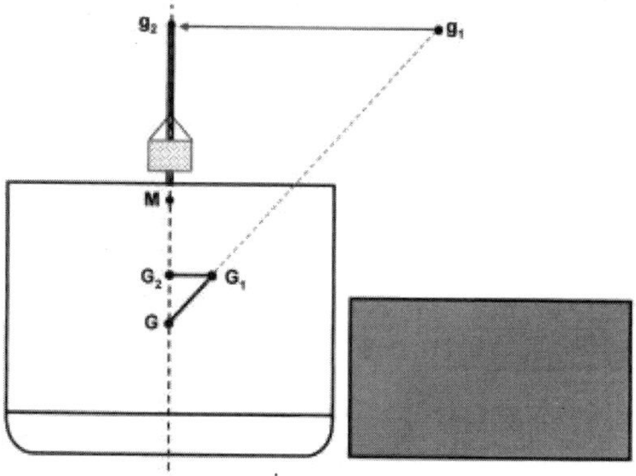

Fig. 13.6

4. Weight landed in the lower hold.

The weight is removed from the derrick head at g_2 as it is landed in the lower hold and finally acts at g_3. G_2 moves to G_3.

<u>Note</u>
The weight is loaded *below* the initial centre of gravity of the ship; so the final position of G, G_3, must be *lower*. KG is *reduced* overall.

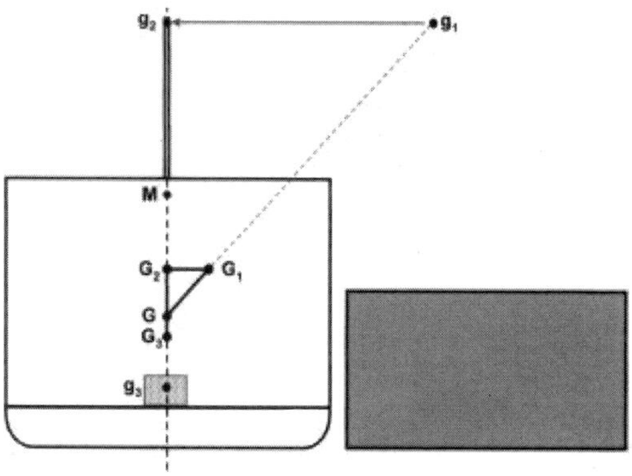

Fig. 13.7

Example 2 illustrates a typical list question involving a heavy lift being loaded. The calculation may be solved by one of two methods:

(1) *Formula method.*
(2) *Taking moments about the keel and the centreline.*

Both methods are shown, however, the moments method is much simpler and will be adopted for all other examples in this section.

<u>*Example 2*</u>
A ship displaces 8850 t, KG 7.15 m and KM 7.98 m. A weight of 40 t is to be loaded from the quay 15.0 m to starboard of the ship's centre line. If the head of the derrick is 27.0 m above the keel when topped to it's maximum extent for the lifting operation, calculate:

(a) *the GM when the weight is suspended;*
(b) *the maximum angle of list;*
(c) *the final angle of list if the weight is placed on deck at Kg 10.40 m, 5.0 m off the centre line to starboard.*
(d) *the weight of ballast to transfer between two double bottom tanks, <u>each</u> having its centre of gravity 4.0 m off the centreline, to bring the ship upright.*
(Assume KM remains constant)

<u>*Solution (Method 1)*</u>
(a) *To calculate the GM when the weight is suspended.*

Load the weight at the derrick head.

$GG_V = \frac{w \times d}{W + w} = \frac{40 \times (27.00 - 7.15)}{8850 + 40} = 0.089\ m$

Initial KG	7.150 m	
GG_V	0.089 m	
Maximum KG	.239 m	
KM	7.980 m	
GM when weight is suspended	0.741 m	(This is the minimum GM)

(b) Calculate the distance that G is off the centre line when the weight is suspended over the quay (GG_H).

$GG_H = \frac{w \times d}{W + w}$ $\quad GG_H = \frac{40 \times 15}{8850 + 40} = 0.067\ m$

$\text{Tan}\ \theta_{MAX.\ LIST} = \frac{GGH}{GM_{MIN.}}$ $\quad \text{Tan}\ \theta_{MAX.\ LIST} = \frac{0.067}{0.741} = 0.09042$ $\quad$ **Maximum list = 5.2° Stbd.**

(c) Calculate the final angle of list when the weight is placed on deck.
(Simply load the weight on deck, ignoring the derrick as in a normal single weight problem.)

$GG_V = \frac{w \times d}{W + w}$ $\quad GG_V = \frac{40 \times (10.40 - 7.15)}{8850 + 40} = 0.015\ m$

Initial KG	7.150 m
GGV	0.015 m
Final KG	7.165 m
KM	7.980 m
Final GM	0.815 m

$GG_H = \frac{w \times d}{W + w}$ $\quad GG_H = \frac{40 \times 5}{8850 + 40} = 0.022\ m$

$\text{Tan}\ \theta_{LIST} = \frac{GG_H}{GM_{FINAL}}$ $\quad \text{Tan}\ \theta_{LIST} = \frac{0.022}{0.815} = 0.02700$ $\quad$ **Final list = 1.5° Stbd.**

(d) Calculate weight of ballast to transfer from Stbd. DB tank to Port DB tank.
In the final condition G is off the centreline by 0.022 m (GG_H)

$GG_H = \frac{w \times d}{W}$ $\quad 0.022 = \frac{w \times 8}{8890}$ $\quad w = \frac{0.022 \times 8890}{8} = 24.5\ t$

Transfer 24.5 t

Solution (Method 2)

(a) To calculate the GM when the weight is suspended.
Load the weight at the derrick head. Take moments about the keel.

weight (t)	Kg (m)	moments (t-m)
8850	7.15	63277.5
40	27.00	1080.0
8890	7.239	64357.5

KM	7.980
KG	7.239
GM	0.741

GM when weight suspended 0.741 m (Minimum GM)

(b) Take moments about the centreline to determine GG_H.

Weight	Dist off CL	Port moments (t-m)	Stbd moments (t-m)
8850	0.000	0.0	0.0
40	15.000		600.0
		0.0	600.0

$GG_H = \frac{\text{Net listing moments}}{\text{Final displacement}} = \frac{600}{8890} = 0.067\ m$

$Tan\theta_{MAX.\ LIST} = \frac{GG_H}{GM_{MIN}}$ $\qquad Tan\ \theta_{MAX.\ LIST} = \frac{0.067}{0.741} = 0.09042$

Maximum list = 5.2° Stbd.

(c) Calculate the final angle of list when the weight is placed on deck. Take moments about the keel.

weight (t)	Kg (m)	moments (t-m)
8850	7.15	63277.5
40	10.40	416.0
8890	7.165	63693.5

KM	7.980
KG	7.165
GM	0.815

Take moments about the centreline to determine GG_H.

Weight	Dist off CL	Port moments (t-m)	Stbd moments (t-m)
8850	0.000	0.0	0.0
40	5.000		200.0
		0.0	200.0

$GG_H = \frac{\text{Net listing moments}}{\text{Final displacement}} = \frac{200}{8890} = 0.022\ m$

$Tan\theta_{MAX.\ LIST} = \frac{GG_H}{GM_{FINAL}}$ $\qquad Tan\ \theta_{MAX.\ LIST} = \frac{0.022}{0.815} = 0.09042$

Final list = 1.5° Stbd.

(d) Calculate weight of ballast to transfer from Stbd. DB tank to Port DB tank.
In the final condition G is off the centreline by 0.022 m (GG_H)

$GG_H = \frac{w \times d}{W}$ $\qquad 0.022 = \frac{w \times 8}{8890}$ $\qquad w = \frac{0.022 \times 8890}{8} = 24.5\ t$

Transfer 24.5 t

Note

If a heavy lift weight is to be *discharged* the same principles apply whereby the maximum list during the operation will occur when the weight is suspended at the derrick or crane head and the weight is plumbed over the ship's side.

13.3 TO CALCULATE THE MAXIMUM PERMISSIBLE KG REQUIRED PRIOR TO LOADING OR DISCHARGING A WEIGHT TO ENSURE THAT A CERTAIN LIST LIMIT IS NOT EXCEEDED

The key point here is to firstly identify the situation during the lifting operation that will create the maximum list. Drawing a diagram will help.

Consider the following example.

<u>*Example 3*</u>

A ship displacing 16200 t is upright and has a 90 t weight on deck at Kg 13.0 m, 6.00 m to port of the centre line. This weight is to be discharged into a lighter on the port side, 14.00 m from the centre line using the ship's heavy lift derrick. If the angle of list is not to exceed 8° at any time during the operation, calculate the maximum allowable KG prior to discharge given that KM is 9.60 m.

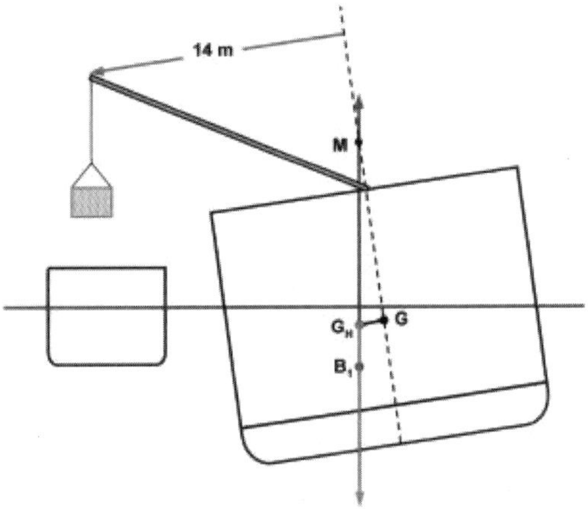

Fig. 13.8

<u>Solution</u>

Maximum list will occur when the weight is suspended at the derrick head and the derrick is plumbed over the port side.

GM will have its minimum value.

$$Tan\theta_{MAX.\ LIST} = \frac{GG_H}{GM_{MIN}}$$

Calculate the distance that G will be off the centre line (GG_H) when the ship is at it's maximum angle of list.

$$GG_H = \frac{w \times d}{W} \quad GG_H = \frac{90 \times (14 - 6)}{16200} = 0.044\ m$$

Maximum allowed list is 8°. GG_H is 0.044 m. This allows the minimum GM to be calculated.

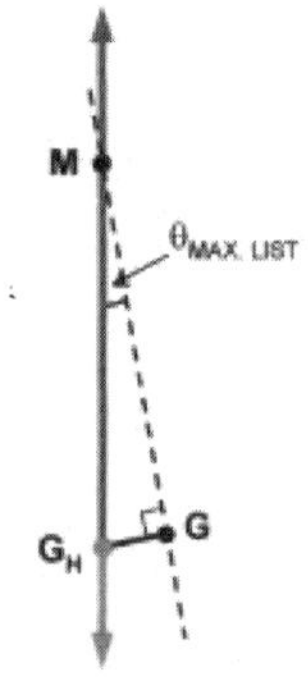

Fig. 13.9

$$Tan\ \theta_{MAX.\ LIST} = \frac{GG_H}{GM_{MIN}}$$

$$Tan\ 8^o = \frac{0.044}{GM_{MIN}}$$

Therefore: $GM_{MIN} = \frac{0.044}{Tan\ 8^o} = 0.313\ m$

A minimum GM of 0.313 m is required when the weight is plumbed over the side at Kg 27.0 m.

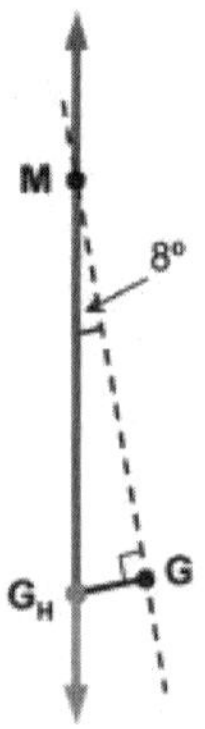

Fig. 13.10

KM	*9.600 m*
Minimum GM	*<u>0.313 m</u>*
Maximum KG	*<u>9.287 m</u>*

Having calculated the maximum allowed KG when the weight is suspended from the derrick head (Kg 27.0 m), shift the weight back to its original stowage position on deck (Kg 13.0) to calculate the maximum initial KG required prior to starting the operation.

Take moments about the keel.

weight (t)	Kg (m)	moments (t-m)
16200	9.287	150449.4
-90	27.00	-2430.0
90	13.00	1170.0
16200	9.209	149189.4

The initial KG must not be greater than ***9.209 m*** *in order to limit the list to 8°.*

SECTION 14 - ASSESSING COMPLIANCE OF A SHIP'S LOADED CONDITION WITH IMO CRITERIA

INTRODUCTION

The minimum intact stability criteria for a number of ship types is specified in the *'Code on Intact Stability for All Types of Ships Covered by IMO Instruments' (IMO).* This section covers the procedures for verifying compliance with such criteria for a typical cargo vessel. The intact stability requirements for passenger vessels are also detailed. (The additional specific requirements for other ship types and conditions of loading are covered in later sections as appropriate). Using the stability data book for *M.V. Almar* the procedures for verifying compliance of a loaded condition will be demonstrated with the aid of worked examples.

Learning Objectives

On completion of this section the learner will achieve the following:

1. Calculate areas under curves using *Simpson's First* and *Second Rules*.
2. Understand the term *Dynamical Stability* and it's relevance to the area under the curve of statical stability.
3. Understand the *IMO* and *M.S. (Load Line) Regulations 1998* intact stability criteria for cargo ships with respect to the curve of statical stability.
4. Verify that a ships loaded condition complies with required minimum criteria.
5. Understand the *IMO* and *M.S. (Passenger Ship Construction: Ships of Classes I, II and II(A) Regulations 1998)* intact stability criteria for passenger ships with respect to the curve of statical stability.
6. Understand the relationship between GZ and GM at small angles of heel.
7. Understand the limitations of using statical stability curve data as a means of assessing ship stability at sea.

14.1 SIMPSON'S RULES FOR CALCULATING AREAS UNDER CURVES

Simpson's Rules provide a simple means of calculating areas under curves without having to resort to integration techniques, which can be somewhat confusing for the non-mathematician.

There are two *Rules* that are used to calculate areas under the curve of statical stability, these being necessary to verify that a ship's proposed loaded condition complies with the intact stability criteria laid down by IMO.

14.1.1 Simpson's first rule

Consider the shape shown:

A, ***B*** and ***C*** are known as *ordinates*, having lengths expressed in metres.

The spacing between each of the ordinates must be the same, with ***h*** being the distance between the ordinates, known as the *Common Interval*, expressed in metres.

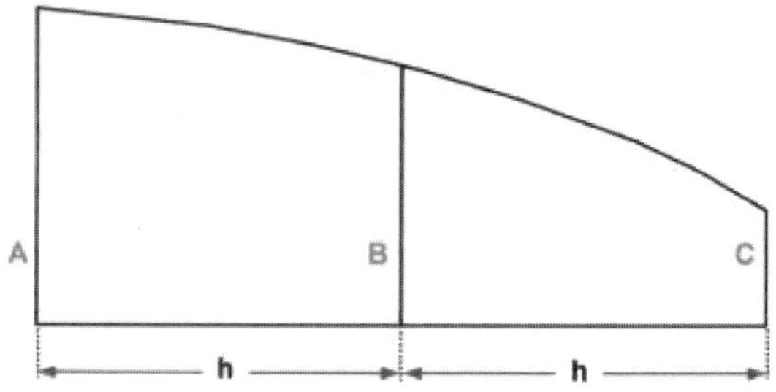

Fig. 14.1

To calculate the area of the shape:

AREA = $^1/_3$ × h × (1A + 4B + 1C)

where the numbers ***1***, ***4***, and ***1*** are known as *Simpson's Multipliers*.

This is Simpson's first Rule.

<u>*Example 1*</u>

A section of steel plate to be used in the construction of a ship's deck has dimensions as shown. Calculate the area of the plate.

Two approaches to the solution are shown.

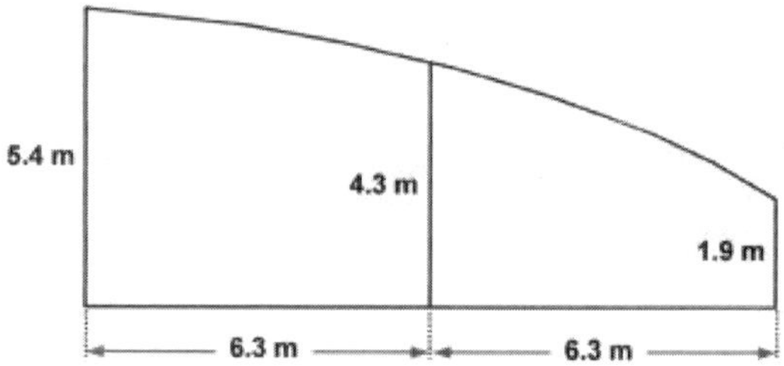

Fig. 14.2

<u>*Solution (1)*</u>

Area = $^1/_3$ × h × (1A + 4B + 1C)

Area = $^1/_3$ × 6.3 × [(1 × 5.4)+(4 × 4.3)+(1×1.9)]

Area = 2.1 × (5.4 + 17.2 + 1.9)

Area = 51.45 m^2

The calculation is very tedious in the format shown. A tabular approach makes the calculation much easier as follows.

<u>*Solution (2)*</u>

Area = $^1/_3$ × h × (1A + 4B + 1C)

Using a table, first calculate what is in the brackets.

Ordinate (m)	SM	Area Fn.
5.4	1	5.4
4.3	4	17.2
1.9	1	1.9
		24.5

Area = $^1/_3$ × h × Sum

Area = $^1/_3$ × 6.3 × 24.5

Area = 51.45 m^2

14.1.2 *Extension of the first rule*

Consider the shape of a ship's half water-plane area shown. The area has *five* ordinates. One way

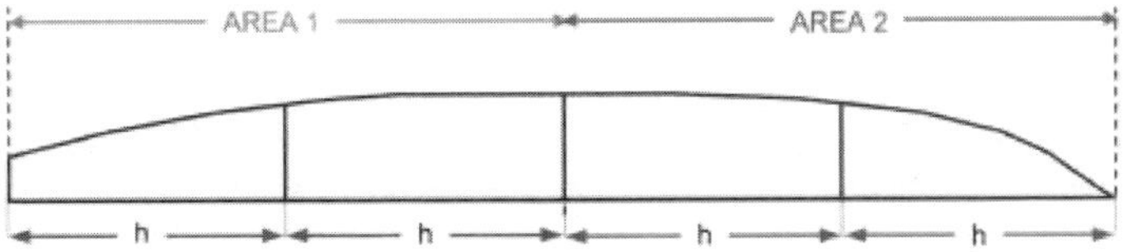

of calculating the whole area would be to divide it up into two, use Simpson's first rule to calculate both areas 1 and 2 separately and then sum them up to work out the total.

Fig. 14.3

A more convenient way is to consider the Simpson's multipliers for both of the areas concerned.

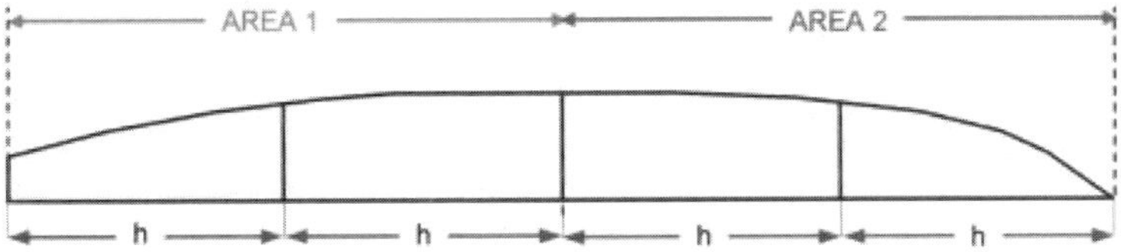

Simply sum the multipliers for the ordinate that forms the boundary of both shapes and treat the whole as a *single* shape. This gives multipliers of 14241.

Fig. 14.4

<u>*Example 2*</u>

A ship's water-plane area has half-ordinates from aft to forward as follows:

0.6 m, 1.5 m, 1.6 m, 1.4 m and 0.0 m. If the ***half-ordinates*** *are equally spaced at 4.2 m apart, calculate:*

(a) the total water-plane area;

(b) the TPC if the ship is floating in salt water (RD 1.025).

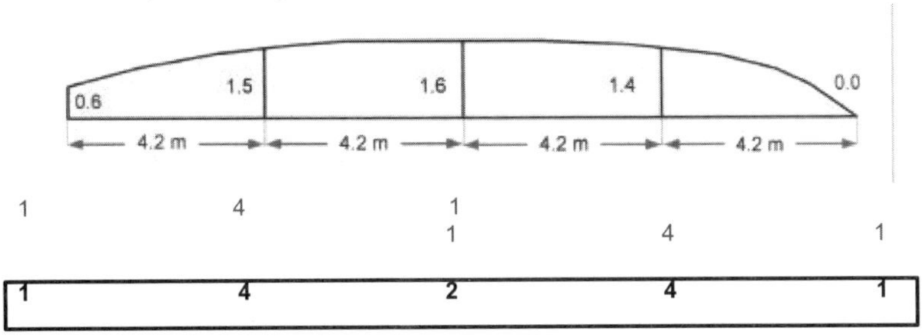

Fig. 14.5

<u>*Solution*</u>

(a) Calculate the area of the half water-plane area

Ordinate (m)	SM	Area Fn.
0.6	1	0.6
1.5	4	6.0
1.6	2	3.2
1.4	4	5.6
0.0	1	0.0
		15.4

Area $= \frac{1}{3} \times h \times Sum$

Area $= \frac{1}{3} \times 4.2 \times 15.4 = 21.56\ m^2$

Total WPA $= 2 \times 21.56 = \mathbf{43.12\ m^2}$

(b) $TPC = \frac{WPA}{100} \times \rho$ $\qquad TPC = \frac{43.12}{100} \times 1.025 = \mathbf{0.442}$

Note Simpson's first rule can be used whenever there are an odd number of ordinates; hence it is often referred to as the *'odd ordinate rule'*.

Thus:
With 3 ordinates the Simpson's multipliers are: 141
With 5 ordinates the Simpson's multipliers are: 14241
With 7 ordinates the Simpson's multipliers are: 1424241
With 9 ordinates the Simpson's multipliers are: 142424241 and so on...

14.13 Simpson's second rule

Consider the shape shown:

AREA = $^3/_8$ × h × (1A + 3B + 3C + 1D)

The Simpson's multipliers are ***1***, ***3***, ***3***, and ***1***.

Follow the worked example.

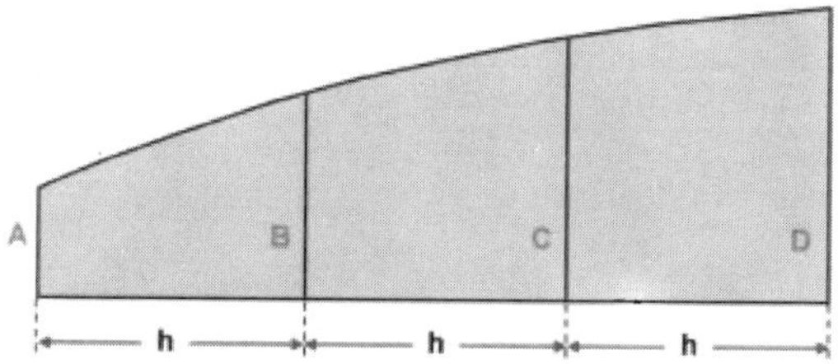

Fig. 14.6

Example 3

A plate section has dimensions as shown. Calculate the area.

Solution

Area = $^3/_8$ × h × (1A + 3B + 3C + 1D)

Using a table, calculate what is in the brackets.

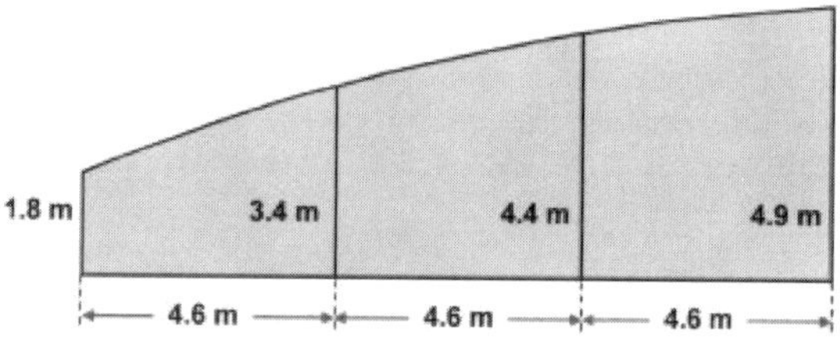

Fig. 14.7

Ordinate (m)	SM	Area Fn.
1.8	1	1.8
3.4	3	10.2
4.4	3	13.2
4.9	1	4.9
		30.1

Area = $^3/_8$ × h × Sum

Area = $^3/_8$ × 4.6 × 30.1

Area = 51.92 m^2

14.1.4 Extension of the second rule

Consider the shape of a ship's half water-plane area shown. The area has *seven* ordinates. The approach is the same as before.

The multipliers in this case are 1332331. Consider the example.

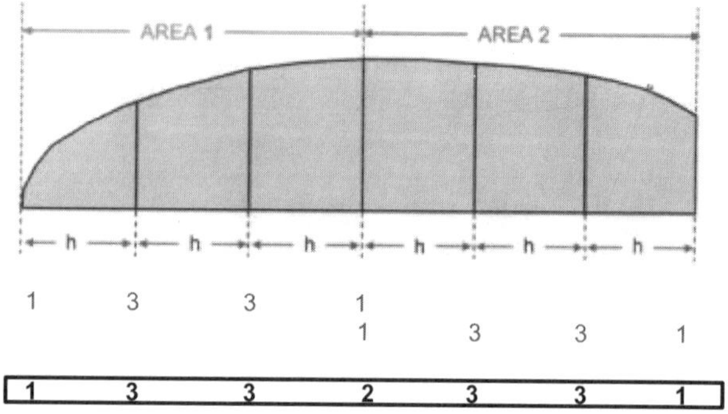

Fig. 14.8

Example 4

A small boat has a half water-plane area with equally spaced half-ordinates as follows:

0.20m, 1.20m, 1.70m, 1.82m, 1.75m, 1.65m and 1.21m.

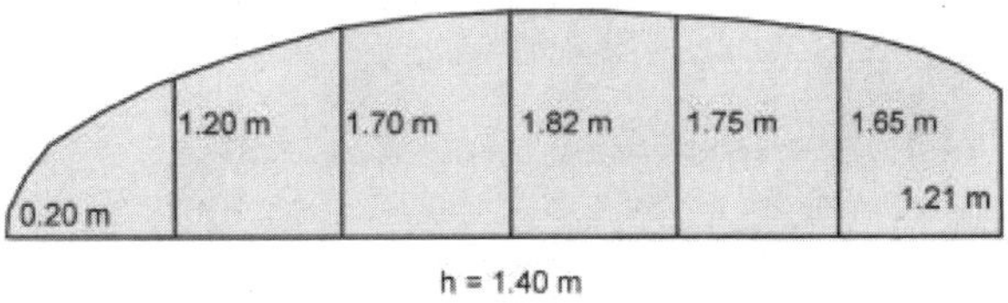

Fig. 14.9

The half-ordinates are equally spaced at 1.40 m apart.
Calculate the water-plane area.

Solution

Ordinate (m)	SM	Area Fn.
0.20	1	0.20
1.20	3	3.60
1.70	3	5.10
1.82	2	3.64
1.75	3	5.25
1.65	3	4.95
1.21	1	1.21
		23.95

Area of half WPA = $^3/_8 \times h \times Sum$

Area of half WPA = $^3/_8 \times 1.40 \times 23.95$

Area of half WPA = $12.57\ m^2$

Total WPA = $2 \times 12.57 =$ $\mathbf{25.15\ m^2}$

Note Simpson's second rule can be used whenever there is a number of ordinates such that:

$$\frac{\text{Number of ordinates - 1}}{3} = \text{a whole number}$$

With 4 ordinates the Simpson's multipliers are: 1331

where: $\frac{4-1}{3} = 1$

With 7 ordinates the Simpson's multipliers are: 1332331

where: $\frac{7-1}{3} = 2$

With 10 ordinates the Simpson's multipliers are: 1332332331

where: $\frac{10-1}{3} = 3$

and so on....

There may be instances when *either* rule may be used, such as with the previous example having 7 ordinates.

Simpson's first and second rules will be applied to the calculation of areas under the curve of statical stability.

14.2 DYNAMICAL STABILITY – THE RELEVANCE OF THE AREA UNDER THE CURVE OF STATICAL STABILITY

14.2.1 Dynamical stability defined

The *'dynamical stability'* of a ship at any particular angle of inclination may be defined as *'the work required by the external forces (wind, waves etc.) to heel the ship to that angle of heel'.*

When assessing the transverse stability of a ship a curve of statical stability (GZ curve) is produced. If the term *dynamical stability* is considered it is more appropriate to consider a *curve of righting moments*, whereby all GZ values calculated at specified angles of heel (for which KN values are available) are multiplied by the ship's displacement i.e.

Righting moment (t-m) = GZ (m) × Displacement (t)

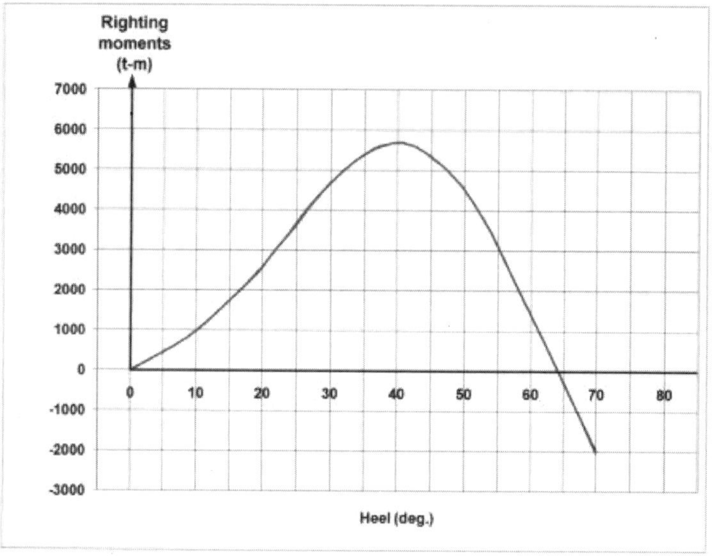

Fig. 14.10

The term *dynamical stability* can now be more readily appreciated. Consider a ship that has been inclined by external forces to an angle of heel of 25°. In order for the external forces to achieve this, *it is necessary that they overcome the sum of all the righting moments that the ship inherently has up to the angle of heel of 25°.* The shaded area in figure 14.11 represents this.

It is now clear that dynamical stability is determined by consideration of the *area under the curve of righting moments* up to the angle of heel concerned.

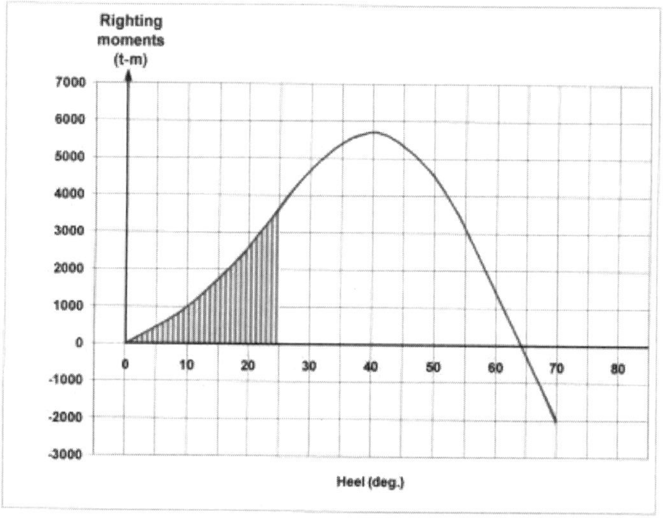

Fig. 14.11

Therefore: **DYNAMICAL STABILITY = AREA UNDER RM CURVE (0° to θ°)**

where the units of dynamical stability are *tonne-metre-radians* (since the minimum IMO criteria for area is expressed in *metre-radians* instead of *metre-degrees!)*

Of course, in practice it is a GZ curve that is produced and since: $\textbf{GZ (m)} = \dfrac{\textbf{Righting moment(t-m)}}{\textbf{Displacement (t)}}$

it follows that dynamical stability is *proportional to the area under the GZ curve.*
In conclusion:

DYNAMICAL STABILITY (t-m-r) = DISPLACEMENT (t) × AREA UNDER GZ CURVE (0° to θ°) (m-r)

14.2.2 The distinction between 'dynamical stability' and 'transverse statical stability'

'Transverse statical stability' is the term used to describe the ability of a ship to return to the upright when it has been forcibly heeled by an external force and is *momentarily at rest* when floating in *still water.*
It is calculated by the formula:

RIGHTING MOMENT (t-m) = GZ (m) × DISPLACEMENT (t)

where GZ is a measure of how far G and B are *horizontally* separated at a particular angle of heel.
The *'dynamical stability'* of a ship at any particular angle of inclination is *'the work required by the external forces (wind, waves etc.) to heel the ship to that angle of heel'.*

It is assessed by consideration of the *area under the righting moment curve* up to the angle of heel concerned.

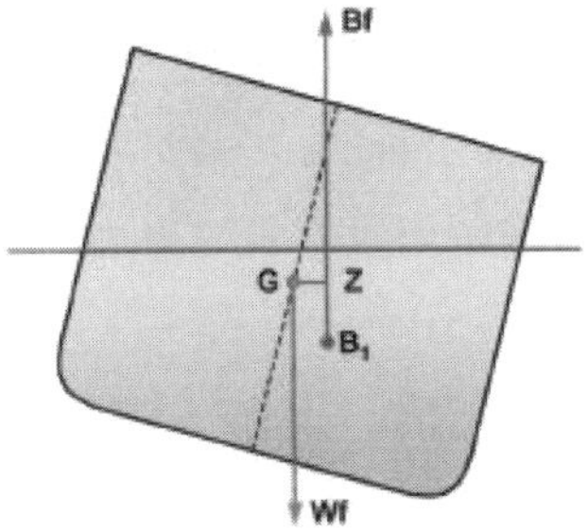

Fig. 14.12

DYNAMICAL STABILITY = AREA UNDER RM CURVE (0° to θ°)
or (in practice):

DYNAMICAL STABILITY (t-m-r) = DISPLACEMENT (t) × AREA UNDER GZ CURVE (0° to θ°) (m-r)
The distinction between the two terms is made even clearer if the curve of statical stability in figure 14.13 is considered.

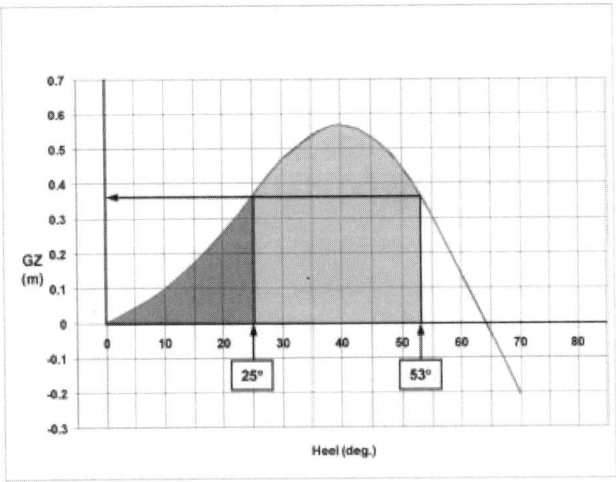

Fig. 14.13

The moment of statical stability will be the same for when the ship is heeled to 25° or 53°. However, the dynamical stability will obviously be much greater at 53° since more 'work' is required by the external forces to heel the ship over to the larger angle of heel.

The relationship between GZ and dynamical stability can be further appreciated if a comparison of the values of GZ and dynamical stability are compared at different angles of heel.

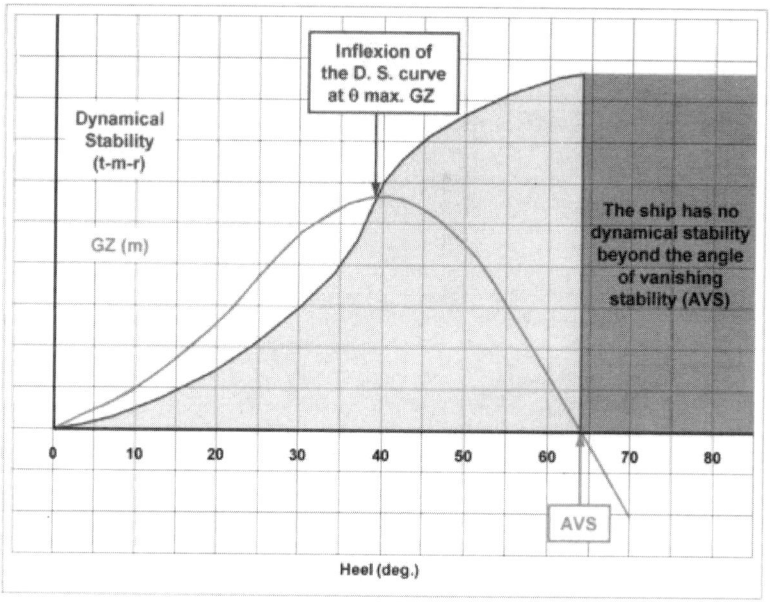

Fig. 14.14

It follows that if dynamical stability is a measure of the 'work' to be done by external forces to heel the ship over to a particular angle of heel, *dynamical stability will continue to increase with heel as long as the ship continues to resist such heeling* i.e. as long as the ship has positive righting levers. Once heeled beyond the angle of vanishing stability (AVS) the ship will capsize on its own.

Note

It must be appreciated that the explanation given is only true for a ship that is *heeled in still water*, is *momentarily at rest* and is *not heeled beyond the angle of progressive flooding*. Furthermore, it is assumed that the position of the centre of gravity of the ship does not move, even when heeled to such large angles for which a GZ curve is normally plotted. Clearly, in practice, the situation when a ship heels at sea is completely different! (See section 14.7).

14.3 MINIMUM INTACT STABILITY CRITERIA FOR CARGO SHIPS

Chapter 3 of the *Code on Intact Stability for All Types of Ships Covered by IMO Instruments (IMO)* details the minimum intact stability criteria to be satisfied by all cargo ships when at sea. Similar requirements are stipulated in *MSN 1752(M)* that accompanies the *M.S. (Load Line) Regulations 1998,* being applicable to all UK registered ships.

Requirements for other types of vessels are also included in the *IMO Code* and the MCA publication *'Load Lines - Instructions for the Guidance of Surveyors'*. The various requirements in the above publications will be covered as deemed necessary in this and subsequent sections.

14.3.1 Recommended general criteria for cargo ships (IMO)

This is as follows:

* *The area under the righting lever curve (GZ curve) should not be less than 0.055 metre-radian up to 30° angle of heel and not less than 0.09 metre-radian up to 40° or the angle of downflooding θ_f, if this angle is less than 40°. Additionally, the area under the righting lever curve (GZ curve) between the angles of heel of 30° and 40° or between 30° and θ_f, if this angle is less than 40°, should not be less than 0.03 metre-radian.*
* *The righting lever GZ should be at least 0.20 m at an angle of heel equal to or greater than 30°.*
* *The maximum righting arm should occur at an angle of heel preferably exceeding 30°, but not less than 25°.*
* *The initial metacentric height GM should not be less than 0.15 m.*
  (θ_f is an angle of heel at which openings in the hull, superstructures or deck-houses which cannot be closed weathertight immerse. In applying this criterion, small openings through

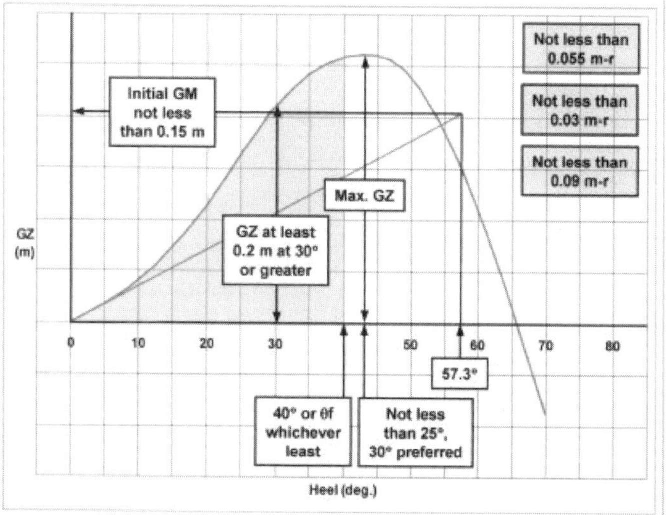

which progressive flooding cannot take place need not be considered as open.)

Fig. 14.15 (IMO criteria)

14.3.2 Intact stability criteria for cargo ships assigned freeboards under the M.S. (Load Line) Regulations 1998 (as specified in MSN 1752(M))

This is as follows:

The design and construction of the ship shall be such as to ensure that its stability in all probable loading conditions shall be sufficient for the freeboards assigned, and for this purpose due consideration shall be given to the intended service of the ship and to the following criteria.

* *The area under the curve of righting levers (GZ curve) shall not be less than:*

(i) 0.055 metre-radians up to an angle of 30°;
(ii) 0.09 metre-radians up to an angle of 40° or the angle at which the lower edge of any openings in the hull, superstructures or deckhouses which cannot be closed weathertight, are immersed if that angle is less; and
(iii) 0.03 metre-radians between the angles of heel of 30° and 40° or such lesser angle as referred to in subparagraph (ii) above.

* *The righting lever (GZ) shall be at least 0.20 m at an angle of heel equal to or greater than 30°.*

* *The maximum righting lever shall occur at an angle of heel not less than 30°.*

* *The initial transverse metacentric height shall not be less than 0.15 m. In the case of a ship carrying a timber deck cargo that complies with the area requirements above by taking into account the volume of timber deck cargo, the initial transverse metacentric height shall not be less than 0.05 m.*

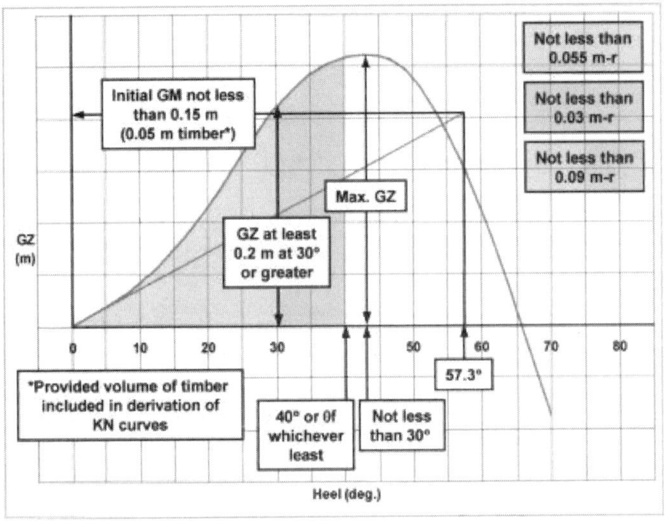

Fig.14.16 (M.S. (Load Line) Regulations 1998 criteria)

These requirements are very similar to those specified by IMO. The specific requirements for timber deck cargoes where a ship has been assigned timber freeboards will be covered in Section 27.

The initial metacentric height requirement is always a value of GM that has been corrected for the effects of free surfaces in tanks.

There are additional requirements for passenger ships and other specific ship types. Some of the more common ship type requirements will be covered in subsequent sections as necessary. Passenger ship requirements are covered in section 14.5.

14.4 ASSESSING COMPLIANCE OF A SHIP'S LOADED CONDITION

14.4.1 Checking compliance when the angle of progressive flooding (θ_f) is greater than 40°

Example 5

M.V. Almar completes loading with a displacement of 26000 tonnes and an effective KG of 8.86 m. Produce a curve of statical stability for the loaded condition and verify that the ship complies with the minimum IMO intact stability criteria.

Solution

Enter hydrostatic data and obtain value for KM. Calculate effective GM.

KM	9.310
KG FLUID	8.860
GM FLUID	**0.450**

Using KN values calculate the values of GZ for the loaded condition.

Heel	**10**	**20**	**30**	**40**	**60**	**80**
KN	1.64	3.30	5.04	6.50	8.06	8.14
KG*Sin Heel	1.54	3.03	4.43	5.70	7.67	8.73
GZ	**0.10**	**0.27**	**0.61**	**0.80**	**0.39**	**-0.59**

Plot the curve of statical stability.

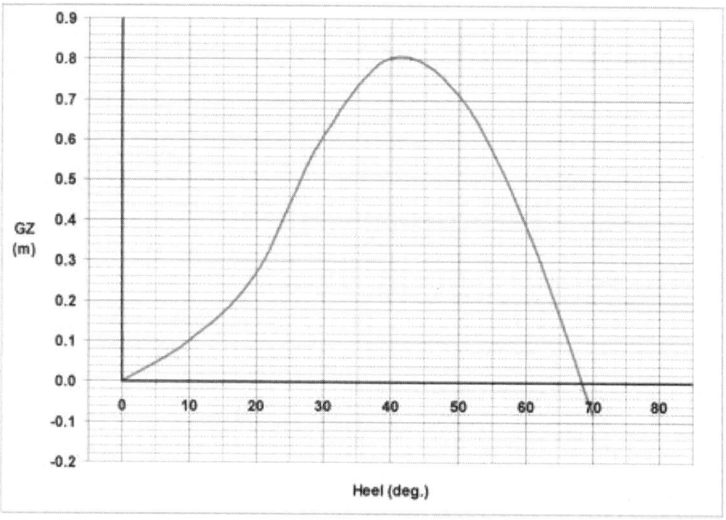

Fig. 14.17

Using Simpson's Rules calculate the areas under the curve.

Area 0° to 30°

Heel	GZ	SM	Area Fn.
0	0.00	1	0.000
10	0.10	3	0.300
20	0.27	3	0.810
30	0.61	1	0.610
		SUM	**1.720**

$$Area = \frac{3}{8} \times \frac{10}{57.3} \times 1.720$$

Area = 0.113 m-r

Area 0° to 40°

Heel	GZ	SM	Area Fn.
0	0.00	1	0.000
10	0.10	4	0.400
20	0.27	2	0.540
30	0.61	4	2.440
40	0.80	1	0.800
		SUM	**4.180**

Area $= \frac{1}{3} \times \frac{10}{57.3} \times 4.180$ ***Area = 0.243 m-r***

Area 30° to 40°

Take the difference of the two areas just calculated.
Area = 0.243 – 0.113 = ***0.130 m-r***

Note The area requirements are expressed in metre-radians. This means that the values of GZ are in metres; since the common interval, h, is 10° simply dividing this value by 57.3 will give a common interval expressed in radians (since 1 Radian is 57.3°).

Consideration of the GZ curve and the calculated areas gives the following answer.

	IMO Criteria (Minimum)	Actual	Complies
GM	Not less than 0.15 m	**0.450**	**YES**
Area 0 to 30	Not less than 0.055 m-r	**0.113**	**YES**
Area 0 to 40 (X)	Not less than 0.09 m-r	**0.243**	**YES**
Area 30-40 (X)	Not less than 0.03 m-r	**0.130**	**YES**
Max GZ	At least 0.2 m	**0.81**	**YES**
Heel max GZ	At least 30 deg.	**42 deg.**	**YES**

It is essential that all the criteria be met.

14.4.2 Checking compliance when the angle of progressive flooding (θ_f) is less than 40°

Under normal loaded conditions with reasonable trim it is usual for the angle of progressive flooding to occur at an angle of heel greater than 40° for most cargo ships. However, there may be instances when this is not the case, particularly in the case of offshore supply vessels and tugs, where the low freeboard aft in way of the working deck will result in early angles of deck edge immersion and subsequent earlier flooding angles depending on the arrangement of openings on the after deck.

Example 6 considers compliance for MV Almar where the angle of progressive flooding occurs at 36°. This would not occur on the ship for which the data for MV Almar is based.

Example 6
M.V. Almar completes loading with a displacement of 26000 tonnes and an effective KG of 8.86 m. Produce a curve of statical stability for the loaded condition and verify that the ship complies with the minimum IMO intact stability criteria ***given that the angle of heel at which progressive flooding takes place is 36°.***

Solution
Enter hydrostatic data and obtain value for KM. Calculate effective GM.

KM	9.310
KG FLUID	8.860
GM FLUID	**0.450**

Using KN values calculate the values of GZ for the loaded condition.

Heel	**10**	**20**	**30**	**40**	**60**	**80**
KN	1.64	3.30	5.04	6.50	8.06	8.14
KG*Sin Heel	1.54	3.03	4.43	5.70	7.67	8.73
GZ	**0.10**	**0.27**	**0.61**	**0.80**	**0.39**	**-0.59**

Plot the curve of statical stability.

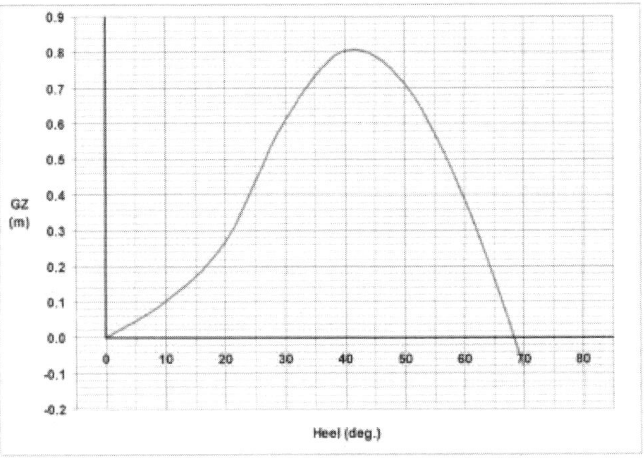

Fig. 14.18

Using Simpson's Rules calculate the areas under the curve.

Heel	GZ	SM	Area Fn.
0	0.00	1	0.000
10	0.10	3	0.300
20	0.27	3	0.810
30	0.61	1	0.610
		SUM	**1.720**

Area 0° to 30°

$$Area = \frac{3}{8} \times \frac{10}{57.3} \times 1.720$$

Area = 0.113 m-r

Area 0° to 36° (the angle of progressive flooding)

To calculate this area it is necessary to obtain GZ values from the curve drawn using a suitable common interval. Always aim for an interval of around 10° - in this case 9° has been chosen.

From the curve obtain values of GZ for the angles of heel 9°, 18°, 27° and 36° and calculate the area under the curve from 0° to 36° in the normal manner using either the first rule or second rule as appropriate.

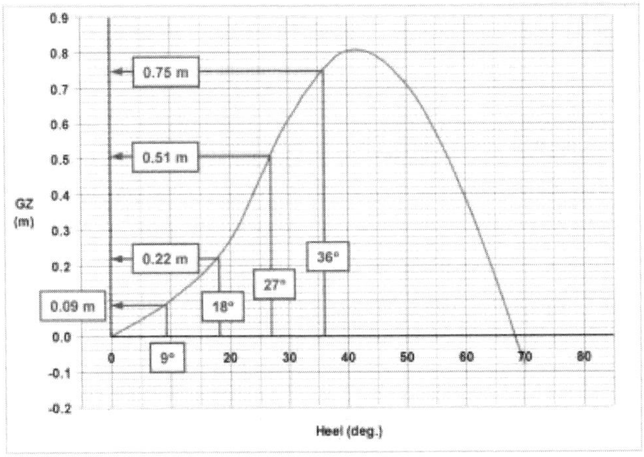

Fig. 14.19

Heel	GZ	SM	Area Fn.
0	0.00	1	0.000
9	0.09	4	0.360
18	0.22	2	0.440
27	0.51	4	2.040
36	0.75	1	0.750
		SUM	**3.590**

Area $= \frac{1}{3} \times \frac{10}{57.3} \times 3.590$ ***Area = 0.209 m-r***

Area 30° to 36°

Take the difference of the two areas just calculated.

Area = 0.209 – 0.113 = ***0.096 m-r***

Consideration of the GZ curve and the calculated areas gives the following answer.

	IMO Criteria (Minimum)	**Actual**	**Complies**
GM	Not less than 0.15 m	**0.450**	**YES**
Area 0 to 30	Not less than 0.055 m-r	**0.113**	**YES**
Area 0 to 40 (X)	Not less than 0.09 m-r	**0.209**	**YES**
Area 30-40 (X)	Not less than 0.03 m-r	**0.096**	**YES**
Max GZ	At least 0.2 m	**0.81**	**YES**
Heel max GZ	At least 30 deg.	**42 deg.**	**YES**

Note

X is 36°, the lesser angle of progressive flooding being less than 40°.

14.5 MINIMUM INTACT STABILITY CRITERIA FOR PASSENGER SHIPS

14.5.1 Additional IMO criteria for passenger ships

Passenger ships must demonstrate compliance with all the requirements laid down in section 14.3.1 (as applicable to cargo ships). However, additional requirements take account of the effects of crowding of all passengers to one side of the ship and the effects of heeling during turning at service speed.

These additional requirements are summarised as follows:

* *The angle of heel on account of crowding of passengers to one side (as defined below) should not exceed 10°.*

    * *A mass of 75 kg should be assumed for each passenger except that this value may be reduced to not less than 60 kg where this can be justified. In addition, the mass and distribution of the luggage should be determined by the Administration.*

    * *The height of the centre of gravity should be assumed equal to:*

        (1) *1.0 m above deck level for passengers standing upright. Account may be taken, if necessary, of camber and sheer of deck;*

        (2) *0.30 m above the seat in respect of seated passengers.*

    * *Passengers and luggage should be considered to be in the spaces normally at their disposal.*

    * *Passengers without luggage should be considered as distributed to produce the most unfavourable combination of heeling moment and/or metacentric height at no more than 4 persons per square metre.*

* *The angle of heel on account of turning should not exceed 10° when calculated using the following formula:*

$$\text{Heeling moment (kN-m)} = 0.196 \times \frac{V^2 \times W}{L} \times \left(KG - \frac{d}{2}\right)$$

where: V = service speed (m/s)
L = length of ship at waterline (m)
W = displacement (t)
KG = height of centre of gravity above baseline (m)

Note
This formula gives a value of heeling moment in kN-m. The value calculated must be converted into tonnes-metres and may then be plotted as a heeling arm on the curve of righting moments whereby intersection of the heeling moment and righting moment curves will indicate the angle of heel due to turning.
Use of this formula will be discussed fully in Section 23 (There exists much confusion between the terms kN and tonnes and it is here that these terms will be explained).

14.5.2 Intact stability criteria for passenger ships (M.S. (Passenger Ship Construction: Ships of Classes I, II and II(A)) Regulations 1998

These alternative requirements apply to UK registered passenger ships and are similar to those requirements for cargo ships laid out in section 14.3.2 and are to be found in Schedule 1 of MSN 1698(M). These are as follows:

1. After correcting for the effect of free surface of liquids in tanks:

(1) The area under the curve of righting levers (GZ curve) shall not be less than:

(a) 0.055 metre-radian up to an angle of 30°;

(b) 0.09 metre-radian up to an angle of 40° or the angle at which the lower edges of any openings in the hull, superstructures or deckhouses, being openings which cannot be closed weathertight, are immersed if that angle be less; and

(c) 0.03 metre-radian between the angles of heel of 30° and 40° or such lesser angle as referred to in subparagraph (b).

(2) The righting lever (GZ) shall be at least 0.20 m at an angle of heel equal to or greater than 30°.

(3) The maximum righting lever shall occur at an angle of heel not less than 30° provided that this angle may be permitted to be reduced, having regard to the design of a particular ship.

(4) The initial transverse metacentric height shall not be less than 0.15 m.

2. Where it is not possible, due to the particular design or operating conditions of a particular ship, to comply with the criteria of this Schedule, the application of alternative criteria may be permitted if it gives a standard of stability at least as effective.

Arguably, the aforementioned requirements are virtually the same as those for UK registered cargo ships; they have been included for the purpose of completeness of this particular section.

14.6 THE RELATIONSHIP BETWEEN GM AND THE INITIAL SLOPE OF THE CURVE OF STATICAL STABILITY

When plotting the GZ curve it is usual to draw a vertical at 57.3° (1 radian) from the baseline equal to the effective GM value as measured on the GZ scale. This allows the construction of a line emanating from the origin that will indicate the initial trend of the GZ curve within *small angles of heel*. The purpose of this is to simply aid in the sketching of the curve at small angles of heel between the plotted GZ values as derived from the KN values provided.

(The actual distinction between stability at small and large angles of heel is discussed in section 16.)

The proof of the relationship between GZ at small angles of heel and GM is as follows:

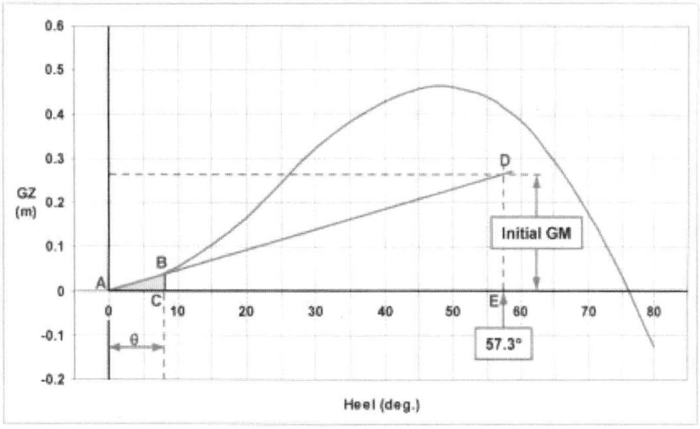

Fig. 14.20

Consider figure 14.20.

AD is a line drawn as a tangent to the GZ curve that emanates from the origin at A.

AD cuts a line drawn vertically upwards from the heel scale at E, 57.3° (1 radian).

Line DE has length equal to the ship's effective GM as measured on the GZ scale.

BC is a GZ value close to the origin at a small angle θ°.

Triangles ABC and ADE are similar.

$$\therefore \quad \frac{DE}{AE} = \frac{BC}{AC}$$

$$\therefore \quad \frac{DE}{57.3^\circ} = \frac{GZ \text{ at } \theta^\circ}{\theta^\circ}$$

If sides AC and AE are expressed in radians:

AE = 1 radian *AC = θ radians*

$$\therefore \quad \frac{DE}{1 \text{ radian}} = \frac{GZ \text{ at } \theta^\circ}{\theta \text{ radians}}$$

Since DE = Initial GM then:

$$\therefore \quad \frac{\text{Initial GM}}{1 \text{ radian}} = \frac{GZ \text{ at } \theta^\circ}{\theta \text{ radians}}$$

Rearranging this gives:

Initial GM × θ expressed in radians = GZ at θ° × 1

Thus: **Initial GM × θ expressed in radians = GZ at θ°**

Within the range of small angles, the value of any angle, expressed in radians, is very close in value to the Sine of the angle in question. Consider the table below.

Angle in degrees	Sine of angle	Angle expressed in radians
1	0.0175	0.0175
2	0.0349	0.0349
3	0.0523	0.0524
4	0.0698	0.0698
5	0.0872	0.0873
6	0.1045	0.1047
7	0.1219	0.1222
8	0.1392	0.1396
9	0.1564	0.1571
10	0.1736	0.1745

Thus, in the above formula ***θ expressed in radians'*** *may be substituted for* **'Sine θ'** *where θ is expressed in degrees.*

Therefore: ***Initial GM × Sine θ = GZ at θ° (θ°being a small angle)***

i.e. ***GZ = GM × Sineθ***

14.7 THE UNRELIABILITY IN PRACTICE OF USING STATICAL STABILITY CURVE DATA FOR ASSESSING A SHIP'S STABILITY AT SEA

Consider the definition of the term *transverse statical stability – it relates to the ability of a ship to return to the upright condition when it has been forcibly inclined by an external force, is* ***momentarily at rest*** *and is* ***floating in still water***.

At sea the ship will be subjected to forces and moments that are not taken into account in calculations that assume 'static' conditions. The ship will be actively rolling, pitching and heaving and as such a more relevant dynamic approach is more appropriate to what is essentially a dynamic problem. The problem that faces modern ship designers is how such a more accurate means of stability assessment can be achieved.

The dynamic forces, acting either individually or cumulatively, can be substantial and have been the cause of the loss or near loss of ships which have had statical stability in excess of IMO, M.S. (Load Line) Regulations or other statutory requirements.
The limitations of using statical stability curve data are summarised in the following sub-sections

14.7.1 Light displacement and KG assumptions

For any KG calculation to be valid the correct lightship KG and displacement values must be used. Section 19 describes the procedure for calculating these values by means of an inclining experiment. In service, however, the light KG and displacement will alter with age by reasons of changes of equipment, fittings, paint coatings, corrosion, and accumulation of spares to name but a few. Structural changes might even take place whereby these values will have changed significantly. When any modification to the vessel takes place the changes in KG and light displacement must be accurately determined and the ship re-inclined if necessary.

Furthermore, the ship as completed might not be exactly to design (drawing) dimensions and the possibility also exists whereby data extracted from drawings can be in error.

It is essential that periodic 'constant' calculations be performed, whereby the draughts as read are used to determine the ship's actual hydrostatic displacement and this in turn is compared to the calculated displacement and draughts so that the error (constant) can be calculated. The constant is a value of an imaginary weight loaded (or discharged) from some position to correct the draughts as calculated to be the same as those actually read. It is not possible to determine the KG at which this weight must be loaded (or discharged). The only way to obtain an up to date lightship KG value is by conducting another inclining experiment.

14.7.2 Calculation inaccuracies

The information given by a curve of statical stability can only be valid if the ship is in the condition of loading assumed by the person doing the calculations. To be valid the ship must:

(a) be at the assumed displacement;
(b) be at the trim stated on the hydrostatic particulars and KN tables (which is rarely the case);
(c) be loaded or ballasted to the assumed effective KG in the calculation whereby free surface moments have been fully accounted for;
(d) be intact, displacing water at all compartments which can be maintained watertight.

14.7.3 Effects of free trim

This is the effect of the ship changing trim, usually further by the stern, in response to heeling to such an angle that the fore and aft distribution of buoyancy changes. This is fully discussed in section 26 as it is particularly relevant to offshore supply vessels.

14.7.4 Dynamic effects of the ship's motion at sea in general

Mechanisms that will reduce stability and might lead to capsize in waves of any heading to the ship, either in isolation or in combination, arise because of the ship's movement in a seaway, in particular pitching, rolling and heaving.

14.7.4.1 Changes in stability caused by heaving, rolling and pitching

These motions create changes in the magnitude and position of application of the upward buoyancy force. The acceleration of the ship as a result of these motions is also not accounted for.

14.7.4.2 The effect of steady wind moments or asymmetric icing

These create a steady heel to the ship and reduce the ship's ability to cope with isolated sudden external forces such as gusting winds, individual exceptionally large waves or the impact of breaking waves.

Wind heeling and ice accretion effects are discussed in section 25.

14.7.4.3 Stability loss on a wave crest

Stability is reduced when the ship is on a wave crest and increased when in a trough.

If an 'end on' wave, equal to the length of the ship, has its crest amidships (where wall-sided) and troughs at the ends (where fine-lined) there will be a reduction in water plane area compared with the still water level. This creates a reduction in BM and a loss in GM (see *wall-sided formula* in section 16). As BM is a directly related to the size of the water plane area and because of the volumes of displacement at the ends of the ship there will be a reduced outward movement of B as the vessel is heeled resulting in reduced GZ values. Consider figure 14.21.

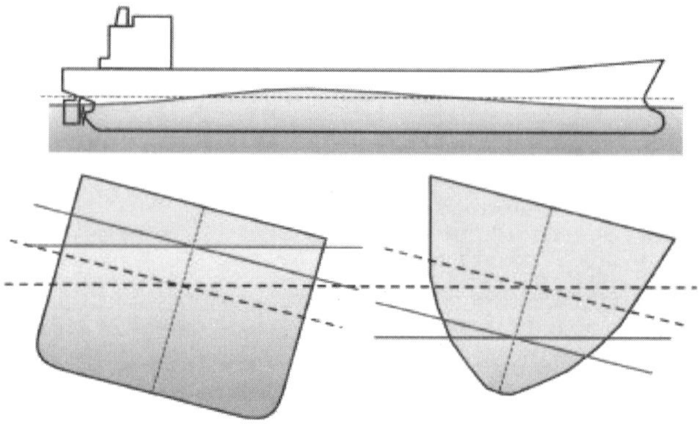

(1) Wave crest amidships – the transfer of wedge of buoyancy when ship heeled is similar to that for the still water condition as the ship is wall-sided amidships.

(2) At the ends of the ship (trough) the transfer of wedge of buoyancy is smaller than that for the still water condition causing overall outboard movement of B to be reduced.

Fig. 14.21

The diagrams in figure 14.21 show that the crest amidships does not affect the amount of buoyancy transferred across at amidships, but it is reduced at the ends of the ship. A reduced outward movement of B implies a reduction in BM value and reduced GZ value. When the trough is amidships the opposite will be true.

When the ship is beam on to the waves the crest/trough influence on the position of B is insignificant but the loss of buoyancy force in the crest applies throughout the ship's length. There is a significant loss of stability due to this cause alone.

14.7.4.4 Parametric resonance

This is the increase in roll (or apparent loss of stability) due to the periodic passage of regular waves that causes the ship to pitch. It is particularly associated with container ships that require large deck spaces for container stowage and fine lined hulls for fast service speeds. Such ships have hull forms that feature fine lined bows and wide sterns in order to maximise deck space aft. This variation between bow and stern hull form is such that it causes a tendency for the ship's pitching motion to induce rolling – a phenomenon known as *parametric resonance*.

14.7.4.5 Dynamic movement of water on deck

Water shipped on deck will not be accounted for. This will cause an increase in KG for the following reasons:

(1) added weight high up will cause G to rise, and;
(2) associated free surface moments causing a further rise in G.

Water on deck presents further problems for the ship if it is actively rolling. The dynamic movement of the water might at times be out of phase with the ships rolling motion, as such it would behave as a *passive stabilising (flume)* tank in a favourable manner (the principles behind such tanks are discussed in section 26 as they are often utilised in offshore supply vessels). However, this dynamic effect of the movement of water must necessarily be assumed to be detrimental, whereby its movement is in phase with the rolling of the ship. The transverse movement of G (which is the true effect of a free surface) causes a reduction in the ship's GZ values.

At the limit of the waters travel: Loss of GZ = $GG_H \times \text{Cosine } \theta$

where: GG_H is the distance that G has moved off the centre line as a result of the transverse movement of water on deck, and;
θ is the angle of heel for which the loss of GZ is being considered.

(The derivation of this formula is fully discussed in section 17)

Since $GG_H = \frac{w \times d}{W}$

$$\text{Loss of GZ} = \frac{\text{mass of water} \times \text{distance off CL}}{\text{Displacement}} \times \text{Cosine } \theta$$

The maximum static effect of the movement of water on deck is illustrated in figure 14.22.
The real effect of the movement of water on deck will be greater by reason of its momentum when surging across the deck.

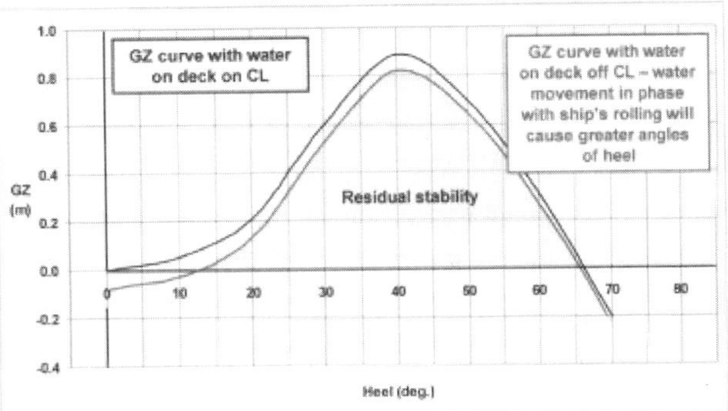

Fig. 14.22

14.7.4.6 Broaching

Broaching occurs when a ship is travelling with the direction of approach of the waves from a near astern direction. If, when sailing away from waves the crest of a particularly large wave overtakes the ship and hits one quarter (rather than squarely onto the stern) the ship will tend to be thrown round into a direction in which the wave is moving. This will bring the ship beam onto the sea resulting in severe heeling.

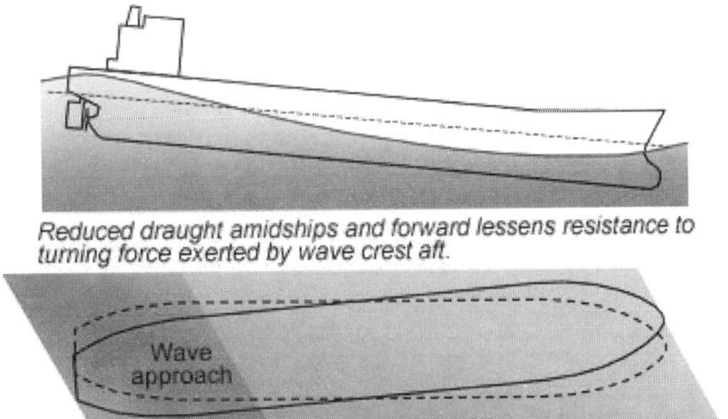

Reduced draught amidships and forward lessens resistance to turning force exerted by wave crest aft.
Wave approach
CREST
TROUGH
Ship turns beam on to the sea.

Fig. 14.23

Once beam on to the waves stability is severely compromised as evident in figure 14.24. The effect of waves acting beam on to the ship causes reduced righting levers when compared to those that would have existed had the ship been heeled to the same angle in still water. Of course, the stability of the ship will always be affected when waves approach the ship from any direction, being different to the assumed still water conditions for which the curve of statical stability is produced.

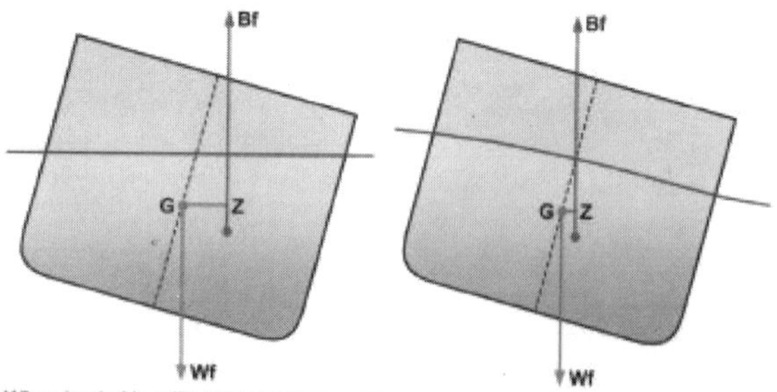

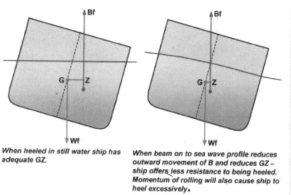

When heeled in still water ship has adequate GZ.

When beam on to sea wave profile reduces outward movement of B and reduces GZ – ship offers less resistance to being heeled. Momentum of rolling will also cause ship to heel excessively.

Fig. 14.24

Synchronism is another a problem associated with waves whereby the period of encounter of waves is similar to the natural roll period of the ship causing the ship to roll excessively even in relatively calm seas. The effect of this is covered in detail in Section 25.

14.7.5 Summary

It is clear that a 'dynamical' approach should be adopted for determining a ship's seaworthiness in terms of stability. Investigations worldwide are ongoing to find a more realistic dynamic approach to stability assessment. However, the problem to be overcome is that of the random nature in which the environmental forces such as wind and waves operate, and being random, makes them very difficult to predict realistically!

As technology advances the use of 'movement sensors' may become more widely adopted whereby the ship's movement will be monitored in all planes of motion and ship accelerations will be monitored to produce a more meaningful dynamical picture of the ship's sea-keeping and stability characteristics. Such systems have been in use for some 25 years now on Dynamically Positioned (D.P.) vessels where station keeping is achieved by computer control of main engines, thrusters and rudders. These systems do not have any 'dynamical stability monitoring' capability, but I am in no doubt that such systems are currently under development.

SECTION 15 – CURVES OF STATICAL STABILITY FOR VARYING CONDITIONS

INTRODUCTION

In section 7 *stable*, *unstable* and *neutral* conditions of stability were discussed in terms of the relative positions of G, B and M. In section 11 *list* was discussed whereby a ship became inclined due to G being off the centre line in a stable ship. In section 10 the curve of statical stability was introduced and this was further examined in way of the required minimum intact criteria in the previous section.

Now all of the above is drawn together so that by consideration of the *shape* of the curve of statical stability alone, it will be possible for the actual condition of stability of the ship to be recognised.

An examination question might take the form:

'Consider the curves of statical stability illustrated. For each state the condition of stability of the ship and identify the angle of inclination that the ship would be lying at, indicating the cause of such inclination.'

It is the purpose of this section that you be able to answer this and other similar type questions.

It is of particular importance that the differences in the shape of the curve of statical stability at the initial angles of heel are appreciated and understood for each condition.

Learning Objectives

On completion of this section the learner will achieve the following:

1. Identify the features of the curve of statical stability for a ship in a *stable* condition.
2. Identify the features of the curve of statical stability for a ship in a *neutral* condition.
3. Identify the features of the curve of statical stability for a ship in an *unstable* condition.
4. Identify the features of the curve of statical stability for a ship in a *listed* condition.
5. Know the safe procedures for correcting an angle of loll and an angle of list.

15.1 CURVE OF STATICAL STABILITY FOR A SHIP IN A STABLE CONDITION

A ship is in a *stable* condition of stability if, when heeled by an external force in *still water* to a *small angle* of inclination*, it returns to the upright* when the external force is removed.

Consider a stable ship being progressively heeled from the upright within small angles of inclination.

KM - KG = GM; which has a *positive* value.

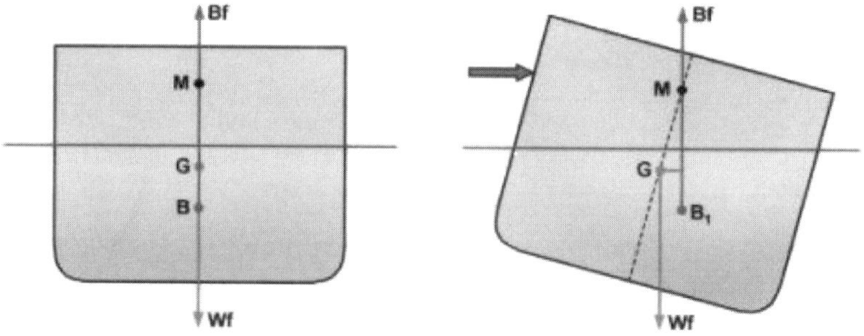

(1) Ship upright – GZ zero
(2) Ship heeled to a small angle – GZ positive

Fig. 15.1

In the heeled condition GZ is positive, which will act to right the ship when the external force is removed.

A typical curve of statical stability for a stable ship is depicted in figure 15.2 where diagrams (1) and (2) of figure 15.1 are related to the curve shown.

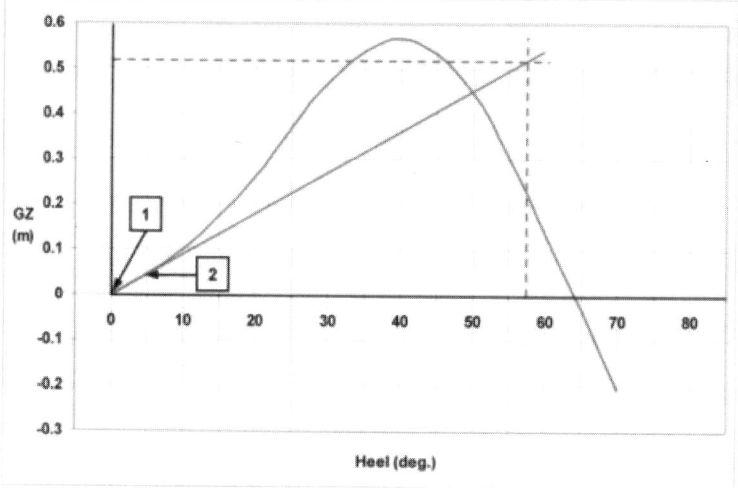

Fig. 15.2

As the ship is heeled beyond small angles the GZ values will depart from the tangential line of construction based on initial GM as shown.

15.2 CURVE OF STATICAL STABILITY FOR A SHIP IN A NEUTRAL CONDITION

A ship is in a *neutral* condition of stability if, when heeled by an external force in *still water* to a *small angle* of inclination, *it comes to rest at an indeterminate angle of heel within small angles of inclination.*

Consider a ship that is in a neutral condition of stability being progressively heeled from the upright within small angles of inclination. The initial transverse metacentre (M) is at the same height as G.

i.e. KM - KG = 0; *GM = 0*

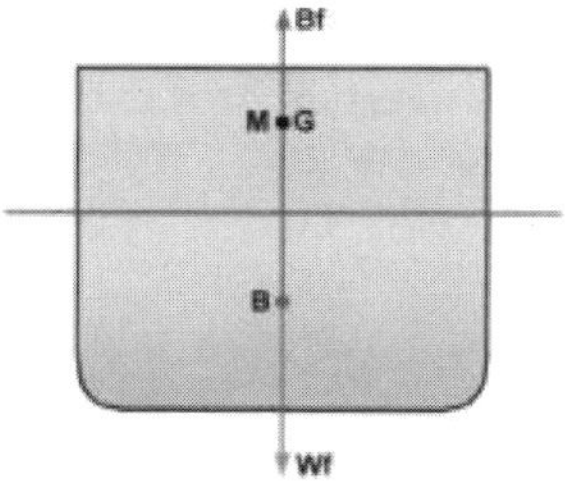

(1) Ship upright – GZ is zero

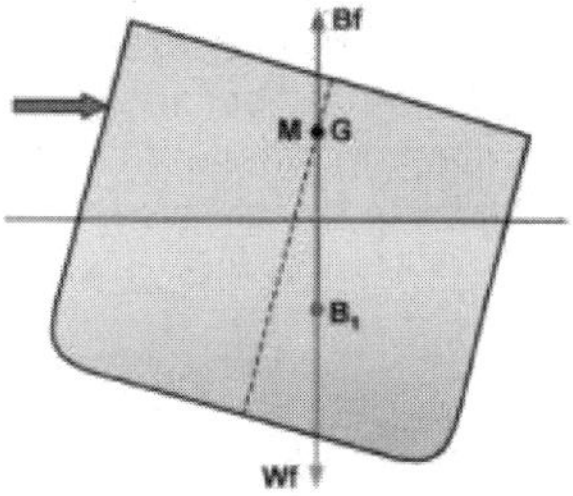

(2) Ship heeled to a small angle – GZ remains zero

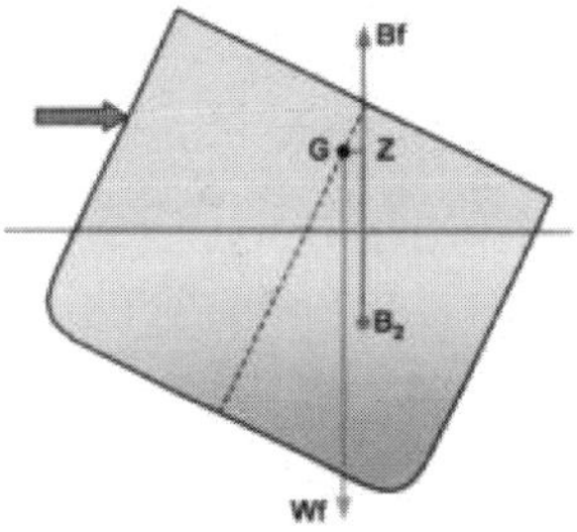

(3) Ship heeled beyond small angles – GZ becomes

Fig. 15.3

The curve of statical stability for such a ship is depicted in figure 15.4 where diagrams (1), (2) and (3) are related to the curve shown.

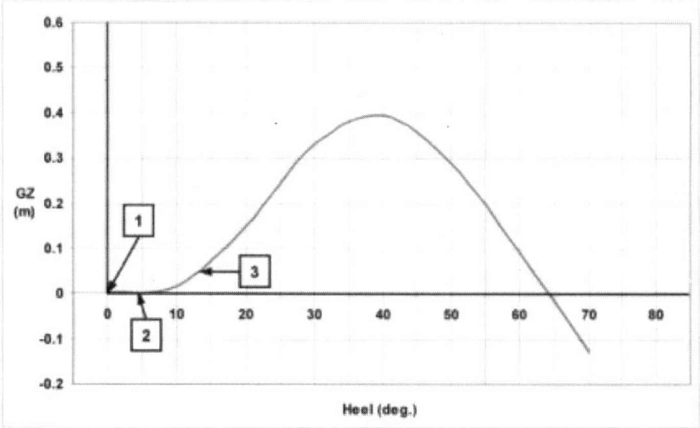

Fig. 15.4

15.3 CURVE OF STATICAL STABILITY FOR A SHIP IN AN UNSTABLE CONDITION (ANGLE OF LOLL)

A ship is in an *unstable* condition if, when heeled by an external force in still water to a small angle, *it continues to heel further when the external force is removed.*
Consider an unstable ship being progressively inclined from the upright. The initial transverse metacentre (M) is below G.
i.e. KM - KG = GM; which has a *negative* value.

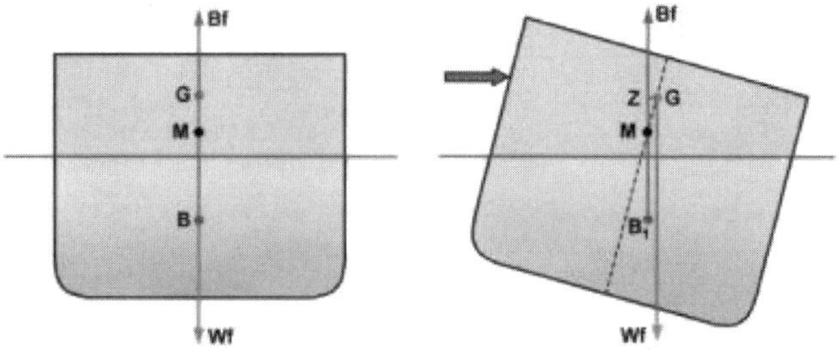

(1) ***Ship upright – GZ is zero (Ship would not remain upright, it would loll to either port or starboard)***

(2) ***Ship inclined to a small angle – GZ is negative (acting to capsize the ship)***

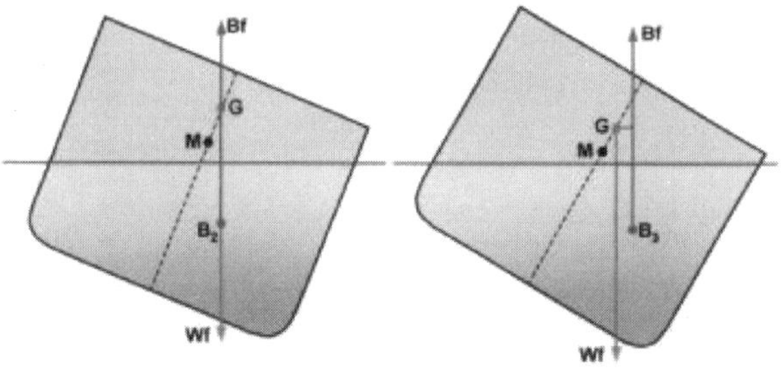

(3) ***Ship comes to rest at angle of loll – GZ is zero***

(4) ***Ship inclined beyond angle of loll – GZ becomes positive***

Fig. 15.5

The curve of statical stability for such a ship is depicted in figure 15.6 where diagrams (1), (2) (3) and (4) are related to the curve shown.

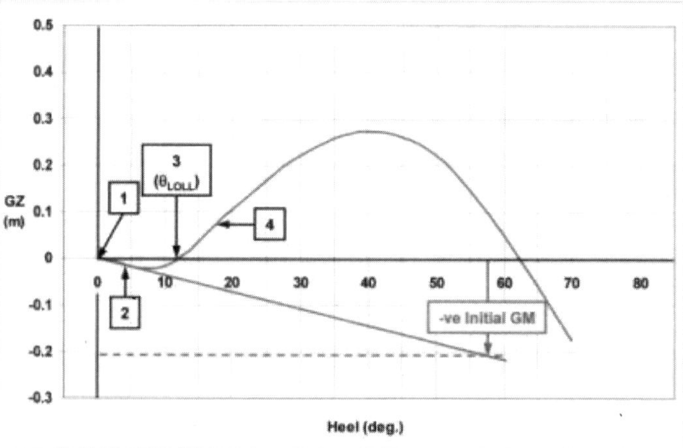

Fig. 15.6

15.4 CURVE OF STATICAL STABILITY FOR A LISTED SHIP

When a ship is listed the centre of gravity of the ship is off the centre line to port or starboard by a distance GG_H.
Consider a listed ship being progressively inclined from the upright. The initial transverse metacentre (M) is above G so the ship is stable in terms of metacentric height (GM).

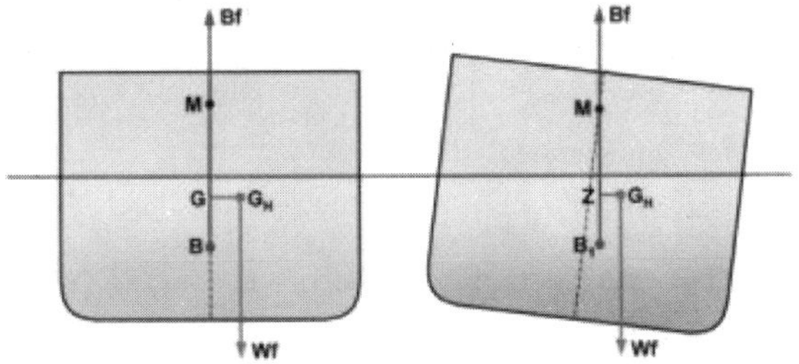

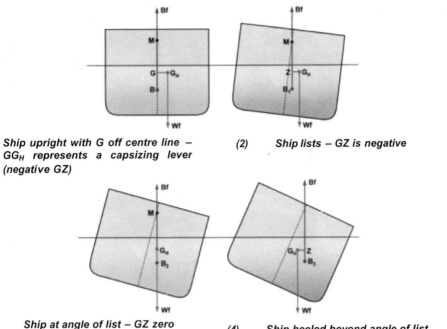

(1) ***Ship upright with G off centre line – GG_H represents a capsizing lever (negative GZ)***

(2) ***Ship lists – GZ is negative***

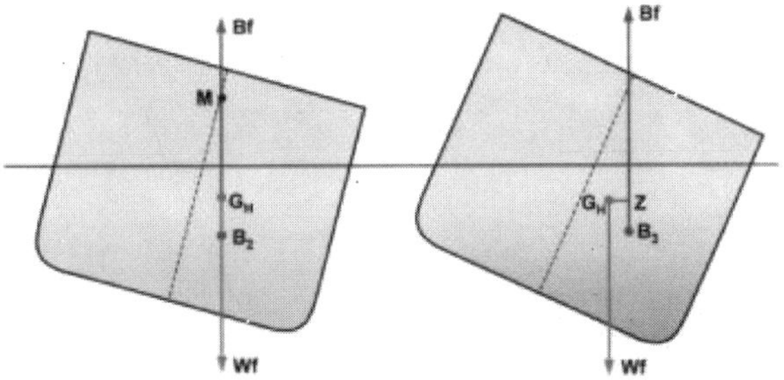

(3) ***Ship at angle of list – GZ zero***

(4) ***Ship heeled beyond angle of list – GZ is positive***

Fig. 15.7

The curve of statical stability for such a ship is depicted in figure 15.8 where diagrams (1), (2) (3) and (4) are related to the curve shown.

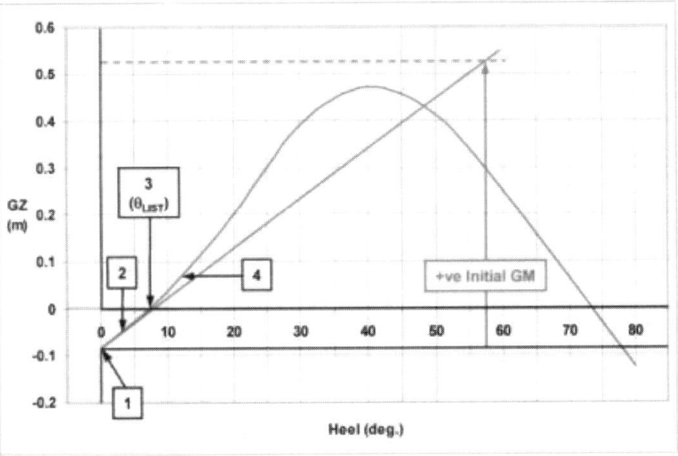

Fig. 15.8

It should be noted here that the curves for unstable (loll) and a listed ship within small angles of heel are similar and must not be confused.

15.5 PROCEDURES FOR CORRECTING AN ANGLE OF LOLL AND LIST

During the course of a voyage the stability of the ship should be closely monitored. It is recommended that a calculation of *fluid GM* and a corresponding GZ curve be produced for the *worst anticipated condition*. Calculations should be done for both departure and anticipated arrival conditions, these being adjusted to suit any changes that may take place as the voyage progresses.

An angle of loll situation can arise in a ship for a number of reasons.

(1) *Ships carrying timber deck cargoes*
Deck cargoes will absorb moisture that will cause G to rise. An allowance of 15% of the weight of timber carried on deck should be made when conducting calculations and determining GZ values for the condition in question.

(2) *Consumption of fuel and water and introduction of free surfaces*
Fuel and water will be consumed from low down in the ship raising G due to the removal of weight from low down in the ship and the introduction of free surfaces in tanks that may have been initially full. Even ballast tanks that are initially full may become slack as a voyage progresses due to the constant rolling and pitching of the ship at sea causing water to escape from tank air pipes on deck. Tanks may require to be topped up occasionally, particularly when stability is considered marginal at any stage during the voyage. Poor cargo and ballast tank management resulting in excessive free surface moments is the most common cause of loll situations excepting damage scenarios.

(3) *Heavy lift operations using ship's lifting gear*
An instantaneous loss of GM will take place immediately that a weight is lifted either off the deck or from a position over the side. Such large increases in KG must be considered prior to any heavy lift operations and calculations should be conducted prior to any such operation to ensure that:
(a) the ship has adequate stability at all stages during the lift, and;
(b) maximum list is restricted to an acceptable limit.

(4) *Shift of bulk cargo*
The vertical component of a shift of solid bulk cargo may be sufficient to reduce GM sufficiently to cause a loll situation, particularly if accompanied by one of the above. The larger horizontal component will also create listing moments compounding the situation further.

Unfortunately things do not always go to plan and mistakes may be made in calculations. Any number of occurrences might take place such as a collision or a fire where water is introduced into a compartment for fire fighting purposes. Whatever the cause, a situation might arise whereby the ship is lying at an *unexpected* angle of inclination.
It is not always possible to ascertain easily whether a ship is *listed* or *lolled* and since the remedial action for each case is very different it is essential that the cause of the inclination be carefully investigated.

The following procedures should be carefully observed:

1. *Alter course to put the ship's head into the predominant waves.*
If the ship is in a lolled situation it is essential that the ship stays lolled to the *same* side. Wave action may cause the ship to roll through the vertical to loll on the other side. This is a dangerous situation since the ship will heel from the vertical of it's own accord and the momentum it will have in lolling over to the other side may be sufficient to capsize it. In any event, the ship will initially heel beyond the angle of loll before settling at the angle of loll whereby cargo shift may result, which will worsen the situation further.

2. *Check that port and starboard listing moments are the same.*
By verifying tank soundings and checking for cargo shift it should be possible to account for any listing moments that may cause the ship to be in a listed situation. If it is calculated that there are no net listing moments then a case of instability may be assumed and the ship will be lying at an angle of loll. Recalculation of the ship's effective KG should also be undertaken to verify the ship's GM.

3. *Check for slack tanks*
In carrying out (2) above it should also be evident if there are excessive free surface moments causing a loss of GM sufficient enough to make the ship unstable. In this case a loll situation may be confirmed.

If a loll situation is confirmed:

4. *Take action to lower G (reduce KG)*
It would be impractical to consider shifting weights on board using ship's lifting equipment at sea. If the ship has high ballast tanks that are full then these may be emptied, *discharging ballast from the high side tank first - the greater vertical distance between G of the ship and g of the weight being discharged will ensure that the greatest lowering of G will take place in the first instance.* Once the high side tank is empty the one on the low side may then be emptied.

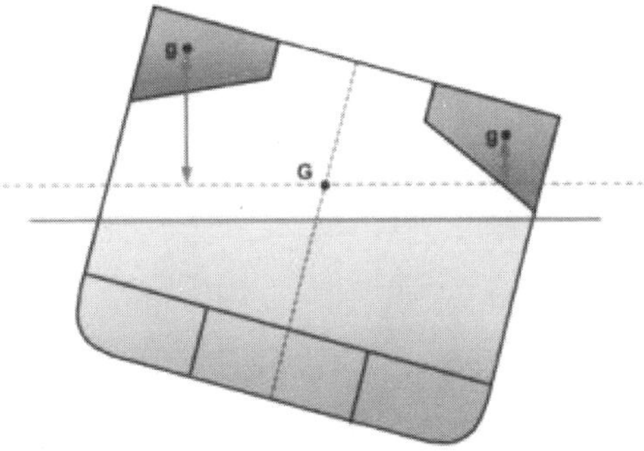

Empty high up ballast tank on the high side first to ensure

Fig. 15.9

5. *Minimise Free surfaces*
Having sounded all the tanks any that are slack will be identified. Minimise the loss of GM due to free surface effect by topping up low down ballast tanks and transferring fuel as necessary. This action alone may remedy the situation.

6. *Ballast tanks low down in the ship*
Select a set of suitably subdivided double bottom tanks to ballast. Ideally start with tanks that have the smallest free surface areas to minimise the effects of free surface whilst filling. The order of filling is as follows and must be strictly adhered to:

(a) Start by filling the tank on the *low side* (No. 1) as shown. *Because of the introduction of more free surfaces whilst filling the first tank the situation will initially worsen.*
(b) When the first tank is completely full, fill the centre tank (No. 2).
(c) When the centre tank is full, fill the final tank (No. 3)
(d) If G is lowered sufficiently then the ship should complete in an *upright condition* (having initially verified that the port and starboard moments were the same).

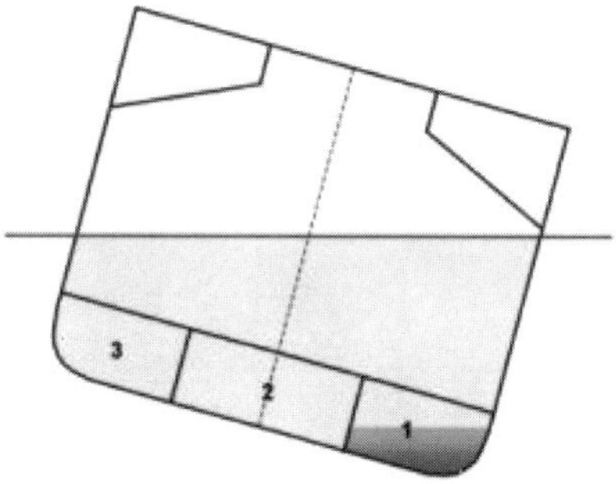

Fill tanks in order shown (low side
Fig. 15.10

The movement of G after completely filling each of the tanks is as depicted in figure 15.11 (ignoring the upward movement of G which arises as a result of the introduced free surface at intermediate stages of filling the tanks).

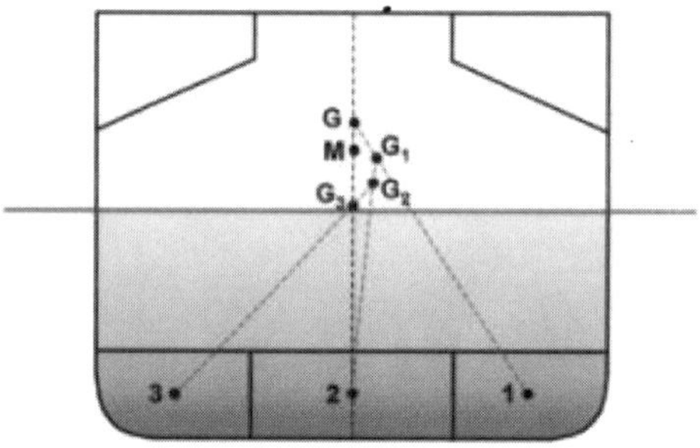

Fig. 15.11

If the situation is not remedied then a second set of tanks must be chosen for filling, the process is repeated.

Note *Once a loll situation is confirmed only ever fill one tank at a time. Always start by filling the* ***low side*** *tank first.*

The angle of loll may initially worsen because the introduced free surfaces when initially starting to fill the tank may cause a greater rise of G than the fall of G caused by the added bottom weight. Hence the importance of filling small tanks first.
If there is any doubt as to whether the ship is lolled or listed, always initially assume it is a lolled situation and take appropriate action, monitoring the situation carefully.
When correcting a *list* it is sufficient to shift a weight to the high side. This may be achieved by shifting weights on deck or by transferring ballast from a listed side tank to a high side tank. Alternatively, excess ballast from the listed side (possibly low down in the ship) may be discharged or a low tank on the high side should be filled.

To treat a loll situation in the same way would have disastrous consequences for reasons already explained!

SECTION 16 – WALL-SIDED FORMULA

INTRODUCTION

In previous sections the term 'small angles of heel' has been repeatedly mentioned. By consideration of the *Wall-sided Formula* for calculating GZ the distinction will be made between stability at small and large angles of heel.

A wall-sided inclination of the ship is one where the waterline on both sides of the ship is in contact with the vertical sides of the ship i.e. the ship is not inclined beyond the angle of heel at which the deck edge becomes immersed or an angle of heel where the turn of the bilge becomes exposed above the waterline.

Learning Objectives

On completion of this section the learner will achieve the following:

1. Understand the distinction between stability at small and large angles of heel by consideration of the *Wall-sided Formula;*
2. Calculate the angle of loll and GM at the angle of loll for a ship that is unstable;
3. Calculate the angle of list caused by a transverse shift of weight when the GM is zero.

16.1 THE DISTINCTION BETWEEN STABILITY AT SMALL AND LARGE ANGLES OF HEEL - THE WALL-SIDED FORMULA

16.1.1 Stability at small angles of heel (initial stability)

Figure 16.1 shows a ship heeled to a small angle by an external force. The centre of buoyancy has moved from B to B_1, which is a movement parallel to, and in the same direction as, the shift of the wedge of buoyancy from b to b_1.

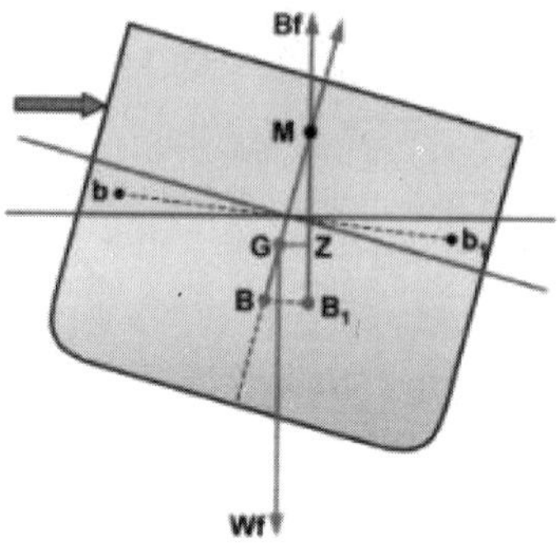

Fig. 16.1

The line of action of buoyancy force acting upwards through B_1 passes through the *initial transverse metacentre (M)*. For small angles of heel (up to about 6°) it is assumed that the movement of B to the low side follows the arc of a circle, BM being the radius of the arc known as the *metacentric radius*.

$$BM = \frac{I}{V}$$

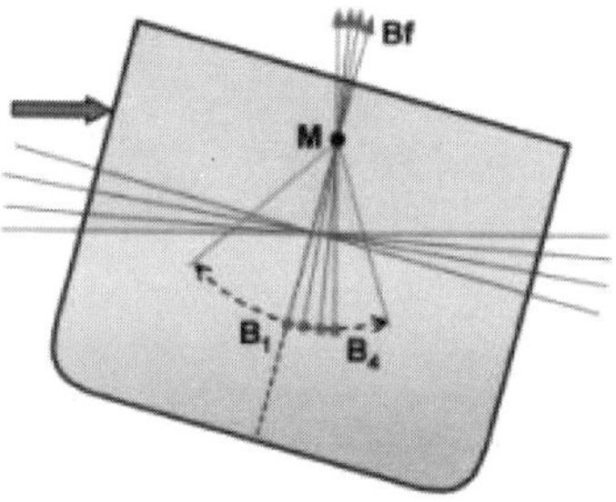

Fig. 16.2

where I is the second moment of area (or moment of inertia) of the water plane area. For a *box-shaped vessel*:

$$BM_{BOX} = \frac{LB^3}{12V}$$

where L and B are the length and breadth of the water plane area respectively and V is the volume of displacement of the vessel (L × B × d).

For small angles of heel the BM can be assumed constant, since there is no significant increase or change of shape of the water plane area as the ship heels, since the value of I must also be assumed constant.

Under these conditions righting lever may be calculated using: **GZ = GM × Sine θ**

and the moment of statical stability or righting moment is given by:

RM = (GM × Sine θ) × Displacement

This measure of stability is referred to as *initial stability* because it is related to the position of the *initial transverse metacentre* that is assumed to be at a fixed point within small angles of heel.

16.1.2 Stability at large angles of heel for wall-sided inclinations

Figure 16.3 shows a ship heeled to a large angle. When heeled to large angles it can no longer be assumed that the centre of buoyancy moves in an arc. The transfer of wedge of buoyancy from high side to low side is such that there is an increasing *vertical* movement of B; the vertical component of transfer of buoyancy increases at a faster rate than the horizontal component and B adopts a position at B_2 rather than some position at B_1 which it would have had if moving in an arc. The water plane area at the larger angle of heel is larger; consequently BM is larger as a result of the greater value of moment of inertia of the water plane area (I). This causes the metacentre to move at larger angles of heel such that it is termed the *'prometacentre'* or moving metacentre (M_2).

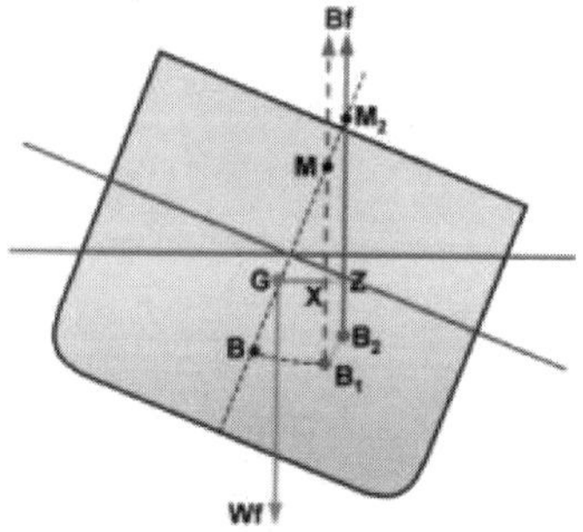

Fig. 16.3

The righting lever arising from this higher position of the centre of buoyancy (B_2) is: **GZ = GX + XZ**

which is greater than the lever GX that would have existed if the upthrust due to buoyancy had been applied at B_1 and passed through M.

The formula for this new GZ that applies for wall-sided inclinations only is:

$$\mathbf{GZ = (GM \times Sine\,\theta) + (½BM \times Tan^2\theta \times Sine\,\theta)}$$

i.e. $$\mathbf{GZ = \quad GX \quad + \quad XZ}$$

This simplifies to: $$\boxed{\mathbf{GZ = (GM + ½BM\ Tan^2\,\theta)\ Sine\,\theta}}$$

where GM and BM are the values for the ship in the upright condition.

A more accurate definition of a small angle of heel is one where XZ is a small (or negligible) value when compared to the value of GX (where GX = GM × Sine θ, this being the value as calculated for a small angle of heel).

When using: **GZ = GM × Sine θ** it should be noted that for a ship that has a large initial GM, the error in using this formula would remain small up to a larger angle of heel than for a ship having a small initial GM value.

<u>Example 1</u>

A box-shaped vessel has length 120 m, breadth 18 m and floats on an even keel draught of 8.0 m in salt water. KG is 6.4 m. Calculate the righting lever (GZ) when the vessel is heeled by an external force to:

(a) 5°;

(b) 30°.

<u>Solution</u>

$$KM = KB + BM$$

$$KB_{BOX} = \frac{draught}{2} = \frac{8.000}{2} = 4.000\ m$$

$$BM_{BOX} = \frac{LB^3}{12V} = \frac{120 \times 18^3}{12 \times (120 \times 18 \times 8)} = 3.375\ m$$

$$\therefore \quad KM = 4.000 + 3.375 = 7.375\ m$$

$$GM = KM - KG \qquad GM = 7.375 - 6.400 = 0.975\ m$$

(a) GZ value at 5°

Because this is a small angle of heel: $GZ = GM \times Sine\ \theta$

$GZ = 0.975 \times Sine\ 5° = \mathbf{0.0849768\ m\ (Ans)}$

Alternatively using the wall-sided formula:

$$GZ = (GM + ½BM\ Tan^2\ \theta)\ Sine\ \theta$$

$$GZ = \left(0.975 + \frac{3.375 \times Tan^2\ 5°}{2}\right) \times Sine\ 5° = \mathbf{0.0861026\ m\ (Ans)}$$

Note *Even within small angles of heel there will be a difference in the answers, because the water plane area of a vessel will increase in reality. The small angle formula for GZ should only be used for angles of heel up to about 5° or 6°.*

(b) *GZ value at 30°*

(The wall-sided formula must be used for this large angle of heel!)

$$GZ = (GM + \tfrac{1}{2}BM\ Tan^2\ \theta)\ Sine\ \theta$$

$$GZ = (0.975 + \frac{3.375 \times Tan^2\ 30^\circ}{2}) \times Sine\ 30^\circ = \mathbf{0.769\ m\ (Ans)}$$

Example 2

A box-shaped vessel has length 116 m, breadth 16 m, and depth 9.8 m and is upright floating on an even keel draught of 5.7m in salt water. KG is 6.0 m. Calculate the moment of statical stability when the vessel is heeled to the angle of deck edge immersion.

Solution

$$KM = KB + BM$$

$$KB_{BOX} = \frac{draught}{2} = \frac{5.700}{2} = 2.850\ m$$

$$BM_{BOX} = \frac{LB^3}{12V} = \frac{116 \times 16^3}{12 \times (116 \times 16 \times 5.7)} = 3.743\ m$$

$$\therefore \quad KM = 2.850 + 3.743 = 6.593\ m$$

$$GM = KM - KG \qquad GM = 6.593 - 6.000 = 0.593\ m$$

To calculate the angle of heel at which deck edge immersion takes place, consider figure 16.4.

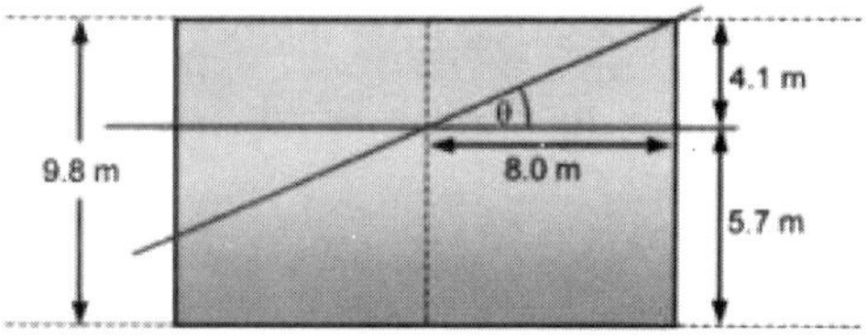

Fig. 16.4

$$Tan\ \theta = \frac{OPP}{ADJ} = \frac{4.1}{8} = 0.51250 \therefore \theta = 27.14^\circ$$

$$GZ = (GM + \tfrac{1}{2}BM\ Tan^2\ \theta)\ Sine\ \theta$$

$$GZ = (0.593 + \frac{3.743 \times Tan^2\ 27.14^\circ}{2}) \times Sine\ 27.14^\circ = \mathbf{0.495\ m}$$

$$RM = GZ \times Displacement$$

$$RM = 0.495 \times (116 \times 16 \times 5.7 \times 1.025) = \mathbf{5368\ t\text{-}m\ (Ans)}$$

16.2 ANGLE OF LOLL

16.2.1 Calculating the angle of loll using the wall-sided formula

A ship with a negative GM will not remain upright. It will capsize, either to port or starboard, until the centre of buoyancy is able to attain a position vertically below the centre of gravity (G) at B_2 (figure 16.5).

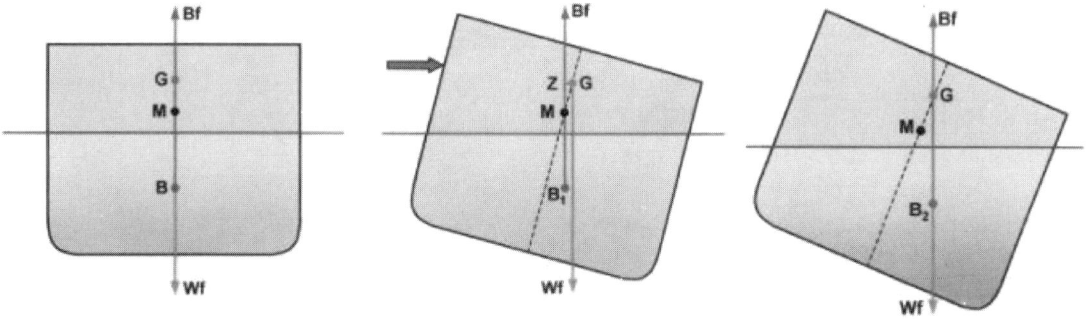

1. Ship upright with negative GM; G above M.
2. Ship starts to capsize as a result of the negative GZ, B moves outward.
3. Ship will settle at angle of loll with B below G. GZ is zero.

Fig. 16.5

At the angle of loll GZ is zero. The accurate formula for calculating GZ for wall-sided inclinations is:

$$\mathbf{GZ = (GM + ½BM\ Tan^2\theta)\ Sine\,\theta}$$

A formula for calculating the angle of loll value can be derived from this as follows:
Expanding the above formula gives:

$$GZ = (GM \times Sine\ \theta) + (½BM \times Tan^2\theta \times Sine\ \theta)$$

At the angle of loll GZ is zero;

$$\therefore \quad 0 = (GM \times Sine\ \theta) + (½BM \times Tan^2\theta \times Sine\ \theta)$$

$$\therefore \quad -(GM \times Sine\ \theta) = (½BM \times Tan^2\theta \times Sine\ \theta)$$

Dividing both sides by Sine θ gives:

$- GM = ½BM \times Tan^2\theta$, or $\quad - GM = \dfrac{BM \times Tan^2\theta}{2}$

$$\therefore \quad \frac{-2 \times GM}{BM} = Tan^2\theta \qquad \therefore \quad \mathbf{Tan\ \theta_{LOLL} = \sqrt{\frac{-2 \times GM}{BM}}}$$

In this equation the values of GM and BM used are the original upright values. Because the upright GM is negative, the quantity within the square root becomes positive.

<u>*Example 3*</u>

In the upright condition a ship has KB 4.26 m, KG 7.15 m and BM 2.84 m. Calculate the angle of loll.

<u>*Solution*</u>

$KM = KB + BM \qquad KM = 4.26 + 2.84 = 7.10\ m$

$GM = KM - KG \qquad GM = 7.10 - 7.15 = -0.05\ m$

$$Tan\ \theta_{LOLL} = \sqrt{\frac{-2 \times GM}{BM}} \quad Tan\ \theta_{LOLL} = \sqrt{\frac{-2 \times -0.05}{2.84}}$$

$$Tan\ \theta_{LOLL} = \sqrt{\frac{0.10}{2.84}} \qquad = 0.18765$$

θ_{LOLL} = 10.63° (to port or starboard) (Ans)

16.2.2 Calculating the effective GM at the angle of loll

If the ship is heeled beyond the angle of loll righting levers become positive to act to right the ship back to the angle of loll. It follows that the ship must have acquired a new positive GM for this to happen as shown in figure 16.6.

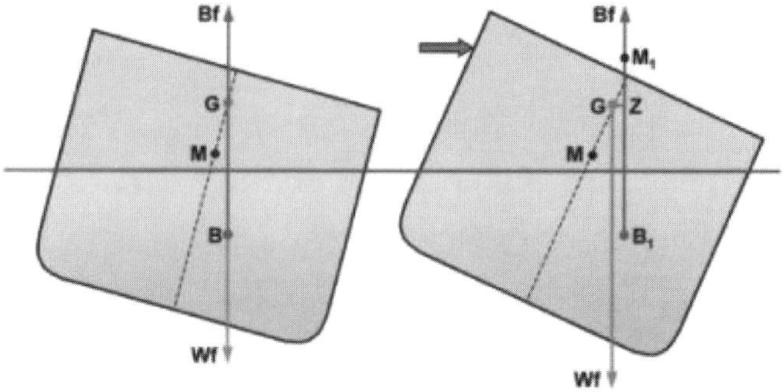

Fig. 16.6

This new metacentric height is the value shown as GM_1 and is given by the formula:

$$\textbf{GM at the angle of loll} = \frac{-2GM}{\cos\theta}$$

where GM is the initial upright GM which is a negative value and θ is the angle of loll. It should be noted that the metacentre at this stage (M_1) need not be on the centre line and will constantly move as the ship is heeled further beyond the angle of loll.

Example 4

An upright ship displaces 12500 t and has KG 7.84 m. 500 t is discharged from a position on the centre line Kg 6.00 m. Calculate the resulting angle of loll given that KB is 3.95 m and KM is 7.85 m in the final condition and the effective GM at the angle of loll.

Solution

Calculate the KG.

$$GG_V = \frac{w \times d}{W - w} = \frac{500 \times (7.84 - 6.00)}{12500 - 500} = 0.077 \text{ m upwards}$$

Final KG = 7.840 + 0.077 = 7.917 m

Final GM = KM – KG   Final GM = 7.850 – 7.917 = - 0.067 m

BM = KM – KB   BM = 7.850 –3.950 = 3.900 m

$$\tan\theta_{LOLL} = \sqrt{\frac{-2 \times GM}{BM}} \quad \tan\theta_{LOLL} = \sqrt{\frac{-2 \times -0.067}{3.900}} = 0.18536$$

θ_{LOLL} = 10.50º (to port or starboard) (Ans)

Calculate the effective GM at the angle of loll.

$$\text{GM at the angle of loll} = \frac{-2GM}{\cos\theta} = \frac{-2 \times -0.067}{\cos 10.50^\circ} = \mathbf{0.136\ m\ (Ans)}$$

16.3 CALCULATING THE ANGLE OF LIST CAUSED BY A TRANSVERSE SHIFT OF WEIGHT WHEN GM IS ZERO

Consider a ship that is upright in a condition of neutral stability where GM = 0 with a weight 'w' on deck. The weight is moved transversely across the deck causing G to move off the centre line to G_H. The ship lists over and comes to rest when the centre of buoyancy attains a position below the centre of gravity.

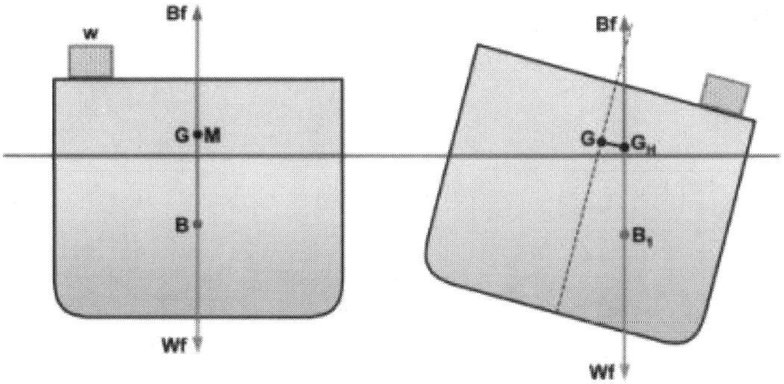

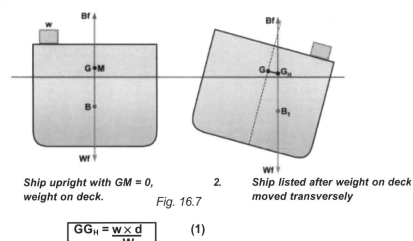

1. Ship upright with GM = 0, weight on deck.

2. Ship listed after weight on deck moved transversely

Fig. 16.7

$$GG_H = \frac{w \times d}{W} \qquad (1)$$

In the listed condition the horizontal component of GG_H is represented by GX (figure 16.8). Had the ship been heeled by an external force to the same angle of heel, instead of being listed by the movement of the weight, a righting lever GZ would have existed, being the same length as GX.

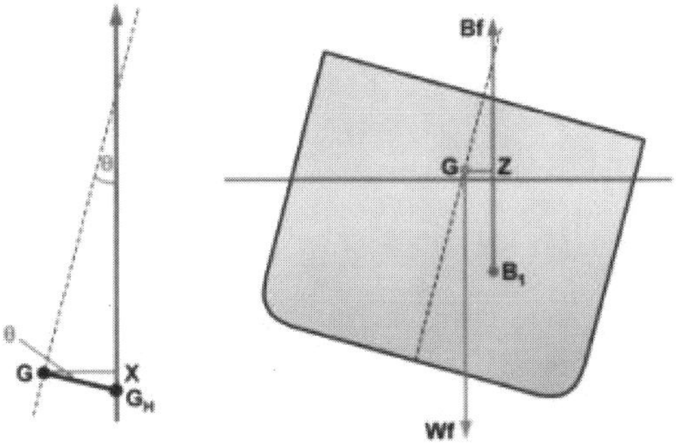

3. For the listed ship GX is the horizontal component of GG_H.

4. GX is the same length as GZ for the ship that had been heeled to the same angle instead.

Fig. 16.8

In triangle GG_HX: $\quad \text{Cosine } \theta = \frac{ADJ}{HYP} \quad \therefore \quad \text{Cosine } \theta = \frac{GX}{GG_H}$

$$\therefore \qquad GX = \text{Cos } \theta \times GG_H \qquad (2)$$

Combining formulae (1) and (2) gives:

$$GX = \frac{\cos\theta \times w \times d}{W}$$

Since GZ (for the ship heeled) = GX (the horizontal component of GG_H), and the formula for GZ at large angles of heel being the wall-sided formula; then:

$$GX = (GM + \tfrac{1}{2}BM \tan^2\theta)\ \text{Sine}\ \theta$$

$$\therefore \qquad \frac{\cos\theta \times w \times d}{W} = (GM + \tfrac{1}{2}BM \tan^2\theta)\ \text{Sine}\ \theta$$

Since the GM = 0:

$$\frac{\cos\theta \times w \times d}{W} = \tfrac{1}{2}BM \tan^2\theta \times \text{Sine}\ \theta$$

Dividing both sides by Cos θ gives:

$$\frac{w \times d}{W} = \tfrac{1}{2}BM \tan^3\theta$$

(Because: $\tan\theta = \frac{\sin\theta}{\cos\theta}$)

$$\frac{w \times d}{W} = \frac{BM \tan^3\theta}{2}$$

Rearranging the above gives:

$$\frac{2 \times w \times d}{BM \times W} = \tan^3\theta$$

Therefore:

$$\mathbf{\tan\theta_{LIST\ WHEN\ GM\ =\ 0} = \sqrt[3]{\frac{2 \times w \times d}{BM \times W}}}$$

Example 5

Calculate the list of a ship displacing 10000 tonnes when a weight of 20 tonnes is shifted transversely through 10 m given that BM is 4.80 m, GM is 0.00 m.

Solution

$$\tan\theta_{LIST\ WHEN\ GM\ =\ 0} = \sqrt[3]{\frac{2 \times w \times d}{BM \times W}}$$

$$\tan\theta_{LIST\ WHEN\ GM\ =\ 0} = \sqrt[3]{\frac{2 \times 20 \times 10}{4.80 \times 10000}} = 0.20274$$

Tan $\boldsymbol{\theta_{LIST\ WHEN\ GM\ =\ 0} = 11.46^o}$ ***(Ans)***

Note

In any calculation that asks for the list to be calculated and a former part of the calculation gives a GM of exactly zero, then the above formula must be used.

Example 6

A ship initially upright has displacement 12500 tonnes, KB 4.2 m, BM 4.6 m and a KG of 8.7 m has a weight of 50 t stowed on deck on the centre line at Kg 4.00 m. Calculate the list when the weight is lifted by the ship's crane, the head of which is 29.0 m above the keel, and then swung outboard 10 m from the centre line.

Solution
Calculate the KG when the crane lifts the weight.

$$GG_V = \frac{w \times d}{W} = \frac{50 \times (29.0 - 4.00)}{12500} = 0.100 \text{ m upwards}$$

Final KG = 8.700 + 0.100 = 8.800 m

KM = KB + BM *KM = 4.200 + 4.600 = 8.800 m*
Final GM = KM – KG *Final GM = 8.800 – 8.800 = 0.000 m*

Calculate list

$$Tan\ \theta_{LIST\ WHEN\ GM\ =\ 0} = \sqrt[3]{\frac{2 \times w \times d}{BM \times W}}$$

$$Tan\ \theta_{LIST\ WHEN\ GM\ =\ 0} = \sqrt[3]{\frac{2 \times 50 \times 10}{4.60 \times 12500}} = 0.25909$$

$$\boldsymbol{Tan\ \theta_{LIST\ WHEN\ GM\ =\ 0} = 14.53^{\circ}\ (Ans)}$$

SECTION 17 – FACTORS AFFECTING THE SHAPE OF THE CURVE OF STATICAL STABILITY

INTRODUCTION

The shape and area under the curve of statical stability is influenced by how the ship is loaded; it is essential that the person(s) responsible for loading the ship understand each of the factors that will affect its shape, GZ and area values. In this section each of the various factors are discussed separately in detail, but it must be appreciated that in practice the curve will be affected cumulatively by a number of these factors at any one time when changes in the condition of loading occur.

Considerations when loading the ship include:

* The ship must be loaded at all times to satisfy minimum intact stability criteria.

* The ship must not be unduly stiff (causing excessive stability) or tender (whereby the ship is stable but has insufficient stability which causes it to roll to excessive angles of heel);

* The need to understand how to improve the stability of the ship to rectify any non-compliance with minimum intact stability criteria is essential.

* The consequences of changes that will take place during the voyage, such as the consumption of fuel from low down in the ship, introduction of free liquid surfaces, cargo shift etc. must be fully understood with respect to the curve of statical stability to prevent unacceptable stability loss.

This section is aimed at the learner increasing his/her familiarity with the curve of statical stability so that realistic decisions can be made in order to rectify inadequate stability situations.

Learning Objectives

On completion of this section the learner will achieve the following:

1. Understand the effect of a *change of KG* on the curve of statical stability;
2. Understand the effect of a *transverse shift of weight (list)* on the curve of statical stability;
3. Understand the effect of a *change of freeboard* on the curve of statical stability;
4. Appreciate the differences between stability of a ship in the light and loaded conditions;
5. Understand the influence of *ship's beam* on the curve of statical stability;
6. Understand the effect of *trim* on the curve of statical stability.

17.1 EFFECT OF A CHANGE OF KG

17.1.1 Causes of a change in KG

The KG of a ship may change as a result of the following:

1. Loading, discharging and shifting of general cargo items;
2. Loading, discharging and transfer of ballast, fuel and lube oil;
3. Increase in KG due to suspension of a weight during lifting operations with ship's gear and subsequent load, discharge or shift of that cargo;
4. Changes during the course of a voyage:
   - consumption of fuel, fresh water and stores;
   - introduction of free surface moments caused by tanks becoming slack;
   - absorption of moisture by timber or similar deck cargoes;
   - ice accretion on decks;
   - accumulation of shipped water on deck and water entrapment in deck cargo;
   - vertical component (upward) of a shift of solid bulk cargo such as grain.
5. Ingress of water due to damage situations.

The effects of the above can be quantified in terms of a reduction or increase in the value of the righting lever (GZ) as detailed in section 17.1.2.

17.1.2 Calculating the increase/decrease in GZ as a result of a change of KG

Consider a ship heeled by an external force to some angle (large or small) (figure 17.1).

If G was ***raised*** (KG increased), GZ would ***decrease*** and the ship would become ***less stable***.
If G was ***lowered*** (KG decreased), GZ would ***increase*** and the ship would become ***more stable***.

The increase or decrease in GZ at a particular angle of heel can be easily calculated.

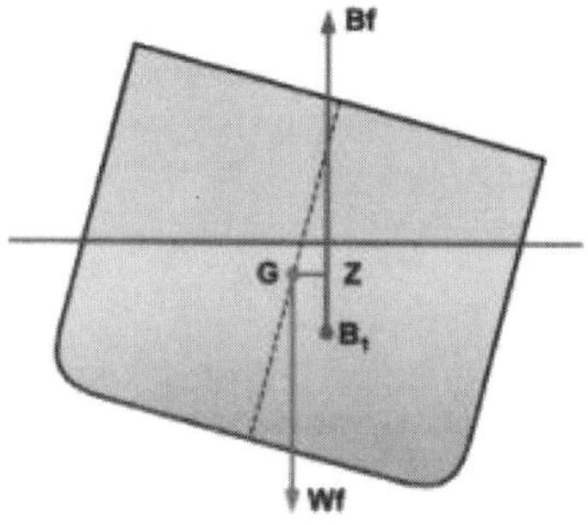

Fig. 17.1

Consider figure 17.2.

If G is raised to G_1 and the ship heeled to the same angle:
GX = ***Loss*** of righting lever.

In triangle GG_1X: $\text{Sine } \theta = \frac{OPP}{HYP} = \frac{GX}{GG_1}$

$\therefore$ **$GX = GG_1 \times \text{Sine } \theta$**

If G is lowered to G_2 and the ship heeled to the same angle:
G_2Y = ***Increase*** in righting lever

In triangle GG_2Y: $\text{Sine } \theta = \frac{OPP}{HYP} = \frac{GY}{GG_2}$

$\therefore$ **$G_2Y = GG_2 \times \text{Sine } \theta$**

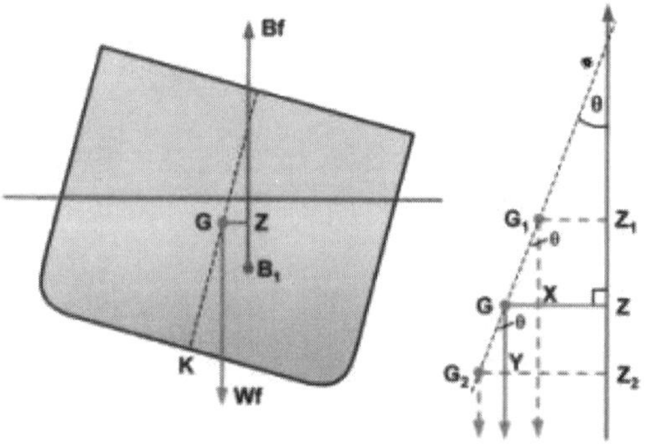

Fig. 17.2

If KG changes the effect on GZ at any angle of heel can be determined by:

LOSS/INCREASE IN GZ = $GG_v \times$ Sine θ

where θ is the angle of heel for which the loss or increase in GZ is being calculated.
Note: Always check that the correction is being applied to the original GZ value in the correct way!

17.1.3 *Effect on the curve of statical stability of a change of KG*

For the purpose of explanation only, assume a ship has a *range of stability* of 90° and KG is *increased* by a weight being shifted upwards within the ship.

If G is raised (KG increased) the loss of GZ at any particular angle of heel can be found by:

$$\textbf{Loss of GZ} = GG_V \times \sin\theta$$

Since Sine 0° = 0.00 and Sine 90° = 1.00 it follows that:

LOSS OF GZ WILL INCREASE AS THE ANGLE OF HEEL INCREASES.

The effect on the curve of statical stability is shown.

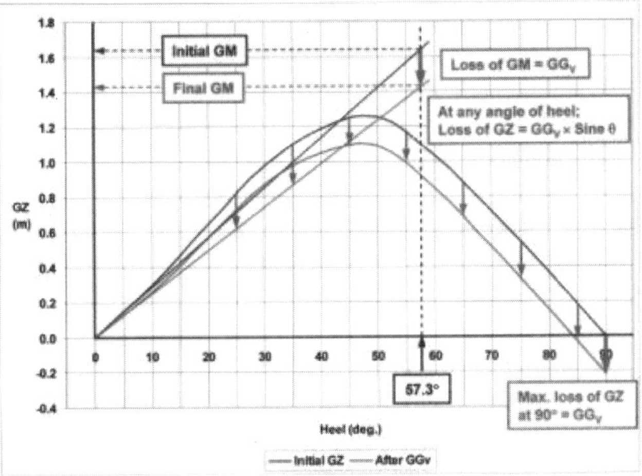

Fig. 17.3

The effect of ***increasing KG*** is as follows:

- * *Initial GM is reduced (by an amount equal to GG_V);*
- * *All GZ values across the range of stability are reduced, particularly at the larger angles of heel;*
- * *Dynamical stability (area under the curve) is reduced making the ship less able to resist heeling by external forces;*
- * *Range of stability is reduced;*
- * *The angle at which deck edge immersion occurs (point of inflexion of the curve – not shown) remains unchanged as freeboard has not changed.*

In effect, most aspects of stability are worsened!

If G were ***lowered*** causing ***KG to reduce*** then all values of GZ would be ***increased***. Initial GM would be increased. Most aspects of stability would be improved!

<u>Example 1</u>

M.V. Almar has a displacement of 23000 tonnes and KG 8.34 m.

(a) *Plot the curve of statical stability for this condition.*

(b) *1240 tonnes of cargo is shifted from a hold position (Kg 3.70 m) to a position on deck (Kg 16.70 m). By correcting the original GZ values plot the curve of statical stability for the new condition and determine the changes in the values of the following:*
   (i) *GM;*
   (ii) *range of stability;*
   (iii) *maximum GZ and angel of heel at which maximum GZ occurs.*

Solution
Enter hydrostatic data with displacement 23000 tonnes and obtain value for KM. Calculate effective GM.

KM	9.398
KG	8.340
GM	**1.058**

Using KN values calculate the values of GZ for the loaded condition.

Heel	10	20	30	40	60	80
KN	1.650	3.340	5.150	6.720	8.230	8.220
KG*Sin Heel	1.448	2.852	4.170	5.361	7.223	8.213
GZ	**0.202**	**0.488**	**0.980**	**1.359**	**1.007**	**0.007**

Plot the curve of statical stability (shown in figure 17.4).

Calculate GG_V caused by shifting the cargo.

$$GG_V = \frac{w \times d}{W} \qquad GG_V = \frac{1240 \times (16.70 - 3.70)}{23000} = \mathbf{0.701\ m\ upwards}$$

Using: ***Loss of GZ = $GG_V \times$ Sine θ*** *calculate the corrections to apply to the initial GZ values and hence calculate the final GZ values. Plot the curve of statical stability for the final condition.*

Heel	10	20	30	40	60	80
Initial GZ	0.202	0.488	0.980	1.359	1.007	0.007
GGv Sin Deg.	0.122	0.240	0.350	0.451	0.607	0.690
After GGv	**0.080**	**0.248**	**0.630**	**0.908**	**0.400**	**-0.683**

Both curves are shown in figure 17.4.

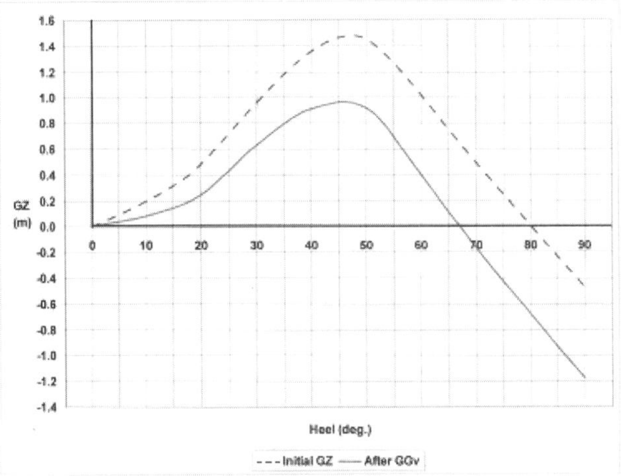

Fig. 17.4

Answers

(b) *(i)* *Initial GM* *1.058 m*
GG_V (up) *0.701 m*
FINAL GM *0.357 m* ***Final GM 0.357 m***

(ii) *From the curves drawn, the range of stability has* ***reduced from 0° to 80°, to, 0° to 67° approximately.***

(iii) *Initial maximum GZ was approximately 1.48 m at 48°. Final maximum GZ is approximately 0.97 m at 47°.*

17.2 EFFECT OF A TRANSVERSE SHIFT OF WEIGHT (LIST)

17.2.1 Causes of a list

A list might arise in a ship as a result of the following:

1. Loading, discharging and shifting of general cargo items about the centre line;
2. Loading, discharging and transfer of ballast, fuel and lube oil abou the centre line;
3. Transverse shift of G due to suspension of a weight outboard during lifting operations with ship's gear and subsequent load, discharge or shift of the weight about the centre line;
4. Changes during the course of a voyage:
   - consumption of fuel, fresh water and stores from off centre line locations;
   - absorption of moisture by timber or similar deck cargoes located off the centre line;
   - unsymmetrical ice accretion on decks;
   - accumulation of shipped water on deck and water entrapment in deck cargo in locations off the centre line;
   - horizontal component of a shift of solid bulk cargo such as grain or the transverse shifting of any cargo in heavy weather.
5. Ingress of water due to damage situations.

17.2.2 Calculating the decrease in GZ as a result of a transverse shift of weight

Consider a ship, initially upright with G on the centre line, heeled by an external force to some angle θ (large or small) with a weight 'w' on one side (figure 17.5). The righting lever is GZ.

The weight is then moved across the deck to the other side causing G to move parallel to and in the same direction as the shift of weight to G_H.

Figure 17.6 shows the ship now heeled to the same angle of heel as before.

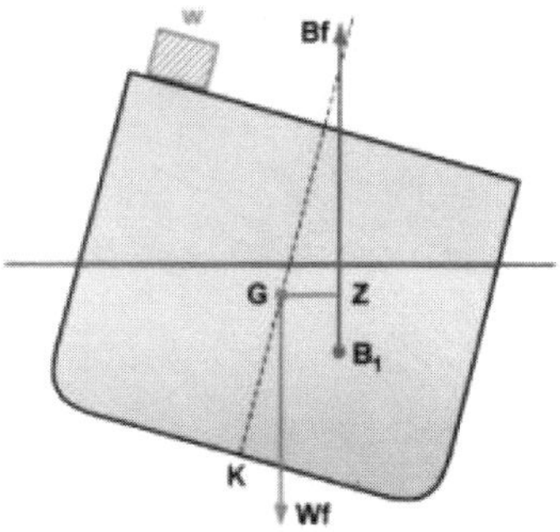

Fig. 17.5

The righting lever has been reduced from GZ to G_HZ_1 as a result of the transverse shift of weight.

The decrease in GZ at a particular angle of heel can be easily calculated.

GX = ***Loss*** of righting lever.

In triangle GG_HX: $\text{Cosine}\ \theta = \frac{ADJ}{HYP} = \frac{GX}{GG_H}$

∴ $\mathbf{GX = GG_H \times Cosine\,\theta}$

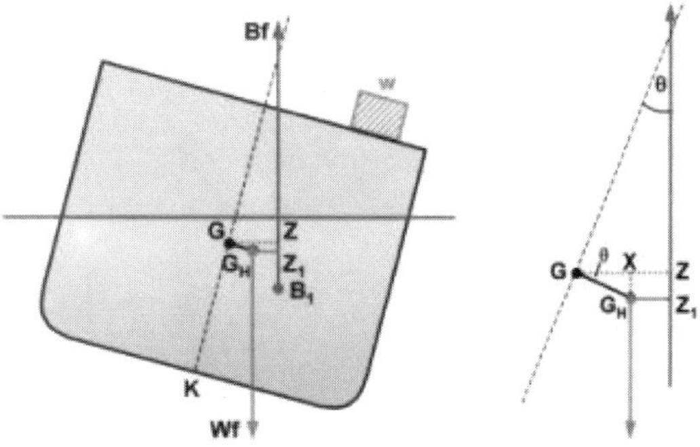

Fig. 17.6

If the ship is listed the loss of GZ at any angle of heel can be determined by:

$$\textbf{LOSS OF GZ} = GG_H \times \text{Cosine}\,\theta$$

where θ is the angle of heel for which the loss of GZ is being calculated.

17.2.3 Effect on the curve of statical stability of list

For the purpose of explanation only, assume a ship has a *range of stability* of 90°.

If G is caused to move off the centre line to G_H the loss of GZ at any particular angle of heel can be found by:

$$\textbf{Loss of GZ} = GG_H \times \textbf{Cosine } \theta$$

Since Cosine 0° = 1.00 and Cosine 90° = 0.00 it follows that:

THE LOSS OF GZ WILL DECREASE AS THE ANGLE OF HEEL INCREASES i.e. THE GREATEST LOSS OF GZ WILL BE WHEN THE SHIP IS UPRIGHT (The ship will come to rest at the angle of list in still water conditions where GG_H will represent a negative value of GZ when the ship is upright!)

The effect on the curve of statical stability is shown.

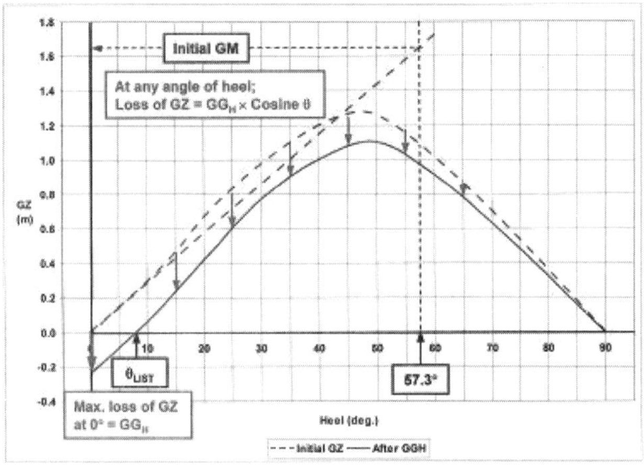

Fig. 17.7

The effect of list is as follows:

- *Initial GM is unchanged (since only vertical movements of G will cause this to change);*
- *All GZ values across the range of stability are reduced, particularly at the smallest angles of heel (when the ship is upright GG_H acts as a capsizing lever causing the ship to heel over to the angle of list);*
- *Dynamical stability (area under the curve) is reduced. Since the ship is already listed, less work is required by the external forces to heel the ship over to dangerous angles of heel on the listed side!*
- *Range of stability is reduced (at both ends of the range for a ship having an initial range of stability less than 90°).*
- *The angle of heel at which deck edge immersion occurs remains unchanged but there is less 'work' required by the external forces to reach it on the listed side.*

Note

The *IMO* and *M.S. (Load Line) Regulations* intact stability criteria do not specify that the ship must be upright at all times at sea. It should be evident that list has a detrimental effect on the stability of the ship whereby area under the GZ curve at the smallest angles of heel can be substantially reduced; this might result in the ship being heeled to dangerous angles of heel on the listed side. The *International Grain Code (IMO)* recognises this fact and to minimise the adverse effects of grain shift it is a requirement that the Master ensures that the ship is *upright prior to sailing.* It should always be borne in mind that in extreme circumstances there may be a potential for cargo shift, which may further significantly reduce the stability of an already listed ship.

Example 2

M.V. Almar has a displacement 26000 tonnes and KG 8.86 m.

(a) *Plot the curve of statical stability for this condition.*

(b) *324 tonnes of deck cargo shifts through a distance of 6.0 m transversely in bad weather. By correcting the original GZ values plot the curve of statical stability for the new condition and determine the following:*
  (i) *the angle of list;*
  (ii) *the change in the range of stability;*
  (iii) *the change in the value of maximum GZ and angel of heel at which maximum GZ occurs.*

(c) *Compare the initial and final values of righting moment available at an angle of heel 20°.*

Solution

Enter hydrostatic data with displacement 26000 tonnes and obtain value for KM. Calculate effective GM.

KM	9.310
KG	8.860
GM	**0.450**

Using KN values calculate the values of GZ for the loaded condition.

Heel	10	20	30	40	60	80
KN	1.640	3.300	5.040	6.500	8.060	8.140
KG*Sin Heel	1.539	3.030	4.430	5.695	7.673	8.725
GZ	**0.101**	**0.270**	**0.610**	**0.805**	**0.387**	**-0.585**

Plot the curve of statical stability (see figure 17.8).

Calculate GG_H caused by the transverse shift of the deck cargo.

$$GG_H = \frac{w \times d}{W} \qquad GG_H = \frac{324 \times 6}{26000} = \mathbf{0.075\ m}$$

Using: ***Loss of GZ = GG_H × Cosine θ*** *calculate the corrections to apply to the initial GZ values and hence calculate the final GZ values.*

Heel	10	20	30	40	60	80
Initial GZ	0.101	0.270	0.610	0.805	0.387	-0.585
GG_H Cos Deg.	0.074	0.070	0.065	0.057	0.037	0.013
After GG_H	**0.028**	**0.199**	**0.545**	**0.748**	**0.350**	**-0.598**

Plot the curve of statical stability for the final condition.

Remember that the loss of GZ at 0° heel = GG_H = 0.075 m, therefore the new GZ value at 0° will now be –0.075 m.

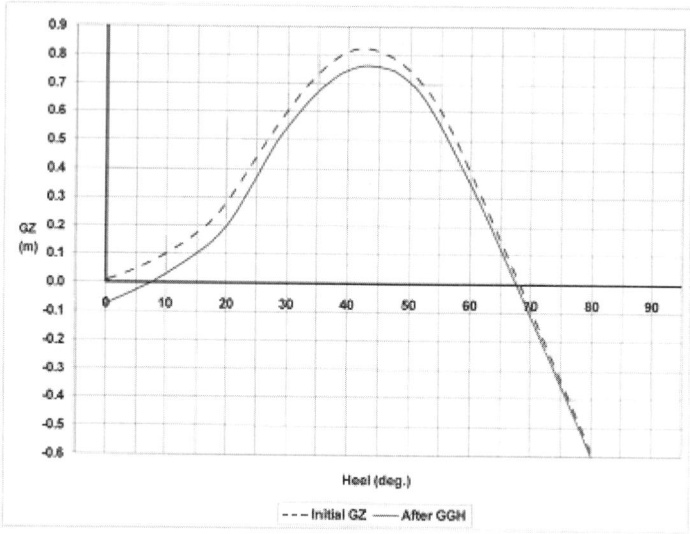

Fig. 17.8

<u>*Answers*</u>

(b) *(i)* *Approximate angle of list as a result of cargo shift is* ***7½°***

(ii) *Range of stability has* ***reduced from 0° to 68°, to, 7½° to 67° approximately.***

(iii) *Initial maximum GZ was 0.82 m at 43° approximately. Final maximum GZ is 0.77 m at 44° approximately.*

(c) *Displacement = 26000 tonnes*

At 20° heel initial GZ = 0.270 m

Initial righting moment at 20° heel = 0.270 × 26000 = ***7020 t-m***

After transverse shift of cargo GZ at 20° heel = 0.199 m

Final righting moment at 20° heel = 0.199 × 26000 = ***5174 t-m***

(This is the new value of righting moment available if the ship where to be heeled beyond the angle of list of 7½° on the listed side.)

17.3 EFFECT OF A CHANGE IN FREEBOARD

17.3.1 Causes of a change in freeboard

A change in freeboard might arise in a ship as a result of the following:

1. Loading and discharging of cargo causing a change in draught;
2. Loading and discharging of ballast, fuel and lube oil as (2);
3. Ice accretion (particularly on small vessels) and absorption of moisture by deck cargoes;
4. Ingress of water in a damage situation.
5. Shipping heavy seas on deck.

17.3.2 Effect of a change in freeboard for constant beam, draught and KG

Consider two ships of similar characteristics having the same beam, draught and KG but one having a greater freeboard as shown.

At angles of heel up to the angle of deck edge immersion of the smaller freeboard ship the curve of statical stability will be exactly the same.

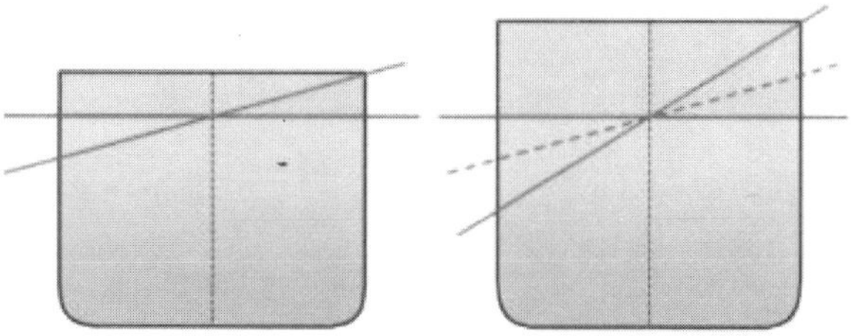

Fig. 17.9

At angles of heel beyond the angle of deck edge immersion of the smaller freeboard ship, values of GZ will be greater for the larger freeboard ship since curve steepness continues to increase up to a larger angle of heel i.e. angle of inflexion which coincides with deck edge immersion will occur at a larger angle of heel. This is a result of the continuing increase in size of the water plane area resulting in a larger BM value – see wall-sided formula in section 16.

17.3.3 Effect on the curve of statical stability of increase in freeboard

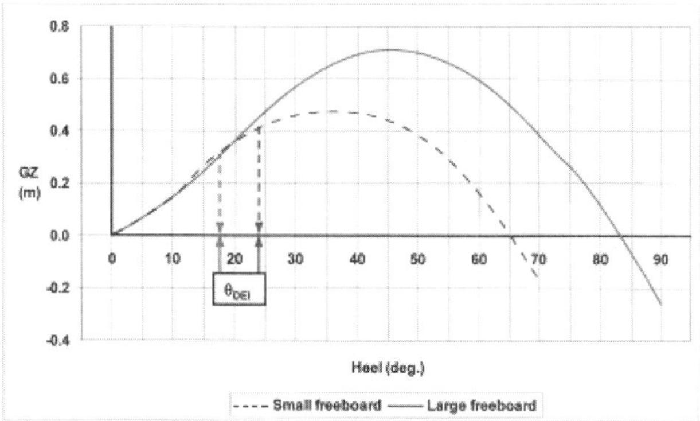

Fig. 17.10

The effect of an increase in freeboard is as follows:

* *Initial GM is unchanged (since only vertical movements of G will cause this to change);*

* *GZ values will be increased at angles of heel beyond the angle of heel at which deck edge immersion takes place for the smaller freeboard ship;*

* *Dynamical stability (area under the curve) is increased at angles of heel beyond the angle of heel at which deck edge immersion takes place.*

* *Range of stability is increased.*

If freeboard where to be reduced then GZ values would be similarly reduced.

17.4 COMPARISON OF STABILITY OF A SHIP IN THE LIGHT AND FULLY LOADED CONDITIONS

Figure 17.11 shows the metacentric diagram for M.V. Almar. As the ship is progressively loaded from the light condition (draught 2.33 m) to the summer load condition (draught 10.20 m) KM decreases (with a slight increase occurring for draughts 8.60 m upwards).

KM = KB + BM

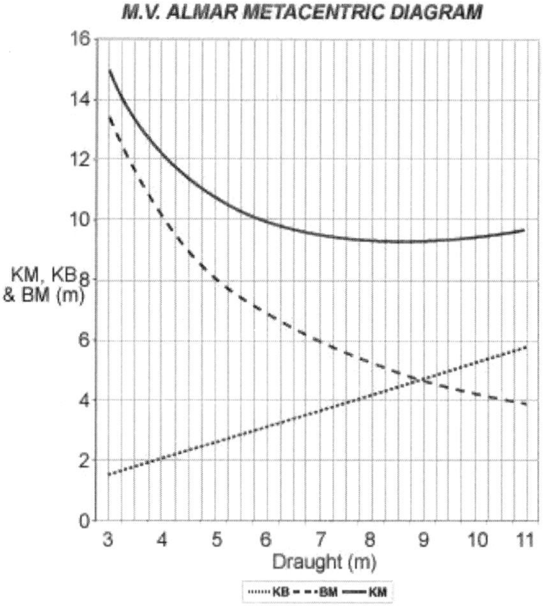

Fig. 17.11

KB obviously increases with draught whereas BM reduces as explained below. Consider figure 17.12.

The movement of B for any angle of heel can be calculated using:

$$BB_1 = \frac{v \times bb_1}{V}$$

where:

- ***v*** is the volume of the transferred wedge;
- ***bb_1*** is the distance through which the centroid of the wedge has moved, and;
- ***V*** is the volume of displacement of the ship.

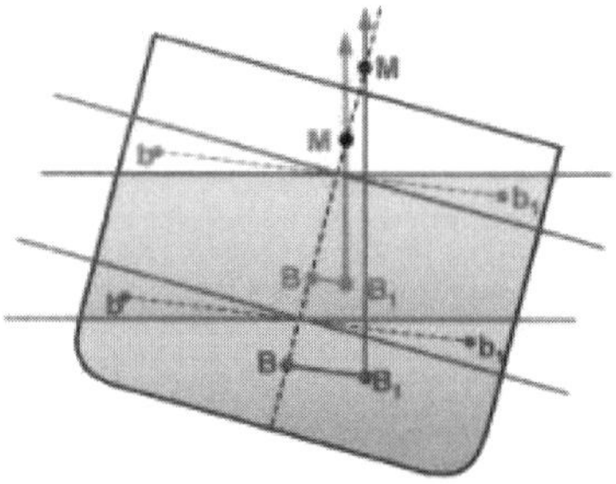

Fig.17.12

At the *load draught (displacement)* the volume of the transferred wedge of buoyancy (v) represents a *smaller part* of the *total volume of displacement* of the ship (V) than it would at the *light draught (displacement).*

Thus: *BM decreases as draught increases. For the normal range of operational draughts of a ship KM will generally decrease as draught increases with a slight increase again at the deepest draughts as evidenced by the metacentric diagram for M.V. Almar (figure 17.11).*

Figure 17.13 makes a comparison of the curves of statical stability for M.V Almar in the light condition and fully loaded condition assuming a constant value of KG (blue curves). The red curve is for a lesser value of KG that would provide a more suitable condition of loading (as recommended in a loading condition in the stability book on which M.V. Almar was based).

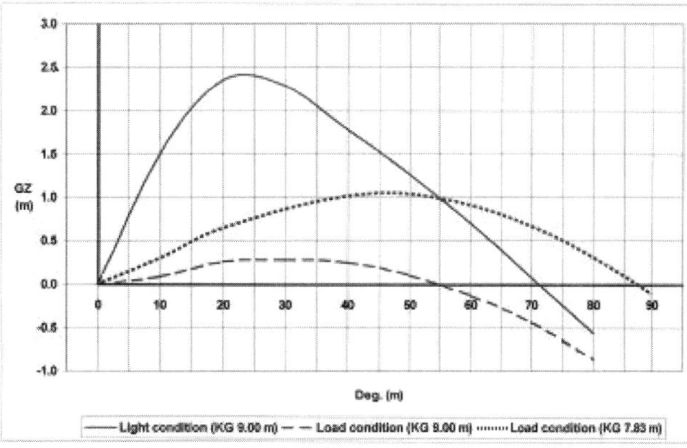

Fig. 17.13

In terms of GZ values alone, for a given KG value the ship will become less stable the more it is loaded, however:

RIGHTING MOMENT (t-m) = GZ (m) × DISPLACEMENT (t)

The righting moment curves show that the extra *weight* of the loaded ship will require more 'work' by the external forces to heel the ship to a particular angle of heel (figure 17.14).

In terms of *righting moment*, provided that the ship has a suitable value of KG in the loaded condition then in reality the ship will have greater stability as more 'work' will be required to heel the vessel to a particular angle of heel as a consequence of the *increased displacement*.

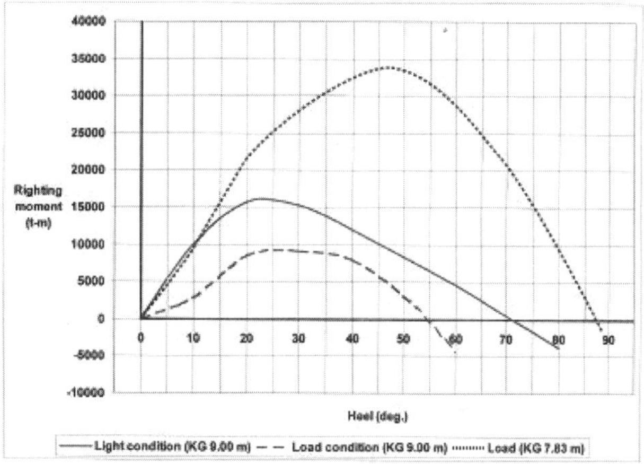

Fig. 17.14

17.5 EFFECT OF BEAM

17.5.1 Effect of increasing beam for constant draught and freeboard

Figure 17.15 shows two box-shaped vessels, one narrow and the other broad, having the same draught and KG heeled to a small angle.

As each vessel is heeled the outward movement of the centre of buoyancy may be calculated by:

$$BB_1 = \frac{v \times bb_1}{V}$$

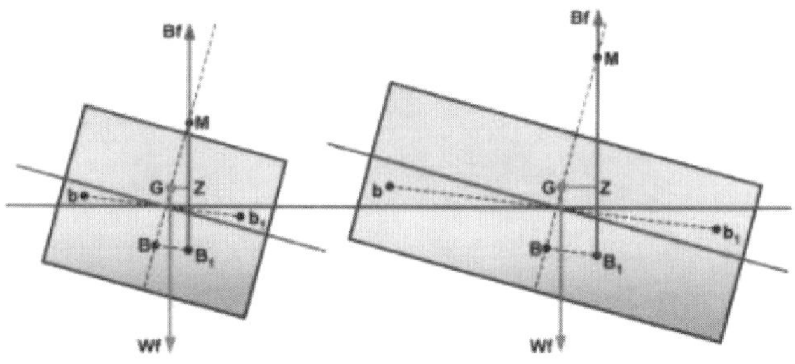

Fig. 17.15

where: ***v*** is the volume of the transferred wedge of buoyancy;
bb₁ is the distance through which the centroid of the transferred wedge of buoyancy has travelled, and;
V is the volume of displacement of the vessel.

Because the volume of the wedge of buoyancy (v) and the distance through which it is transferred (bb_1) is *greater for the broader vessel* the outward movement of B to B_1 is much greater. This creates a larger value of KM (and GM), so initial stability is greater for the broader vessel. The effect of beam is investigated in depth in section 8.

This increase in initial stability is offset by the earlier angle of heel at which deck edge immersion takes place for the broader vessel.

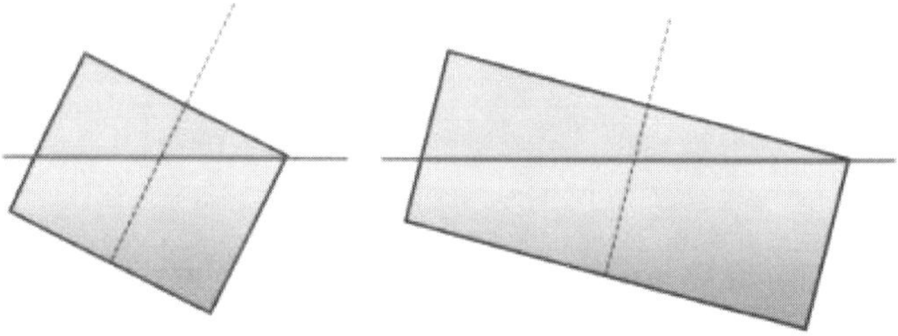

Fig. 17.16

17.5.2 Effect on the curve of statical stability of an increase in beam

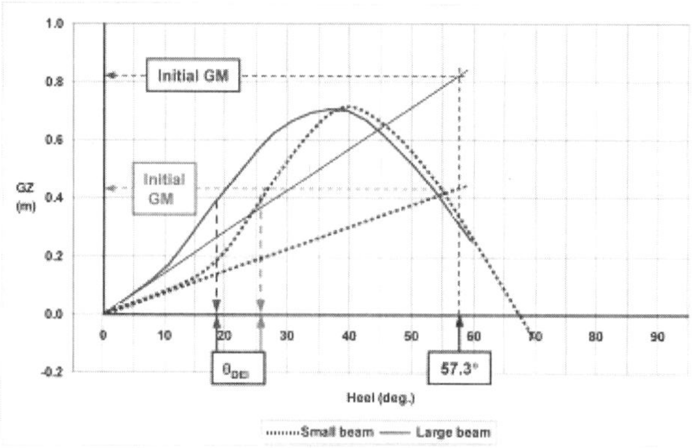

Fig. 17.17

The effect of an increase in beam is as follows:

- * *Initial GM is increased as a result of the increasing BM.*
- * *GZ values will be increased initially.*
- * *Dynamical stability (area under the curve) is increased initially.*
- * *Angle at which deck edge immersion takes place is reduced.*

* *Range of stability may increase nor decrease. This will depend on the initial freeboard and increase in beam for that freeboard being considered. The smaller the freeboard and the greater the increase in the beam, the further the reduction in the angle of heel at which deck edge immersion takes place; this may cause range to reduce. If the freeboard is substantial, any moderate increase in beam will result in the range of stability increasing.*

17.5.3 Ship conversion - practical application of increasing effective beam

Modifications to improve a ship's stability may be required to allow the addition of top weight in a conversion or as a way of compensating for inadequate stability when a ship is inclined on completion. The improvement might be to:

* increase KM;
* increase large angle righting lever values;
* increase the range of positive stability, or;

all of these in order to improve intact stability. Improvements might be required with respect to damaged stability, possibly as result of introduced legislative changes.

When a major improvement in stability is necessary the fitting of *sponson tanks* is an option considered frequently by naval architects. Such tanks are fitted to increase the effective beam (and water plane area) for the range of operational draughts of the ship in order to increase BM (and KM) as already described. In order that sudden stability loss is avoided at larger angles of heel, the *lower edges* of the sponson tanks should be some distance below the lowest operational waterline. This ensures that the sponson does not come out of the water when the ship is heeled (as the benefits of their fitting would immediately be lost). A design criterion might be to ensure that the sponson remains immersed when the ship is at its minimum design operating draught and rolled to at least 5-10°.

Location of the upper edge of the sponson will be governed by whether the sponsons are fitted to provide an increase in GM or whether an increase in the range of stability (as well as GM) is required. Figure 17.18 shows a sponson arrangement that might be fitted to an offshore support vessel where there is a need to operate equipment over the ship's side or the addition of a deck crane that must be operated at sea, whereby stability problems arose as a result of suspended weights.

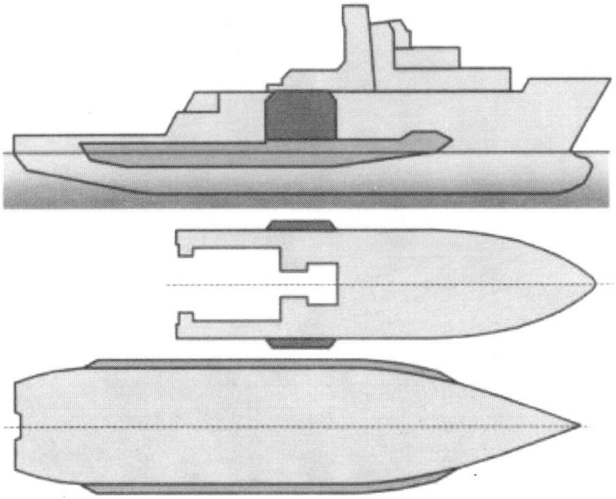

Sponsons fitted to an offshore support vessel. The lower tank increases KM and initial stability; the smaller upper tank increases GZ values at larger angles of heel and improves the range of stability.

Fig. 17.18

17.6 EFFECT OF STERN TRIM

17.6.1 Comparison of even keel and stern trimmed stability characteristics

In still water a ship trimmed by the stern can be expected to have a greater GM than when on an even keel. This is a result of KM being normally greater in the trimmed condition. This greater value of KM arises in part from an increased KB and an increased BM (caused by an increase in the effective length of the water plane area).

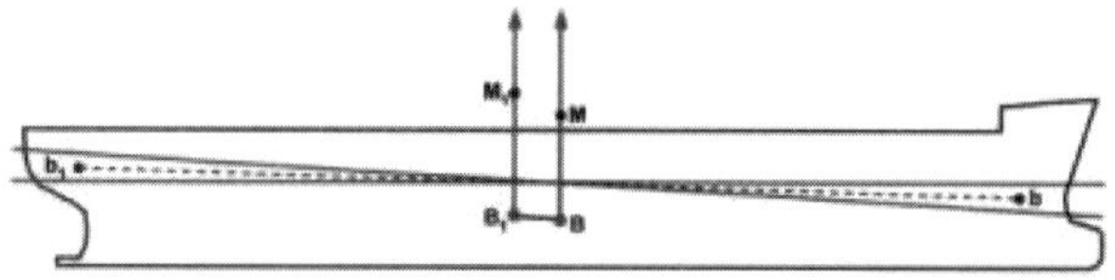

Increase in transverse KM caused

Fig. 17.19

For the trimmed condition KB is slightly higher because of the shape of the underwater volume and BM is higher because of the increased moment of inertia (I) of the water plane area. Consequently, KM is increased and for any given value of KG the values of GM and GZ at small angles of heel are increased.

The improved initial stability (at small angles of heel) is however more than offset against the fact that the freeboard aft is reduced. When on an even keel and heeled to the angle at which deck edge immersion occurs, such immersion occurs simultaneously all along the length of the ship (ignoring the effect of sheer and superstructure that is considered reserve buoyancy). If the ship is trimmed by the stern and then heeled the after deck becomes immersed first (at a smaller angle of heel) resulting in reduced GZ values mid- range in the GZ curve.

17.6.2 Effect on the curve of statical stability of a trim by the stern

The effect is shown in figure 17.20 which is somewhat exaggerated for the purposes of illustration.

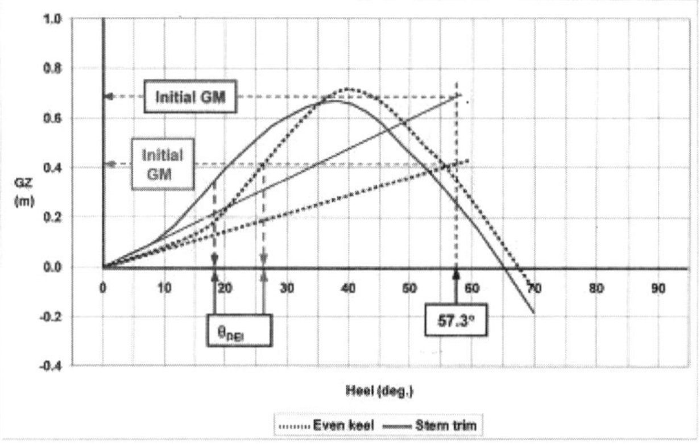

Fig. 17.20

The effect of a trim by the stern is as follows:

- *Initial GM is increased as a result of the increasing KB and BM.*
- *GZ values will be increased initially.*
- *Dynamical stability (area under the curve) is increased initially.*
- *Angle at which deck edge immersion takes place is reduced due to earlier immersion aft.*
- *Range of stability will probably reduce as the increase in initial GM and GZ values at small angles of heel will be minimal.*

The explanation given so far is somewhat over simplified, but might probably suffice for any general question that might be asked on this topic. A more detailed explanation is given in section 26 where the effects of stern trim can seriously affect the stability of offshore supply vessels and tugs, where the low afterdeck characteristics of the hull are a feature of such vessels.

SECTION 18 – THE INTERNATIONAL GRAIN CODE (IMO)

INTRODUCTION

When loading solid bulk cargoes of any type it is recognised that they will have a potential for shifting depending for the main part on:

* how full a compartment is and the available void space remaining;
* the 'ease of flow' of the individual particles of the cargo (evidenced by the *angle of repose* of the cargo), and;
* the extent to which the ship rolls at sea.

A bulk cargo to a certain degree behaves as if it were a free liquid surface in a slack tank. If the ship rolls to such a degree that the cargo shifts then the characteristic nature of liquid behaviour becomes evident but once the shift has taken place the similarity ends, since the bulk cargo will stay to one side, resulting in list. With the ship now rolling about the angle of list, any further shift of bulk cargo in the same direction as before would result in a progressively worsening situation that might lead to the ultimate loss of the ship.

The stability problems associated with the carriage of bulk grain cargoes are equally valid for other cargo types, however, it is the aim of this section to look specifically at the characteristics and carriage requirements for bulk grain cargoes as detailed in the *International Code for the Safe Carriage of Grain in Bulk (International Grain Code)(IMO).*

In this section extensive reference is made to the regulations contained within the *International Grain Code* and also the *Code of Safe Practice for Solid Bulk Cargoes (BC Code)* where appropriate.

Where such references are made the following abbreviations will be used to signify the Code to which the regulation belongs as follows:

* **IG Code** – *International Grain Code*
* **BC Code** - *Code of Safe Practice for Solid Bulk Cargoes*

Learning Objectives

On completion of this section, the learner will achieve the following:

1. Understand the effect on the curve of statical stability of a shift of a solid bulk cargo in general.
2. Know the Grain Code assumptions with respect to an anticipated shift of a bulk grain cargo.
3. Know the grain loading information to be supplied.
4. Know the intact stability criteria for a ship with a *Document of Authorisation* carrying bulk grain.
5. Understand how compensation for the *horizontal component* of assumed grain shift is determined (derivation of the heeling arm curve).
6. Understand how compensation for the *vertical component* of assumed grain shift is applied (assumptions with respect to Kg of the bulk grain cargo within a compartment).
7. Understand the procedure to check compliance with the intact stability requirements of the Code.
8. Methods of improving stability when the minimum *International Grain Code* criteria is not met.
9. Understand the main optional stability requirements to be met by ships without Documents of Authorisation carrying partial cargoes of bulk grain.
10. Understand the use of simplified stability data required for ship's carrying grain built on or after 1st January 1994 (on or after the date that the *International Grain Code* came into force).

18.1 THE EFFECT OF A SHIFT OF SOLID BULK CARGO ON THE CURVE OF STATICAL STABILITY

The requirements for safe stowage and shipment of bulk cargoes are to be found in the *Code of Safe Practice for Solid Bulk Cargoes (BC Code)*.

When loading solid bulk cargoes, the cargo should be trimmed level in each compartment to limit the adverse effects of a shift of the cargo during the voyage.

The ease with which such a cargo will shift is dependant on the *angle of repose* of the cargo.

18.1.1 Angle of Repose

When solid bulk cargoes such as grain are loaded they are usually poured into the ship's hold. If they are poured onto one spot a conical shaped pile will form which will have a certain slope profile. The *angle of repose* is the maximum slope angle of *non-cohesive* (free flowing) granular material. It is the angle between a horizontal plane and the cone slope of such a material.

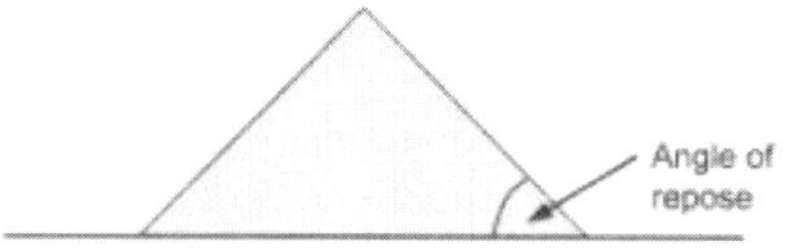

Fig. 18.1

The angle of repose is governed by the shape and surface of the individual particles of cargo within a particular stow and cargo moisture content.

The less the angle of repose of the cargo; the greater the ease with which the cargo will shift!

The BC Code categorises bulk cargoes for trimming purposes as *cohesive* and *non-cohesive*. Cohesive cargoes are generally all damp materials that when poured have high angles of repose. Some dry cargoes also display cohesive properties. Non-cohesive cargoes are free flowing materials like grain that have small angles of repose.

Bulk cargoes are also classed by angle of repose.

18.1.2 Non-cohesive bulk cargoes having an angle of repose less than or equal to 30°.

Materials which flow freely like grain must be carried in accordance with the provisions laid down in the *International Code for the Safe Carriage of Grain in Bulk (International Grain Code)(IMO)*. Such cargoes have a high potential for shifting and the effect on stability is a major consideration.

The term *grain* includes wheat, maize (corn), oats, rye, barley, rice, pulses, seeds and processed forms of the aforementioned whose behaviour is similar to that of grain in its natural state. Grain seeds are well rounded and have an almost polished surface in many cases causing them to have a typical angle of repose of about 23°.

Non-grain cargoes that possess non-cohesive properties similar to grain as defined above must also be carried in accordance with the provisions of the International Grain Code (BC Code - Regulation 5.2.4.2).

18.1.3 Non-cohesive bulk cargoes having an angle of repose from 30° to 35°.

The BC Code criteria for the trimming of these cargoes are shown.

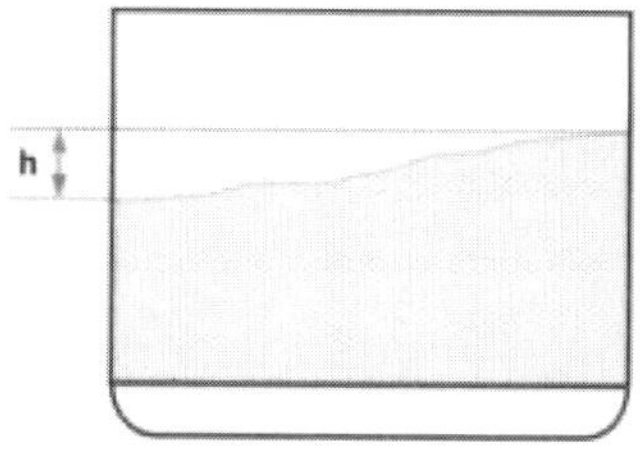

'h' must not exceed B/10 where B is the beam of the ship in metres but 'h' must never exceed 1.5 m. If h cannot be determined then loading must be carried out with approved trimming equipment (BC Code - Regulation 5.2.4.3).

Fig. 18.2

18.1.4 Non-cohesive bulk cargoes having an angle of repose greater than 35°.

The aim with these cargoes is to distribute the material in such a way as to avoid the formation of wide, steeply sloped voids beyond the trimmed surface within the boundaries of the cargo space. The material should be trimmed to an angle *significantly less* than the angle of repose (BC Code - Regulation 5.2.4.4).

18.1.5 The importance of trimming level the bulk cargo surface

Consider a ship loaded with a bulk grain cargo that has a typical angle of repose value of 23°. If the ship is inclined to an angle of heel that is *greater* than the angle of repose the stow will become unstable and shift of cargo will occur.

If the shift occurs as shown (figure 18.3) then the ship will return to an angle of list and will now roll about the angle of list.

Subsequent rolling will result in the ship being heeled to greater angles of heel on the listed side that will lead to further shifts of cargo and increased angles of list if the angle of repose is exceeded a further time.

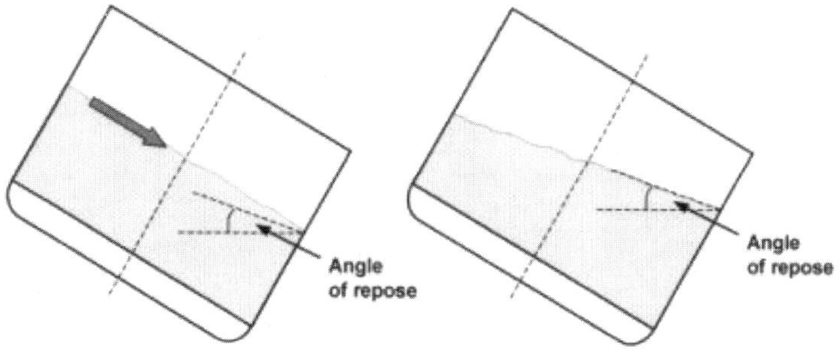

Fig. 18.3

Ship listed after cargo shift.

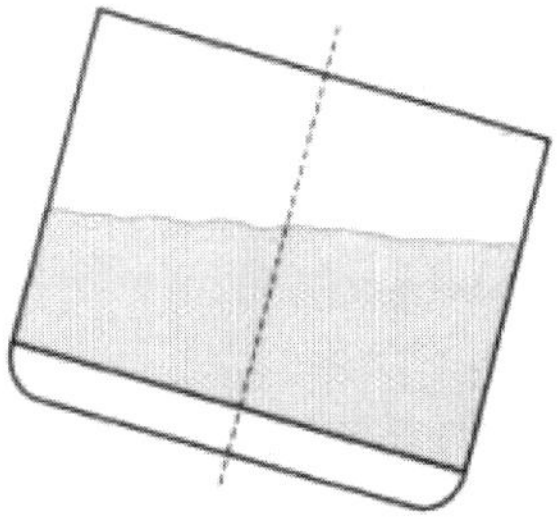

Fig.18.4

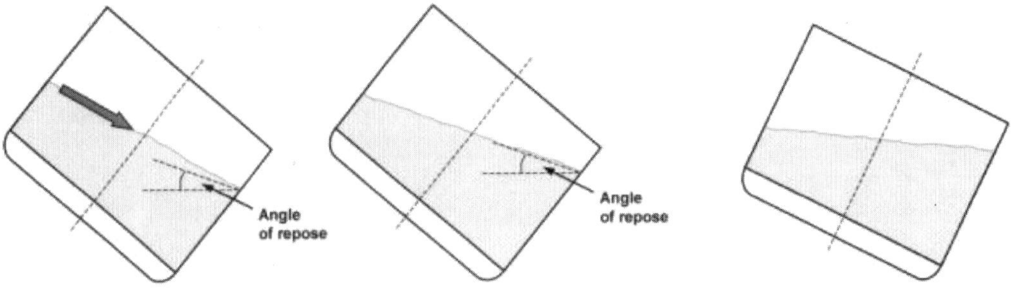

Ship rolls to increased angles of heel on the listed side. If further cargo shift takes place the list will be increased further as shown below.

Fig. 18.5

If these effects continue the ship could ultimately capsize. However, provided that the ship has sufficient stability it should remain in a listed, yet stable, condition. In order to minimise the likelihood of excessive list it is essential that bulk cargoes with small angles of repose are trimmed level before sailing.

18.1.6 The effect on the curve of statical stability of a shift of solid bulk cargo.

Of particular importance is the effect of a shift of solid bulk cargo on the ship's transverse stability. Consider the vessel in figure 18.6 where a shift of cargo has taken place within a hold.

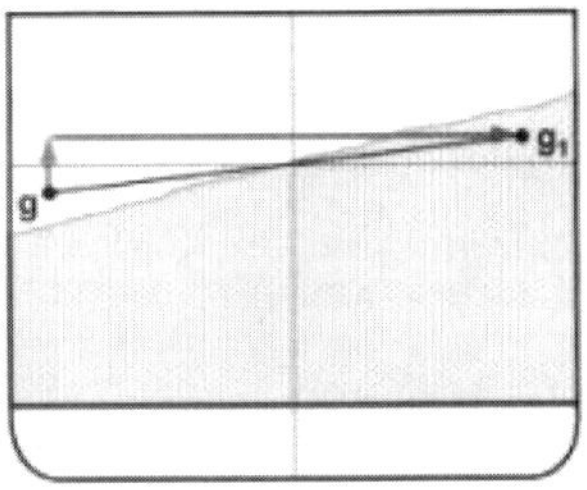

Fig.18.6

Effectively, a wedge of grain has moved from g to g_1. This movement has two components:

- * a small *vertical component* which causes the ship's centre of gravity to rise (GG_v), causing an increase in KG/decrease in GM;
- * a larger *horizontal component* which causes the ship's centre of gravity to move off the centre line (GG_h), causing list.

In section 17 the effects of these individual components of shift was described. The original GZ values will be reduced as a result of both components of the shift of the ship's centre of gravity to give the final condition after the shift of cargo has taken place.

Loss of GZ due to vertical component upwards = $GG_V \times$ Sine θ;

Loss of GZ due to horizontal component = $GG_H \times$ Cosine θ.

As way of an example consider the situation where MV Almar at a displacement of 20000 tonnes is initially upright with KG 9.200 m and initial GM 0.260 m. 180 tonnes of solid bulk cargo in one of the holds subsequently shifts 5 metres upward and 18 metres transversely. The effects of the shift of cargo on the curve of statical stability are seen in figure 18.7.

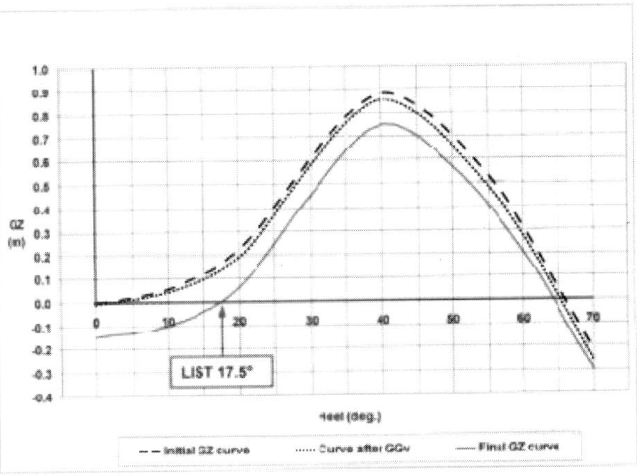

Fig. 18.7

An alternative representation of the losses of GZ is shown in figure 18.8. The values of loss of GZ due to the horizontal component ($GG_H \times$ Cosine θ) are plotted as a *heeling arm curve*, whereby they are plotted from the *graph baseline upwards* instead of from the *GZ curve downwards*.

This is the method of representation adopted by the *International Grain Code* as it makes calculation of the residual area easier.

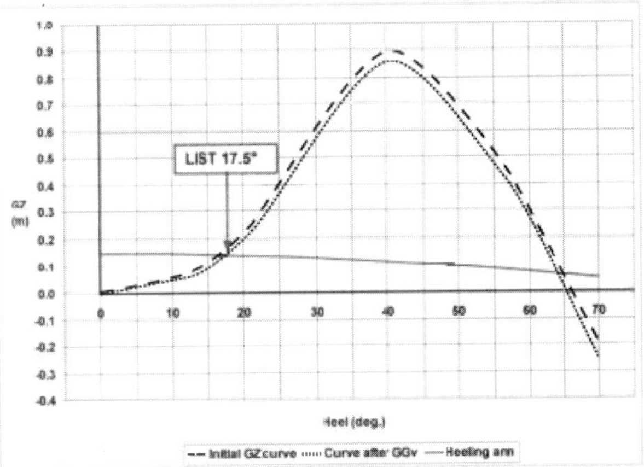

Fig. 18.8

18.2 ASSUMPTIONS OF THE *INTERNATIONAL GRAIN CODE* WITH RESPECT TO ANTICIPATED SHIFT OF GRAIN CARGO

18.2.1 General principles of the International Grain Code

The Grain Code is based on the recognition that in a compartment nominally filled with grain void spaces will exist between the surface of the grain and the upper boundaries of the compartment and that, due to the ship's rolling motion in a seaway, a possibility will always exist for the grain to shift transversely into such voids causing loss of stability due to list effect. The Code aims to limit this possibility by requiring that the grain surface be trimmed level to ensure that a large angle of heel be required to cause the grain surface to shift or, alternatively, by physically restraining the grain surface against such movement.

The Code recognises that the stability of the ship is a critical consideration at all times and as such, it requires demonstration by calculation that at all times during a voyage the ship will have sufficient intact stability to provide adequate residual dynamic stability after taking into account the adverse effect of a grain shift, should it occur. The magnitude of any grain shift cannot be precisely anticipated, since it will depend upon various dynamic factors, so the Code assumes angles of grain shift from the horizontal (trimmed) state. It then specifies a minimum level of acceptable stability for the carriage of grain based in terms of the resultant angle of list due to the assumed grain shift, the required residual dynamical stability after such shift and initial metacentric height (GM). *It should be noted that the assumed pattern of grain movement prescribed in the Code is not intended to portray the actual movement of the grain surfaces as the ship moves in a seaway. However, it is intended that the calculated heeling moment based on this prescribed pattern of grain movement adequately represent the actual effects that may be experienced.*

18.2.2 Specific assumptions

Calculations involving shifts of bulk grain cargoes are based on the following assumptions:

(a) In full compartments there will be a void space under all upper boundary surfaces having an inclination of less than 30° to the horizontal (30° being a figure based on the non-cohesive bulk cargo category for cargoes having an angle of repose less than or equal to 30° detailed in the BC Code – see section 18.1.2). (IG Code – Regulation B 1.1.1)

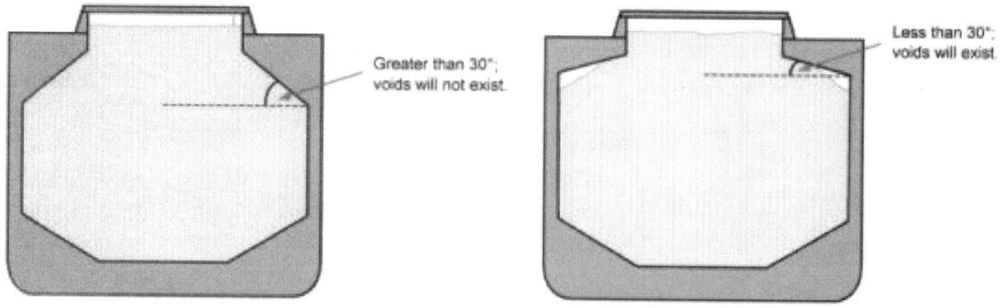

IG Code - Regulation B 1.1.1

Fig. 18.9

(b) In filled and trimmed hatchways the void is to be taken as 150 mm below the lowest point of the hatch or the top of the hatch side coaming, whichever is lower. The volume of any open void within the hatch cover is to be added (IG Code – Regulation B 1.1.2).

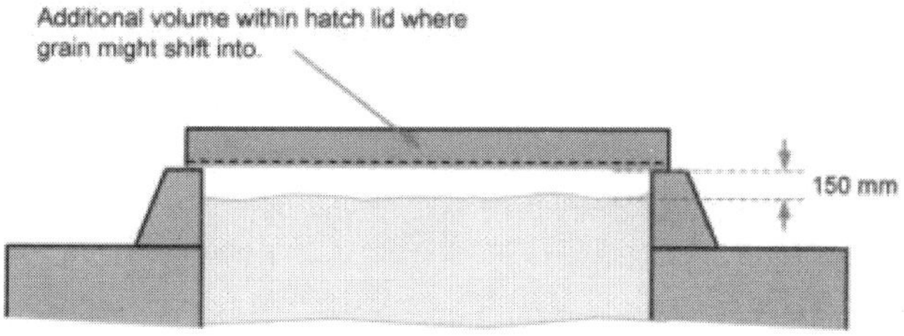

IG Code – Regulation B 1.1.2

Fig. 18.10

(c) In the void spaces of *full* compartments the grain surface is assumed to shift 15° from the horizontal (IG Code – Regulation B 2.3).

In *partially filled* compartments the grain surface is assumed to shift 25° from the horizontal (IG Code – Regulation B 5.1).

(A compartment may be considered full if it is filled to a level within the vertical sides of the coaming.)

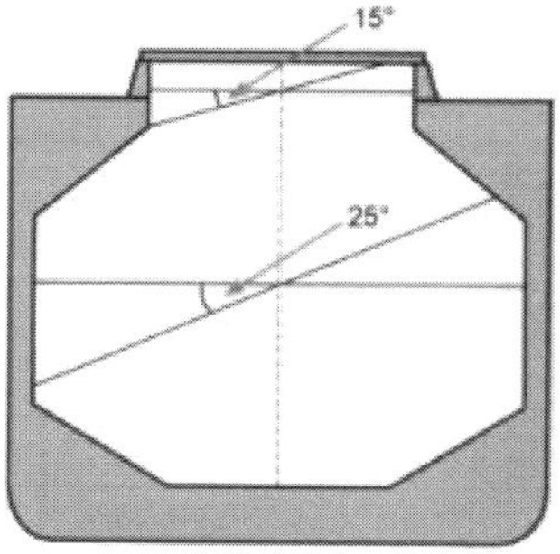

IG Code – Regulations B 2.3 & B 5.1

Fig. 18.11

(d) Many bulk cargoes will settle as the voyage progresses so it is assumed that void spaces will *always exist*, even in full compartments, so it is anticipated that any cargo will have some potential to shift should the ship heel excessively.

18.3 GRAIN LOADING INFORMATION TO BE SUPPLIED

18.3.1 Document of authorisation to carry grain cargoes

One of the principles of the SOLAS conventions is that member nations will be responsible for the details of compliance with the requirements of the appropriate IMO Codes and that other nations will accept, on good faith, that the details contained within such Codes are properly observed. However, each nation retains the right to ascertain that any ship which conducts commerce from it's ports has, in fact, been subjected to regulatory checks by it's home Administration. In the case of ships carrying grain in bulk, the mechanism for accomplishing this is the *Document of Authorisation* described in IG Code – Regulation A 3.

The *Document of Authorisation* is a certification made by an Administration which is signatory to the Convention or by an agency authorized to act on behalf of that Administration (such as the MCA), that a specific ship under it's registry is capable of carrying grain in bulk and that the information in the *Grain Loading Manual* defining such capability, has been reviewed and is approved as being in compliance with the requirements of the Code. Since so many nations are signatory to the Convention, this means that the *Document of Authorisation* will be accepted at almost every port worldwide.

18.3.2 Information regarding ship's stability and grain loading

IG Code - Regulation A 6 lists the specific data and information which is to be included in the *Grain Loading Manual*.

This information shall include:

6.2.1 ship's particulars;
6.2.2 light ship displacement and KG;
6.2.3 table of liquid free surface moments (or I values) for ship's tanks to allow a free surface correction to be calculated;
6.2.4 capacities and centres of gravities of compartments;
6.2.5 curve or table of angle of flooding, where less than 40°, at all permissible displacements;
6.2.6 hydrostatic data curves or tables suitable for the range of operating draughts; and
6.2.7 cross curves of stability (KN curves) that are sufficient in number to verify stability criteria compliance and to include curves for 12° and 40° heel.

In addition to the above:

6.3.1 curves or tables of volumes, vertical centres of volumes, and assumed volumetric heeling moments for every compartment, filled or partly filled, or combination thereof, including the effects of temporary fittings;
6.3.2 tables or curves of maximum permissible grain heeling moments for varying displacements and ship's KG values to allow the master to demonstrate compliance with the minimum stability criteria (this requirement only applies to ships built on or after the entry into force of the Code – for UK ship's the Code is enforced by the M.S. (Carriage of Cargoes) Regulations 1999 which came into force on the 15th March 1999);
6.3.3 details of the scantlings of any temporary fittings and, where applicable, the provisions necessary to meet the requirements of the Code (including the requirements for ships not issued with a document of authorisation carrying partial cargoes of bulk grain);
6.3.4 loading instructions in the form of notes summarising the requirements of the Code;
6.3.5 a worked example of the grain loading calculations for the guidance of the master; and
6.3.6 typical loaded service departure and arrival conditions and where necessary intermediate worst service conditions based on three representative values of grain stowage factor e.g. 1.25, 1.50 and 1.75 m^3/t.

18.4 INTACT STABILITY CRITERIA FOR SHIPS CARRYING GRAIN ISSUED WITH A DOCUMENT OF AUTHORISATION

A document of authorisation is issued to many ships and is accepted as evidence that the ship is capable of complying with the requirements of the International Grain Code. The specific content of this document has already been detailed.

The intact stability requirements that must be met throughout the voyage for any ship carrying grain issued with such a document are detailed in IG Code – Regulation A 7 below:

7.1.1 the angle of heel due to the shift of grain shall not be greater than 12°, or in the case of ships constructed on or after 1st January 1994 the angle at which the deck edge is immersed, whichever is the lesser;

7.1.2 in the statical stability diagram, the net or residual area between the heeling arm curve and the righting arm (GZ) curve up to the angle of heel of maximum difference between the ordinates of the two curves, or 40° or the angle of flooding (θ_f), whichever is the least, shall in all conditions of loading be not less than 0.075 metre-radians; and

7.1.3 the initial metacentric height (GM), after correction for the free surface effects of liquids in tanks, shall be not less than 0.30 metres.

7.2 Before loading bulk grain the master shall, if so required by the Contracting Government of the country of the port of loading, demonstrate the ability of the ship at all stages of any voyage to comply with the stability criteria required by this section.

7.3 After loading, the master shall ensure that the ship is upright before proceeding to sea.

Figure 18.12 details the stability requirements with respect to the curve of statical stability.

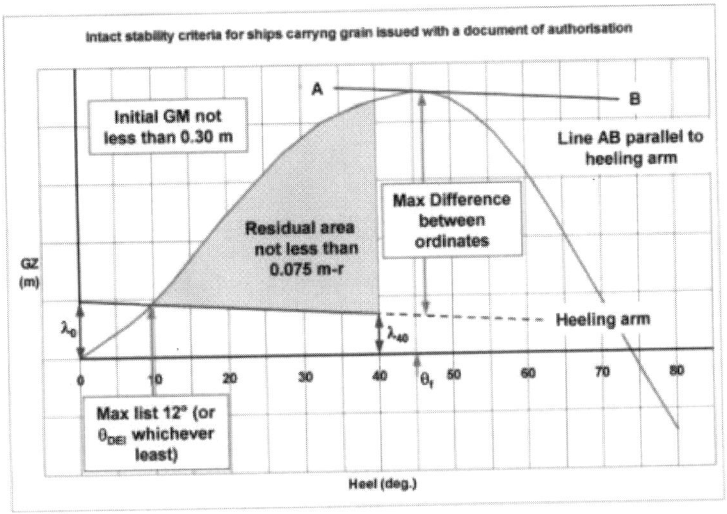

Fig. 18.12.

Because the maximum permitted list after assumed grain shift is 12° (or θ_{DEI}), the curve of statical stability must be derived from cross-curves (KN curves) that are sufficient in number to accurately define the curve for the purpose of these requirements, and, shall include cross-curves for the values of heel 12° and 40°.

18.5 DERIVATION OF THE HEELING ARM

The heeling arm represents the loss of GZ at various angles of heel as a result of the assumed *horizontal component* of the shift of grain.

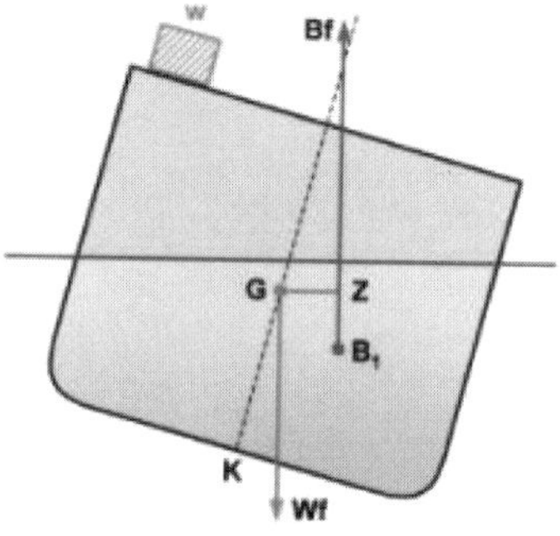

Fig. 18.13

The derivation of this curve is as follows:

Figure 18.13 shows an upright ship with a weight w on one side heeled to some angle by an external force where the righting lever is GZ.

The weight is shifted transversely across the deck causing G to move off the centre line to G_H and the ship is again heeled to the same angle as before.

The righting lever has been reduced from GZ to G_HZ_1 as a result of the transverse shift of weight.

GX = ***Loss*** of righting lever.

In triangle GG_HX: Cosine $\theta = \frac{ADJ}{HYP} = \frac{GX}{GG_H}$

$\therefore$ **$GX = GG_H \times \text{Cosine}\,\theta$**

If the ship is listed the loss of GZ at any angle of heel is determined by:

LOSS OF GZ = $GG_H \times \text{Cosine}\,\theta$

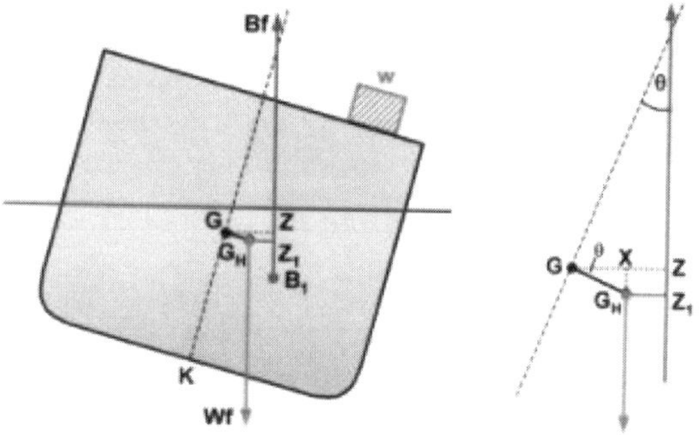

Fig. 18.14

where θ is the angle of heel for which the loss of GZ is being calculated.

The loss of GZ at 0° heel = GG_H (since Cosine 0° = 1.000)

The loss of GZ at 40° heel = $GG_H \times$ Cosine 40°

The International Grain Code (IMO) substitutes the notation GG_H for the symbol λ.
Therefore, for the horizontal component of a shift of grain:

The loss of GZ at 0° heel = λ_0

The loss of GZ at 40° heel = λ_{40}

where λ_0 and λ_{40} are the values that create the heeling arm to be plotted on the curve of statical stability (see figure 18.12).

To calculate λ_0:

Since $\lambda_0 = GG_H$ and; $GG_H = \frac{w \times d}{W}$ it follows that: $\lambda_0 = \frac{w \times d}{W}$

Since the stowage factor of the grain cargo is not known until arrival at the loading port the actual weight of cargo loaded is not known. Consequently, the weight of the wedge of grain that is assumed to shift is not known either.

Since: $\text{mass (t)} = \frac{\text{volume (m}^3\text{)}}{\text{SF (m}^3\text{/t)}}$

$$\lambda_0 = \frac{\text{volume} \times d}{SF \times W}$$

where: *(volume (m^3) × distance (m))* gives a value of *Volumetric Heeling Moments (m^4)*

Values of *Volumetric Heeling Moments (VHM's)* are calculated for each hold or compartment designated for the carriage of grain by the naval architect and are based on the *movement of a volume of grain in cubic metres through a horizontal distance in metres* across the hold. The volume of grain shifted is based on the assumed 15° and 25° shift of grain surface (depending on whether a compartment is full or part full).

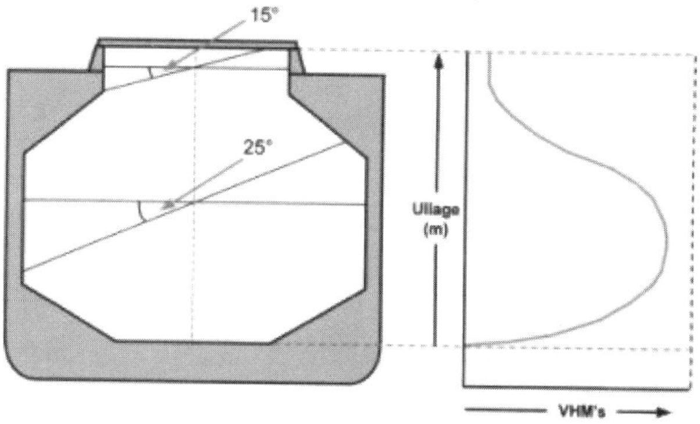

Fig. 18.15

VHM values will be given in the ship's *Grain Loading Manual*, either in tabular format (as in the stability data book for M.V Almar, or, in the form of curves as depicted in figure 18.15.

Thus:

$$\lambda_0 = \frac{\Sigma \text{ VHM's}}{\text{SF} \times \text{W}}$$

To calculate λ_{40}:

$$\lambda_{40} = \lambda_0 \times \text{Cosine } 40^\circ$$

where Cosine 40° = 0.766044…..

The *International Grain Code* allows an approximation of Cosine 40° of 0.8; therefore the other end of the heeling arm to be plotted at 40° is found by:

$$\lambda_{40} = 0.8 \times \lambda_0$$

A straight line is used to join the two points of the heeling arm (the Code ignores the fact that it should really be a cosine curve).

18.6 COMPENSATION FOR THE VERTICAL COMPONENT OF SHIFT OF GRAIN

Part B – Calculation of assumed heeling moments and general assumptions in the Code details the method for compensating for the adverse effect of the *vertical component* of the shift of grain. This is based upon the assumptions of the shift of the grain surface in a full compartment (15°) and a partly filled compartment (25°).

Consider figure 18.16.

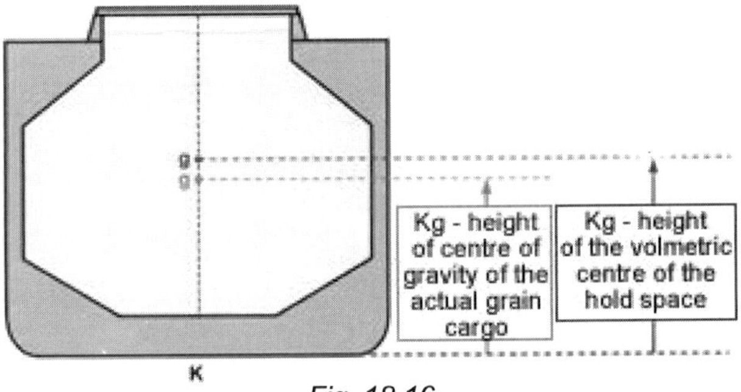

Fig. 18.16

In the calculation of the ship's effective KG (and GM) it is common to use the height of the geometric centre of the total volume of the hold (which also takes account of the space within the hatch coaming). This will be *higher than the actual Kg of the cargo* if any void spaces at the top of the grain stow are also considered.

If this higher geometric centre position is used then any adverse effect of the vertical component of the shift of grain can be ignored.

However, if the *lesser* value of the Kg of the actual grain cargo is used for the calculation of the ship's effective KG (and GM) then the volumetric heeling moments for that compartment must be increased by a factor as follows:

In a *full compartment* the VHM's are increased by: **VHM's × 1.06** (IG Code – Regulation B 1.3)

In a *part full compartment* the VHM's are increased by: **VHM's × 1.12** (IG Code – Regulation B 1.5)

The reasoning behind this is as follows:

Figure 18.17 (a) shows the basic list triangle GG_HM where:

$$\tan \theta_{LIST} = \frac{GG_H}{GM}$$

(a) ***Basic list triangle***

(b) ***Increasing list by raising G (vertical component of grain shift)***

(c) ***Increasing list by increasing GG_H (increasing VHM's for hold concerned)***

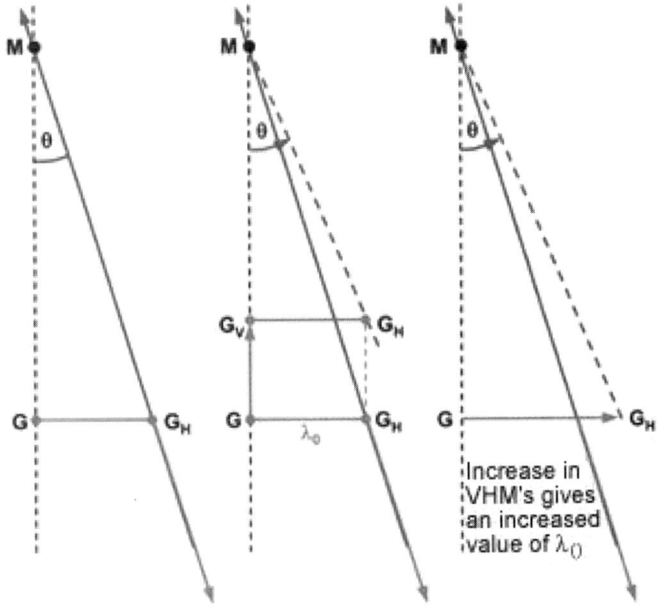

Fig. 18.17

For a given value of GG_H (caused by an excess of listing moments to one side) the list may be caused to increase in one of two ways:

(1) Shifting a weight upwards causing G to rise to G_V (this being the true effect of the vertical component of the shift of grain as depicted in figure 18.17 (b)), or;

(2) Increasing the listing moments further to give a greater value of GG_H (the effect is realised by increasing the value of the VHM's of the grain to give a greater value of λ_0, since:

$$\lambda_0 = \frac{\Sigma \text{ VHM's}}{\text{SF} \times \text{W}}$$

as depicted in figure 18.17 (c))

The factors 1.06 (for full compartments) and 1.12 (for part full compartments) are such that they will create an increase in the list of the ship that is equivalent to the effect of the vertical component of the shift of the wedge of grain, should the grain surface shift as assumed by the code i.e. 15° and 25° for part full and full compartments respectively.

In practice it is normal to use the Kg of the hold (the volumetric centre of the hold) when the compartment is full and to use the Kg of the actual grain as obtained from the hold data for compartments that are only partially filled. It is essential that these correction factors are understood and applied as appropriate since valuable marks for a question will be lost otherwise. This aspect of the Code is widely misunderstood!

Under no circumstances must the Kg of the grain cargo be increased by these factors – a common mistake made by many!

18.7 PROCEDURE TO VERIFY COMPLIANCE OF A SHIP'S LOADED CONDITION WITH MINIMUM *INTERNATIONAL GRAIN CODE* CRITERIA.

The following worked example will demonstrate the procedure to be followed for verifying the compliance of a ship's loaded condition. Each stage should be carefully studied and the example represents the method that should be adopted in practice.

Example 1
Prior to loading a grain cargo M.V. Almar has a displacement of 8420 t and solid KG of 10.46 m. Free surface moments due to slack tanks on board amount to 860 t-m.
Grain of SF 1.36 m^3/t is loaded into the holds as follows:

Hold No. 1	***Ullage 0.0 m***	***(Full)***
Hold No. 2	***Ullage 0.0 m***	***(Full)***
Hold No. 3	***Ullage 0.0 m***	***(Full)***
Hold No. 4	***Ullage 6.0 m***	***(Part full)***
Hold No. 5	***Ullage 2.5 m***	***(Part full)***
Hold No. 6	***Ullage 0.0 m***	***(Full)***

KG assumptions: ***Full compartments – use the Kg of the actual hold space;***
Part full compartm ents – use the KG of the actual grain cargo.

Part A
Determine the following:

(a) *weight of grain loaded in tonnes;*

(b) *the total volumetric heeling moments;*

(c) *the final solid and effective KG and final displacement;*

(d) *values λ_0 and λ_{40} (the heeling arm);*

Part B
(e) *By calculating the GZ values for the ship's loaded condition plot the curve of statical stability and the heeling arm due to grain shift (using values calculated in Part A (d)).*

(f) *Verify that the ship's loaded condition meets the intact stability requirements specified in the International Grain Code.*

Solution – Part A
A tabular approach is adopted.

(1) *Enter the cargo hold data tables with ullage given and obtain values for grain volume, VCG and VHM's.*

(2) *The weight of grain in each compartment is calculated by:* $\text{mass (t)} = \dfrac{\text{volume } (m^3)}{\text{SF } (m^3/t)}$

(3) *The tabulated VHM's are multiplied by the correction factor where appropriate to give the actual VHM's (Holds 4 and 5 are part full and the Kg used is that of the actual grain cargo in*

the hold; for all other holds the Kg of the actual hold space is used, so no correction is applied).

Compartment	Ullage (m)	Volume (m3)	Weight (t)	VCG (m)	Tabulated VHM's	Corr'n factor	Actual VHM's
1	0.0	5010	3684	8.220	370	1.00	370
2	0.0	5460	4015	7.650	381	1.00	381
3	0.0	5350	3934	7.650	371	1.00	371
4	6.0	3640	2676	5.800	2730	1.12	3058
5	2.5	4420	3250	7.050	565	1.12	633
6	0.0	5680	4176	7.740	408	1.00	408
TOTALS			**21735**				**5221**

Ans (a) ***weight of grain loaded is 21735 tonnes***

Ans (b) ***total VHM's 5221 m^4***

(4) Take moments about the keel to calculate the final KG and displacement.

	Weight	Kg	moments
Initial displ.	8420	10.46	88073
Hold 1	3684	8.220	30282
Hold 2	4015	7.650	30715
Hold 3	3934	7.650	30095
Hold 4	2676	5.800	15521
Hold 5	3250	7.050	22913
Hold 6	4176	7.740	32322
FINAL	**30155**	**8.288**	249921

FSE (m)	**0.029**

KG solid	8.288
FSE (m)	0.029
KG fluid	**8.316**

Note: $FSE\ (m) = \frac{\text{Free surface moments (t-m)}}{\text{Displacement}} = \frac{860}{30155} = 0.029\ m$

Ans (c) ***Final displacement 30155 tonnes***
Solid KG 8.288 m
Effective (fluid) KG 8.316 m

(5) Calculate the heeling arm values

$\lambda_0 = \frac{\Sigma \text{ VHM's}}{SF \times W}$ $\lambda_0 = \frac{5221}{1.36 \times 30155}$ $= \mathbf{0.127\ m}$

$\lambda_{40} = 0.8 \times \lambda_0$ $\lambda_{40} = 0.8 \times 0.127$ $= \mathbf{0.102\ m}$ ***(Ans. (d))***

Solution – Part B

(6) Obtain KN values for the ship's loaded displacement and calculate values of GZ (using the effective KG!).

Heel	10	20	30	40	60	80
KN	1.65	3.31	4.88	6.21	7.79	8.05
KG*Sin Heel	1.44	2.84	4.16	5.35	7.20	8.19
GZ	**0.21**	**0.47**	**0.72**	**0.86**	**0.59**	**-0.14**

(7) Enter hydrostatic data with displacement value and obtain KM; calculate effective GM.

KM	9.423
KG	8.316
GM	**1.107**

(8) *Plot the curve of statical stability and heeling arm (figure 18.18).*

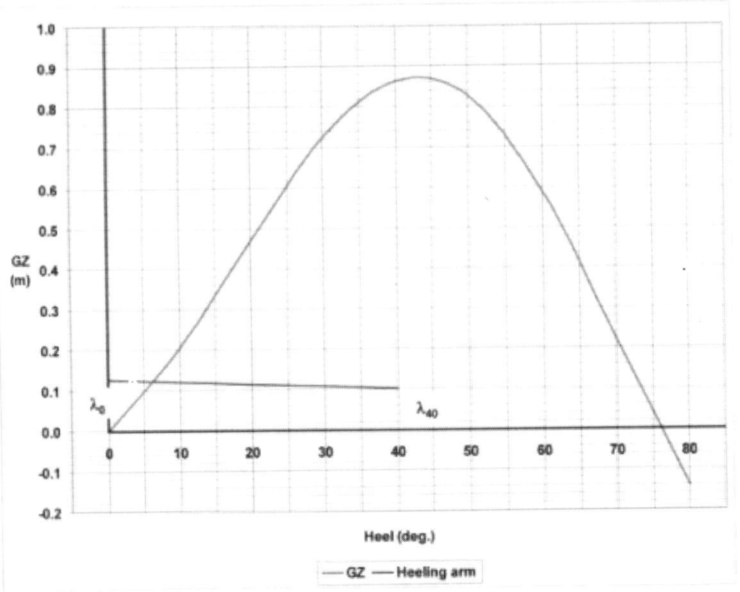

Fig. 18.18

From the curve it can be seen that the angle of heel if grain shift takes place as assumed by the Code will be approximately 6°.

(9) *Verify compliance with the Code*

To calculate the residual area (which must be not less than 0.075 m-r) the area under the GZ curve from the angle of list (6° in this instance) to 40° must be first calculated. In this case 40° is the upper limit, since the angle of heel at which maximum difference between the ordinates of the two curves occurs is greater than 40°. Since there are no curves of flooding angle then it must be assumed that at all operational draughts the angle of heel at which progressive flooding takes place will always be greater than 40°.

It is recommended that ordinates (GZ values) be taken from the curve to allow Simpson's multipliers of 14241 to be used.

The common interval $h = \frac{40° - 6°}{4} = 8\frac{1}{2}°$

GZ values are taken from the curve plotted for angles of heel 6°, 14½°, 23°, and 31½° as shown in figure 18.19. The value for 40° has already been calculated using the KN value given.

Once the area under the GZ curve has been determined (between 6° and 40°) the area under the trapezium bounded by the GZ value at 6°, the heeling arm and λ_{40} *is then calculated. This is taken away from the area under the GZ curve to give the residual area value to be compared for compliance.*

Study figure 18.19 and revisit figure 18.12 in section 18.4 for clarification.

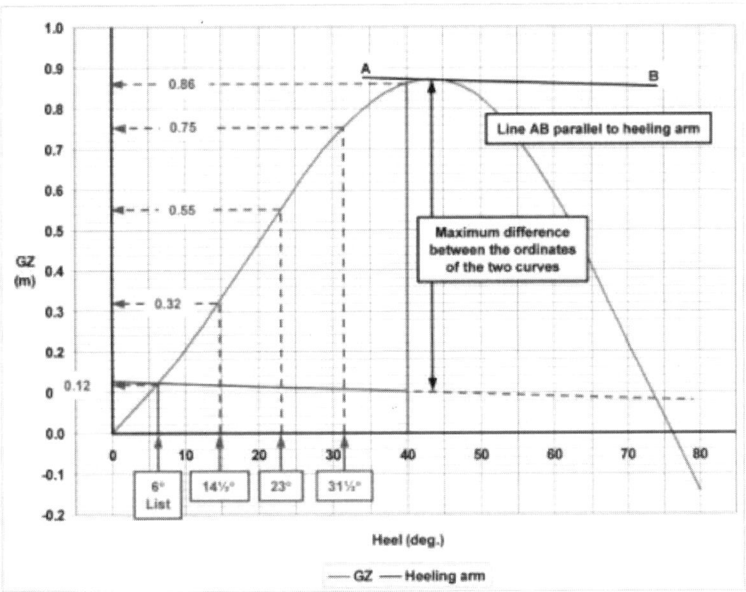

Fig. 18.19

Calculate area under GZ curve from 6° to 40°.

	Heel (deg)	GZ (m)	SM	Area fn.
List value	6	0.12	1	0.12
	14.5	0.32	4	1.28
	23	0.55	2	1.10
	31.5	0.75	4	3.00
	40	0.86	1	0.86
			Sum	**6.36**

Area = ? × h × Sum $\qquad$ *Area = ?* $\times \frac{8\frac{1}{2}}{57.3} \times 6.36 = 0.314$ *m-r*

Calculate area under trapezium

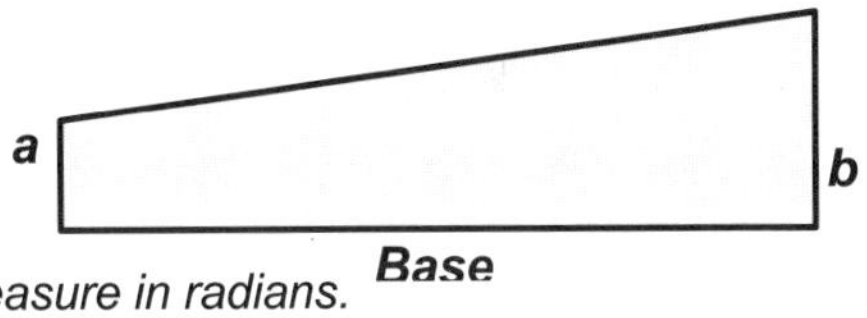

Note that area under trapezium = $\frac{(a + b)}{2} \times base$

where the base in degrees is divided by 57.3° to give a measure in radians.

Area under trapezium = $\frac{(0.120 + 0.102)}{2} \times \frac{36^\circ}{57.3^\circ} = 0.070$ *m-r*

Residual area = 0.314 – 0.070 = ***0.244 m-r*** *(0.075 m-r)*

Effective GM = ***1.107 m*** *(0.30 m)*

Angle of list = ***6°*** *(12°)*

The ship's loaded condition complies with the minimum intact stability of the International Grain Code.

18.8 METHODS OF IMPROVING STABILITY WHEN THE MINIMUM *INTERNATIONAL GRAIN CODE* CRITERIA IS NOT SATISFIED

In the event that stability calculations for a proposed loading condition do not meet the stability requirements of IG Code - Regulation A 7, alternative stowage arrangements should be considered. If this is not successful, other, usually more cost effective alternatives are available as follows:

18.8.1 Ballasting

If there is sufficient reserve deadweight and the ship is not at the respective load line draught taking on ballast will be helpful. Double bottom tanks should be filled to eliminate free surface effects. The added low weight will increase the displacement and reduce the KG.

18.8.2 Saucers

The grain heeling moments can be significantly reduced in a filled compartment by constructing a saucer as described in IG Code - Regulation A 14 in the square of the hatchway. This device has the same effect as a centreline, grain-tight bulkhead in that it prevents the grain from shifting across the entire breadth of the compartment as illustrated in figure 18.20.

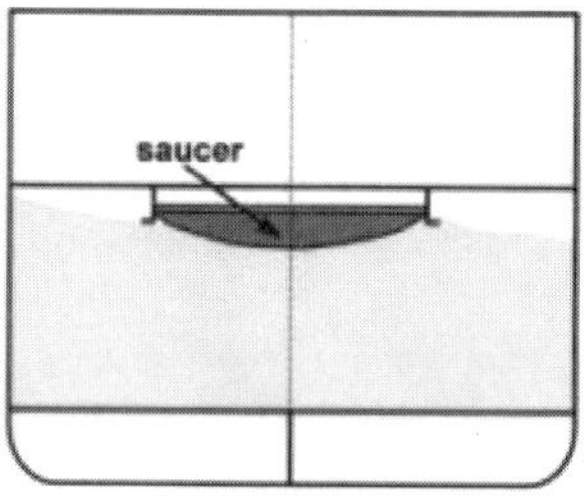

Grain condition after shift.
Fig. 18.20

Unless there are grain-tight divisions forward and aft of the hatchway, the effect is limited to the longitudinal length of the saucer. The volumetric heeling moments that apply in a specific compartment when a saucer is fitted must be included in the approved *Grain Loading Manual* if this option is to be available to the ship.

The specific requirements relating to the use and construction of saucers are given in IG Code - Regulation A 14 as follows:

14.1 *For the purpose of reducing the heeling moment a saucer may be used in place of a longitudinal division in way of a hatch opening only in a filled, trimmed, compartment as defined in A 2.2, except in the case of linseed and other seeds having similar properties, where a saucer may not be substituted for a longitudinal division. If a longitudinal division is provided, it shall meet the requirements of A 10.9.*

14.2 *The depth of the saucer, measured from the bottom of the saucer to the deck line, shall be as follows:*

.1 *For ships with a moulded breadth of up to 9.1 m, not less than 1.2 m.*
.2 *For ships with a moulded breadth of 18.3 m or more, not less than 1.8 m.*
.3 *For ships with a moulded breadth between 9.1 m and 18.3 m, the minimum depth of the saucer shall be calculated by interpolation.*

14.3 *The top (mouth) of the saucer shall be formed by the underdeck structure in way of the hatchway, i.e. hatch side girders or coamings and hatch end beams. The saucer and hatchway above shall be completely filled with bagged grain or other suitable cargo laid down on a separation cloth or its equivalent and stowed tightly against adjacent structure so as to have a bearing contact with such structure to a depth equal to or greater than one half of the depth specified in A 14.2. If hull structure to provide such bearing surface is not available, the saucer shall be fixed in position by steel wire rope, chain, or double steel strapping as specified in A 17.4 and spaced not more than 2.4 m apart.*

18.8.3 Bundling of bulk grain

Whereas a saucer is formed by a volume of bagged grain or similarly restrained cargo, the same result of preventing a transverse shift of grain across the entire breadth of the compartment, as illustrated in figure 18.20, may be achieved by constructing a single, large bag of bulk grain which fills the hatchway and which is fixed in position by the structural boundaries of the hatchway. This is termed 'bundling of bulk grain' and is an acceptable alternative to a saucer.

The volumetric heeling moment which applies when bundling of bulk grain is used in a specific compartment is the same as that which applies for a saucer used in the same location, and it must be listed in the *Grain Loading Manual* if this option is to be available for use by the vessel.

The specific requirements pertaining to the method of 'bundling of bulk grain' are given in IG Code - Regulation A 15, as listed below. It is to be noted that the limitations on its use are the same as those that apply to a saucer and are specified in IG Code - Regulation A 14.1.

As an alternative to filling the saucer in a filled, trimmed compartment with bagged grain or other suitable cargo a bundle of bulk grain may be used provided that:

15.1 The dimensions and means for securing the bundle in place are the same as specified for a saucer in A 14.2 and A 14.3.

15.2 The saucer is lined with a material acceptable to the Administration having a tensile strength of not less than 2687 N per 5 cm strip and which is provided with suitable means for securing at the top.

15.3 As an alternative to A 15.2, a material acceptable to the Administration having a tensile strength of not less than 1344 N per 5 cm strip may be used if the saucer is constructed as follows:

.3.1 Athwartship lashings acceptable to the Administration shall be placed inside the saucer formed in the bulk grain at intervals of not more than 2.4 m. These lashings shall be of sufficient length to permit being drawn up tight and secured at the top of the saucer.

.3.2 Dunnage not less than 25 mm in thickness or other suitable material of equal strength and between 150 mm and 300 mm in width shall be placed fore and aft over these lashings to prevent the cutting or chafing of the material which shall be placed thereon to line the saucer.

15.4 The saucer shall be filled with bulk grain and secured at the top except that when using material approved under A 15.3 further dunnage shall be laid on top after lapping the material before the saucer is secured by setting up the lashings.

15.5 If more than one sheet of material is used to line the saucer they shall be joined at the bottom either by sewing or by a double lap.

15.6 The top of the saucer shall be coincidental with the bottom of the beams when these are in place and suitable general cargo or bulk grain may be placed between the beams on top of the saucer.

Consider figure 18.21.

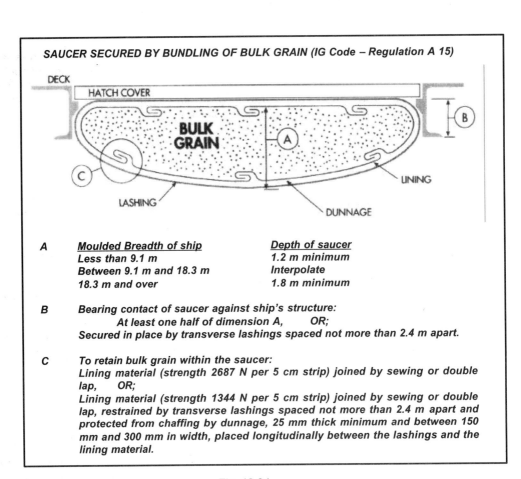

SAUCER SECURED BY BUNDLING OF BULK GRAIN (IG Code – Regulation A 15)

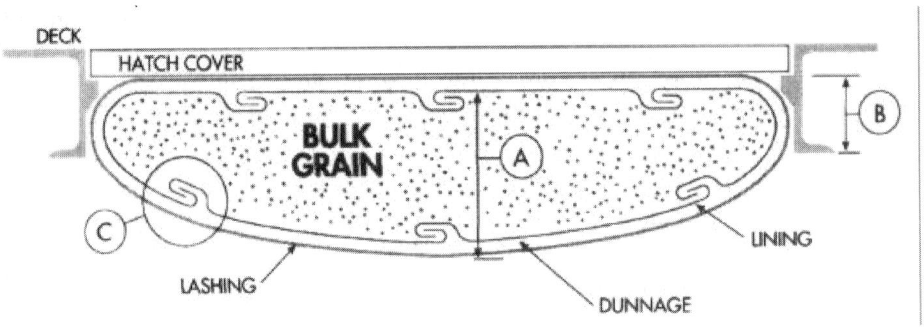

A	***Moulded Breadth of ship***	***Depth of saucer***
	Less than 9.1 m	***1.2 m minimum***
	Between 9.1 m and 18.3 m	***Interpolate***
	18.3 m and over	***1.8 m minimum***

B ***Bearing contact of saucer against ship's structure:***
At least one half of dimension A, OR;
Secured in place by transverse lashings spaced not more than 2.4 m apart.

C ***To retain bulk grain within the saucer:***
Lining material (strength 2687 N per 5 cm strip) joined by sewing or double lap, OR;
Lining material (strength 1344 N per 5 cm strip) joined by sewing or double lap, restrained by transverse lashings spaced not more than 2.4 m apart and protected from chaffing by dunnage, 25 mm thick minimum and between 150 mm and 300 mm in width, placed longitudinally between the lashings and the lining material.

Fig. 18.21

18.8.4 Overstowing arrangements

If one or more of the grain compartments is partly filled, the grain heeling moments for such compartments is much greater than it is for the filled compartments. The grain heeling moment for a partly filled compartment can be eliminated, i.e., reduced to zero by securing the slack surface against shifting by overstowing it with bagged grain or with other cargo which will have the similar effect of restraining the grain surface against any movement. A reduction in the total grain heeling moment, achieved by this means, may be sufficient to bring the proposed stowage arrangement within acceptable limits.

This option does not require any special information or endorsement in the *Grain Loading Manual.* The specific requirements for overstowing are given in IG Code - Regulation A 16, as follows:

16.1 *Where bagged grain or other suitable cargo is utilized for the purpose of securing partly filled compartments, the free grain surface shall be level and shall be covered with a separation cloth or equivalent or by a suitable platform. Such platform shall consist of bearers spaced not more than 1.2 m apart and 25 mm boards laid thereon spaced not more than 100 mm apart. Platforms may be constructed of other materials provided they are deemed by the Administration to be equivalent.*

16.2 *The platform or separation cloth shall be topped off with bagged grain tightly stowed and extending to a height of not less than one sixteenth of the maximum breadth of the free grain surface or 1.2 m, whichever is the greater.*

16.3 *The bagged grain shall be carried in sound bags which shall be well filled and securely closed.*

16.4 *Instead of bagged grain, other suitable cargo tightly stowed and exerting at least the same pressure as bagged grain stowed in accordance with A 16.2 may be used.*

18.8.5 Strapping or lashing

Partly filled compartments have the greatest volumetric heeling moments because they have a large volume of open space above the grain surface into which the grain can shift and, also, because the regulations assume a 25° shift instead of the 15° shift which applies when the compartment is filled. Consequently, a significant reduction in grain heeling moments can be achieved by totally preventing a grain shift in a partly filled compartment. This may be accomplished by fabricating a somewhat costly construction that completely covers the slack grain surface and physically restrains it against any movement that may be generated by the motions of the ship at sea.

The use of this option does not require any special information or endorsement in the *Grain Loading Manual*. The specific requirements pertaining to the details of construction are given in IG Code - Regulation A 17, as given below:

When, in order to eliminate heeling moments in partly filled compartments, strapping or lashing is utilized, the securing shall be accomplished as follows:

17.1 *The grain shall be trimmed and levelled to the extent that it is very slightly crowned and covered with burlap separation cloths, tarpaulins or the equivalent.*

17.2 *The separation cloths and/or tarpaulins shall overlap by at least 1.8 m.*

17.3 *Two solid floors of rough 25 mm x 150 mm to 300 mm lumber shall be laid with the top floor running longitudinally and nailed to an athwartships bottom floor. Alternatively, one solid floor of 50 mm lumber, running longitudinally and nailed over the top of a 50 mm bottom bearer not less than 150 mm wide, may be used. The bottom bearers shall extend the full breadth of the compartment and shall be spaced not more than 2.4 m apart. Arrangements utilizing other materials and deemed by the Administration to be equivalent to the foregoing may be accepted.*

17.4 *Steel wire rope (19 mm diameter or equivalent), double steel strapping (50 mm x 1.3 mm and having a breaking load of at least 49 kN), or chain of equivalent strength, each of which shall be set tightly by means of a 32 mm turnbuckle, may be used for lashings. A winch tightener, used in conjunction with a locking arm, may be substituted for the 32 mm turnbuckle when steel strapping is used, provided suitable wrenches are available for setting up as necessary. When steel strapping is used, not less than three crimp seals shall be used for securing the ends. When wire is used, not less than four clips shall be used for forming eyes in the lashings.*

17.5 *Prior to the completion of loading the lashing shall be positively attached to the framing at a point approximately 450 mm below the anticipated final grain surface by means of either a 25 mm shackle or beam clamp of equivalent strength.*

17.6 *The lashings shall be spaced not more than 2.4 m apart and each shall be supported by a bearer nailed over the top of the fore and aft floor. This bearer shall consist of lumber of not less than 25 mm x 150 mm or its equivalent and shall extend the full breadth of the compartment.*

17.7 *During the voyage the strapping shall be regularly inspected and set up where necessary.*

Figure 18.22 illustrates details of these arrangements.

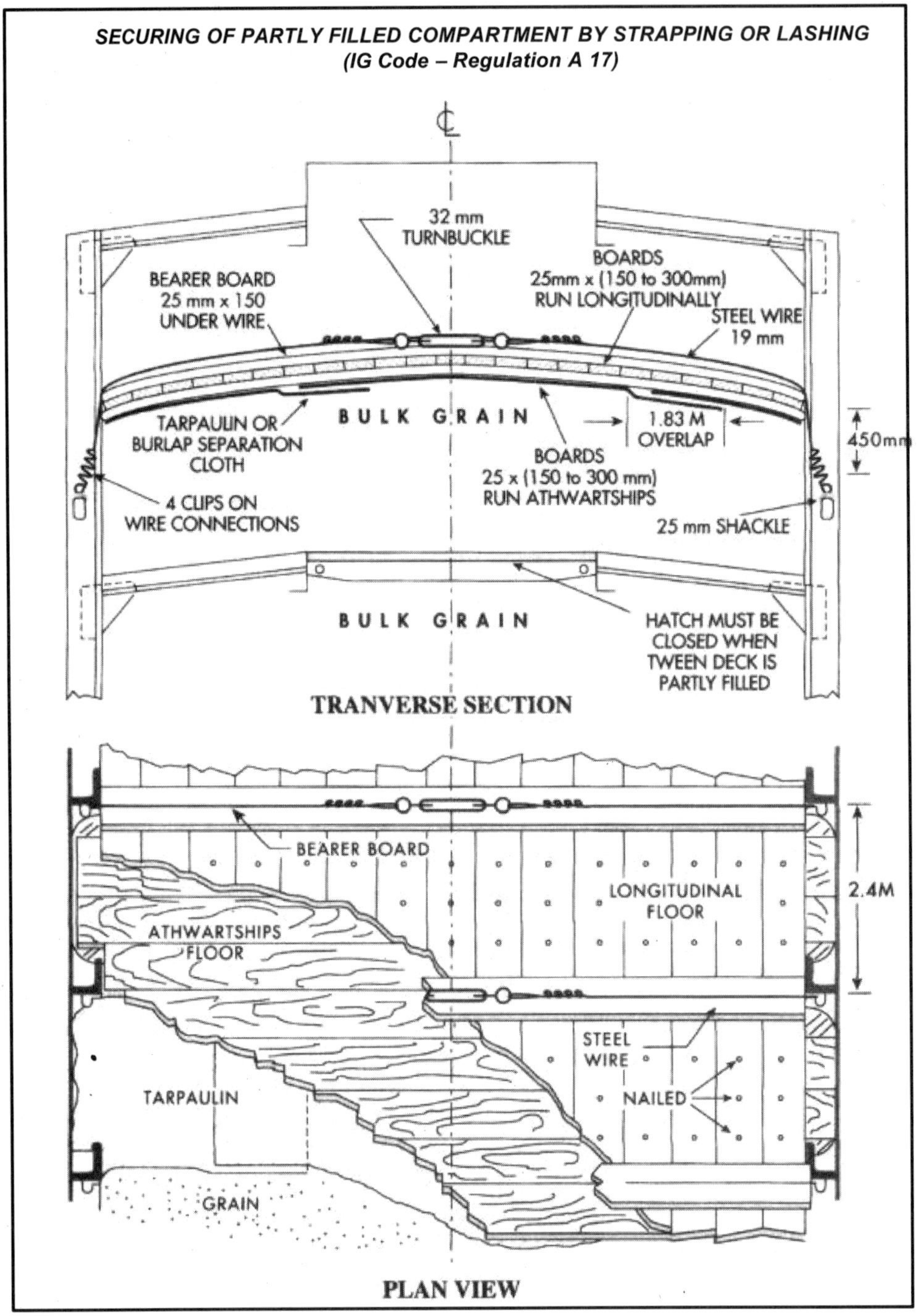

Fig. 18.22

18.8.6 Securing with wire mesh

This method of preventing a slack grain surface from shifting and thereby reducing the grain heeling moment to zero, is essentially the same as 'Strapping or Lashing' except that the principal restraining force of the transverse cables spaced every 2.4 meters for the length of the hold, is transmitted to the overall, fabric-covered surface of the grain by means of a stiff, wire mesh of the type used to reinforce concrete instead of through a deck constructed of dunnage.

The use of this option does not require any special information or endorsement in the *Grain Loading Manual*. The specific requirements pertaining to the details of construction are given in IG Code - Regulation A 18, as given below:

When, in order to eliminate grain heeling moments in partly filled compartments, strapping or lashing is utilized, the securing may, as an alternative to the method described in A 17, be accomplished as follows:

18. 1 The grain shall be trimmed and levelled to the extent that it is very slightly crowned along the fore and aft centreline of the compartment.

18.2 The entire surface of the grain shall be covered with burlap separation cloths, tarpaulins, or the equivalent. The covering material shall have a tensile strength of not less than 1344 N per 5 cm strip.

18.3 Two layers of wire reinforcement mesh shall be laid on top of the burlap or other covering. The bottom layer is to be laid athwartships and the top layer is to be laid longitudinally. The lengths of wire mesh are to be overlapped at least 75 mm. The top layer of mesh is to be positioned over the bottom layer in such a manner that the squares formed by the alternate layers measure approximately 75 mm x 75 mm. The wire reinforcement mesh is the type used in reinforced concrete construction. It is fabricated of 3 mm diameter steel wire having a breaking strength of not less than 52 kN/cm^2 welded in 150 mm x 150 mm squares. Wire mesh having mill scale may be used but mesh having loose, flaking rust may not be used.

18.4 The boundaries of the wire mesh, at the port and starboard side of the compartment, shall be retained by wood planks 150 mm x 50 mm.

18.5 Hold-down lashings, running from side to side across the compartment, shall be spaced not more than 2.4 m apart except that the first and the last lashing shall not be more than 300 mm from the forward or after bulkhead, respectively. Prior to the completion of the loading, each lashing shall be positively attached to the framing at a point approximately 450 mm below the anticipated final grain surface by means of either a 25 mm shackle or beam clamp of equivalent strength. The lashing shall be led from this point over the top of the boundary plank described in A 18.4, which has the function of distributing the downward pressure exerted by the lashing. Two layers of 150 mm x 25 mm planks shall be laid athwartships centred beneath each lashing and extending the full breadth of the compartment.

18.6 The hold-down lashings shall consist of steel wire rope (19 mm diameter or equivalent), double steel strapping (50 mm x 1.3 mm and having a breaking load of at least 49 kN), or chain of equivalent strength, each of which shall be set tight by means of a 32 mm turnbuckle. A winch tightener, used in conjunction with a locking arm, may be substituted for the 32 mm turnbuckle when steel strapping is used, provided suitable wrenches are available for setting up as necessary. When steel strapping is used, not less than three crimp seals shall be used for securing the ends. When wire rope is used, not less than four clips shall be used for forming eyes in the lashings.

18.7 During the voyage the hold-down lashings shall be regularly inspected and set up where necessary.

Figure 18.23 illustrates these arrangements.

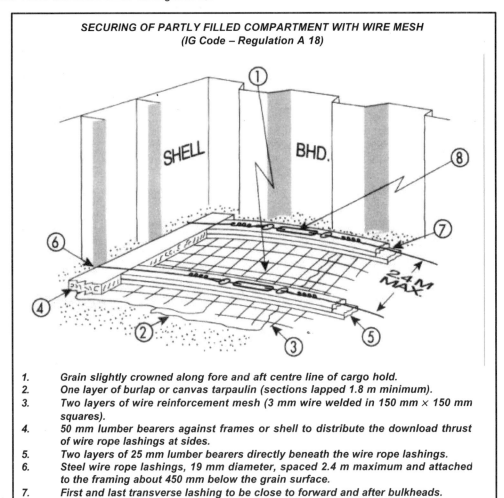

SECURING OF PARTLY FILLED COMPARTMENT WITH WIRE MESH
(IG Code – Regulation A 18)

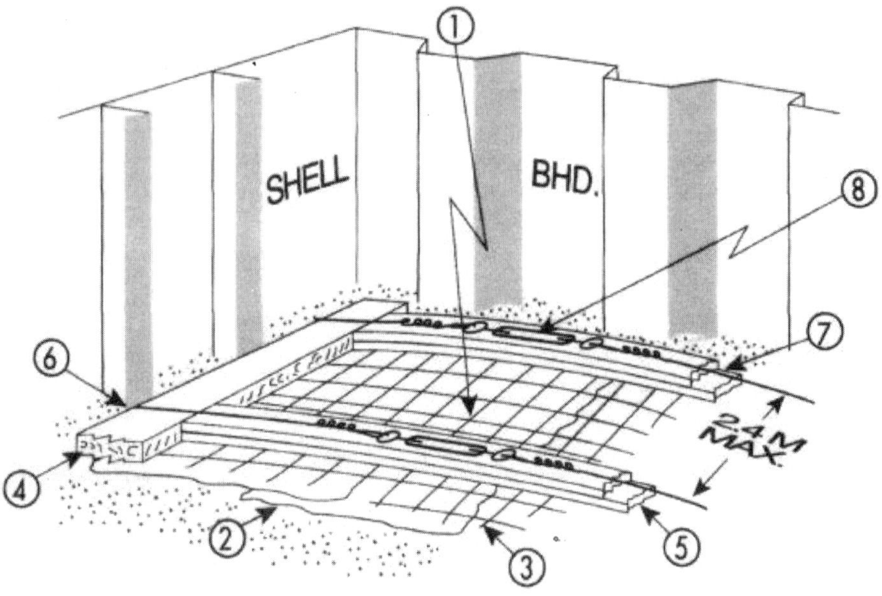

1. *Grain slightly crowned along fore and aft centre line of cargo hold.*
2. *One layer of burlap or canvas tarpaulin (sections lapped 1.8 m minimum).*
3. *Two layers of wire reinforcement mesh (3 mm wire welded in 150 mm × 150 mm squares).*
4. *50 mm lumber bearers against frames or shell to distribute the download thrust of wire rope lashings at sides.*
5. *Two layers of 25 mm lumber bearers directly beneath the wire rope lashings.*
6. *Steel wire rope lashings, 19 mm diameter, spaced 2.4 m maximum and attached to the framing about 450 mm below the grain surface.*
7. *First and last transverse lashing to be close to forward and after bulkheads.*
8. *32 mm turnbuckle to tension lashing.*

Fig. 18.23

18.9 OPTIONAL STABILITY REQUIREMENTS TO BE MET BY SHIPS WITHOUT DOCUMENTS OF AUTHORISATION CARRYING PARTIAL CARGOES OF BULK GRAIN

It is not a requirement that every cargo ship have a *Document of Authorisation*. Instead this Document is optional for ships, usually bulk carriers, for which it greatly facilitates their operations. The Code provides two options under which, subject to certain limitations, a ship without a Document of Authorisation may load grain in bulk.

(a) Under IG Code - Regulation A 3.5:

The master must provide to its home Administration, plans and calculations that demonstrate that the proposed stowage arrangements and loading condition complies with the requirements of the Code. The calculations must include derivation of the volumetric heeling moments that are used as well as the calculations demonstrating compliance with regulation A 7.1. When the home Administration approves the calculations, the master must present the approval at the port of loading. Alternatively, and only if the home Administration so authorises, the authorities at the port of loading may review and approve the calculations prior to permitting loading.

(b) Under IG Code - Regulation 9:

A ship without a Document of Authorisation may carry a partial cargo of bulk grain without performing all the detailed calculations required under option (a) above, by utilising the provisions of IG Code - Regulation A 9 quoted below. Authority to use this option must be obtained from the home Administration.

9.1 A ship not having on board a document of authorisation issued in accordance with A 3 of this Code may be permitted to load bulk grain provided that:

.1 the total weight of the bulk grain shall not exceed one third of the deadweight of the ship;

.2 all filled compartments, trimmed, shall be fitted with centreline divisions extending, for the full length of such compartments, downwards from the underside of the deck or hatch covers to a distance below the deck line of at least one eighth of the maximum breadth of the compartment or 2.4 m, whichever is the greater, except that saucers constructed in accordance with A 14 may be accepted in lieu of a centreline division in and beneath a hatchway except in the case of linseed and other seeds having similar properties;

.3 all hatches to filled compartments, trimmed, shall be closed and covers secured in place;

.4 all free grain surfaces in partly filled cargo space shall be trimmed level and secured in accordance with A 16, A 17 or A 18;

.5 throughout the voyage the metacentric height after correction for the free surface effects of liquids in tanks shall be 0.3 m or that given by the following formula, whichever is the greater:

$$GM_R = \frac{L\ B\ Vd\ (0.25B - 0.645\ \sqrt{Vd\ B})}{SF \times \Delta \times 0.0875}$$

where:
L = total combined length of all full compartments (metres)
B = moulded breadth of the vessel (metres)
SF = stowage factor (cubic metres per tonne)

Vd = calculated average void depth calculated in accordance with regulation B 1 (metres — Note: not millimetres)
Δ = displacement (tonnes); and

.6 *the master demonstrates to the satisfaction of the Administration or the Contracting Government of the port of loading on behalf of the Administration that the ship will comply with the requirements of this section.*

The factor Vd, average void depth, needed for the calculation required by this option necessitates reference to Part B of the Code, which contains the details needed by naval architects to prepare *Grain Loading Manuals*.

Interpretation of this regulation implies a permitted loaded condition whereby no grain stability calculations are required. If, in accordance with IG Code - Regulation A 9.1.4 all the bulk grain cargo is carried in *partly filled* holds *and secured*, and the total weight of grain is limited as per IG Code – Regulation A 9.1.1 then there is no grain stability requirement. However, if the Administration imposes a cargo ship stability requirement, then IG Code – Regulation A 9 would still apply.

18.10 SIMPLIFIED STABILITY DATA FOR SHIPS CARRYING GRAIN BUILT ON OR AFTER 1ST JANUARY 1994 (ON OR AFTER DATE THAT THE *INTERNATIONAL GRAIN CODE* TAKES EFFECT).

18.10.1 Presentation of simplified grain data

The requirement to construct a curve of statical stability and to verify compliance with the Code criteria as detailed in section 18.7 has been greatly simplified by the use of *Tables* or *Curves of Maximum Permissible Grain Heeling Moments (tonnes-metres)*. IG Code - Regulation A 6.3.2 requires such data to be provided for all ship's built on or after the date of entry into force of the Code (1st January 1994).

Instead of calculating the fluid GM, assumed angle of list and residual area, the effective KG for the displacement being considered (including the grain) is calculated along with the actual total grain heeling moment.

The actual grain heeling moment calculated is then compared with the maximum permissible value obtained from the table or curves that are entered with arguments of displacement and effective KG.

An extract from a table of maximum permissible grain heeling moments is illustrated below.

TABLE OF MAXIMUM GRAIN HEELING MOMENTS (t-m)										
DISPLACEMENT	FLUID KG (metres)									
tonnes	6.50	6.60	6.70	6.80	6.90	7.00	7.10	7.20	7.30	7.40
14500	6141	5820	5499	5179	4858	4537	4217	3896	3575	3255
14000	5957	5647	5338	5028	4719	4409	4099	3790	3480	3171
13500	5924	5625	5327	5028	4730	4431	4132	3834	3535	3237
13000	5934	5647	5359	5072	4784	4497	4209	3922	3634	3347
12500	5891	5614	5338	5062	4785	4509	4232	3956	3679	3403
12000	5857	5591	5326	5061	4795	4630	4265	3999	3734	3468
11500	5893	5639	5385	5130	4876	4622	4368	4113	3859	3605
11000	5944	5701	5457	5214	4971	4728	4484	4241	3998	3755
10500	5948	5716	5484	5251	5019	4787	4555	4323	4090	3858
10000	5940	5719	5498	5276	5055	4834	4613	4392	4171	3950
9500	5961	5751	5541	5331	5121	4911	4701	4491	4281	4071
9000	6027	5828	5629	5430	5231	5032	4833	4634	4435	4236
8500	6127	5939	5751	5563	5375	5187	4999	4811	4623	4435
8000	6210	6033	5856	5679	5502	5325	5148	4971	4795	4618
7500	6252	6087	5921	5755	5589	5423	5257	5091	4926	4760
7000	6343	6189	6034	5879	5724	5569	5415	5260	5105	4950
6500	6550	6406	6262	6118	5975	5831	5687	5543	5400	5256
6000	6832	6699	6566	6434	6301	6168	6035	5903	5770	5637
5500	7120	6998	6877	6755	6633	6512	6390	6268	6147	6025
5000	7320	7209	7099	6988	6877	6767	6656	6546	6435	6325

These tables (or curves) are produced by the naval architect. Provided that the actual grain heeling moments are less then the maximum permissible as tabulated, then the ship will meet all the intact stability criteria specified in the Code. The values given in the tables are based on the same assumptions with respect to grain movement as previously discussed.

Simplified data is not required to be carried by ships built before 1st January 1994 however, most ships will be provided with it because of the time saved by its use.

18.10.2 Using simplified grain data

Actual Grain Heeling Moments (AGHM's) (t-m) may be calculated using: $$\textbf{AGHM's (t-m)} = \frac{\Sigma \textbf{VHM's}}{\textbf{SF}}$$

(the term 'displacement' is simply removed from the formula for calculating the value of λ_0).

Follow the example that illustrates their use. Note that the table of *maximum permissible grain heeling moments* used is **not** that for the ship M.V. Almar, such data was not available for the ship on which the data booklet provided was based.

Example 2

A ship displaces 4200 tonnes and has effective KG 7.420 m. Grain of SF 1.42 m³/t is loaded as detailed below:

Hold	***Vol. (m³)***	***Kg (m)***	***Tabulated VHM's (m⁴)***
No. 1 (Full)	***1406***	***6.92***	***340***
No. 2 (Full)	***2220***	***6.84***	***402***
No. 3 (Full)	***2364***	***6.84***	***460***
No. 4 Part full)	***680***	***3.82***	***2420***
No. 5 (Full;	***2624***	***6.80***	***530***

KG assumptions: ***Full compartments, the Kg of the volume of the hold is given; Part full compartments, the Kg of the actual cargo is given.***

An extract from the Table of Maximum Permissible Grain Heeling Moments (t-m) is given:

TABLE OF MAXIMUM GRAIN HEELING MOMENTS (t-m)										
DISPLACEMENT	FLUID KG (metres)									
tonnes	6.50	6.60	6.70	6.80	6.90	7.00	7.10	7.20	7.30	7.40
12500	5891	5614	5338	5062	4785	4509	4232	3956	3679	3403
12000	5857	5591	5326	5061	4795	4630	4265	3999	3734	3468
11500	5893	5639	5385	5130	4876	4622	4368	4113	3859	3605
11000	5944	5701	5457	5214	4971	4728	4484	4241	3998	3755
10500	5948	5716	5484	5251	5019	4787	4555	4323	4090	3858
10000	5940	5719	5498	5276	5055	4834	4613	4392	4171	3950
9500	5961	5751	5541	5331	5121	4911	4701	4491	4281	4071
9000	6027	5828	5629	5430	5231	5032	4833	4634	4435	4236

For the loaded condition determine:

(a) the final displacement and KG of the ship;
(b) the actual grain heeling moments (t-m)
(c) whether the ship's loaded condition complies with the stability requirements of the International Grain Code;
(d) the approximate angle of list should the grain shift as assumed by the Code.

Solution

A tabular approach is adopted. Calculate the actual weight of grain in each hold and take moments about the keel to determine the final displacement and KG.

Compartment	Volume (m3)	Weight (t)	VCG (m)	Moments (t-m)	Tabulated VHM's	Corr'n factor	Actual VHM's
1	1406	990	6.920	6851	340	1.00	340
2	2220	1563	6.840	10691	402	1.00	402
3	2364	1665	6.840	11389	460	1.00	460
4	680	479	3.820	1830	2420	1.12	2710
5	2624	1848	6.800	12566	530	1.00	530
Initial displ.		4200	7.420	31164			
TOTALS		10745	6.933	74491			4442

(a) *Final displacement = **10745 tonnes**; final KG = **6.933 m (Ans).***

(b) *Enter the VHM's as given and correct as necessary; in this case those given for No. 4 Hold. Sum the VHM's to give a total value (4442 m^4).*

Calculate the actual grain heeling moments (AGHM's) (t-m).

$$AGHM\text{'s (t-m)} = \frac{\Sigma VHM\text{'s}}{SF}$$

$$AGHM\text{'s (t-m)} = \frac{4442}{1.42} = \mathbf{3128\ t\text{-}m\ (Ans)}$$

(c) *Enter table with Displacement, KG and actual grain heeling moment values.*

TABLE OF MAXIMUM GRAIN HEELING MOMENTS (t-m)										
DISPLACEMENT	FLUID KG (metres)									
tonnes	6.50	6.60	6.70	6.80	6.90	7.00	7.10	7.20	7.30	7.40
12500	5891	5614	5338	5062	4785	4509	4232	3956	3679	3403
12000	5857	5591	5326	5061	4795	4630	4265	3999	3734	3468
11500	5893	5639	5385	5130	4876	4622	4368	4113	3859	3605
11000	5944	5701	5457	5214	4971	4728	4484	4241	3998	3755
10500	5948	5716	5484	5251	5019	4787	4555	4323	4090	3858
10000	5940	5719	5498	5276	5055	4834	4613	4392	4171	3950
9500	5961	5751	5541	5331	5121	4911	4701	4491	4281	4071
9000	6027	5828	5629	5430	5231	5032	4833	4634	4435	4236

Given that: Displacement = 10745 tonnes;
KG = 6.933 m; and
*AGHM's = 3128 t-m, the **ship complies with the requirements.***

(d) *To calculate the approximate angle of list should assumed grain shift takes place interpolation is required. The formula is:*

$$\textbf{Approximate list} = \frac{\textbf{Actual Grain Heeling Moments (t-m)}}{\textbf{Max. Permissible Grain Heeling Moments (t-m)}} \times 12^{\circ}$$

To determine the AGHM's value consider the table:

TABLE OF MAXIMUM GRAIN HEELING MOMENTS (t-m)										
DISPLACEMENT	FLUID KG (metres)									
tonnes	6.50	6.60	6.70	6.80	6.90	7.00	7.10	7.20	7.30	7.40
12500	5891	5614	5338	5062	4785	4509	4232	3956	3679	3403
12000	5857	5591	5326	5061	4795	4630	4265	3999	3734	3468
11500	5893	5639	5385	5130	4876	4622	4368	4113	3859	3605
11000	5944	5701	5457	5214	4971	4728	4484	4241	3998	3755
10500	5948	5716	5484	5251	5019	4787	4555	4323	4090	3858
10000	5940	5719	5498	5276	5055	4834	4613	4392	4171	3950
9500	5961	5751	5541	5331	5121	4911	4701	4491	4281	4071
9000	6027	5828	5629	5430	5231	5032	4833	4634	4435	4236

(1) *Interpolate for actual displacement of 10745 t to obtain MPGHM values for KG 6.90 m and KG 7.00 m.*

Displ.	***6.90***	***7.00***
11000	*4971*	*4728*
10745	***4995***	***4758***
10500	*5019*	*4787*

(2) *Interpolate for the actual KG value of 6.933 m to obtain MPGHM value.*

Displ.	***6.90***	*6.933*	***7.00***
10745	***4995***	***4924***	***4758***

$\therefore$ *Approximate list =* $\dfrac{3128}{4924} \times 12^{o} =$ ***7.6º (Ans.)***

In practice it is sufficient to verify that the actual grain heeling moments are within acceptable limits, however the approximate angle of list has been asked in examinations on past occasions.

Note

It must be emphasised that the ship must comply with the stability requirements of the Code at *all* stages of the voyage and not just on departure. Compliance should be tested for the ship's worst anticipated condition and rechecked as circumstances dictate during the voyage.

SECTION 19 – INCLINING EXPERIMENT

INTRODUCTION

Chapter 2 of the *Code on Intact Stability for all Types of Ships Covered by IMO Instruments (IMO)*, hereafter being referred to as the *Code*, details the information that must be provided to the master of all ships in order that stability calculations may be accurately conducted to ensure the ship's safe operation. A key element of this information is the *Inclining Test Report* that details the calculation procedure conducted to determine the ship's light KG and displacement.

Learning Objectives

On completion of this section, the learner will achieve the following:

1. Know the stability information that must be provided for the master.
2. Understand the correct procedures for conducting an inclining experiment.

19.1 STABILITY INFORMATION TO BE PROVIDED TO THE MASTER

The regulations in Chapter 2 of the Code details the stability information requirements as follows:

2.1.1 *Stability data and associated plans should be drawn up in the working language of the ship and any other language the Administration may require. Reference is also made to the International Safety Management (ISM) Code, adopted by the Organization by resolution A.741(18). All translations of the stability booklet should be approved.*

2.1.2 *Each ship should be provided with a stability booklet, approved by the Administration, which contains sufficient information to enable the master to operate the ship in compliance with the applicable requirements contained in the Code. The Administration may have additional requirements. On a mobile offshore drilling unit, the stability booklet may be referred to as an operating manual. The stability booklet may include information on longitudinal strength. This Code addresses only the stability-related contents of the booklet.*

2.1.3 *The format of the stability booklet and the information included will vary dependent on the ship type and operation. In developing the stability booklet, consideration should be given to including the following information:*

.1 *a general description of the ship;*
.2 *instructions on the use of the booklet;*
.3 *general arrangement plans showing watertight compartments, closures, vents, downflooding angles, permanent ballast, allowable deck loadings and freeboard diagrams;*
.4 *hydrostatic curves or tables and cross-curves of stability calculated on a free-trimming basis, for the ranges of displacement and trim anticipated in normal operating conditions;*
.5 *capacity plan or tables showing capacities and centres of gravity for each cargo stowage space;*
.6 *tank sounding tables showing capacities, centres of gravity, and free surface data for each tank;*
.7 *information on loading restrictions, such as maximum KG or minimum GM curve or table that can be used to determine compliance with the applicable stability criteria;*
.8 *standard operating conditions and examples for developing other acceptable loading conditions using the information contained in the stability booklet;*
.9 *a brief description of the stability calculations done, including assumptions;*
.10 *general precautions for preventing unintentional flooding;*
.11 *information concerning the use of any special cross-flooding fittings with descriptions of damage conditions which may require cross-flooding;*
.12 *any other necessary guidance for the safe operation of the ship under normal and emergency conditions;*
.13 *a table of contents and index for each booklet;*
.14 *inclining test report for the ship, or:*
  .14.1 *where the stability data are based on a sister ship, the inclining test report of that sister ship along with the light-ship measurement report for the ship in question; or*
  .14.2 *where light-ship particulars are determined by other methods than from inclining of the ship or its sister, a summary of the method used to determine those particulars;*
.15 *recommendation for determination of ship's stability by means of an in-service inclining test.*

Regulation 2.2 allows for the provision of an approved stability-calculating program to supplement the above information requirements but it is not compulsory that one be provided.
Schedule 6 of MSN 1752 (M) (which accompanies the *M.S. (Load Line) Regulations 1998*), applicable to UK registered ships, should be consulted by students studying for the MCA examinations.

19.2 THE INCLINING EXPERIMENT

19.2.1 Purpose

Chapter 7 Regulation 7.1.1 of the Code requires that every passenger ship regardless of size and every cargo ship of 24 m or over be inclined on completion in order to determine the value of the *KG in the light condition*. This must be determined accurately because the light KG and displacement values are the basis from which the KG is determined for every other condition. An error in the KG calculated for any condition of loading will result in all stability parameters dependant on this value being incorrect also i.e. GM, GZ values and dynamical stability parameters will be in error.

During the experiment the longitudinal position of the centre of gravity (LCG) for the light condition will also be determined.

19.2.2 Calculation of KG in the inclined condition

It is unlikely that the ship will be in the true light displacement condition when inclined. Often the experiment will be conducted when the ship is near completion, usually towards the end of the fitting out stage. Once the KG and displacement has been determined for the inclined condition, any weights that remain still to come on board, or be removed, must then be accounted for and also the effects of any free liquid surfaces must be considered for slack tanks present at the time of the experiment.

19.2.2.1 Derivation of the inclining experiment formula

Prior to starting the experiment the ship must be exactly upright to ensure that the centre of gravity, G, is on the centre line. Figure 19.1 shows that f a known weight is then shifted transversely across the deck through a certain distance in metres, G will move off the centre line to G_H, causing the ship to list.

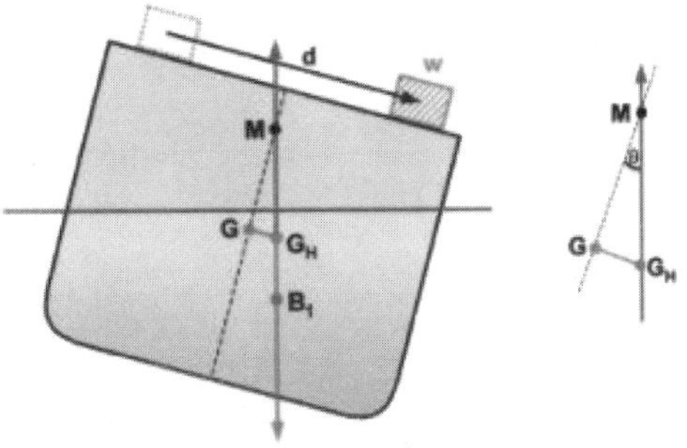

Fig. 19.1

The distance GG_H is calculated by the formula:

$$GG_H = \frac{w \times d}{W} \qquad (1)$$

If a plumb line is suspended at O such that it crosses a batten at X, then as the ship lists a deflection XY will be observed and can be measured (figure 19.2).

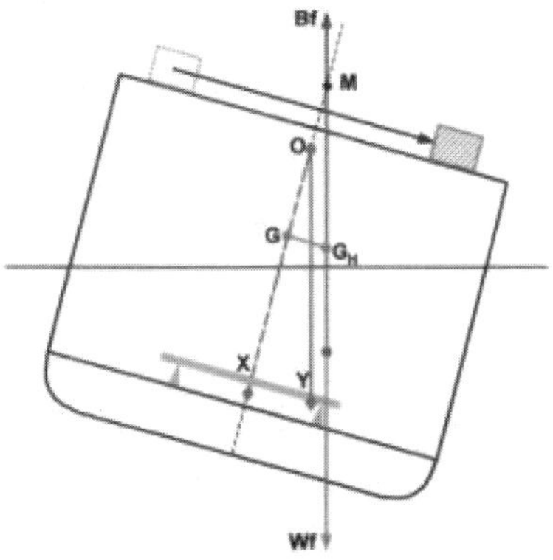

Fig. 19.2

Triangles MGG_H and OXY are similar.

In triangle MGG_H: $\tan\theta = \frac{OPP}{ADJ} = \frac{GG_H}{GM}$

In triangle OXY: $\tan\theta = \frac{OPP}{ADJ} = \frac{XY}{OX}$

Therefore: $\frac{GG_H}{GM} = \frac{XY}{OX}$

so: $\frac{GG_H}{GM} = \frac{\text{Deflection of the pendulum}}{\text{Pendulum length}}$

Rearranging this gives:

$$GM = \frac{GG_H \times \text{Pendulum length}}{\text{Deflection of the pendulum}} \qquad (2)$$

Combining formulae (1) and (2) gives:

$$\mathbf{GM = \frac{w \times d \times Pendulum\ length}{W \times Deflection}}$$

The GM in the inclined condition will be a *fluid GM* as it will include the effects of any free liquid surfaces in slack tanks.

Having calculated the effective GM as inclined: **KG = KM - GM**

where KM is obtained from the ship's hydrostatic data for the true mean draught as calculated from the observed draughts (Calculation of the *true mean draught* is discussed in Section 20).

Example 1

A ship initially upright has a displacement of 6420 tonnes and KM of 7.42 m as ascertained from the ship's hydrostatic particulars. An inclining weight of 10 tonnes is moved transversely across the deck through a distance of 12.4 m. Deflection in a pendulum 8.0 metres in length is observed to be 14.2 cm. Calculate the effective KG of the ship in the inclined condition.

Solution

Calculate GM as inclined: $GM = \frac{w \times d \times Pendulum\ length}{W \times Deflection}$ $GM = \frac{10 \times 12.4 \times 8.0}{6420 \times 0.142} = 1.088\ m$

Calculate KG as inclined:

KG = KM – GM; *KG = 7.420 – 1.088 =* ***6.332 metres (Ans)***

In practice, more than one pendulum will be used whereby mean deflection values will be used for the calculation of the GM.

19.2.2.2 Calculation of the ship's actual light KG and displacement

Chapter 7 Regulation 7.2.4 of the Code defines the lightship condition as being:

the ship complete in all respects, but without consumables, stores, cargo, crew and effects, and without any liquids on board except that machinery and piping fluids, such as lubricants and hydraulics are at operating levels.

Careful note should be made of this definition as items such as 'water in the boiler at operating level' and its associated free surface moments are often mistakenly removed in the KG calculation when reducing the inclined condition to the true light displacement values in examination questions.

Example 2

A Ro-Ro vessel is to be inclined at a displacement of 11100 t, KM 11.70 m. During the experiment liquid in the tanks are as follows:

No. 3 DB (slack) contains 110 t SW ballast (RD 1.025) (free surface moment 800 t-m, basis FW)
N0. 4 DB (slack) contains 38 t of fuel oil (RD 0.88) (free surface moment 670 t-m, basis FW)

The movement of 14 t through a transverse distance of 22.2 m causes a 15.2 cm deflection of a 12 m long pendulum.

(a) *Calculate the effective KG as inclined.*
(b) *The following changes are required to bring the ship to the light condition:*

Discharge: *28 t inclining weights, Kg 16.0 m*
41 t equipment, Kg 9.0 m
110 t SW ballast, Kg 1.1 m
38 t fuel oil, Kg 0.9 m
Load: *19 t machinery, Kg 5.5 m*

Calculate the lightship displacement and lightship KG.

Solution

(a) Calculate GM as inclined: $GM = \frac{w \times d \times \text{Pendulum length}}{W \times \text{Deflection}}$ $GM = \frac{14 \times 22.2 \times 12.0}{11100 \times 0.152} = 2.211m$

Calculate KG as inclined:

KG = KM – GM; KG = 11.700 –2.211 = **9.489 m (Ans)**

(b) *The free surface moments as given are basis FW. These must first be corrected to give values appropriate to the actual density of the liquid in the slack tanks.*

SW ballast (RD 1.025) Actual FSM's $= 800 \times \frac{1.025}{1.000} = 820$ t-m

Fuel oil (RD 0.88) Actual FSM's $= 670 \times \frac{0.88}{1.000} = 590$ t-m

Take moments about the keel to calculate the lightship KG and displacement.

	Weight (t)	KG (m)	Moments (t-m)
Ship as inclined	11100	9.489	105328
Inclining weights (-)	-28	16.000	-448
Equipment (-)	-41	9.000	-369
SW ballast (-)	-110	1.100	-121
SW ballast FSM's (-)			-820
Fuel oil (-)	-38	0.900	-34
Fuel oil FSM's (-)			-590
Machinery (+)	19	5.500	105
FINAL	**10902**	**9.452**	**103051**

*Lightship displacement = **10902 t (Ans)***
*Lightship KG = **9.452 m (Ans)***

Note The free surface moments must also be removed, since in the lightship condition, if all the tanks are empty, no free surface moments can exist!

19.2.3 Preparations for the inclining test

Before the inclining test can be done the ship's personnel may be required to assist in the following preparations:

(1) The ship should be moored in quiet sheltered waters free from the effects of passing vessels. There must be adequate depth of water to ensure that the ship will not contact the bottom during the inclination.

(2) Moorings should be slack and any shore side gangways landed to allow unrestricted heeling.

(3) All temporary material and equipment such as toolboxes, staging, welding equipment etc. should be reduced to an absolute minimum. Excess crew and personnel not directly involved in the test should be sent ashore.

(4) All fittings and equipment such as accommodation ladders, lifeboats and derricks/cranes should be stowed in their normal seagoing positions.

(5) All tanks should be verified as being completely empty or full. The number of slack tanks should be kept to an absolute minimum. Ideally tanks with rectangular free surfaces should only be slack so that the free surface effect can be accurately determined. Slack tanks must have the contents accurately determined with respect to liquid mass and Kg.

(6) Decks should be free of water. Any water trapped on deck will move during the test and reduce the accuracy of the result. Snow and ice must also be removed.

(7) The following information must be provided to the person in charge of the inclining test:

- (a) lines plan;
- (b) hydrostatic curves or hydrostatic data;
- (c) general arrangement plan;
- (d) capacity plan showing the VCG and LCG of all cargo spaces, tanks etc. When the ship is to be inclined using ballast water transfer the transverse and vertical centres of gravity for the applicable tanks, for *each* angle of inclination, must be available;
- (e) tank sounding tables;
- (f) draught mark locations; and
- (g) docking drawing with keel profile and draught mark corrections (if available).

(8) Efficient two-way communication must be established between a person in charge of the operation at the central control station, the weight handlers and each pendulum station.

19.2.4 Precautions taken by the surveyor to ensure accuracy of the calculation

Annex 1 of the Code provides detailed guidance for the conduct of an inclining test and this should be referred to. The requirements to ensure an accurate result are summarised as follows:

1) The ship should be as complete as possible at the time of the test. The mass and Kg of items remaining to be fitted must be accurately known, if this is not the case for any item, the test should be conducted after the item in question has been fitted.

2) The ship must be as upright as possible and have sufficient draught to avoid any significant changes in water plane area as the ship is listed. A deviation from design trim of up to 1% of LBP is normally acceptable when using hydrostatic data calculated for a design trim. Otherwise, the hydrostatic data should be calculated for the actual trim of the ship during the experiment.

3) The mass of the inclining weight(s) used should be sufficient to provide a minimum list of 1° and a maximum list of 4° to each side. This is to ensure that the formula: $\tan \theta_{LIST} = \frac{GG_H}{GM}$ remains valid, being applicable to small angles of inclination only. The inclining weights themselves must be marked with an identification number and their mass. Re-certification of the test weights should be carried out prior to the inclining.
As an alternative to the use of inclining weights, water ballast transfer may be carried out, if acceptable to the Administration. This method will be more appropriate on very large ships.

4) The use of three pendulums (but no less than two) is recommended to allow bad readings at any one station to be identified. The pendulum weight should be suspended in a trough of hydraulic oil to dampen movement. The pendulums should be long enough to give a measured deflection to each side of upright of at least 15 cm. This will require a pendulum length of at least 3 metres. Usually, the longer the pendulum the greater the accuracy of the test; however, if excessively long pendulums are used on a tender ship the pendulums may not settle down and the accuracy of the readings will be questionable. On large ships with a high GM, pendulum lengths in excess of the above- recommended length may be required to obtain the minimum deflection. In such cases the trough should be filled with a high-viscosity oil.
The pendulum wire should be piano-wire and the top connection should allow unrestricted rotation at the pivot point (a washer with the pendulum wire attached suspended from a nail would suffice).

5) Battens should be smooth, light coloured wood, 1-2 cm thick, and should be securely fixed in position to prevent inadvertent movement by the person making the measurements. The batten should be aligned close to the pendulum wire but not in contact with it. A suitable arrangement is shown in figure 19.3.

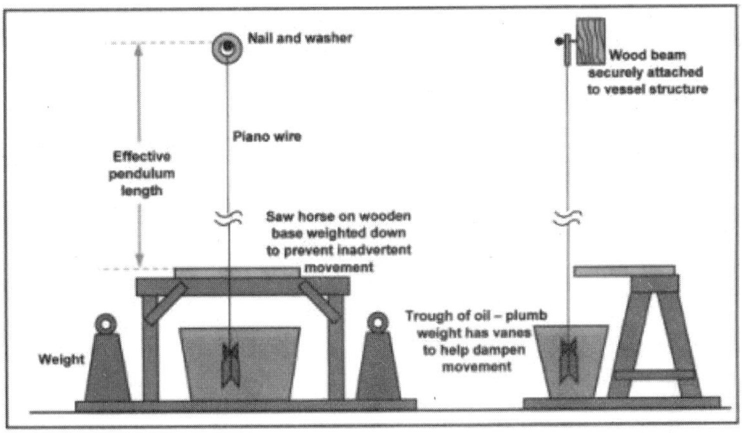

Fig. 19.3

6) It is recommended that at least five freeboard readings approximately equally spaced on each side of the ship be taken or that all draught marks (forward, aft and amidships) be read on each side of the ship. Draught mark readings should be taken to assist in determining the waterline defined by freeboard readings, or to verify the vertical location of draught marks on ships where their location has not been confirmed. A small boat should be available for this purpose. Such readings allow determination of the displacement of the ship immediately prior to the test. Dock water density readings will also be taken from sufficient depth (not the surface as this may be affected by rain run-off) to allow the displacement obtained from the hydrostatic data to be corrected for the actual water density observed.

7) The mean draught (average of port and starboard readings taken in (6) above) should be calculated for each of the locations where the freeboard and draught readings where taken and plotted on the ship's line drawings or outboard profile to ensure that all readings are consistent and together define the correct waterline. The plot should give a straight line or a waterline that is hogged or sagged whereby a hog/sag correction must be determined and applied. If inconsistent readings are obtained, the freeboards/draughts should be retaken.

8) The standard test employs eight distinct weight movements whereby a straight-line plot must be achieved as illustrated in figure 19.4. If a straight-line plot is not achieved, those weight movements that did not give an acceptable plot must be repeated.

As well as calculating the lightship displacement and KG, draught and trim readings at the time of the experiment will be used to determine the ship's longitudinal centre of gravity for the inclining condition. This will then be corrected by calculation to obtain the true lightship LCG.

On completion of the test a report will be written and included as part of the ship's stability data book.

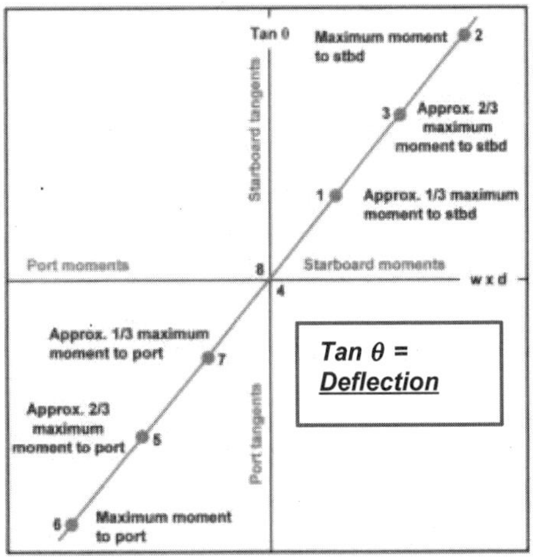

Fig. 19.4

19.2.5 The occasions when an inclining experiment and lightweight survey must be conducted.

Chapter 7 – Regulations 7.1.1 to 7.1.6 details the occasions on which a ship must be inclined and is as follows:

7.1.1 Every passenger ship regardless of size and every cargo ship having a length, as defined in the International Convention on Load Lines, 1966, of 24 m and upwards should be inclined upon its completion and the elements of its stability determined.

7.1.2 Where any alterations are made to a ship so as to materially affect the stability, the ship should be re-inclined.

7.1.3 At periodic intervals not exceeding five years, a light-weight survey should be carried out on all passenger ships to verify any changes in lightship displacement and longitudinal centre of gravity. The ship should be re-inclined whenever, in comparison with the approved stability information, a deviation from the light-ship displacement exceeding 2% or a deviation of the longitudinal centre of gravity exceeding 1% of L is found, or anticipated.

7.1.4 The Administration may allow the inclining test of an individual ship as required by paragraph 7.1.1 to be dispensed with provided basic stability data are available from the inclining test of a sister ship and it is shown to the satisfaction of the Administration that reliable stability information for the exempted ship can be obtained from such basic data.

7.1.5 The Administration may allow the inclining test of an individual ship or class of ships especially designed for the carriage of liquids or ore in bulk to be dispensed with when reference to existing data for similar ships clearly indicates that, due to the ship's proportions and arrangements, more than sufficient metacentric height will be available in all probable loading conditions.

7.1.6 The inclining test prescribed is adaptable for ships with a length below 24 m if special precautions are taken to ensure the accuracy of the test procedure.

Annex 3 of the Code details a means of approximately determining the initial stability (GM) of small ships up to 70 m in length by consideration of the rolling period.

SECTION 20 – TRIM USING HYDROSTATIC DATA

INTRODUCTION

This section introduces the methods used for calculating trim in real situations. Use is made of the hydrostatic particulars found in the stability data book for *M.V. Almar* provided.

Students are often unsure as to the level of accuracy required when using hydrostatic data. Consider the extract from the hydrostatic particulars for *M.V. Almar*.

DRAUGHT m	DISPL. t SW RD 1.025	TPC t SW RD 1.025	MCTC t-m SW RD 1.025	LCB m FOAP	LCF m FOAP	KB m	KML m Above Base	KMT m Above Base
3.00	8770	31.35	302	87.34	87.31	1.55	586	14.94
3.10	9090	31.39	303	87.34	87.26	1.60	566	14.58
3.20	9400	31.43	304	87.33	87.21	1.66	548	14.23
3.30	9720	31.48	305	87.33	87.15	1.71	531	13.92
3.40	10030	31.52	306	87.32	87.11	1.76	515	13.62
3.50	10350	31.55	306	87.32	87.06	1.81	500	13.32

For consistency the accuracy used when interpolating for hydrostatic values in this section shall be as follows:

* *Draughts will be calculated to three decimal places e.g. 7.236 m.*

* *All other hydrostatic data values will be calculated to the same number of decimal places as adopted in the table.*

* *When calculating moments, values will be rounded to the nearest whole number.*

Learning Objectives

On completion of this section the learner will achieve the following:

1. Understand the terms *Arithmetic Mean Draught (AMD)* and *True Mean Draught (TMD)* and recognise the importance of using the true mean draught for obtaining the ship's actual displacement when trimmed.
2. Calculate the true mean draught for a trimmed ship.
3. Calculate the final draughts for a ship when loading and/or discharging weights by taking moments about the mean LCF using hydrostatic data.
4. Calculate the final draughts for a ship when loading and/or discharging weights by consideration of the relative positions of the longitudinal centre of buoyancy (LCB) and the longitudinal centre of gravity (LCG) using hydrostatic data.
5. Conduct a variety of calculations that might be encountered in examination situations.
6. Calculate the change of draught and trim due to change in water density.

20.1 TRUE MEAN DRAUGHT – DISPLACEMENT WHEN TRIMMED

20.1.1 True mean draught when LCF is amidships

A ship's hydrostatic particulars will only be accurate for the condition of trim assumed. This will be the case for those provided for *M.V. Almar* where the cautionary note given states:
'These hydrostatics have been developed with the vessel floating on an even keel'.

If the LCF is *amidships* the displacement given when entering the hydrostatic particulars with the *Arithmetic Mean Draught (AMD)* will always be correct, where:

$$\textbf{AMD} = \frac{\textbf{Draught at FP + Draught at AP}}{\textbf{2}}$$

Consider the ship shown floating on an even keel with the longitudinal centre of flotation (F) amidships where a weight is moved along the deck.

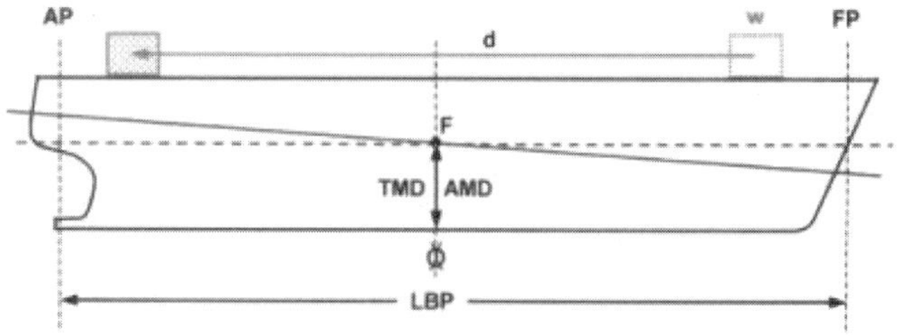

Fig. 20.1

The waterline will rotate about F where the draught amidships, being the arithmetic mean draught (AMD), will be the same as the draught at F, known as the *True Mean Draught (TMD)*.

When the LCF is amidships: **TMD = AMD**

20.1.2 True mean draught when LCF is not amidships

Consideration of the hydrostatic particulars shows that the position of the LCF changes with draught. The position of the LCF is seldom amidships.

Figure 20.2 shows a ship where the LCF is *aft of amidships*.

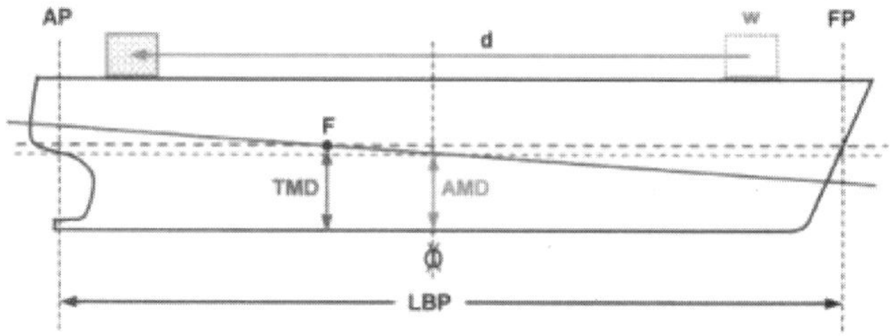

Fig. 20.2

If the weight is moved aft the waterline will rotate about F as shown. In this case the draught amidships, being the AMD, *reduces*. Entering the hydrostatic particulars with this reduced AMD will result in a *lesser displacement value* that will be in *error*.

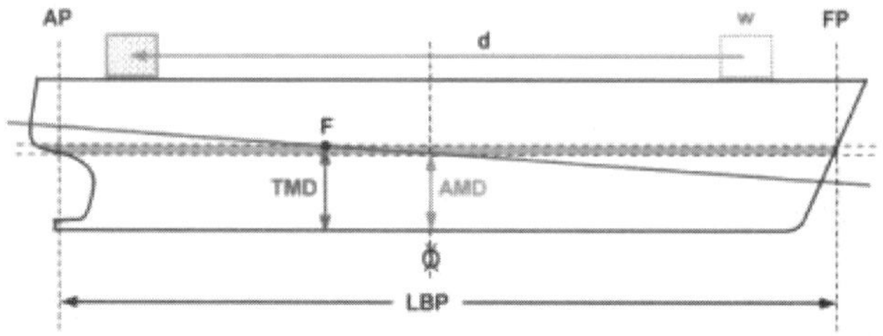

Fig. 20.3

The error in the displacement will be equivalent to the weight of the slice or *layer* of water shaded.

For this reason the displacement value should always be obtained using the True Mean Draught, being the draught at the position of the longitudinal centre of flotation.

The difference between the displacement obtained for the Arithmetic Mean Draught and that obtained for the True Mean Draught is termed the *layer correction* and will be additive or subtractive from the Arithmetic Mean Draught displacement depending on whether the LCF is aft or forward of amidships and whether the ship is trimmed by the head or by the stern.

20.1.3 Calculating the True Mean Draught

The True Mean Draught (TMD) is easily calculated. Figure 20.4 shows a ship trimmed by the stern with LCF *aft* of amidships.

Here a correction must be *added* to the AMD to obtain the TMD at the LCF.

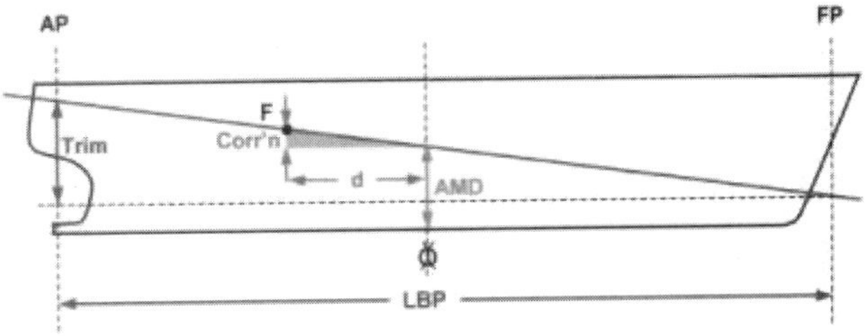

Fig. 20.4

Consider the similar triangles where:

$$\frac{\text{Correction to AMD}}{\text{Distance LCF from amidships}} = \frac{\text{Trim}}{\text{LBP}}$$

It follows that:

$$\textbf{Correction to AMD} = \frac{\textbf{Trim} \times \textbf{Distance LCF from amidships}}{\textbf{LBP}}$$

Example 1

A ship LBP 148 m floats at draughts F 4.60 m A 5.80 m and has LCF 69.0 m foap. Calculate the True Mean Draught.

Solution

Draw a simple sketch!

TMD = AMD + Correction

$$AMD = \frac{4.60 + 5.80}{2} = 5.20\ m$$

Correction to AMD

$$\frac{Trim \times d}{LBP} = \frac{1.20 \times (74.0 - 69.0)}{148} = 0.041 m$$

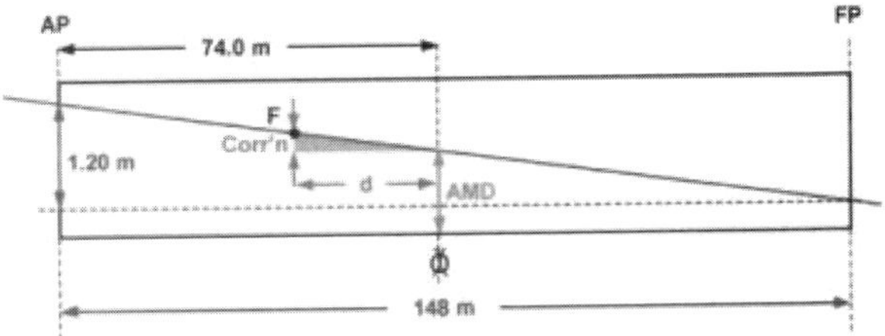

Fig. 20.5

Therefore; True Mean Draught = 5.200 + 0.041 = ***5.241 m (Ans)***

In all cases the correction to the AMD will be *added* or *subtracted* depending on two factors:

(1) *whether the ship is trimmed by the head or by the stern;*
(2) *whether LCF is forward or aft of amidships.*

Consider the *four* possibilities shown in figure 20.6.

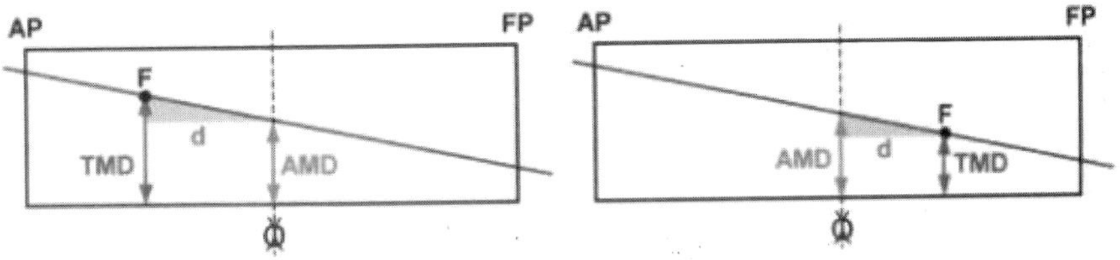

(1) Ship trimmed by stern, LCF aft of amidships:

TMD = AMD + Correction

(2) Ship trimmed by stern, LCF forward of amidships:

TMD = AMD - Correction

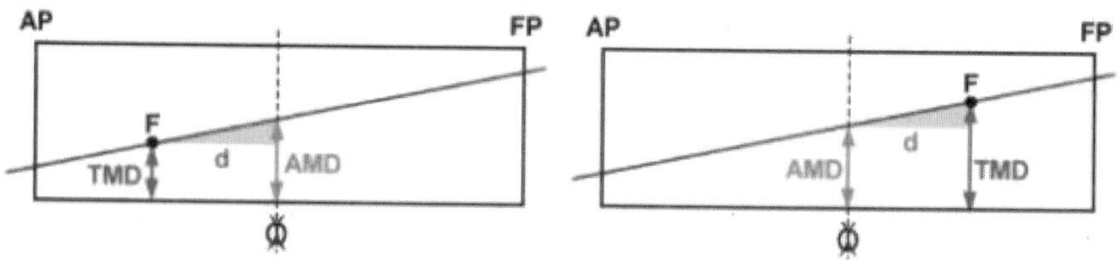

(3) Ship trimmed by head, LCF aft of amidships:

TMD = AMD - Correction

(4) Ship trimmed by head, LCF forward of amidships:

TMD = AMD + Correction

Fig. 20 .6

Example 2

A ship LBP 120 m floats at draughts F 4.62 m A 5.40 m. Calculate the true mean draught if the LCF is 66 m foap.

Solution

TMD = AMD – Correction

$$AMD = \frac{4.62 + 5.40}{2} = 5.01\ m$$

$$\text{Correction to AMD} = \frac{Trim \times d}{LBP}$$

$$\frac{0.78 \times (66.0 - 60.0)}{120} = 0.039\ m$$

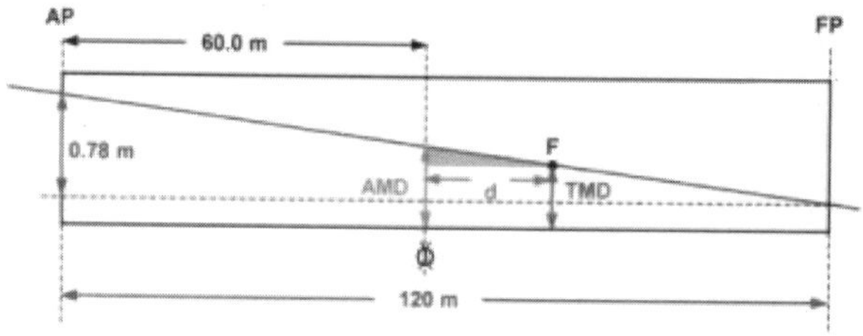

Fig. 20.7

Therefore; True Mean Draught = 5.010 - 0.039 = ***4.971 m (Ans)***

Example 3

A ship LBP 166 m floats at draughts F 7.32 m A 6.84 m. Calculate the true mean draught if the LCF is 80 m foap.

Solution

TMD = AMD – Correction

$$AMD = \frac{7.32 + 6.84}{2} = 7.08\ m$$

$$\text{Correction to AMD} = \frac{Trim \times d}{LBP}$$

$$\frac{0.48 \times (83.0 - 80.0)}{166} = 0.009\ m$$

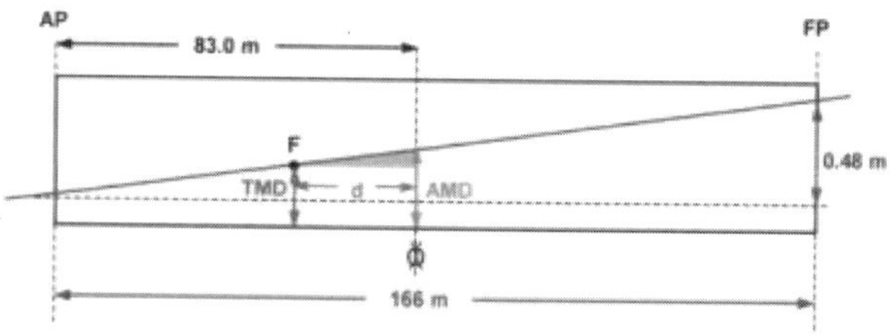

Fig. 20.8

Therefore; True Mean Draught = 7.080 - 0.009 = ***7.071 m (Ans)***

Provided that a simple sketch is made this method shown for calculating the true mean draught is very useful because the formula can be easily derived. However, the following formula may be used as an alternative provided that it is applied exactly in the form in which it is stated below:

$$\mathbf{TMD = dA - \left(\frac{(dA - dF)}{LBP} \times LCF\ foap \right)}$$

where: ***dA*** is the draught aft;

dF is the draught forward;

LCF foap is the position of the LCF expressed as being so many metres forward of the aft perpendicular;

LBP is the length between perpendiculars.

It is important that the expression (dA – dF) is left as it is and not reversed. If the trim is by the head then (dA – dF) will give a *negative* value.

Consider the previous examples (2 & 3) calculated using this formula.

Example 4

A ship LBP 120 m floats at draughts F 4.62 m A 5.40 m. Calculate the true mean draught if the LCF is 66 m foap.

Solution

$$TMD = dA - \left(\frac{(dA - dF)}{LBP} \times LCF\ foap \right)$$

$$TMD = 5.40 - \left(\frac{(5.40 - 4.62)}{120} \times 66 \right)$$

$$TMD = 5.40 - \left(\frac{0.78}{120} \times 66 \right)$$

TMD = 4.971 m (Ans)

Example 5

A ship LBP 166 m floats at draughts F 7.32 m A 6.84 m. Calculate the true mean draught if the LCF is 80 m foap.

Solution

$$TMD = dA - \left(\frac{(dA - dF)}{LBP} \times LCF\ foap \right)$$

$$TMD = 6.84 - \left(\frac{(6.84 - 7.32)}{166} \times 80 \right)$$

$$TMD = 6.84 - \left(\frac{-0.48}{166} \times 80 \right)$$

$TMD = 6.84 - (-0.231)$

$TMD = 6.84 + 0.231$

TMD = 7.071 m (Ans)

The aforementioned formula will be used for calculating the true mean draught in all the following examples that appear in this section. If you prefer the previous method then use that, but remember to draw a sketch to ensure that the correction is applied the correct way!

20.2 TRIM CALCULATIONS USING HYDROSTATIC DATA – TAKING MOMENTS ABOUT THE MEAN LCF

The *hydrostatic particulars* in the trim and stability booklet for *M.V. Almar* will be used throughout the remainder of this section. When loading and discharging weights, if the difference between the initial draught and final draught is substantial, it is essential that *mean hydrostatic values* are used to ensure as accurate an answer as possible is obtained for the final draughts. Interpolation will also be necessary for extracting intermediate data values not tabulated.

The first approach to solving trim problems is by the method used in *Section 12 - Introduction to Trim*, where moments are taken about the LCF.

The scenario to be considered is as follows. *M.V. Almar* arrives in port with certain draughts forward and aft. Cargo is worked, being discharged and/or loaded. The anticipated draughts on completion of cargo must be calculated and if necessary, ballast may have to be transferred to ensure a suitable trim for departure.

The procedure for calculation by taking moments about the mean LCF is as follows:

1. Calculate the *initial true mean draught (TMD)*.
2. Enter the hydrostatic particulars with the *initial TMD* and obtain values for *Displacement*, *MCTC* and *LCF position*, interpolating as necessary.
3. Calculate the *final displacement*.
4. Enter the hydrostatic particulars with the *final displacement* value and obtain values for *TMD*, *MCTC* and *LCF position*, interpolating as necessary.
5. Calculate the *mean MCTC* and *mean LCF position* values.
6. Take moments about the *mean LCF position* to determine the net trimming moments (by the head or by the stern).
7. Using the *mean MCTC* value, calculate the *change of trim (COT)*.
8. Apply the COT calculated in (7) to the *initial trim* and calculate the *final trim* of the ship.
9. Calculate the change of draughts aft and forward due to trim (Ta and Tf) by apportioning the *final trim* in accordance with the *position of the LCF for the final waterline*.
10. Apply Ta and Tf to the final TMD that was obtained in (4) to obtain the final anticipated draughts.
11. If necessary calculate the change of trim required to bring the ship to the desired departure trim, and using the formula: $COT = \frac{w \times d}{MCTC}$ calculate the weight of ballast to be transferred between the chosen tanks.

Follow example 6 referring to the hydrostatic particulars where necessary.

Example 6
M.V. Almar arrives in port with draughts F 4.00 m A 4.20 m.
Cargo is to be loaded as follows:

Hold No. 1	*1400 t at lcg 144.94 m foap;*
Hold No. 3	*2900 t at lcg 103.94 m foap;*
Hold No. 5	*3104 t at lcg 62.05 m foap;*
Hold No. 6	*3285 t at lcg 42.31 m foap;*

(a) *Calculate the final draughts.*

(b) *Calculate the weight of ballast to transfer from 6 P+S DB ballast tank (lcg 42.19 m foap) to the fore peak tank (lcg 162.04 m foap) to ensure that the ship sails with a trim of 0.60 m by the stern.*

(LBP is 167.87 m for all calculations - see general particulars in stability data book.)

Solution (a)

(1) Calculate initial TMD

$$AMD = \frac{4.00 + 4.20}{2} = 4.10\ m$$

Enter data with AMD and obtain approximate LCF position.
AMD 4.10 m; LCF = 86.78 m foap. Use this to calculate the TMD.

$$TMD = dA - \left(\frac{(dA - dF)}{LBP} \times LCF\ foap \right)$$

$$TMD = 4.20 - \left(\frac{0.20}{167.87} \times 86.78 \right)$$

TMD = 4.200 - 0.103 = **4.097 m**

(2) Enter data with TMD 4.097 m

$$Initial\ displacement = 11930 + (310 \times \frac{0.097}{0.1}) = 12231\ t$$

MCTC = 308 t-m (no interpolation needed)

$$LCF = 86.86 + (-0.08 \times \frac{0.097}{0.1}) = 86.78\ m\ foap$$

(3) Calculate the final displacement

Initial displacement	12231
Load	1400
Load	2900
Load	3104
Load	3285
Final displacement	**22920**

(4) Enter data with final displacement 22920 t

TMD = 7.400 m; MCTC = 343 t-m; LCF = 85.19 m foap.
(No interpolation needed)

(5) Calculate mean MCTC and mean LCF

$$Mean\ MCTC = \frac{308 + 343}{2} = 325.5\ t\text{-}m.\ Use\ 326\ t\text{-}m$$

$$Mean\ LCF = \frac{86.78 + 85.19}{2} = 85.985\ m\ foap.\ Use\ 85.99\ m\ foap$$

(6) Take moments about the mean LCF position to determine net trimming moments

Weight (t)	Mean LCF (m foap)	Weight lcg (m foap)	Dist from mean LCF (m)	Head moments (t-m)	Stern moments (t-m)
1400	85.99	144.94	58.95	82530	
2900	85.99	103.94	17.95	52055	
3104	85.99	62.05	23.94		74310
3285	85.99	42.31	43.68		143489
TOTAL				134585	217799
					134585
					83214

(7) Calculate the change of trim using the mean MCTC

$$COT\ (cms) = \frac{Trimming\ moments}{MCTC_{MEAN}} = \frac{83214}{326} = 255.3\ cms$$

COT = 2.553 m by the stern

(8) *Calculate the final trim*

Initial trim	*0.200 m by the stern*
COT (by the stern)	*2.553 m*
FINAL TRIM	*2.753 m by the stern*

(9) *Apportion the final trim using the LCF position for the final waterline.*

$$Ta = COT \times \frac{a}{LBP} \quad Ta = 2.753 \times \frac{85.19}{167.87} = 1.397\ m$$

$$Tf = COT - Ta \quad Tf = 2.753 - 1.397 = 1.356\ m$$

(10) *Apply Ta and Tf to the final TMD to obtain final draughts.*

	Fwd	Aft
Final TMD	7.400	7.400
Trim (by stern)	1.356	1.397
Final draughts	**6.044**	**8.797**

Solution (b)

Trim on completion of cargo	*2.753 m by the stern*
Required	*0.600 m by the stern*
COT required	*2.153 m by the HEAD*

$$COT\ (cms) = \frac{w \times d}{MCTC} \qquad 215.3 = \frac{w \times (162.04 - 42.19)}{343}$$

$$215.3 = \frac{w \times 119.85}{343}$$

w = 616.2 tonnes to transfer (Ans)

20.3 TRIM CALCULATIONS USING HYDROSTATIC DATA – TRIM BY CONSIDERATION OF THE RELATIVE POSITIONS OF THE LCB AND LCG

Using mean values of MCTC and the LCF position certainly improves accuracy when calculating the final draughts. However, when using the *mean* values of MCTC and LCF position it is assumed that their values will change *linearly* between the draughts concerned. This is rarely the case because the shape of a ship's hull seldom changes linearly with draught - the hull is curved in form, especially at the ends.

Another problem with taking moments about the position of the LCF is that it is easy to mistakenly apply the moments of individual weights in the table the wrong way. We have all done it and it can be very frustrating.

An alternative approach to trim problems is to consider the relative positions of the LCB and LCG when the ship is momentarily 'held' in the even keel condition. The horizontal distance between the LCB and LCG represents a *trimming lever* which, when multiplied by the displacement gives a value of *trimming moment*. Knowledge of this and the MCTC for the even keel waterline in question will allow the change of trim from the even keel, the *actual trim*, to be determined.

This approach is always adopted when dealing with trim calculations in real situations, with a few exceptions where the previous method might be considered more appropriate.

Let us now consider this *easier* and *more accurate* approach.

Figure 20.9 illustrates a ship floating on an *even keel* with a weight on deck.

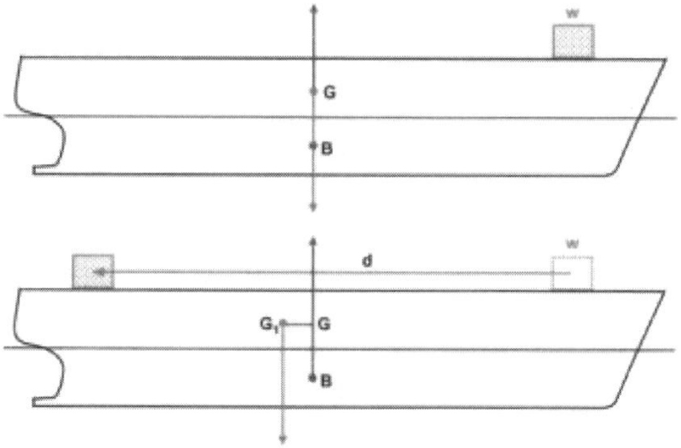

Fig. 20.9

For the ship to float at even keel it can be seen that the longitudinal positions of the centre of gravity (LCG) and the centre of buoyancy (LCB) must be the *same*.

The weight is moved aft causing a movement of G to G_1 (LCG moves aft). $GG_1 = \frac{w \times d}{W}$

Therefore: $GG_1 \times W = w \times d$

where: $GG_1 \times W = \text{Trimming moment} = w \times d$

GG_1 is the horizontal distance between the LCB and the LCG, representing a *trimming lever* that will act to trim the ship by the *stern*.

Since: $\text{COT (cms)} = \frac{\text{Trimming moment}}{\text{MCTC}}$

the *change of trim from even keel* may be calculated using:

$$\mathbf{COT_{FROM\ EVEN\ KEEL} = \frac{W \times (LCB{\sim}LCG)}{MCTC}}$$

where: ***'W'*** is the displacement of the ship;

'(LCB~LCG)' is the horizontal distance between the LCB and the LCG that exists when the ship is 'held' at even keel;

'MCTC' is the MCTC value for the current draught.

In order to calculate the position of the LCG for the final loaded condition moments are taken about the aft perpendicular in exactly the same way as they would be taken about the keel to find the final KG.

Consider example 7 where *M.V. Almar* is initially on an even keel prior to loading cargo.

20.3.1 Calculating the final draught – ship initially on an even keel

Example 7

M.V. Almar has an even keel draught of 5.10 m. Cargo is worked as follows:

Discharge 356 t from lcg 148 m foap;
Discharge 404 t from lcg 59 m foap;
Load 566 t at lcg 120 m foap;
Load 800 t at lcg 102 m foap;
Load 200 t at lcg 81 m foap;
Load 1600 t at lcg 44 m foap.

Calculate the final draughts.

Solution

(1) *Calculate the initial TMD*
Because the ship is on an even keel:AMD = TMD = 5.100 m

(2) *Enter data with TMD and obtain Displacement and LCB values*
Initial displacement is 15440 t
LCB is 87.09 m foap.
Because the ship is on an even keel the positions of the LCB and LCG will be the same.

Therefore:
Initial LCG position = LCB position = 87.09 m foap

(3) *Take moments about the AP to find the final LCG position.*

Weight (t)	Weight (t)	lcg (m foap)	Moments (t-m)
Initial displ.	15440	87.09	1344670
	-356	148.00	-52688
	-404	59.00	-23836
	566	120.00	67920
	800	102.00	81600
	200	81.00	16200
	1600	44.00	70400
FINAL	**17846**	**84.29**	**1504266**

(4) *Enter data with final displacement and obtain TMD, MCTC, LCB and LCF positions.*

$$\text{Final TMD} = 5.80 + \left(0.1 \times \frac{156}{330}\right) = 5.847 \text{ m}$$

MCTC = 319 t-m *LCB = 86.98 m foap*

$$\text{LCF} = 86.12 + \left(-0.03 \times \frac{156}{330}\right) = 86.11 \text{ m foap}$$

(5) *Calculate the change of trim from even keel for the final condition.*

$$COT_{\text{FROM EVEN KEEL}} = \frac{W \times (LCB \sim LCG)}{MCTC}$$

$$COT_{\text{FROM EVEN KEEL}} = \frac{17846 \times (86.98 - 84.29)}{319} = 150.5 \text{ cms}$$

A simple sketch will indicate whether the COT is by the head or by the stern.

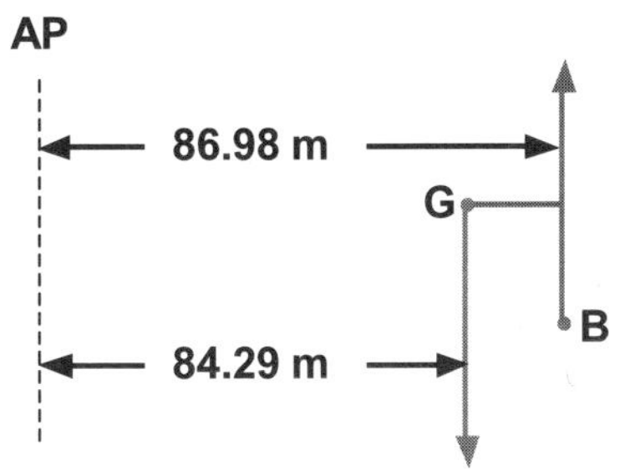

The ship will trim by the stern.

Fig. 20.10

(6) *Apportion the change of trim from even keel to the forward and aft draughts, applying Ta and Tf to the final even keel draught (TMD).*

$$Ta = COT \times \frac{a}{LBP} \qquad Ta = 150.5 \times \frac{86.11}{167.87} = 77.2 \text{ cms} = 0.772 \text{ m}$$

$$Tf = COT - Ta \quad Tf = 150.5 - 77.2 = 73.3 \text{ cms} = 0.733 \text{ m}$$

	Fwd	Aft
Final TMD	5.847	5.847
Trim (by stern)	0.733	0.772
Final draughts	**5.114**	**6.619**

20.3.2 Calculating the final draught – ship initially trimmed

If the ship is initially trimmed then the LCB and LCG must be in different positions to cause the ship to trim from the even keel condition. In this situation the initial true mean draught must first be calculated and the hydrostatic data entered to determine initial values of displacement, MCTC and the LCB position. Obviously the direction of trim, whether by the head or stern, will be known.

Using the formula:

$$COT_{FROM\ EK} = \frac{W \times (LCB \sim LCG)}{MCTC}$$

will allow the initial trimming lever causing the trim, (LCB~LCG), to be calculated. Knowledge of the direction of trim will allow the value of (LCB~LCG) to be applied to the initial LCB to obtain an initial value of the position of LCG.

To allow comparison of the two different methods, example 6 will be reworked using the (LCB~LCG) method.

<u>Example 8 (same as example 6)</u>
M.V. Almar arrives in port with draughts F 4.00 m A 4.20 m.
Cargo is to be loaded as follows:

Hold No. 1   1400 t at lcg 144.94 m foap;
Hold No. 3   2900 t at lcg 103.94 m foap;
Hold No. 5   3104 t at lcg 62.05 m foap;
Hold No. 6   3285 t at lcg 42.31 m foap;

(a) *Calculate the final draughts.*

(b) Calculate the weight of ballast to transfer from 6 P+S DB ballast tank (lcg 42.19 m foap) to the fore peak tank (lcg 162.04 m foap) to ensure that the ship sails with a trim of 0.60 m by the stern.

Solution (a)

(1) Calculate initial TMD

AMD = 4.10 m
Enter data with AMD and obtain LCF position.
LCF = 86.78 m foap.
Use this to calculate the TMD.

$$TMD = dA - \left(\frac{(dA - dF)}{LBP} \times LCF\ foap \right)$$

$$TMD = 4.20 - \left(\frac{0.20}{167.87} \times 86.78 \right)$$

TMD = **4.097 m**

(2) Enter data with TMD 4.097 m

$$\text{Initial Displacement} = 11930 + \left(310 \times \frac{0.097}{0.1}\right) = 12231\ t$$

MCTC = 308 t-m LCB = 87.27 m foap

(3) Calculate the initial trimming lever (LCB~LCG)

$$COT_{FROM\ EVEN\ KEEL} = \frac{W \times (LCB\sim LCG)}{MCTC} \qquad 20.0 = \frac{12231 \times (LCB\sim LCG)}{308}$$

$$(LCB\sim LCG) = \frac{20.0 \times 308}{12231} = 0.50\ m$$

(4) Calculate initial LCG position.
The ship is trimmed by the stern. LCB is 87.27 m foap.
(LCB~LCG) is 0.50 m.

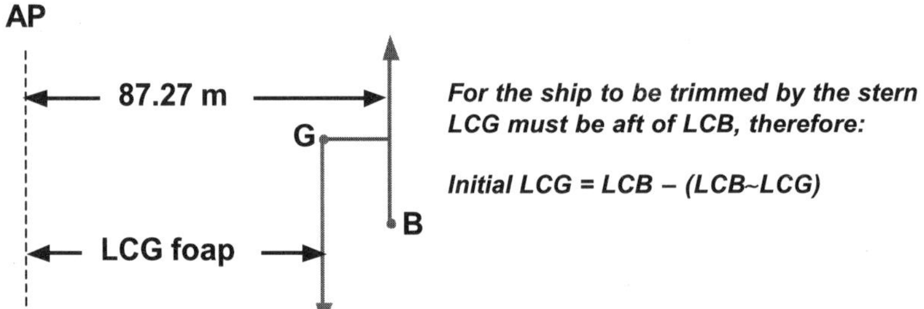
AP
87.27 m
G
B
LCG foap
For the ship to be trimmed by the stern LCG must be aft of LCB, therefore:
Initial LCG = LCB – (LCB~LCG)

Fig. 20.11

Initial LCG = 87.27 – 0.50 = 86.77 m foap

(5) Take moments about the AP to find the final LCG.

Weight (t)	Weight (t)	lcg (m foap)	Moments (t-m)
Initial displ.	12231	86.77	1061284
	1400	144.94	202916
	2900	103.94	301426
	3104	62.05	192603
	3285	42.31	138988
FINAL	**22920**	**82.78**	**1897217**

(6) *Enter data with final displacement and obtain TMD, MCTC, LCB and LCF positions.*
Final TMD = 7.400 m MCTC = 343 t-m
LCB = 86.70 m foap LCF = 85.19 m foap

(7) *Calculate the change of trim from even keel for the final condition.*

$$COT_{FROM\ EVEN\ KEEL} = \frac{W \times (LCB \sim LCG)}{MCTC}$$

$$COT_{FROM\ EVEN\ KEEL} = \frac{22920 \times (86.70 - 82.78)}{343} = \mathbf{261.9\ cms}$$

A simple sketch will indicate whether the COT is by the head or by the stern.

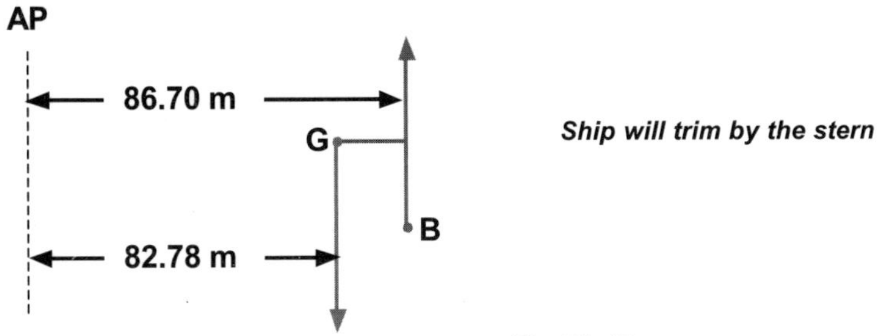

Fig. 20.12

(8) *Apportion the change of trim from even keel to the forward and aft draughts, applying Ta and Tf to the final even keel draught (TMD).*

$$Ta = COT \times \frac{a}{LBP} \qquad Ta = 261.9 \times \frac{85.19}{167.87} = 132.9\ cms$$

$$Tf = COT - Ta \quad Tf = 261.9 - 132.9 = 129.0\ cms$$

	Fwd	Aft
Final TMD	7.400	7.400
Trim (by stern)	1.290	1.329
Final draughts	**6.110**	**8.729**

Solution (b)

Trim on completion of cargo	*2.619 m by the stern*
Required	*0.600 m by the stern*
COT required	*2.019 m by the HEAD*

$$COT\ (cms) = \frac{w \times d}{MCTC} \qquad 201.9 = \frac{w \times (162.04 - 42.19)}{343}$$

$$201.9 = \frac{w \times 119.85}{343} \qquad \mathbf{w = 577.8\ tonnes\ to\ transfer\ (Ans)}$$

Note

The answers obtained using the previous method where:

(a) F 6.044 m A 8.797 m

(b) 616.2 tonnes

Inaccuracy in these answers is caused by the assumption that the hydrostatic data changed linearly between the range of draughts concerned when mean values of MCTC and LCF are used to calculate the change of trim. Since no mean values are used in the (LCB~LCG) method the answers are much more accurate.

When calculating the draughts and trim for a proposed condition of loading it is usual to complete a 'loading sheet' itemising *all* items of deadweight and their moments about the after perpendicular. Different circumstances will dictate the approach that should be adopted. When loading and/or discharging only a few weights to modify a loaded condition it may be appropriate to start with the arrival draughts and modify the 'loading sheet' to find the departure draughts. On the other hand, if the departure condition is going to be significantly different, it may be more appropriate to redo the full ship calculation. Examples of this will be covered in *Section 30 - Practical ship loading Problems*.

In the remainder of this section a number of different problems that commonly occur in examinations are discussed. Taking moments about the LCF is often the easier option to choose as will be seen.

20.4 VARIOUS EXAMINATION STYLE PROBLEMS INVOLVING TRIM

20.4.1 Maximum cargo to load in each space for the ship to complete at the maximum draught

Example 9

M.V. Almar is loading a bulk cargo in port and has draughts F 7.36 m A 8.24 m in salt water. Calculate the maximum amount of cargo to load in each of the spaces available so that the maximum draught on departure will be 8.40 m. Space is available as follows:

No. 2 Hold, lcg 124.38 m foap;
No. 6 Hold, lcg 42.31 m foap.

(Note: the requirement is that the maximum amount of cargo be loaded and the draught is not to exceed 8.40 m. This means that the ship must complete on an even keel draught of 8.40 m.)

Solution (a) – Taking moments about the mean LCF

(1) *Calculate initial TMD*

AMD = 7.80 m
Enter data with AMD and obtain LCF position.
LCF = 84.82 m foap.
Use this to calculate the TMD.

$$TMD = dA - \left(\frac{(dA - dF)}{LBP} \times LCF\ foap\right)$$

$$TMD = 8.24 - \left(\frac{0.88}{167.87} \times 84.82\right)$$

$$TMD = \mathbf{7.795\ m}$$

(2) *Enter data with TMD 7.795 m*

$$\text{Initial Displacement} = 23920 + \left(330 \times \frac{0.095}{0.1}\right) = 24234\ t$$

MCTC = 351 t-m

$$LCF = 84.92 + \left(-0.1 \times \frac{0.095}{0.1}\right) = 84.83\ m\ foap$$

(3) *Enter data with required even keel draught (Final TMD) 8.40 m*

Final displacement = 26270 t *MCTC 365 t-m*
LCF 84.17 m foap

(4) *Calculate cargo to load*

Cargo to load = Final displacement – Initial displacement
*Cargo to load = 26270 – 24234 = **2036 t***

(5) *Calculate mean MCTC and mean LCF*

$$\text{Mean } MCTC = \frac{351 + 365}{2} = 358\ t\text{-}m$$

$$\text{Mean } LCF = \frac{84.83 + 84.17}{2} = 84.50\ foap$$

(6) *Calculate COT required*

Initial trim	*0.88 m by the stern*
Required trim	*0.00 m even keel*
COT required	*0.88 m by the head*

(7) *Calculate the required trimming moments to achieve this*

$$COT = \frac{w \times d}{MCTC_{MEAN}} = \frac{\text{Trimming moments}}{MCTC_{MEAN}}$$

$$88 = \frac{\text{Trimming moments}}{358}$$

*Trimming moments = **31504 t-m by the head***

(8) *Take moments about the mean LCF*

Let x = cargo to load in No.2 Hold; (2036 – x) cargo to load in No. 6 Hold

Space	Weight (t)	Mean LCF (m foap)	Weight lcg (m foap)	Dist from mean LCF (m)	Head moments (t-m)	Stern moments (t-m)
No. 2	x	84.50	124.38	39.88	39.88x	
No. 6	(2036 - x)	84.50	42.31	42.19		(85899 - 42.19x)

Required head moments (31504 t-m) = Head moments – Stern moments

∴ *31504 = 39.88x – (85899 – 42.19x)*

∴ *31504 = 39.88x – 85899 + 42.19x*

∴ *31504 + 85899 = 39.88x + 42.19x*

∴ *117403 = 82.07x*

∴ *x =* ***1431 tonnes in No. 2 Hold;***

(2036 – 1431) = ***605 tonnes in No. 6 Hold (Ans)***

Solution (b) – By (LCB~LCG) method taking moments about AP

(1) *Calculate initial TMD*

AMD = 7.80 m

Enter data with AMD and obtain LCF position.

LCF = 84.82 m foap.

Use this to calculate the TMD.

$$TMD = dA - \left(\frac{(dA - dF)}{LBP} \times LCF\ foap \right)$$

$$TMD = 8.24 - \left(\frac{0.88}{167.87} \times 84.82 \right)$$

TMD = ***7.795 m***

(2) *Enter data with TMD 7.795 m*

$$\text{Initial Displacement} = 23920 + \left(330 \times \frac{0.095}{0.1}\right) = 24234\ t$$

LCB = 86.61 m foap

MCTC = 351 t-m

(3) *Calculate the initial trimming lever (LCB~LCG)*

Trim = 88 cms by the stern

$$COT_{FROM\ EVEN\ KEEL} = \frac{W \times (LCB{\sim}LCG)}{MCTC} \qquad 88 = \frac{24234 \times (LCB{\sim}LCG)}{351}$$

$$(LCB{\sim}LCG) = \frac{88 \times 351}{24234} = \mathbf{1.27\ m}$$

(4) *Calculate initial LCG position.*

The ship is trimmed by the stern. LCB is 86.61 m foap.

(LCB~LCG) is 1.27 m.

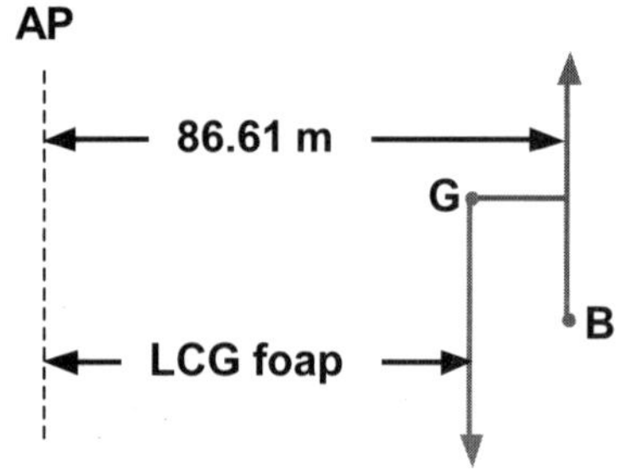

For ship to be trimmed by the stern LCG must be aft of LCB, therefore:

Initial LCG = LCB – (LCG~LCB)

Fig. 20 .13

Initial LCG = 86.61 –1.27 = ***85.34 m foap***

(5) *Enter data with required even keel draught (Final TMD) 8.40 m*
Final displacement = 26270 t *MCTC 365 t-m*
LCB =86.44 m foap *LCF 84.17 m foap*

(6) *Calculate cargo to load*
Cargo to load = Final displacement – Initial displacement
Cargo to load = 26270 – 24234 = ***2036 t***

(7) *Determine required final LCG*
To complete on even keel LCG = LCB = 86.44 m foap

(8) *Take moments about the AP*

Let x = cargo to load in No.2 Hold; (2036 – x) cargo to load in No. 6 Hold

	Weight (t)	lcg (m foap)	moments (t-m)
Initial displ.	24234	85.34	2068130
No. 2	x	124.38	124.38x
No. 6	(2036 - x)	42.31	(86143 - 42.31x)
Final	**26270**	**86.44**	

Note that the final displacement and final LCG are already known.

$\therefore \quad 86.44 = \dfrac{\text{Sum of the moments (t-m)}}{\text{Final displacement (t)}}$

$\therefore \quad 86.44 = \dfrac{2068130 + 124.38x + 86143 - 42.31x}{26270}$

$\therefore \quad 2270779 = 2068130 + 124.38x + 86143 - 42.31x$

$\therefore \quad 2270779 - 2068130 - 86143 = 124.38x - 42.31x$

$\therefore \quad 116506 = 82.07x$

x = ***1420 tonnes in No. 2 Hold;***
(2036 – 1420) = ***616 tonnes in No. 6 Hold (Ans)***

<u>Note</u> Again it is seen that there is a difference in the answers obtained by the different methods of calculation; *1431 tonnes in No. 2 Hold and 605 tonnes in No. 6 Hold* by the previous method which is less accurate.

20.4.2 Maximum cargo to load in each space for the ship to complete at the load displacement with a desired trim

<u>Example 10</u>
M.V. Almar has draughts F 9.46 m A 10.14 m in salt water and is to complete loading to the summer displacement. The remaining cargo is to be loaded into hold no. 2 and hold no. 5. How much of the remaining cargo must be loaded into each hold for the ship to complete cargo with a trim of 0.2 m by the stern.

<u>Solution (a) – Taking moments about the mean LCF</u>
(1) *Calculate initial TMD*

AMD = 9.80 m
Enter data with AMD and obtain LCF position.
LCF = 82.70 m foap.

Use this to calculate the TMD.

$$TMD = dA - \left(\frac{(dA - dF)}{LBP} \times LCF\ foap \right)$$

$$TMD = 10.14 - \left(\frac{0.68}{167.87} \times 82.70 \right)$$

TMD = ***9.805 m***

(2) *Enter data with TMD 9.805 m*

$$Initial\ Displacement = 31090 + (350 \times \frac{0.005}{0.1}) = 31108\ t$$

$$MCTC = 401 + (3 \times \frac{0.005}{0.1}) = 401\ t\text{-}m$$

$$LCF = 82.70 + (-0.1 \times \frac{0.005}{0.1}) = 82.70\ m\ foap$$

(3) *Calculate cargo to load*
Cargo to load = Summer displacement – Initial displacement
From ship particulars Summer displacement = 32485 t
Cargo to load = 32485 – 31108 = ***1377 t***

(4) *Enter data with Summer draught 10.20 m*
MCTC = 411 t-m LCF = 82.32 m foap

(5) *Calculate mean MCTC and mean LCF*

$$Mean\ MCTC = \frac{401 + 411}{2} = 406\ t\text{-}m$$

$$Mean\ LCF = \frac{82.70 + 82.32}{2} = 82.51\ m\ foap$$

(6) *Calculate COT required*

Initial trim	*0.68 m by the stern*
Required trim	*0.20 m by the stern*
COT required	*0.48 m by the head*

(7) *Calculate the required trimming moments to achieve this*

$$COT = \frac{w \times d}{MCTC_{MEAN}} = \frac{Trimming\ moments}{MCTC_{MEAN}}$$

$$48 = \frac{Trimming\ moments}{406}$$

Trimming moments = ***19488 t-m by the head***

(8) *Take moments about the mean LCF*

Let x = cargo to load in No.2 Hold; (1377 – x) cargo to load in No. 5 Hold

From stability data book: lcg No. 2 Hold = 124.38 m foap;
lcg No. 5 Hold = 62.05 m foap.

Space	Weight (t)	Mean LCF (m foap)	Weight lcg (m foap)	Dist from mean LCF (m)	Head moments (t-m)	Stern moments (t-m)
No. 2	x	82.51	124.38	41.87	41.87x	
No. 5	(1377 - x)	82.51	62.05	20.46		(28173 - 20.46x)

Required head moments (19488 t-m) = Head moments – Stern moments

$\therefore$ 19488 = 41.87x – (28173 – 20.46x)
$\therefore$ 19488 = 41.87x – 28173 + 20.46x
$\therefore$ 19488 + 28173 = 41.87x + 20.46x
$\therefore$ 47661 = 62.33x
$\therefore$ x = **765 tonnes in No. 2 Hold;**
(1377 – 765) = **612 tonnes in No. 5 Hold (Ans)**

Solution (b) – By (LCB~LCG) method taking moments about AP

(1) Calculate initial TMD

AMD = 9.80 m
Enter data with AMD and obtain LCF position.
LCF = 82.70 m foap.

Use this to calculate the TMD.

$$TMD = dA - \left(\frac{(dA - dF)}{LBP} \times LCF\ foap \right)$$

$$TMD = 10.14 - \left(\frac{0.68}{167.87} \times 82.70 \right)$$

TMD = **9.805 m**

(2) Enter data with TMD 9.805 m

$$\text{Initial Displacement} = 31090 + \left(350 \times \frac{0.005}{0.1}\right) = 31108\ t$$

$$MCTC = 401 + \left(3 \times \frac{0.005}{0.1}\right) = 401\ t\text{-}m$$

$$LCB = 85.97 + \left(-0.04 \times \frac{0.005}{0.1}\right) = 85.97\ m\ foap$$

(3) Calculate the initial trimming lever (LCB~LCG)
Trim = 68 cms by the stern

$$COT_{FROM\ EVEN\ KEEL} = \frac{W \times (LCB\sim LCG)}{MCTC} \qquad 68 = \frac{31108 \times (LCB\sim LCG)}{401}$$

$$(LCB\sim LCG) = \frac{68 \times 401}{31108} = \mathbf{0.88\ m}$$

(4) Calculate initial LCG position.
The ship is trimmed by the stern. LCB is 85.97 m foap.
(LCB~LCG) is 0.88 m.

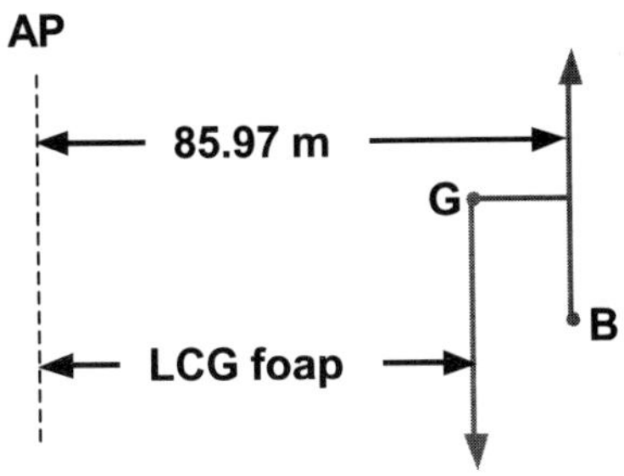

For ship to be trimmed by the stern LCG must be aft of LCB, therefore:

Initial LCG = LCB – (LCG~LCB)

Fig. 20 .14

Initial LCG = 85.97 –0.88 = **85.09 m foap**

(5) Calculate cargo to load
Cargo to load = Summer displacement – Initial displacement
From ship particulars Summer displacement = 32485 t
Cargo to load = 32485 – 31108 = **1377 t**

(6) Enter data with Summer draught 10.20 m
MCTC = 411 t-m LCB = 85.82 m foap LCF = 82.32 m foap

(7) Calculate required final LCG to desired trim of 0.20 m by the stern

$$COT_{FROM\ EVEN\ KEEL} = \frac{W \times (LCB{\sim}LCG)}{MCTC} \qquad 20 = \frac{32485 \times (LCB{\sim}LCG)}{411}$$

$$(LCB{\sim}LCG) = \frac{20 \times 411}{32485} = \mathbf{0.25\ m}$$

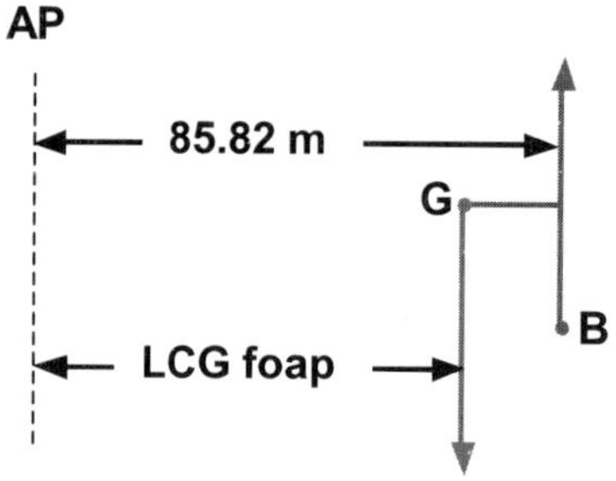

For the ship to trim by the stern LCG must be aft of the LCB, therefore:

LCG = LCB – (LCB~LCG)

Fig. 20.15

Required final LCG = 85.82 – 0.25 = **85.57 m foap**

(8) Take moments about the AP
Let x = cargo to load in No.2 Hold; (1377 – x) cargo to load in No. 5 Hold
From stability data book: lcg No. 2 Hold = 124.38 m foap;
lcg No. 5 Hold = 62.05 m foap.

	Weight (t)	lcg (m foap)	moments (t-m)
Initial displ.	31108	85.09	2646980
No. 2	x	124.38	124.38x
No. 5	(1377 - x)	62.05	(85443 - 62.05x)
Final	**32485**	**85.57**	

Note that the final displacement and final LCG are already known.

$$\therefore \quad 85.57 = \frac{\text{Sum of the moments (t-m)}}{\text{Final displacement (t)}}$$

$$\therefore \quad 85.57 = \frac{2646980 + 124.38x + 85443 - 62.05x}{32485}$$

$$\therefore \quad 2779741 = 2646980 + 124.38x + 85443 - 62.05x$$

$$\therefore \quad 2779741 - 2646980 - 85443 = 124.38x - 62.05x$$

$$\therefore \quad 47318 = 62.33x$$

x = **759 tonnes in No. 2 Hold;**
(1377 – 759) = **618 tonnes in No. 5 Hold (Ans)**

Note Again it is seen that there is a difference in the answers obtained by the different methods of calculation; *765 tonnes in No. 2 Hold; 612 tonnes in No. 5 Hold* by taking moments about the mean LCF which is less accurate.

20.4.3 Where to load a single weight to keep the aft draught constant

Example 11
M.V. Almar has draughts F 4.24 m A 4.98 m and 436 tonnes of deck cargo remains to be loaded. Calculate:
(a) the position foap to load the weight in order that the aft draught remains constant;
(b) the final draught forward.

Solution (a)
(1) Calculate initial TMD

AMD = 4.61 m
Enter data with AMD and obtain LCF position.

$$LCF = 86.41 + \left(-0.03 \times \frac{0.01}{0.1}\right) = 86.41m \text{ foap}$$

Use this to calculate the TMD.

$$TMD = dA - \left(\frac{(dA - dF)}{LBP} \times LCF \text{ foap}\right)$$

$$TMD = 4.98 - \left(\frac{0.74}{167.87} \times 86.41\right)$$

$$TMD = \mathbf{4.599\ m}$$

(2) Enter data with TMD 4.599 m

$$\text{Initial Displacement} = 13520 + \left(320 \times \frac{0.099}{0.1}\right) = 13837\ t$$

TPC = 31.84 MCTC = 310 t-m LCF = 86.41 m foap

Note With this type of problem it is not usually required to use mean hydrostatic values.

(3) Consider figure 20.16

If the 436 tonnes of cargo is initially loaded at the LCF the vessel will experience uniform sinkage.

The cargo must then be shifted to a position forward of the LCF in order that the ship trims by the head to reduce the draught aft back to its original value.

For the draught aft to remain constant:

Sinkage = Ta

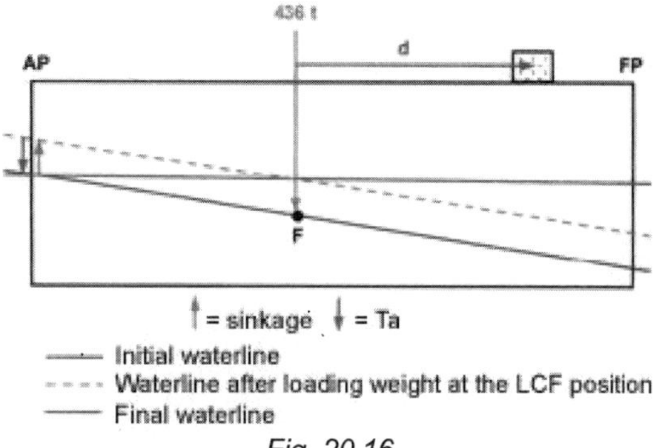

Fig. 20.16

where Ta is the change of draught aft due to trim caused by moving the weight forward.

Therefore:

$$\frac{w}{TPC} = COT \times \frac{a}{L}$$

Thus, to keep the draught aft constant when loading a known weight:

$$\frac{w}{TPC} = \frac{w \times d}{MCTC} \times \frac{a}{L}$$

Calculating the distance 'd' will allow the position foap to be determined.

(4) *Calculate the position to load the weight*

$$\frac{w}{TPC} = \frac{w \times d}{MCTC} \times \frac{a}{L}$$

$$\frac{436}{31.84} = \frac{436 \times d}{310} \times \frac{86.41}{167.87}$$

$$\frac{436}{31.84} = 0.724d \qquad d = 18.91 \text{ m forward of the LCF}$$

Therefore, the weight must be loaded: 86.41 + 18.91 = ***105.32 m foap (Ans)***

Solution (b)
The position to load the weight is now known.

$$Sinkage = \frac{w}{TPC} \qquad Sinkage = \frac{436}{31.84} = 13.7 \text{ cms}$$

$$COT = \frac{w \times d}{MCTC} \qquad COT = \frac{436 \times 18.91}{310} = 26.6 \text{ cms}$$

$$Ta = COT \times \frac{a}{L} \quad Ta = 26.6 \times \frac{86.41}{167.87} = 13.7 \text{ cms}$$

$$Tf = COT - Ta \quad Tf = 26.6 - 13.7 = 12.9 \text{ cms}$$

Calculate the final draughts.

	Fwd	Aft
Initial	4.240	4.980
Sinkage	0.137	0.137
	4.377	5.117
Trim	0.129	0.137
Final draughts	**4.506**	**4.980**

Final forward draught = ***4.506 m (Ans)***

Calculating both draughts provides a check on part (a) of the calculation.

20.4.4 Calculating the weight to load to reduce the deepest draught by a given amount

Example 12
M.V. Almar has draughts F 5.62 m A 6.48 m.
(a) *Calculate the amount of ballast to pump into the fore peak tank (lcg 162.04 m foap) to reduce the draught aft to 6.20 m.*
(b) *Calculate the final draught forward.*

Solution (a)
(1) *Calculate initial TMD*

AMD = 6.05 m

Enter data with AMD and obtain LCF position.

$$LCF = 86.05 + \left(-0.04 \times \frac{0.05}{0.1}\right) = 86.03 \text{ m foap}$$

Use this to calculate the TMD.

$$TMD = dA - \left(\frac{(dA - dF)}{LBP} \times LCF \text{ foap}\right)$$

$$TMD = 6.48 - \left(\frac{0.86}{167.87} \times 86.03\right)$$

TMD = ***6.039 m***

(2) *Enter data with TMD 6.039 m*

$$\text{Initial Displacement} = 18340 + \left(320 \times \frac{0.039}{0.1}\right) = 18465 \text{ t}$$

$$TPC = 32.34 + \left(0.04 \times \frac{0.039}{0.1}\right) = 32.36$$

MCTC = 321 t-m

$$LCF = 86.05 + \left(-0.04 \times \frac{0.039}{0.1}\right) = 86.03 \text{ m foap}$$

Note With this type of problem it is not usually required to use mean hydrostatic values.

(3) *Consider figure 20.17*

If the weight (ballast) is initially loaded at the LCF the vessel will experience uniform sinkage.

The weight must then be shifted to the fore peak tank in order that the ship trims by the head to give the required reduction in draught aft.

For the draught aft to be reduced:

Reduction in dA = Ta - Sinkage

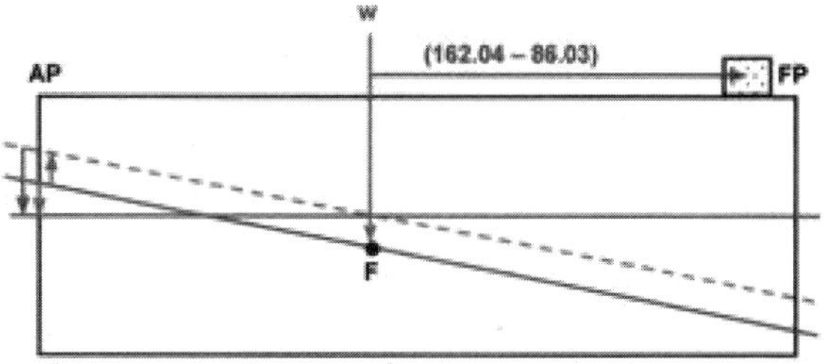

Fig. 20.17

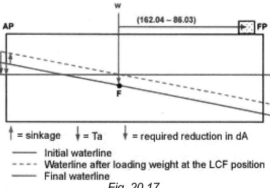

where Ta is the change of draught aft due to trim caused by moving the weight (ballast) forward.

Therefore: $$\text{Reduction in dA} = \left(COT \times \frac{a}{L}\right) - \frac{w}{TPC}$$

Thus, to reduce the draught aft: $$\textbf{Reduction in dA} = \left(\frac{w \times d}{MCTC} \times \frac{a}{L}\right) - \frac{w}{TPC}$$

Calculating the 'w' to determine the weight of ballast to be loaded in the fore peak.

(4) *Calculate the reduction in draught aft required*

Reduction in dA = 6.48 – 6.20 = 0.28 m = ***28 cms***

(5) *Calculate the weight of ballast to load*

Reduction in dA = $\left(\frac{w \times d}{MCTC} \times \frac{a}{L}\right) - \frac{w}{TPC}$

$$28 = \left(\frac{w \times (162.04 - 86.03)}{321} \times \frac{86.03}{167.87}\right) - \frac{w}{32.36}$$

$$28 = 0.121w - 0.031w$$

$28 = 0.090w$ $\qquad$ *w =* ***311.1 tonnes (Ans)***

Solution (b)

The weight of ballast water in the fore peak is now known.

Sinkage = $\frac{w}{TPC}$ $\qquad$ *Sinkage =* $\frac{311.1}{32.36} = 9.6$ *cms*

$COT = \frac{w \times d}{MCTC}$ $\qquad$ $COT = \frac{311.1 \times (162.04 - 86.03)}{321} = 73.7$ *cms*

$Ta = COT \times \frac{a}{L}$ $\quad$ $Ta = 73.7 \times \frac{86.03}{167.87} = 37.8$ *cms*

$Tf = COT - Ta$ $\quad$ $Tf = 73.7 - 37.8 = 35.9$ *cms*

Calculate the final draughts.

	Fwd	Aft
Initial	5.620	6.480
Sinkage	0.096	0.096
	5.716	6.576
Trim	0.359	0.378
Final draughts	**6.075**	**6.198**

Final forward draught = ***6.075 m (Ans)***

Calculating both draughts provides a check on part (a) of the calculation. The error of 0.002 m in the aft draught is due to rounding up of figures in the calculation.

20.4 CHANGE IN DRAUGHT AND TRIM DUE TO CHANGE IN WATER DENSITY

20.4.1 Cause of a change of trim due to change of water density

The centre of flotation is located at the geometric centre of the water plane area and the centre of buoyancy is at the geometric centre of the underwater volume of the ship. Their longitudinal positions will rarely be the same. Consider the values of LCB and LCF for M.V. Almar as plotted against draught in figure 20.18.

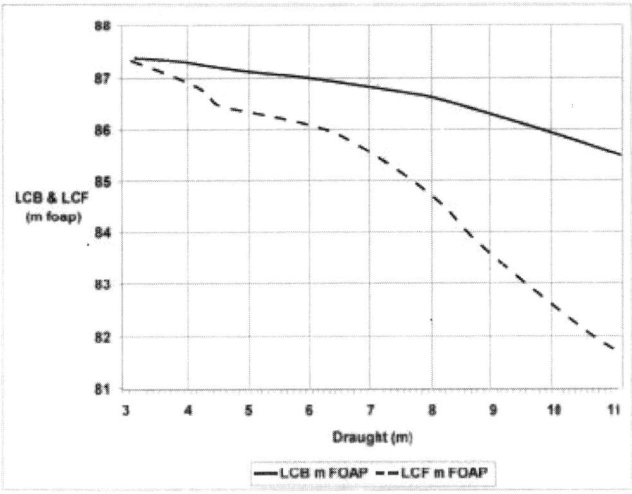

Fig. 20.18

If LCB and LCF were to be in the same longitudinal position (as would be the case for a box shaped vessel on an even keel) and the vessel were to move from water of one density to water of a different density, the change in density would result only in bodily sinkage or rise. When LCF is *not* in the same position as LCF, as is usually the case, a ship will always experience a change in trim also when passing between water of different densities. The reason for this is explained as follows.

Figure 20.19 (a) shows a ship on an even keel in salt water at waterline W_1L_1. In this condition the LCB is vertically below the LCG. On passing into fresh water, being less dense, the ship will initially sink bodily to waterline W_2L_2 (figure 20.19 (b)).

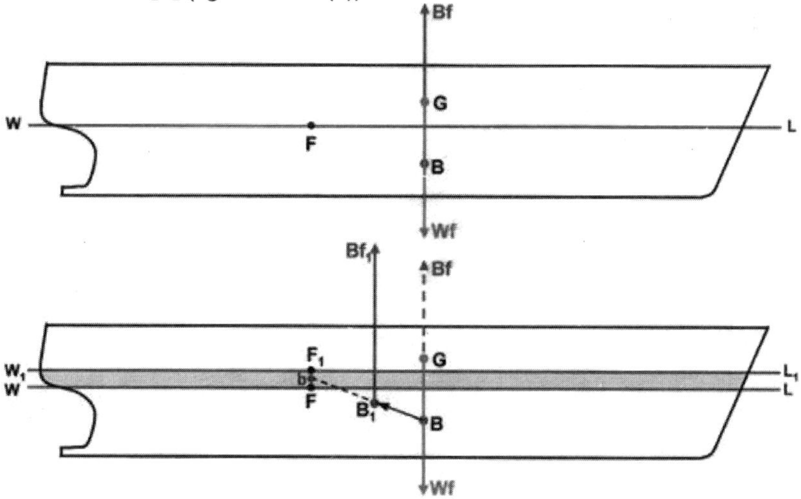

(a) ***Ship in salt***

(b) ***On passing into fresh water ship experiences bodily sinkage to waterline W_1L_1***

Fig. 20.19

At the new waterline the position of the LCF (F_1) can be assumed to be the same as at the initial waterline (F) since the draught will not have significantly changed.

The added layer of buoyancy due to the sinkage will have its centroid at **b** i.e. at the same longitudinal positions as F and F_1.

Because a volume of buoyancy has been effectively added, B will move in a direction directly towards the centroid of the added slice of buoyancy to B_1. This creates a trimming couple that in this case will cause the ship to trim by the head.

20.4.2 Calculating the final draughts

(1) Calculate the bodily sinkage

This will be the fresh water allowance for the displacement in question if the ship passes from salt water to fresh water, or; the dock water allowance if the ship is passing from salt water to dock water.

$$\textbf{fwa (mm)} = \frac{\textbf{Displacement}}{4 \times \textbf{TPC}_{SW}}$$

$$\textbf{dwa (mm)} = \textbf{FWA} \times \frac{(1025 - \textbf{RD}_{DW})}{25}$$

The abbreviations *fwa* and *dwa* are so termed to distinguish between the true fresh water allowance (and dock water allowance) values that would apply to the ship when at the summer displacement. The displacement and TPC values are those corresponding to salt water for the true mean draught in question.

*(2) Calculate the weight of the layer of buoyancy acquired at **b** using:*

$$\textbf{w (tonnes)} = \textbf{Sinkage (cms)} \times \textbf{TPC}_{\textbf{LESSER DENSITY WATER}}$$

The TPC value must be for the fresh (or less dense) water.

(3) Calculate the trimming moment
Consider figure 20.19 (b).
Trimming moment (t-m) = w × *horizontal* distance B to b
where: Bb = BF_1 = (LCB~LCF)

Therefore: **Trimming moment (t-m) = w × (LCB~LCF)**

(4) Calculate the change of trim due to density

$$\textbf{COT (cms)} = \frac{\textbf{Trimming moment}}{\textbf{MCTC}_{\textbf{2nd DENSITY}}}$$

The MCTC must always be for the second density since the ship only trims when at the new waterline after accounting for the sinkage.

(5) Apportion the COT to find Ta and Tf according to the position of the LCF

(6) Apply the sinkage, Ta and Tf to the intial draughts to find the draughts in the new water density.

Note that steps (3) and (4) may be combined for ease of calculation.

Example 13

M.V. Almar has draughts F 9.28 m A 10.32 m when floating in salt water. Calculate the draughts in fresh water.

Solution

(1) *Calculate initial TMD*

AMD = 9.80 m

Enter data with AMD and obtain LCF position.

LCF = 82.70 m foap

Use this to calculate the TMD.

$$TMD = dA - \left(\frac{(dA - dF)}{LBP} \times LCF\ foap\right)$$

$$MD = 10.32 - \left(\frac{1.04}{167.87} \times 82.70\right)$$

$TMD =$ **9.808 m**

(2) *Enter data with TMD 9.808 m*

$$Displacement = 31090 + \left(350 \times \frac{0.008}{0.1}\right) = 31118\ t$$

$$TPC = 34.89 + \left(0.07 \times \frac{0.008}{0.1}\right) = 34.90$$

$$MCTC = 401 + \left(3 \times \frac{0.008}{0.1}\right) = 401\ t\text{-}m$$

$$LCB = 85.97 + \left(-0.04 \times \frac{0.008}{0.1}\right) = 85.97\ m\ foap$$

$$LCF = 82.70 + \left(-0.10 \times \frac{0.008}{0.1}\right) = 82.69\ m\ foap$$

(3) *Calculate the bodily sinkage*

$$fwa\ (mm) = \frac{Displacement}{4 \times TPC_{SW}}$$

$$fwa\ (mm) = \frac{31118}{4 \times 34.90} = 223\ mm = 22.3\ cms$$

(4) *Calculate the weight of the layer of buoyancy*

$$w\ (tonnes) = Sinkage\ (cms) \times TPC_{LESSER\ DENSITY\ WATER}$$

$$w = 22.3 \times 34.90 \times \frac{1.000}{1.025} = 759.3\ tonnes$$

(5) *Calculate the change of trim due to density*

$$COT\ (cms) = \frac{w \times (LCB \sim LCF)}{MCTC_{2nd\ DENSITY}}$$

$$COT\ (cms) = \frac{759.3 \times (85.97 - 82.69)}{\left(401 \times \frac{1.000}{1.025}\right)} = 6.4\ cms$$

Consideration of figure 20.19 (b) will show that the ship will trim by the head.

(6) *Apportion the COT to find Ta and Tf according to the position of the LCF*

$$Ta = COT \times \frac{a}{L} \qquad Ta = 6.4 \times \frac{82.69}{167.87} = 3.2 \text{ cms}$$

$$Tf = COT - Ta \quad Tf = 6.4 - 3.2 = 3.2 \text{ cms}$$

(7) *Apply the sinkage, Ta and Tf to the intial draughts to find the draughts in the new water density.*

	Fwd	Aft
Initial	9.280	10.320
Sinkage	0.223	0.223
	9.503	10.543
Trim	0.032	0.032
Final draughts	**9.535**	**10.511**

Note

In this example the ship trimmed by the head. Had the LCF been forward of the LCB the ship would have trimmed by the stern! For each scenario it is advisable to do a sketch to verify the direction of the change of trim in each case. Alternatively, use the formula in section 20.4.3.

20.4.3 Alternative formula for calculating the change of trim

Having calculated the sinkage the change of trim that arises due to the change of water density may be calculated using the following:

$$\textbf{COT (cms)} = \frac{W(RD_1 - RD_2)(LCF - LCB)}{RD_1 \times MCTC_2}$$

Where: ***'W'*** is the ship's displacement;

'RD_1' is the density of the water from which the ship is leaving;

'RD_2' is the density of the water into which the ship is going;

'$MCTC_2$' is the MCTC for the water into which the ship is going, and;

LCF and ***LCB*** is as before. The term (LCF – LCB) must always be calculated as it is and not changed around. Thus:

if the answer is positive it is a change of trim by the stern, and;
if the answer is negative it is a change of trim by the head.

Verify use of this formula by calculating the change of trim in the previous example.

20.4.4 Considering change of trim due to change of density when conducting trim problems

A trim question might incorporate change of trim due to density as in Example 14.

Example 14

M.V. Almar arrives is port with draughts F 8.60 m A 9.10 m in salt water. The aft peak tank is full. Calculate the amount of ballast water to discharge from the aft peak tank in order that the ship arrives at the berth with a trim by the stern of 0.20 m. The RD of the dock water at the berth is 1.006.

Solution

(1) *Calculate initial TMD*

AMD = 8.85 m

Enter data with AMD and obtain LCF position.

$LCF = 83.72 + \left(-0.1 \times \frac{0.05}{0.1}\right) = 83.67$ m foap

Use this to calculate the TMD.

$$TMD = dA - \left(\frac{(dA - dF)}{LBP} \times LCF \text{ foap}\right)$$

$$TMD = 9.10 - \left(\frac{0.50}{167.87} \times 83.67\right)$$

$TMD =$ **8.851 m**

(2) Enter data with TMD 8.851 m

$$\text{Displacement} = 27630 + \left(340 \times \frac{0.051}{0.1}\right) = 27803 \text{ t}$$

$$MCTC = 375 + \left(3 \times \frac{0.051}{0.1}\right) = 377 \text{ t-m}$$

$$LCB = 86.32 + \left(-0.03 \times \frac{0.051}{0.1}\right) = 86.30 \text{ m foap}$$

$$LCF = 83.72 + \left(-0.10 \times \frac{0.051}{0.1}\right) = 83.67 \text{ m foap}$$

(3) Calculate the change of trim due to density when going from salt water to dock water RD 1.006

$$COT \text{ (cms)} = \frac{W(RD_1 - RD_2)(LCF - LCB)}{RD_1 \times MCTC_2}$$

$$COT = \frac{27803 \times (1.025 - 1.006)(83.67 - 86.30)}{\left(1.025 \times 377 \times \frac{1.006}{1.025}\right)}$$

$$COT = \frac{27803 \times 0.019 \times (-2.63)}{379.262} = \mathbf{-3.7 \text{ cms}}$$

Because the answer is negative the change of trim will be 3.7 cms by the **head**.

(4) Calculate the change of trim required by discharging the ballast water

Initial trim	50.0 cms by the stern
Required	20.0 cms by the stern
COT required	30.0 cms by the head
COT (density)	03.7 cms by the head
COT (ballast discharge)	**26.3 cms by the head**

Because the ship will trim by the head when it goes from salt water to the dock water, the change of trim required by discharging ballast from the aft peak tank will be less. With this problem, consider that the ballast water is discharged in the salt water causing a change of trim of 26.3 cms by the head; the further 3.7 cms is achieved on passage from salt water to the berth.

(5) Calculate the amount of ballast to discharge from the aft peak tank (Lcg 4.66 m foap)

$$COT \text{ (cms)} = \frac{w \times d}{MCTC} \qquad 26.3 = \frac{w \times (83.67 - 4.66)}{377}$$

w = 125.5 tonnes (Ans)

SECTION 21 – DRY-DOCKING

INTRODUCTION

It is a requirement that all ships be dry-docked for inspection and maintenance below the waterline. When a ship is being dry-docked additional forces acting at the keel take effect, being the reaction or upthrust afforded by the blocks onto which the ship is being landed. These forces can create undue loads on the stern structure and cause loss of stability of the ship. This section investigates these effects.

Learning Objectives

On completion of this section the learner will achieve the following:

1. Understand the sequence of events that takes place whilst a ship is being dry-docked.
2. Calculate the upthrust at the blocks (P force) at any stage during dry-docking of the ship.
3. Understand the loss of stability during dry-docking and calculate the loss of stability as either a rise of the ship's centre of gravity (increase in KG) or as a fall of the metacentre (reduction in KM).
4. Conduct dry-docking calculations.
5. Understand the practical considerations during the dry-docking of a ship.

21.1 SEQUENCE OF EVENTS DURING DRY-DOCKING

Figures 21.1 to 21.3 illustrate what happens as the ship enters the dry dock and the water is pumped out of the dock.

1. The ship enters the dry dock with a small trim by the stern and is floated into position.

2. The gates are closed and water is pumped out of the dock until the ship touches the blocks aft. Immediately the ship touches the blocks aft this denotes the start of the *critical period* (it is now that the ship will start to experience a loss of stability, hence the term).

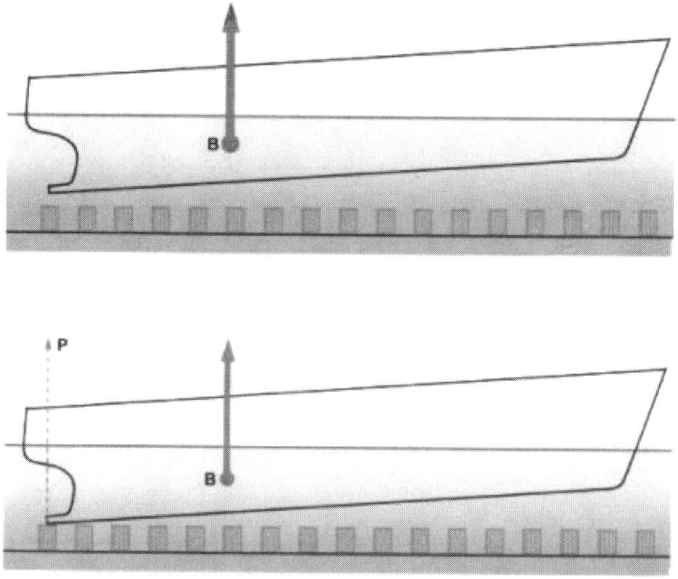

1. Ship enters dock with a small trim by the stern.

2. Water is pumped out of the dock until the ship touches the blocks aft.

Fig. 21.1

3. As more water is pumped out of the dock the *true mean draught* will start to reduce as the ship experiences more and more support at the stern. The upthrust afforded by the blocks at the stern is termed the *'P force',* this continues to increase as the buoyancy force reduces. Throughout the docking process the ship will displace a progressively lessening volume of water as the true mean draught reduces and the P force increases to provide more support for the ship (in effect, the P force takes over supporting the ship and the role of the buoyancy force in supporting the ship reduces). At this stage the aft draught will be reducing at a greater rate than what the forward draught is increasing, the ship will be trimming by the head as the overall true mean draught reduces. For reasons discussed later, the loss of stability will also be increasing as the P force increases.

4. Eventually the ship will come to rest on the blocks along it's entire length, this *critical instant* denotes the end of the critical period, since for a flat bottomed ship the problem of stability loss is no longer of concern.

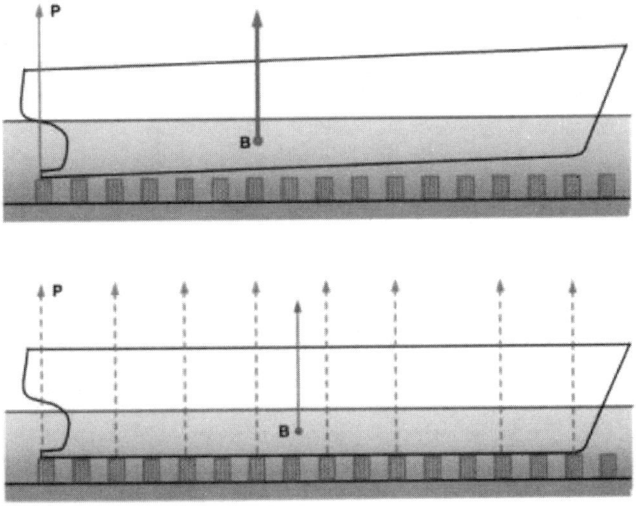

3. ***During the critical period P force increases as the effect of the Bf reduces – overall TMD reduces as the ship trims by the head.***

4. ***On touching the blocks fore and aft the draughts start to reduce uniformly forward and aft.***

Fig. 21.2

5. After settling on the blocks forward and aft water continues to be pumped from the dock and the draught reduces at the same rate forward and aft. The upthrust P becomes uniformly distributed along the ship's length and continues to increase as the effective buoyancy force reduces.

6. When the dock becomes nearly empty and the ship is fully dry the upthrust P will be equal to the ship's displacement having now replaced all the upthrust afforded by the buoyancy force.

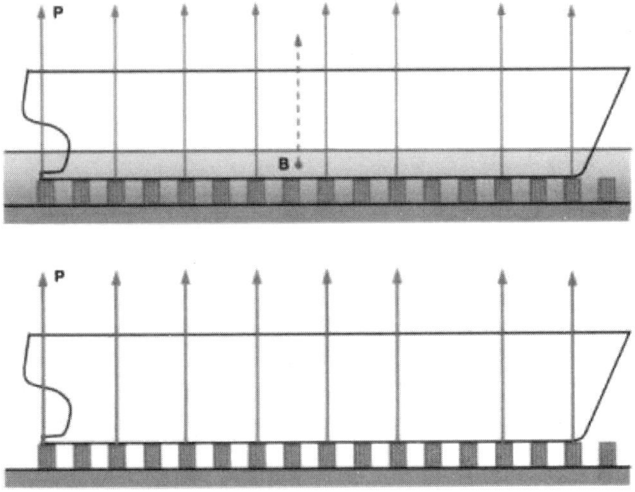

5. ***On touching the blocks forward and aft (critical instant) draughts reduce uniformly and P force becomes distributed along the ship's length***

6. ***Once the ship is dry the P force has completely taken over from the buoyancy force.***

Fig. 21.3

21.2 CALCULATING THE P FORCE

21.2.1 Calculation of P force at any stage during dry-docking

Throughout the dry-docking procedure the true mean draught reduces as it would if the ship were rising out of the water due to weights being discharged.

Consider the formula:

$$\textbf{Rise (cms)} = \frac{\textbf{w (t)}}{\textbf{TPC}}$$

The P force may be considered to have the same effect on true mean draught as if a weight had actually been discharged, therefore: Reduction in TMD (cms) = $\frac{\text{P force (t)}}{\text{TPC}}$

or:

$$\textbf{P force (t) = Reduction in TMD (cms)} \times \textbf{TPC}$$

This formula may be used to calculate the upthrust at the blocks at *any* stage in the docking process since the true mean draught is always reducing as water is taken out of the dock.

21.2.2 Calculation of P force during the critical period when dry-docking

In the period between the ship touching the blocks aft (start of the critical period) and touching the blocks forward and aft (the critical instant) the ship undergoes a change of trim.

The change of trim at any stage during the critical period may be considered to be the same as the change of trim that would have occurred had a weight 'w' been discharged from a position at the aft perpendicular equivalent to the upthrust P in tonnes (if it is assumed that the ship is on the blocks aft at the aft perpendicular).

Consider the formula: COT (cms) = $\frac{w \times d}{\text{MCTC}}$

If the force P is considered to have the same effect as a weight discharged at the aft perpendicular, then: COT (cms) = $\frac{P \times d}{\text{MCTC}}$

or:

$$\textbf{P} = \frac{\textbf{COT (cms)} \times \textbf{MCTC}}{\textbf{Dist LCF foap}}$$

This can be used to calculate the P force during the *critical period only*.

Use of both of these formulae will be seen in subsequent dry docking calculation examples.

21.3 LOSS OF STABILITY WHEN DRY-DOCKING

Loss of stability commences as soon as the ship touches the blocks aft and continues to worsen as the value of the P force increases. The maximum loss of GM of concern occurs the instant immediately prior to the ship settling on the blocks forward and aft – this time being termed the critical instant. Once the ship is flat on the blocks it will be in a safe condition as the risk of heeling over as a result of becoming unstable will have passed (most ship's having a substantial area of flat bottom). For ships that have a relatively small percentage of flat bottom area additional measures must also be taken such as using side shores to support the ship in the upright condition when in the dry dock.

Either of two methods of calculation of the loss of GM may be used.

21.3.1 Loss of GM as a result of a rise in G (increase in KG)

Consider the upward movement of G that would occur if a weight 'w' is discharged from a position at the keel (Kg = 0 m). When discharging a weight the centre of gravity of the ship, G, will move directly away from the centre of gravity of the discharged weight to G_V as shown in figure 21.4.

GGv will be equal to the loss of GM where:

$$GG_V = \frac{w \times d}{W - w}$$

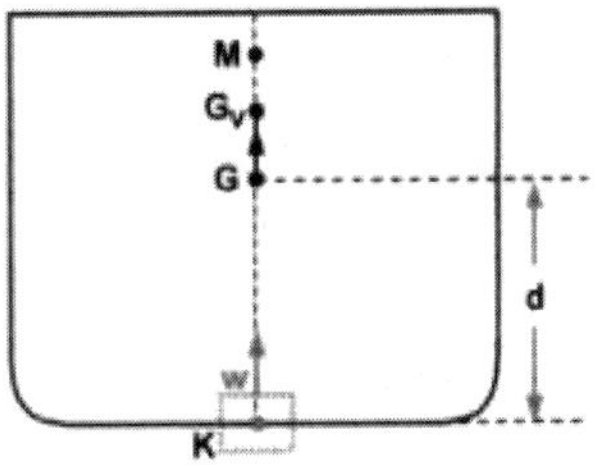

Fig. 21.4

'd' is the distance between the centre of gravity of the ship (G) and the centre of gravity of the discharged weight which was at the keel 'K'. Therefore distance 'd' is the initial KG of the ship.

(It should be noted also that KM changes as a result of a reduction in the ship's draught.)

If the P force is considered to have the same effect as discharging an equivalent weight from the keel then:

$$\text{Loss of GM} = \frac{P \times KG}{W - P}$$

The effect on the ship's stability is made clearer if the available righting moment at a particular angle of heel is considered. Figure 21.5 shows a ship during the critical period where it has taken the blocks at the aft end only. During docking the ship becomes heeled to a small angle of inclination by an external force such as the wind.

The forces acting are as follows:

Wf is the total weight force acting downwards through the centre of gravity at G;

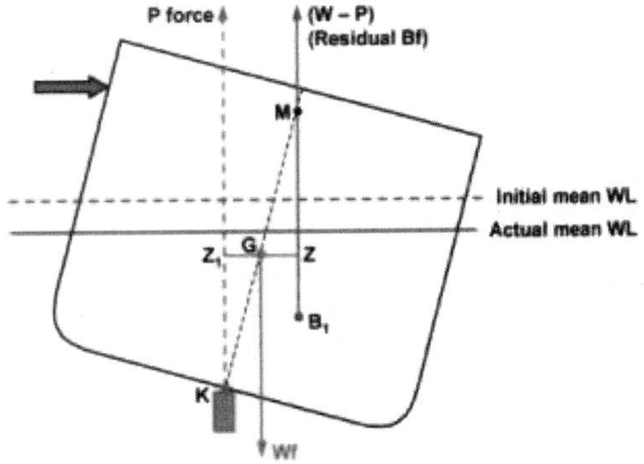

Fig. 21.5

(W – P) is the remaining, or residual, buoyancy force acting upwards through the geometric centre of the underwater volume at B_1;

P is the upthrust of the blocks exerted at the keel aft.

$(W - P) \times GZ$ represents a *righting moment*;

$P \times GZ_1$ represents a *capsizing moment*.

Therefore the available righting moment is given by:

$$\textbf{Available righting moment} = \left[(W - P) \times GZ\right] - \left[P \times GZ_1\right]$$

It is essential that the righting moment afforded by the upward acting (remaining) buoyancy force remains greater than the capsizing moment afforded by the upthrust of the P force acting at the keel at all times prior to the ship touching the blocks forward and aft. If the ship should become unstable during the critical period it will lurch off the blocks to one side resulting in structural damage to the ship, movement of the blocks and great embarrassment!

It is for this reason that the loss of GM is calculated for the critical instant (when the ship touches the blocks forward and aft) to ensure that adequate stability is maintained prior to the ship taking the blocks overall.

21.3.2 Loss of GM as a result of a fall in M (decrease in KM)

Consider figure 21.6 that illustrates the ship heeled by an external force such as the wind during the critical period where the ship has taken the blocks at the aft end only.

The total weight force of the ship acts downwards through G. Counteracting this are the two upward forces; the P force acting upwards at the keel and the residual buoyancy force (W – P) acting upwards through the centre of buoyancy (B_1). The *resultant* of the two upward acting forces acts through the new metacentre (M_1) such that:

$$P \times x = (W - P) \times y \qquad \textbf{(1)}$$

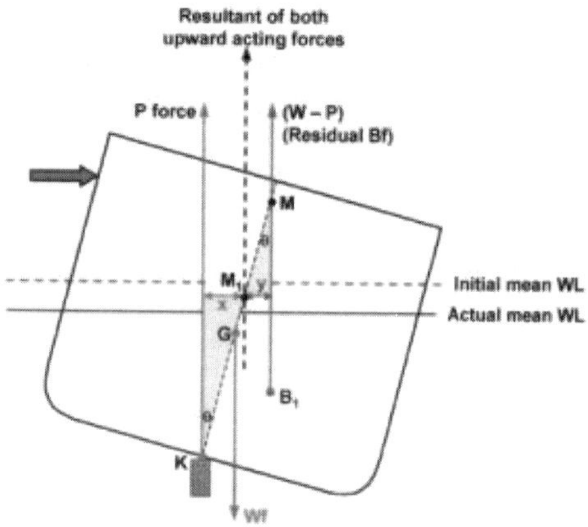

Fig. 21.6

MM_1 represents the resulting fall of the transverse metacentre (or loss of GM).
Consider the two similar triangles:

$$\text{Sine } \theta = \frac{y}{MM_1} \qquad \text{therefore:} \qquad y = \text{Sine } \theta \times MM_1 \qquad \textbf{(2)}$$

Also:

$$\text{Sine } \theta = \frac{x}{KM_1} \qquad \text{therefore:} \qquad x = \text{Sine } \theta \times KM_1 \qquad \textbf{(3)}$$

Combining formulae 1, 2 and 3 above gives: $(W - P) \times \text{Sine } \theta \times MM_1 = P \times \text{Sine } \theta \times KM_1$

Divide both sides by Sine θ: $(W - P) \times MM_1 = P \times KM_1$

Expanding this gives: $(W \times MM_1) - (P \times MM_1) = P \times KM_1$

$\therefore \quad (W \times MM_1) = (P \times KM_1) + (P \times MM_1)$

$\therefore \quad (W \times MM_1) = P \times (KM_1 + MM_1)$

$\therefore \quad (W \times MM_1) = P \times \text{Initial KM}$

$\therefore \quad MM_1 = \dfrac{P \times \text{Initial KM}}{W}$

i.e.

$$\textbf{Loss of GM} = \frac{\mathbf{P \times KM}}{\mathbf{W}}$$

Note In this formula the KM value is that which corresponds to the true mean draught for the instant that the loss of GM is being calculated and not that for the initial true mean draught that the ship has prior to docking. It is found by entering the hydrostatic data with a displacement value that corresponds to that given by (W – P).
W in this formula is the ship's *initial* displacement.

21.4 TYPICAL DRY-DOCKING PROBLEMS

In the following example both methods of calculating the loss of GM will be used. An explanation is included to prove that both methods are equally valid.

Example 1

Prior to entering dry dock M.V. Almar has draughts F 4.86 m A 5.24 m and an effective KG of 9.16m. Calculate:

(a) the GM when the ship takes the blocks forward and aft (at the critical instant);

(b) the draughts at the same instant;

Solution (a)

(1) Calculate initial TMD

AMD = 5.05 m

Enter data with AMD and obtain LCF position.

$$LCF = 86.32 + \left(-0.02 \times \frac{0.05}{0.1}\right) = 86.31 \text{ m foap}$$

Use this to calculate the TMD.

$$TMD = dA - \left(\frac{(dA - dF)}{LBP} \times LCF\ foap\right)$$

$$TMD = 5.24 - \left(\frac{0.38}{167.87} \times 86.31\right)$$

TMD = **5.045 m**

(2) Enter data with TMD 5.045 m

$$\text{Displacement} = 15120 + \left(320 \times \frac{0.045}{0.1}\right) = 15264 \text{ t}$$

MCTC = 312 t-m LCF = 86.31 m foap

(3) Calculate the P force at the critical instant

The initial trim of the ship is 38 cms by the stern. When the ship touches the blocks forward and aft the effective trim will be zero i.e. the ship will be on even keel. The ship will have therefore experienced a change of trim of 38 cms by the head – as if a weight equal to the P force had been discharged from the aft perpendicular.

$$P = \frac{COT\ (cms) \times MCTC}{Dist\ LCF\ foap} \qquad P = \frac{38 \times 312}{86.31} = 137.4 \text{ tonnes (138 tonnes)}$$

(4) Enter data with the effective displacement (W – P) at the critical instant to obtain KM

Effective displacement = W – P = 15264 – 138 = 15126 tonnes

$$KM = 10.70 + \left(-0.10 \times \frac{6}{320}\right) = 10.698 \text{ m}$$

(5) Calculate the loss of GM (both methods used)

Method 1

$$\text{Loss of GM} = \frac{P \times KG}{W - P} \quad \text{Loss of GM} = \frac{138 \times 9.16}{(15264 - 138)} = \mathbf{0.084\ m}$$

Method 2

$$\text{Loss of GM} = \frac{P \times KM}{W} \quad \text{Loss of GM} = \frac{138 \times 10.698}{15264} = \mathbf{0.097\ m}$$

(6) *Calculate the GM at the critical instant*

Method 1

KM at critical instant	10.698
KG	9.160
Initial GM	1.538
Loss of GM	0.084
GM at critical instant	**1.454**

Method 2

KM at critical instant	10.698
KG	9.160
Initial GM	1.538
Loss of GM	0.097
GM at critical instant	**1.441**

Both answers are different but are both valid since a true measure of a ship's stability is it's righting moment value at any given angle of heel.
Within small angles of heel the righting moment is given by:

Righting moment (t-m) = Displacement × GM× Sine θ

By method 1
At the critical instant the effective displacement = W – P = 15126 t since the P force acts as a weight being discharged from the keel.
RM = Displacement × GM × Sine θ
RM = 15126 × 1.454 × Sine θ = ***21993Sine θ t-m***

By method 2
By considering the loss of GM as a result of the fall of the metacentre:
RM = Displacement × GM × Sine θ
RM = 15264 × 1.441 × Sine θ = ***21995Sine θ t-m***
(The slight difference arises due to rounding up of values in the calculation.)

Solution (b)
At the critical instant the ship will be on an even keel. The draught at the same instant may be calculated by one of two methods.

Method 1
The initial TMD has already been calculated as being 5.045 m.
Entering the data with this obtain the TPC value. $TPC = 31.96 + (0.04 \times \frac{0.045}{0.1}) = 31.98\ t$

$$\textbf{Reduction in TMD (cms)} = \frac{\textbf{P force (t)}}{\textbf{TPC}}$$

$$\text{Reduction in TMD} = \frac{138}{31.98} = 4.3\ \text{cms}$$

∴ *Draught at critical instant = 5.045 – 0.043 =* ***5.002 m (Ans)***

Method 2
If the effective displacement at the critical instant is (W – P)
Effective displacement = W – P = 15264 – 138 = 15126 tonnes
Enter the data with this displacement value to obtain the TMD at the critical instant.

$$TMD = 5.00 + (0.1 \times \frac{6}{320}) = 5.002\ m$$

Therefore the draught at the critical instant = ***5.002 m (Ans)***
(Clearly method 2 is much easier!)

During the docking operation it is essential that the 'critical instant' draught is determined as both draughts forward and aft will be constantly being read. As the ship's draught approaches that as calculated for the critical instant, also evidenced by the fact that the ship will be in a near even keel condition at that time, the rate at which the water is pumped out of the dock will be slowed down to allow final adjustment of the ship's fore and aft alignment prior to the ship taking the blocks overall. Once on the blocks the rate of pumping will be increased again.

21.5 PRACTICAL CONSIDERATIONS DURING DRY-DOCKING

The major considerations that should be borne in mind are:

(1) that the P force is kept to an acceptable level, and;

(2) that the ship maintains an acceptable positive GM during the critical period.

21.5.1 The requirement to limit the P force

During the critical period prior to taking the blocks fully forward and aft the P force will be acting at a single point on the stern frame of the ship. The stern frame is specially strengthened to accept the forces exerted on it during dry- docking but there will be a maximum limit that must not be exceeded. If the P force becomes too great structural damage will occur. It is usual to have acceptable near-light conditions of loading for dry-docking specified in the ship's stability data book. If an actual P-force value is not quoted then it may be approximated from the recommended condition(s) given by rearranging the dry-docking formulae and calculating it. Under normal circumstances the ship's classification society will investigate any proposed dry-docking condition and verify that it is appropriate. Under exceptional circumstances a ship may be dry-docked in a part-loaded condition but this will only ever be done after taking classification society advice. It would often be more prudent to discharge any cargo on board prior to entering dry dock.

An obvious method to limit the P force during the critical period is to keep the initial trim by the stern small, consider the formula for calculating the P force during the critical period:

$$\mathbf{P = \frac{COT\ (cms) \times MCTC}{Dist\ LCF\ foap}}$$

It is clear from the above that P force is directly proportional to the change of trim that the ship will undergo. Limiting the trim will therefore limit the maximum loads that will be experienced by the stern frame. The greater the displacement of a given ship, the more important will be the need to limit the docking trim.

21.5.2 Limiting the loss of GM

Consideration of the formulae will indicate that the greater the trim of the ship when docking, the greater will be the loss of GM.

$$\mathbf{P = \frac{COT\ (cms) \times MCTC}{Dist\ LCF\ foap}}$$

$$\mathbf{Loss\ of\ GM = \frac{P \times KG}{W - P}} \quad \text{or:} \quad \mathbf{Loss\ of\ GM = \frac{P \times KM}{W}}$$

Clearly, the greater the trim, the greater the P force; the greater the P force, the greater the loss of GM!

Alternatively, the ship should dry-dock with a greater effective GM that will ensure that stability is maintained. Improving the ship's initial GM will be achieved by:

(1) Lowering the effective KG by lowering weights within the vessel, discharging weights from high up or taking on an acceptable amount of ballast in double bottom tanks, or;

(2) Minimising free surface effects by topping up slack tanks wherever possible.

Example 2

M.V. Almar about to dry dock requires a minimum GM of 0.3 m at the time the ship takes the blocks forward and aft. Current draughts are F 6.89 m and A 8.47 m. KG is 8.86 m.

Calculate the maximum permissible trim by the stern on entering the dry dock.

Solution

(1) *Calculate initial TMD*

AMD = 7.68 m

Enter data with AMD and obtain LCF position.

$$LCF = 85.01 + \left(-0.09 \times \frac{0.08}{0.1}\right) = 84.94 \text{ m foap}$$

Use this to calculate the TMD.

$$TMD = dA - \left[\frac{(dA - dF)}{LBP} \times LCF \text{ foap}\right]$$

$$TMD = 8.47 - \left[\frac{1.58}{167.87} \times 84.94\right]$$

$$TMD = \mathbf{7.671\ m}$$

(2) *Enter data with TMD 7.671 m*

$$\text{Displacement} = 23580 + \left(340 \times \frac{0.071}{0.1}\right) = 23821 \text{ t}$$

$$MCTC = 347 + \left(2 \times \frac{0.071}{0.1}\right) = 348 \text{ t-m}$$

$$LCF = 85.01 + \left(-0.09 \times \frac{0.071}{0.1}\right) = 84.95 \text{ m foap}$$

$$KM = 9.37 + \left(-0.01 \times \frac{0.071}{0.1}\right) = 9.363 \text{ m}$$

We must assume that KM remains constant in this case.

(3) *Calculate the allowed loss of GM*

KM	9.363
KG	8.860
Initial GM	0.503
Minimum critical GM	0.300
GM at critical instant	**0.203**

(4) *Calculate the maximum allowed P force and hence the maximum intial trim*

Method 1

$$\text{Loss of GM} = \frac{P \times KG}{W - P} \quad 0.203 = \frac{P \times 8.860}{(23821 - P)}$$

$\therefore \quad 0.203(23821 - P) = 8.860P$

$\therefore \quad 4835.663 - 0.203P = 8.860P$

$\therefore \quad 4835.663 = 8.860P + 0.203P$

$\therefore \quad 4835.663 = 9.063P \qquad \therefore \quad P = 534 \text{ tonnes}$

$$P = \frac{COT \times MCTC}{d} \qquad 534 = \frac{COT \times 348}{84.95}$$

$$COT = \frac{534 \times 84.95}{348} = \mathbf{130\ cms\ (Ans)}$$

To ensure that a GM of 0.3 m is maintained at the critical instant the trim of the ship must not exceed 1.30 m by the stern.

Method 2

$\text{Loss of GM} = \dfrac{P \times KM}{W} \quad 0.203 = \dfrac{P \times 9.363}{23821}$

$P = \dfrac{0.203 \times 23821}{9.363} \qquad \therefore \qquad P = 516 \text{ tonnes}$

$P = \dfrac{COT \times MCTC}{d} \qquad 516 = \dfrac{COT \times 348}{84.95}$

$COT = \dfrac{516 \times 84.95}{348}$ = ***126 cms (Ans)***

SECTION 22 – BILGING

INTRODUCTION

A 'bilged' ship is one that has suffered a breach of the hull through grounding, collision or other means and water has been admitted into the hull. Whenever a ship suffers damage and flooding of compartments takes place there will always be an increase in the draught. However, it does not always follow that the ship's initial stability will be worsened; in some instances stability is improved.

This section investigates the way flooding of compartments can affect the ship's draught and stability for a number of different scenarios. Although calculations involving box-shaped vessels are considered, the principles discussed will apply equally to ship shapes (in fact many ship's hulls almost represent box-shaped vessels if the curvature of the hull form at the ends is ignored!).

Similarity of high block coefficient hull forms to box-shaped vessels.

Fig. 22.1

Learning Objectives

On completion of this section the learner will achieve the following:

1. Calculate the change in draught and stability of a box-shaped vessel when an empty amidships compartment is bilged;
2. Calculate the effects of bilging an empty amidships compartment with a watertight (double bottom);
3. Calculate the effects of bilging a compartment when permeability is less than 100%;
4. Calculate the draughts when an end compartment becomes bilged;
5. Calculate the list when an amidships side compartment is bilged, permeability 100%;
6. Review the principles of bilging to be applied to different flooding scenarios.

22.1 THE EFFECTS OF BILGING AN EMPTY AMIDSHIPS COMPARTMENT

The changes in draught and stability when a compartment becomes flooded due to damage can be investigated by either of two methods:

(1) the lost buoyancy (constant displacement) method, or;

(2) the added weight method.

22.1.1 Calculating the KM of a box-shaped vessel

In order to do bilging calculations involving box-shaped vessels it will be necessary to calculate the KM of a box. This is given by: **KM = KB + BM**

$$KM_{BOX} = \frac{\text{Draught}}{2} + \frac{LB^3}{12V}$$

where: ***'L'*** and ***'B'*** are the length and breadth of the water plane area respectively, and; ***'V'*** is the volume of displacement of the box-shaped vessel when on an even keel.

22.1.2 Lost buoyancy (constant displacement) method

This method assumes that when a compartment becomes flooded there is no change in the displacement or KG of the vessel. The approach is to consider that a certain amount of volume of buoyancy is lost whereby the vessel must sink to regain that amount of buoyancy elsewhere in the remaining intact part of the vessel, since, for a vessel to float:
total weight force acting downward through the centre of gravity (G) must equal the total buoyancy force acting upward through centre of buoyancy (B, being at the centroid of the intact underwater volume).

Figure 22.2 illustrates this approach where an amidships compartment extending the full breadth and depth of the vessel becomes bilged.

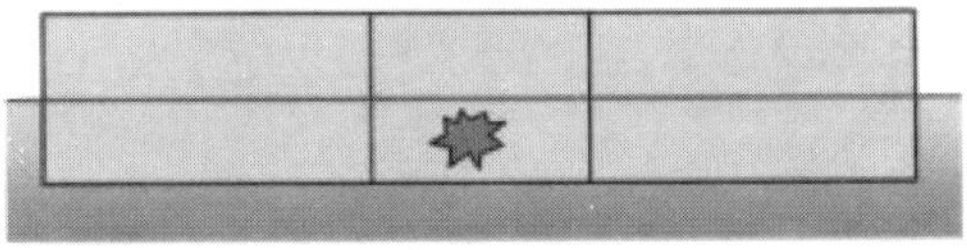

1. Box-shaped vessel suffers substantial side damage amidships.

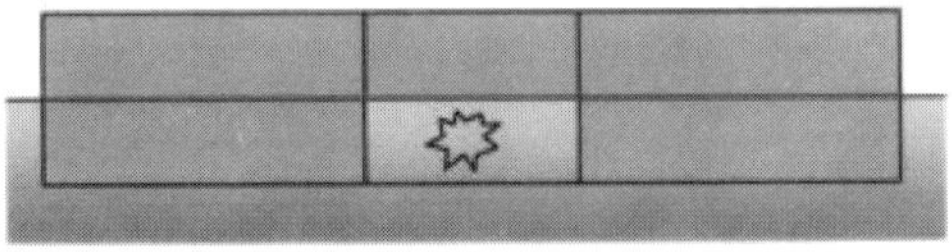

2. Water floods into the compartment. The buoyancy afforded by the damaged compartment is lost creating an excess of weight force. Since the damage is substantial the compartment may now be considered as being 'open to the sea'.

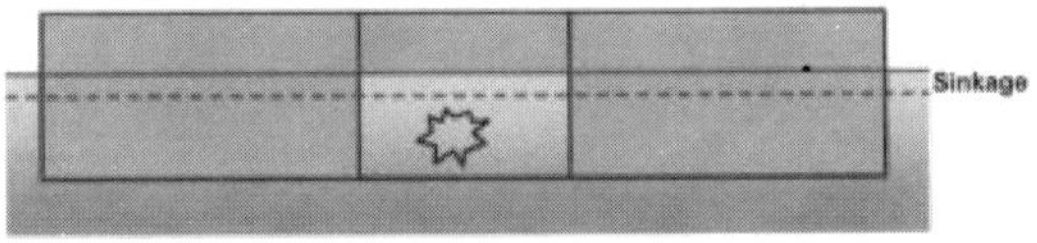

3. The excess of weight force causes the vessel to sink to regain a volume of buoyancy equivalent to that lost.

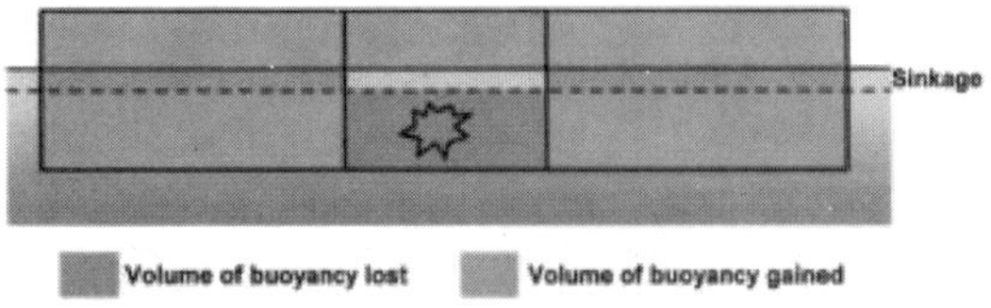

4. The volume of buoyancy lost = The volume of buoyancy gained

(Note that the slice of water (sinkage) in the bilged compartment is not part of the volume gained – since this compartment is offering no support to the vessel – being effectively 'open to the sea'.

Fig. 22.2

So it is assumed that the sinkage of the vessel is caused by the redistribution of the intact underwater volume. Since nothing has been loaded and the effective volume of displacement is the same, the assumptions of this approach are:

(1) Volume of displacement (and displacement) remain constant, and;
(2) KG remains constant.

We must now consider the change in the vessels initial stability. Consider the change in effective water plane area in figure 22.3.

Fig. 22.3

In this case the part of water plane area of the bilged compartment has been lost. Since:

$BM = \frac{I}{V}$ and for a box-shaped vessel: $BM_{BOX} = \frac{LB^3}{12V}$

BM will reduce directly as a result of the reduced water plane area. V, the volume of displacement of the vessel, has not changed, since if displacement remains constant; so does the volume of displacement.

In addition, because the draught has increased due to the sinkage, KB will increase.

$KB_{BOX} = \frac{\text{Draught}}{2}$

This is still valid for the bilged condition since the KB of each of the end compartments will be the same.

Since: KM = KB + BM; it is most probable that KM will change as a result of the increasing KB and the decreasing BM; the changes in both unlikely to be the same.

If KM changes and KG is assumed to remain constant, any change in KM will be the same as the change in GM, being either an increase or decrease.

Consider example 1.
<u>*Example 1 (By lost buoyancy – constant displacement method)*</u>
A box-shaped vessel has length 140 m, breadth 36 m and is on an even keel draught of 6 m in salt water. In the present condition the KG is 12.80 m. An empty amidships compartment extending the full breadth and depth of the vessel 60 m in length is bilged. Calculate:

(a) the draught in the bilged condition;
(b) the initial GM;
(c) the GM in the bilged condition;
(d) the moment of statical stability if the vessel is heeled to 5°.

<u>*Solution (a)*</u>
Do a simple sketch.

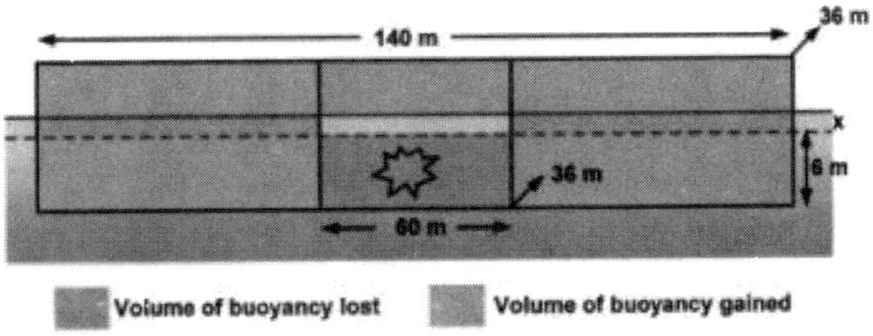

Fig. 22.4

VOLUME OF BUOYANCY LOST = VOLUME OF BUOYANCY GAINED

*Let **x** = sinkage*

$$60 \times 36 \times 6 = (140 - 60) \times 36 \times x$$
$$12960 = 2880x$$
$$x = 4.500 \text{ m}$$

*The draught in the bilged condition = 6.000 + 4.500 = **10.500 m (Ans)***

Solution (b)
To calculate the initial GM, first calculate KM.

$KM_{BOX} = KB + BM$

$$KB = \frac{Draught}{2} = \frac{6.000}{2} = 3.000 \text{ m}$$
$$BM = \frac{LB^3}{12V} = \frac{140 \times 36^3}{12 \times (140 \times 36 \times 6)} = 18.000 \text{ m}$$

Therefore: $KM = 3.000 + 18.000 = 21.000$ m

Calculate GM

$GM = KM - KG$ $\quad GM = 21.000 - 12.800 =$ **8.200 m (Ans)**

Solution (c)
To calculate the GM in the bilged condition, calculate KM.

Remember the assumptions:

KG remains constant;
Displacement (and volume of displacement) remains constant.

$KM_{BOX} = KB + BM$

$$KB = \frac{Draught}{2} = \frac{10.500}{2} = 5.250 \text{ m}$$

$$BM = \frac{LB^3}{12V} = \frac{(140 - 60) \times 36^3}{12 \times (140 \times 36 \times 6)} = 10.286 \text{ m}$$

Therefore: $KM = 5.250 + 10.286 = 15.536$ m

Calculate GM for the bilged condition.

$GM = KM - KG$ $\quad GM = 15.536 - 12.800 =$ **2.736 m (Ans)**

Solution (d)
Righting moment (t-m) = GZ × Displacement
$Displacement_{BOX}$ *= Length × Breadth × Draught × Density of water*
Since the displacement remains constant:
Displacement = 140 × 36 × 6 × 1.025 = 30996 tonnes
At 5°, a small angle of heel: $GZ = GM \times \text{Sine } \theta$
$\therefore$ *Righting moment (t-m) = (GM × Sine θ) × Displacement*
Righting moment (t-m) = (2.736 × Sine 5°) × 30996 = ***7391 t-m (Ans)***

22.1.3 Added weight method

This assumes that the floodwater entering the ship increases the displacement and affects the ship's KG by reason of the effect of added mass and (in some cases) the effect of the introduced free surface. Essentially the problem is approached in the same way that would apply when a tank is either partially or fully filled during routine ship operations. Example 1 will be reworked using this method.

<u>Example 1 (By added weight method)</u>

A box-shaped vessel has length 140 m, breadth 36 m and is on an even keel draught of 6 m in salt water. In the present condition the KG is 12.80 m. An empty amidships compartment extending the full breadth and depth of the vessel 60 m in length is bilged. Calculate:

(a) *the draught in the bilged condition;*
(b) *the initial GM;*
(c) *the GM in the bilged condition;*
(d) *the moment of statical stability if the vessel is heeled to 5°.*

<u>Solution (a)</u>

Do a sketch.

Calculate the mass of floodwater admitted into the compartment.

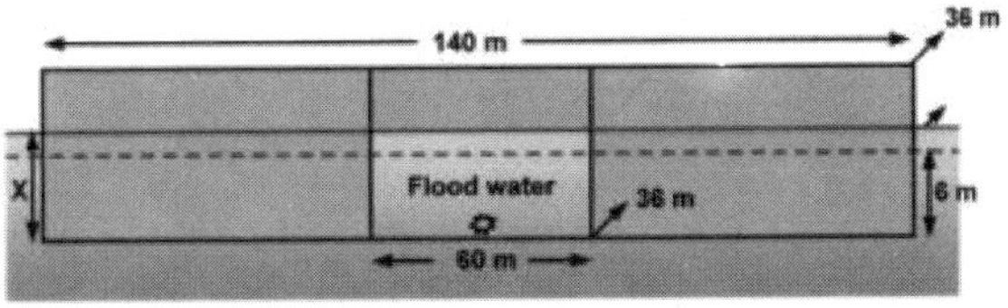

Fig. 22.5

*Let **X** equal the new draught after bilging.*

Added mass of water $= 60 \times 36 \times X \times 1.025 = 2214X$ *tonnes* **(1)**

Calculate the initial displacement.

Initial displacement $= 140 \times 36 \times 6 \times 1.025 = 30996$ *tonnes* **(2)**

Calculate the new displacement.

New displacement $= 140 \times 36 \times X \times 1.025 = 5166X$ *tonnes* **(3)**

Calculate the final draught (X).

New displacement (3) = Initial displacement (2) + mass of floodwater (1)

$5166X = 30996 + 2214X$

$\therefore \quad 5166X - 2214X = 30996$

$\therefore \quad 2952X = 30996$

$\therefore$ *X = draught in the bilged condition =* ***10.500 m (Ans)***

<u>Solution (b)</u>

To calculate the initial GM, first calculate KM.

$KM_{BOX} = KB + BM$

$$KB = \frac{Draught}{2} = \frac{6.000}{2} = 3.000 \text{ m}$$

$$BM = \frac{LB^3}{12V} = \frac{140 \times 36^3}{12 \times (140 \times 36 \times 6)} = 18.000 \text{ m}$$

Therefore: $KM = 3.000 + 18.000 = 21.000$ *m*

Calculate GM

$GM = KM - KG \qquad GM = 21.000 - 12.800 =$ ***8.200 m (Ans)***

<u>Solution (c)</u>

Calculate the final KG.

Initial displacement = 30996 tonnes

Mass of floodwater $= 60 \times 36 \times 10.5 \times 1.025 = 23247$ *tonnes*

Kg of the floodwater $= \frac{10.5}{2} = 5.25$ *m*

Introduced free surface moments $= \frac{lb^3}{12} \times dt = \frac{60 \times 36^3}{12} \times 1.025$

Free surface moments = 239112 t-m

Take moments about the keel.

	Weight (t)	KG (m)	Moments (t-m)
Initial	30996	12.800	396749
Flood water	23247	5.250	122047
FSM's			239112
Final	54243	**13.972**	757908

Calculate the final KM

$KM_{BOX} = KB + BM$

$KB = \frac{Draught}{2} = \frac{10.500}{2} = 5.250$ *m*

$BM = \frac{LB^3}{12V} = \frac{140 \times 36^3}{12 \times (140 \times 36 \times 10.5)} = 10.286$ *m*

Therefore: $KM = 5.250 + 10.286 = 15.536$ *m*

Calculate GM

$GM = KM - KG$ $\quad GM = 15.536 - 13.972 =$ ***1.564 m (Ans)***

Solution (d)

Righting moment (t-m) = GZ × Displacement

Final displacement = 54243 tonnes

At 5°, a small angle of heel: $GZ = GM \times \text{Sine } \theta$

$\therefore$ *Righting moment (t-m) = (GM × Sine θ) × Displacement*

Righting moment (t-m) = (1.564 × Sine 5°) × 54243 = ***7394 t-m (Ans)***

Disregarding the slight difference due to the rounding up of figures in the calculation this gives the same answer as by the lost buoyancy (constant displacement) method. Therefore, both methods of calculation are equally valid.

22.1.4 Method to use for bilging calculations

The two methods of calculation will give identical answers for the final draughts, trim and righting moment. Despite giving different values for GM (and GM_L), when the GM values are allied to the appropriate displacement value for the damaged condition they will give equal values of righting moment; remembering of course that the righting moment is the true measure of a vessels initial stability and not GM alone!

The lost buoyancy (constant displacement) approach is considered more appropriate when the damage is extensive and the floodwater is very much part of the sea. Because damage stability legislation assumes worst case scenarios all damaged stability calculations are conducted using this method. Consequently, *this is the method that should be adopted for examination purposes and will be used for the purposes of all other examples in this section.*

The added weight method may be considered more appropriate when the breach of the hull is small and the floodwater is more contained so that the effect of the water introduced is the same as that if it were introduced into an intact ship. Pumps may be able to limit the amount of water admitted and a level below the external waterline may be maintained, obviously in the calculation the worst-case scenario is considered.

22.2 THE EFFECTS OF BILGING AN EMPTY AMIDSHIPS COMPARTMENT WITH A WATERTIGHT FLAT (DOUBLE BOTTOM)

22.2.1 Floodwater confined below a watertight flat below the original waterline

Example 2

A box-shaped vessel floating on an even keel in salt water has the following particulars; length 110 m, breadth 22 m and draught 5.00 m.

There is an empty amidships bottom compartment 20 m in length extending the full breadth of the vessel with a watertight flat 4.80 m above the keel.

Calculate the change in GM if this compartment becomes bilged.

Solution

By the lost buoyancy (constant displacement) method:

KG remains constant;

Displacement (and volume of displacement) remains constant.

Therefore, any change in KM will equal the change in GM.

Do a simple sketch.

From the sketch it can be seen that the water plane area will remain intact since no part of the hull is flooded above the watertight flat.

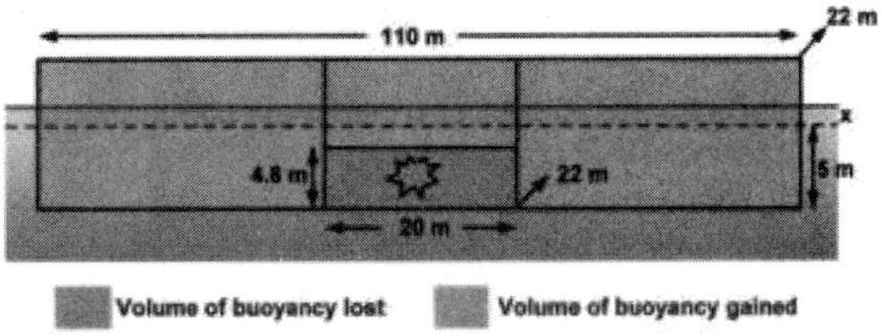

Fig. 22.6

VOLUME OF BUOYANCY LOST = VOLUME OF BUOYANCY GAINED

Let ***x*** *= sinkage*

$$20 \times 22 \times 4.8 = 110 \times 22 \times x$$
$$2112 = 2420x$$
$$x = 0.873 \text{ m}$$

Therefore the draught in the bilged condition = 5.000 + 0.873 = ***5.873 m***

To calculate the change in initial GM, calculate KM for the intact condition and then KM for the bilged condition. The difference in the values calculated will give the change in GM.

Intact KM

$KM_{BOX} = KB + BM$

$$KB = \frac{Draught}{2} = \frac{5.000}{2} = 2.500 \text{ m}$$

$$BM = \frac{LB^3}{12V} = \frac{110 \times 22^3}{12 \times (110 \times 22 \times 5)} = 8.067 \text{ m}$$

Therefore: $KM = 2.500 + 8.067 = 10.567 \text{ m}$

Bilged KM

$KM_{BOX} = KB + BM$

At the final waterline $KB \neq \frac{Draught}{2}$

Consider the shape of the new intact underwater volume of the vessel.

KB in the bilged condition will be greater than half the draught. To calculate the KB for the bilged condition it will be necessary to take 'moments of volume' about the keel in a similar way to taking moments about the keel when solving KG calculations.

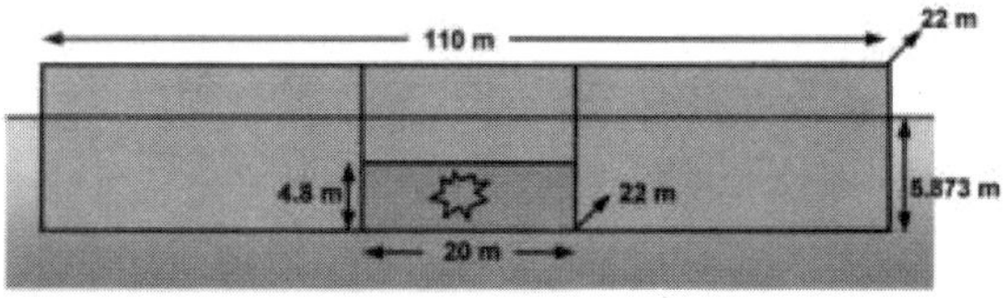

Fig. 22.7

	Volume (m3)	KB (m)	Moments (m4)
Total volume below final WL	(110 x 22 x 5.873)	5.873/2	41735.5
Volume of DB lost	-(20 x 22 x 4.8)	4.8/2	5068.8
Final	(110 x 22 x 5)	**3.030**	36666.7

KB = 3.030 m

(Note that the final volume of displacement (in red) is the same as the initial volume of displacement, so just use the original values!) $BM = \frac{LB^3}{12V}$

However, since the water plane area has remained fully intact and the volume of dsplacement does not change: Initial BM = Final BM = 8.067 m

Therefore: Final KM = 3.030 + 8.067 = 11.097 m

Change in GM = Change in KM

Initial KM	10.567
Final KM	11.097
Change in GM	**0.530**

GM has increased by 0.530 m (Ans)

In this instance the initial stability of the vessel has increased as a result of bilging the compartment. This is due to the addition of bottom weight with no introduced free surface moments (if the added weight method were to be considered).

22.2.2 Final waterline above the watertight flat

Example 3

A box-shaped vessel is floating on an even keel in salt water and has the following particulars: length 100 m, breadth 20 m and draught 5.50 m. There is an empty amidships bottom compartment of 18 m length that extends the full breadth of the vessel with a watertight flat 6.20 m above the keel.

Calculate the change in initial GM if this compartment becomes bilged.

Solution

By the lost buoyancy (constant displacement) method:

KG remains constant;

Displacement (and volume of displacement) remains constant.

Therefore, any change in KM will equal the change in GM.

Do a simple sketch.

Consider figure 22.8. The initial waterline is almost up to the level of the watertight flat. The approach here is to make the following assumption:

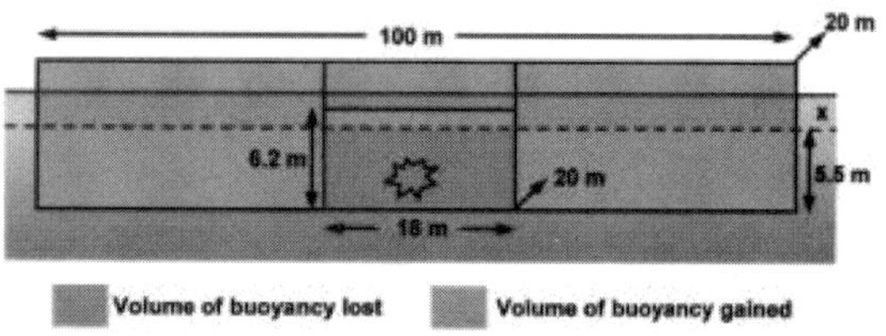

Fig. 22.8

'Assume that the final waterline is above the level of the watertight flat'

Calculate the problem on this basis and if it were found that the new draught is actually less than the height of the watertight flat, rework the problem as if it were an ordinary amidships compartment as in example 1, since the initial assumption made would be incorrect.

Note that the space in the bilged compartment between the initial waterline and the watertight flat is not part of the volume of buoyancy gained, since the compartment is now open to the sea when bilged.

VOLUME OF BUOYANCY LOST = VOLUME OF BUOYANCY GAINED

*Let **x** = sinkage* $(18 \times 20 \times 5.5) = (100 \times 20 \times x) - (18 \times 20 \times (6.2 - 5.5))$

$$1980 = 2000x - 252$$
$$1980 + 252 = 2000x$$
$$2232 = 2000x$$
$$x = 1.116 \text{ m}$$

*Therefore the draught in the bilged condition = 5.500 + 1.116 = **6.616 m***
Since this puts the final waterline above the watertight flat the assumption was correct.
To calculate the change in initial GM, calculate KM for the intact condition and then KM for the bilged condition.

Intact KM
$KM_{BOX} = KB + BM$

$KB = \frac{Draught}{2} = \frac{5.500}{2} = 2.750 \text{ m}$

$BM = \frac{LB^3}{12V} = \frac{100 \times 20^3}{12 \times (100 \times 20 \times 5.5)} = 6.061 \text{ m}$ *Therefore: KM = 2.750 + 6.061 = 8.811 m*

Bilged KM
$KM_{BOX} = KB + BM$
At the final waterline $KB \neq \frac{Draught}{2}$

Consider the shape of the new intact underwater volume of the vessel.

KB in the bilged condition will be greater than half the draught. To calculate the KB for the bilged condition take 'moments of volume' about the keel.

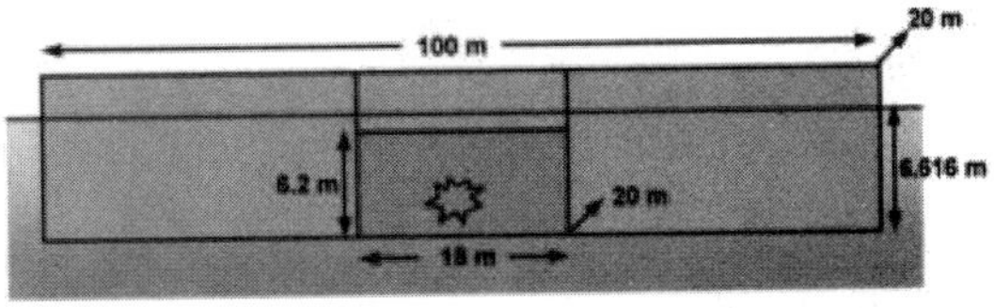

Fig. 22.9

	Volume (m3)	KB (m)	Moments (m4)
Total volume below final WL	(100 x 20 x 6.616)	6.616/2	43771.5
Volume of DB lost	-(18 x 20 x 6.2)	6.2/2	6919.2
Final	(100 x 20 x 5.5)	**3.350**	36852.3

KB = 3.350 m
$BM = \frac{LB^3}{12V}$

However, since the waterplane area has remained fully intact and the volume of displacement does not change: *Initial BM = Final BM = 6.061 m*
Therefore: *Final KM = 3.350 + 6.061 = 9.411 m*

Change in GM = Change in KM

Initial KM	8.811
Final KM	9.411
Change in GM	**0.600**

GM has increased by 0.600 m (Ans)

In this instance the initial stability of the vessel has increased as a result of bilging the compartment. This is due to the addition of bottom weight with no introduced free surface moments (if the added weight method were to be considered).

22.3 BILGING A COMPARTMENT WHEN PERMEABILITY IS LESS THAN 100%

The term *permeability* with respect to any compartment on a ship relates to the amount of space in that compartment that is capable of being filled with floodwater. An empty tank has a permeability of 100% (or 1.00). A completely full tank has a permeability of 0% (or 0.00). A widely used value for permeability of the engine room in a ship is taken as 85% (or 0.85); whereby 15% of the engine room is taken up by the machinery within it and 85% is void space capable of being flooded.

The previous examples assumed that the compartment being bilged was empty before bilging i.e. the compartment permeability was 100%. If the compartment has permeability less than 100%, by reasons of cargo in it for example, less floodwater will be admitted, the ship's bodily sinkage will be smaller, and the change of GM will be different to what would have arisen from bilging a compartment of permeability 100%.

In terms of the lost buoyancy (constant displacement) method, a smaller permeability will mean a smaller loss of buoyancy. Furthermore, if the reduced permeability applies at the final waterline, there will be less loss of water plane area and hence less loss of BM (since the volume of displacement remains constant). Unless there is data to suggest otherwise, the permeability that applies to the loss of volume of buoyancy will apply equally to the loss of water plane area. It should also be evident that some of the volume of buoyancy regained will include that of the cargo in the bilged compartment.

22.3.1 Bilging a compartment when permeability is less than 100% - permeability value given

Example 4

A box-shaped vessel has length 120 m, breadth 16 m and floats at an even keel draught of 6.00 m in salt water. There is an empty amidships compartment of length 20 m extending the full breadth of the vessel that has a permeability of 40%. If this compartment should become bilged calculate:

(a) the new draught, and;

(b) the change in GM.

Solution (a)

By the lost buoyancy (constant displacement) method:

KG remains constant;

Displacement (and volume of displacement) remains constant.

Therefore, any change in KM will equal the change in GM.

Do a simple sketch.

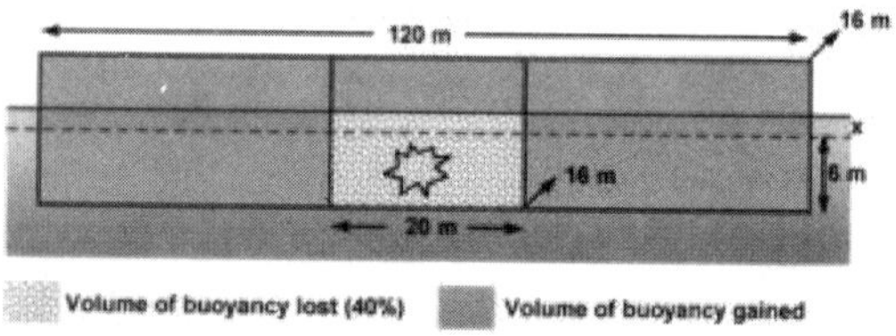

Fig. 22.10

VOLUME OF BUOYANCY LOST = VOLUME OF BUOYANCY GAINED

Let $\boldsymbol{x}$ *= sinkage*

$$(20 \times 16 \times 6 \times 0.40) = [(120 \times 16) - (20 \times 16 \times 0.40)\ x]$$

$$768 = (1920 - 128)x$$

$$768 = 1792x$$

$$x = 0.429\ m$$

Therefore the draught in the bilged condition = 6.000 + 0.429 = ***6.429 m***

Solution (b)

To calculate the change in initial GM, calculate KM for the intact condition and then KM for the bilged condition.

Intact KM

$KM_{BOX} = KB + BM$

$KB = \frac{Draught}{2} = \frac{6.000}{2} = 3.000\ m$

$BM = \frac{LB^3}{12V} = \frac{120 \times 16^3}{12 \times (120 \times 16 \times 6)} = 3.556\ m$

Therefore: $KM = 3.000 + 3.556 = 6.556\ m$

Bilged KM

$KM_{BOX} = KB + BM$

$KB = \frac{Draught}{2} = \frac{6.429}{2} = 3.215\ m$

$BM = \frac{LB^3}{12V}$

In this case not all of the WPA attributable to the bilged compartment is lost – only 40% of it. See figure 22.11.

Because it is the *transverse BM* that is required that portion of the water plane area lost may be considered as a strip running transversely.

Therefore, the remaining intact length of the water plane area is given by:

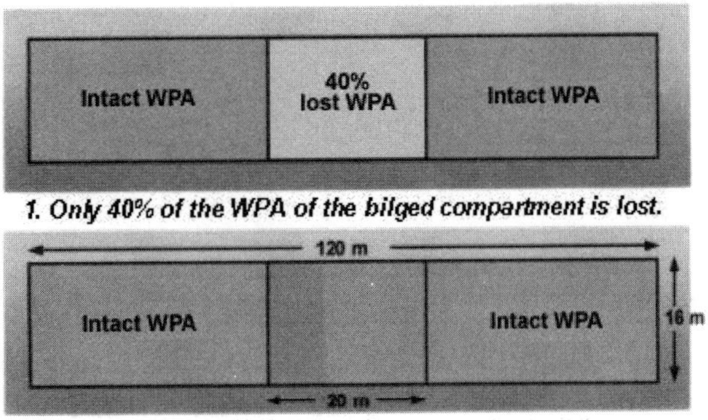

1. Only 40% of the WPA of the bilged compartment is lost.

2. Treating the lost WPA as a transverse strip of the bilged compartment then the effective intact length of the WPA = 120 – (0.40 × 20) metres.

Fig.22.11

Intact WPA length = 120 – (0.40 × 20) = 112 metres

Intact WPA breadth = 16 metres (unchanged)

These are the values that must be used to calculate the bilged condition BM.

Therefore: $BM = \frac{LB^3}{12V}$ $BM = \frac{(120 - (0.40 \times 20)) \times 16^3}{12 \times (120 \times 16 \times 6)} = 3.319\ m$

Therefore: $Final\ KM = 3.215 + 3.319 = 6.534\ m$

Initial KM	6.556
Final KM	6.534
Change in GM	**0.022**

Change in GM = Change in KM

In this instance the initial stability of the vessel has reduced due to the fall in KM.

22.3.2 Calculating the permeability for a compartment

The permeability value for a compartment may be calculated from data relating to the stowage factor and the *true* density of the cargo.

Example 5

A hold has length 30 m, breadth 12 m and a depth of 8 m. Coal having a stowage factor (SF) of 1.36 m^3/t is loaded into the hold until completely full. If the true density of the coal is 1.20 t/m^3, calculate the permeability of the compartment.

Note that the true density is that which applies to the individual pieces of coal cargo and does not take account of any void spaces that might exist in between those coal pieces. SF takes account of the voids in between the pieces of coal.

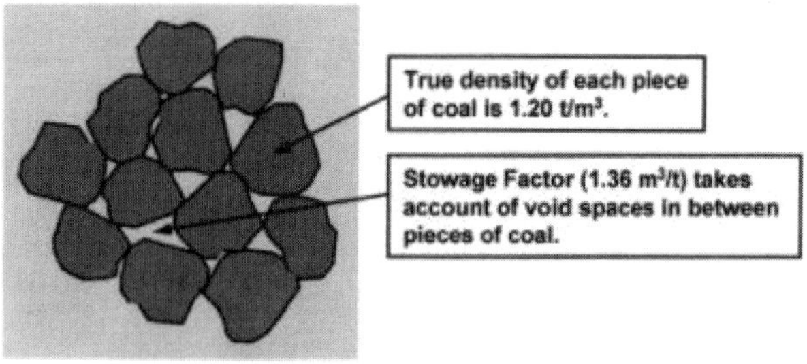
True density of each piece of coal is 1.20 t/m³.
Stowage Factor (1.36 m³/t) takes account of void spaces in between pieces of coal.

Fig. 22.12

Solution (Method 1)

Compartment volume $= 30 \times 12 \times 8 = 2880\ m^3$

Maximum mass of coal that compartment can hold $= \dfrac{\text{Volume}}{\text{SF}} = \dfrac{2880}{1.36} = 2118\ t$

Volume of actual coal in the compartment (ignoring voids) $= \dfrac{\text{mass}}{\text{Density}}$

$$= \frac{2118}{1.20} = 1765\ m^3$$

Therefore, Void space in the compartment $= 2880 - 1765 = 1115\ m^3$

Permeability $= \dfrac{\text{Void space}}{\text{Total space}} = \dfrac{1115}{2880} = $ ***0.387 (38.7%) (Ans)***

A formula for calculating permeability is derived as follows:

$$\text{Permeability} = \frac{\text{Void space}}{\text{Total space}} = \frac{\text{Total space} - \text{Filled space}}{\text{Total space}}$$

Therefore: $\text{Permeability} = \dfrac{(\text{mass} \times \text{SF}) - (\text{mass/density})}{\text{mass} \times \text{SF}}$

where: $\dfrac{\text{mass}}{\text{density}}$ = the 'solid' SF

$$\text{Permeability} = \frac{\text{mass} \times (\text{SF} - 1/\text{density})}{\text{mass} \times \text{SF}}$$

Therefore: $\text{Permeability} = \dfrac{\text{SF} - 1/\text{density}}{\text{SF}}$

The symbol for permeability is μ.

$$\boldsymbol{\mu = \frac{SF - 1/RD}{SF}}$$

Consider the previous example where the coal had density 1.20t/m^3 and SF 1.36 m^3/t.

Solution (Method 2)

$\mu = \dfrac{SF - 1/RD}{SF} = \dfrac{1.36 - 1/1.20}{1.36} = \mathbf{0.387\ (38.7\%)\ (Ans)}$

Example 6 is a particularly awkward problem whereby a compartment above a double bottom tank becomes bilged and permeability has to be calculated.

Example 6

A box-shaped vessel has length 140 m, breadth 26 m and is floating on an even keel draught of 5.80 m in salt water. There is a double bottom tank, depth 1.50 m, with a hold above. Both compartments are 36 m in length and extend the full breadth of the vessel. Homogenous cargo in the hold stows at 1.42 m^3/t and has RD 1.28. The vessel suffers side damage and the hold becomes bilged. Calculate:

(a) the final draught;

(b) the change in GM.

Solution (a)

Calculate the permeability of the bilged compartment. $\mu = \dfrac{SF - 1/RD}{SF} = \dfrac{1.42 - 1/1.28}{1.42} = 0.45\ (45\%)$

By the lost buoyancy (constant displacement) method:

KG remains constant;

Displacement (and volume of displacement) remains constant.

Therefore, any change in KM will equal the change in GM.

Do a simple sketch.

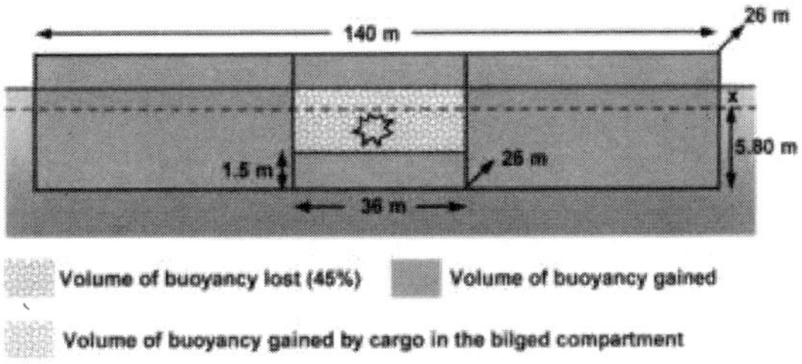

Fig. 22.13

VOLUME OF BUOYANCY LOST = VOLUME OF BUOYANCY GAINED

*Let **x** = sinkage* $36 \times 26 \times (5.8 - 1.5) \times 0.45 = \{(140 \times 26) - (36 \times 26 \times 0.45)\ x\}$

$1811.2 = (3640 - 421.2)x$

$1811.2 = 3218.8x$

$x = 0.563\ m$

*Therefore the draught in the bilged condition = 5.800 + 0.563 = **6.363 m***

Solution (b)

To calculate the change in initial GM, calculate KM for the intact condition and then KM for the bilged condition.

Intact KM

$KM_{BOX} = KB + BM$

$KB = \dfrac{Draught}{2} = \dfrac{5.800}{2} = 2.900\ m$

$BM = \dfrac{LB^3}{12V} = \dfrac{140 \times 26^3}{12 \times (140 \times 26 \times 5.8)} = 9.713\ m$

Therefore: $KM = 2.900 + 9.713 = 12.613\ m$

Bilged KM

$KM_{BOX} = KB + BM$

At the final waterline KB ≠ $\frac{\text{Draught}}{2}$

Consider the shape of the new intact underwater volume of the vessel.

To calculate the KB for the bilged condition take 'moments of volume' about the keel.

Remember that cargo is still displacing water in the bilged space and must be accounted for. The Kb of the bilged hold is calculated by:

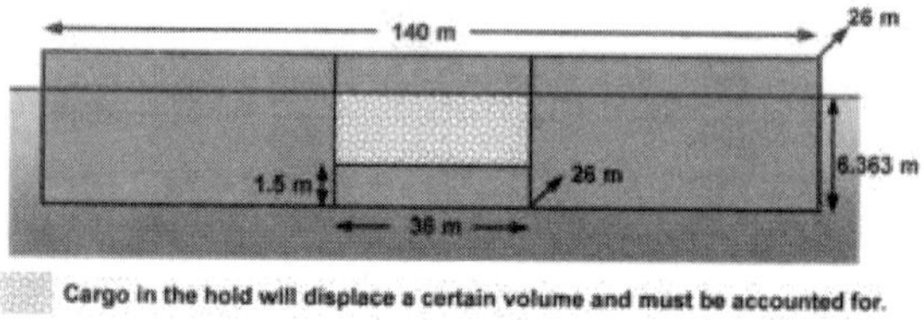

Fig. 22.14

$1.5 + \frac{(6.363 - 1.5)}{2} = 3.932\ m$ *(Study figure 22.14 if in doubt.)*

	Volume (m3)	KB (m)	Moments (m4)
Total volume below final WL	(140 x 26 x 6.363)	6.363/2	73688
Volume of DB lost	-(36 x 26 x 4.863 x 0.45)	3.932	8054
Final	(140 x 26 x 5.8)	**3.109**	65634

KB = 3.109 m

$BM = \frac{LB^3}{12V}$

Only 45% of the water plane area attributable to the bilged hold is lost.

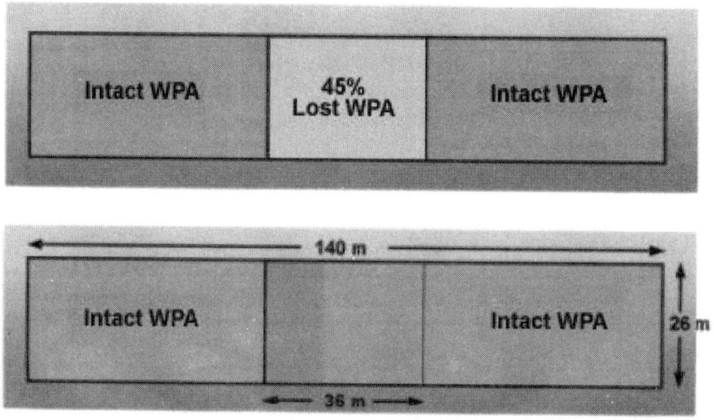

Fig. 22.15

$BM = \frac{LB^3}{12V}$ $BM = \frac{(140 - (36 \times 0.45)) \times 26^3}{12 \times (140 \times 26 \times 5.8)}$ $= 8.589\ m$

Therefore: *Final KM = 3.109 + 8.589 = 11.698 m*

Initial KM	12.613
Final KM	11.698
Change in GM	**0.915**

Change in GM = Change in KM

*GM has **decreased**.*

22.4 CALCULATING THE DRAUGHTS WHEN AN END COMPARTMENT BECOMES BILGED

If an end compartment becomes bilged the vessel will suffer both bodily sinkage and a change of trim. The bodily sinkage is calculated as if the compartment were sited amidships. The compartment is then 'shifted' in the calculation to allow the change of trim to be calculated. The change of trim that takes place will depend on the MCTC value for the bilged condition.

Being a box-shaped vessel, in calculations it is usually required that the MCTC value be calculated using:

$$\mathbf{MCTC = \frac{W \times GM_L}{100LBP}}$$

The derivation of this formula was demonstrated in section 12.6.

In examinations it is (usually) only required to solve questions where the bilged compartment has a permeability of 100%.

22.4.1 Bilging an extreme end compartment with 100% permeability

Example 7

A box-shaped vessel has length 75 m, breadth 12 m and is floating on an even keel draught in salt water of 2.5 m. In this condition the KG is 3.00 m. An empty forward end compartment of length 6 m extending the full breadth and depth of the vessel is bilged.
Calculate the draughts in the flooded condition.

Solution

By the lost buoyancy (constant displacement) method:
KG remains constant;
Displacement (and volume of displacement) remains constant.

By assuming that the compartment is amidships calculate the new mean draught

Do a simple sketch.

1. *Calculate the new mean draught*

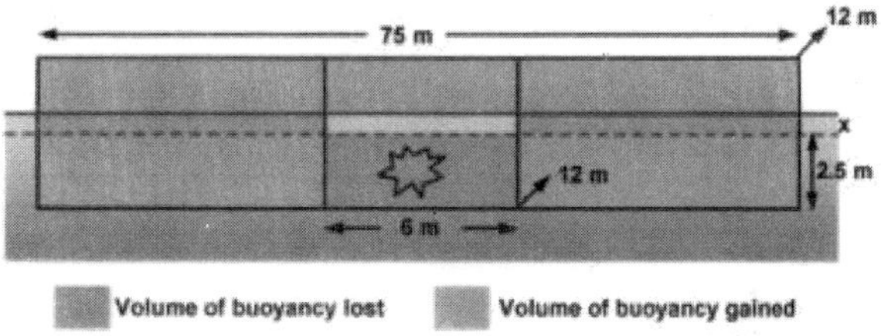

Fig. 22.16

VOLUME OF BUOYANCY LOST = VOLUME OF BUOYANCY GAINED

*Let **x** = sinkage* $6 \times 12 \times 2.5 = \left[(75 - 6) \times 12 \right] x$

$180 = 828x$

$x = 0.217$ m

Therefore the mean draught in the bilged condition = 2.500 + 0.217 = ***2.717 m***

2. *Move the compartment to its actual position and calculate the trimming moment*

Consider figure 22.17.

Initially the LCG and LCB are in the same longitudinal position at amidships (since the vessel is on an even keel). The change of trim is caused by the loss of volume of buoyancy forward which causes the LCB to move aft (B to B_1). This creates a trimming moment given by:

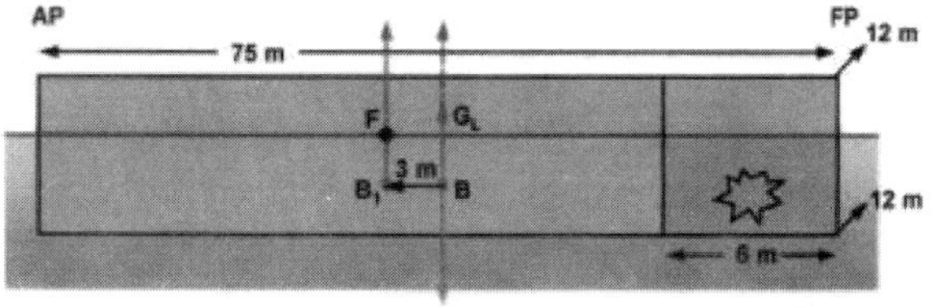

Fig. 22.17

Trimming moment (t-m) = $W \times BB_1$

Because of the symmetry of the intact volume it follows that the trimming lever (BB_1) *= 3 m, being half the length of the bilged compartment.*

∴ *Trimming moment =* $(75 \times 12 \times 2.5 \times 1.025) \times 3 =$ ***6918.75 t-m***
(Displacement remains constant!)

3. *Calculate MCTC*

$$MCTC = \frac{W \times GM_L}{100LBP}$$

where $GM_L = KM_L - KG$
First calculate the KM_L *for the bilged condition.*
$KM_L = KB + BM_L$

In the bilged condition: $KB = \frac{Draught}{2} = \frac{2.717}{2} = 1.359\ m$

$$BM_L = \frac{BL^3}{12V}$$

The water plane area afforded by the bilged compartment has been lost, therefore:

$$BM_L = \frac{12 \times (75-6)^3}{12 \times (75 \times 12 \times 2.5)} = 146.004\ m$$

Therefore: $KM_L = 1.359 + 146.004 = 147.363\ m$

$GM_L = KM_L - KG$ $GM_L = 147.363 - 3.000 = 144.363\ m$
(KG remains constant!)

$$MCTC = \frac{W \times GM_L}{100LBP}$$

$$MCTC = \frac{(75 \times 12 \times 2.5 \times 1.025) \times 144.363}{100 \times 75} = 44.392\ t\text{-}m$$

(Note that LBP is 75 m, do not use the effective length of the remaining water plane area by mistake!)

4. *Calculate the change of trim*

$$COT\ (cms) = \frac{Trimming\ moment}{MCTC} = \frac{6918.75}{44.392} = 155.9\ cms\ by\ the\ head$$

5. *Apportion the change of trim to the forward and aft draughts*

Consider figure 22.17. Because the water plane area afforded by the bilged compartment forward is lost the LCF will move aft. Because of the symmetry of the box shaped vessel the movement of the LCF aft will be the same as the movement of the LCB (BB_1)*, which is 3 m.*
Therefore, the new position of the LCF is 34.5 m foap.

$Ta = COT \times \frac{a}{L}$ $Ta = 155.9 \times \frac{34.5}{75} = 71.7\ cms$

$Tf = COT - Ta$ $Tf = 155.9 - 71.7 = 84.2\ cms$

	Fwd	Aft
Final mean	2.717	2.717
Trim	0.842	0.717
FINAL	**3.559**	**2.000**

Apply Ta and Tf to the final mean draught of 2.717 m.

22.4.2 Bilging an extreme end compartment with a watertight flat - 100% permeability

Example 8

A box-shaped vessel has length 100 m, breadth 18 m and is floating on an even keel draught in salt water of 4.0 m. In this condition the KG is 6.8 m. An empty forward end compartment of length 10 m below a watertight flat 3 m above the keel and extending the full breadth of the vessel is bilged. Calculate the draughts in the flooded condition.

Solution

By the lost buoyancy (constant displacement) method:

KG remains constant;

Displacement (and volume of displacement) remains constant.

By assuming that the compartment is amidships calculate the new mean draught

Do a simple sketch

1. *Calculate the new mean draught*

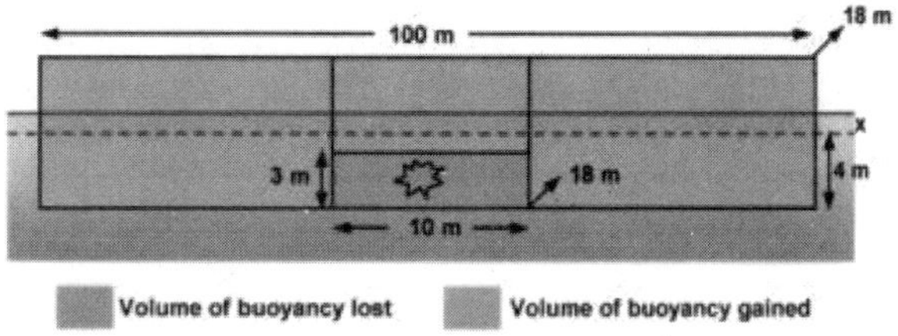

Fig. 22.18

VOLUME OF BUOYANCY LOST = VOLUME OF BUOYANCY GAINED

*Let **x** = sinkage*

$$10 \times 18 \times 3 = (100 \times 18 \times)\, x$$
$$540 = 1800x$$
$$x = 0.300 \text{ m}$$

*Therefore the mean draught in the bilged condition = 4.00 + 0.300 = **4.300 m***

2. *Move the compartment to its actual position and calculate the trimming moment Consider figure 22.19.*

Initially the LCG and LCB are in the same longitudinal position at amidships (since the vessel is on an even keel). The change of trim is caused by the loss of volume of buoyancy forward which causes the LCB to move aft (B to B_1) where the trimming moment is given by:

Trimming moment (t-m) = $W \times BB_1$

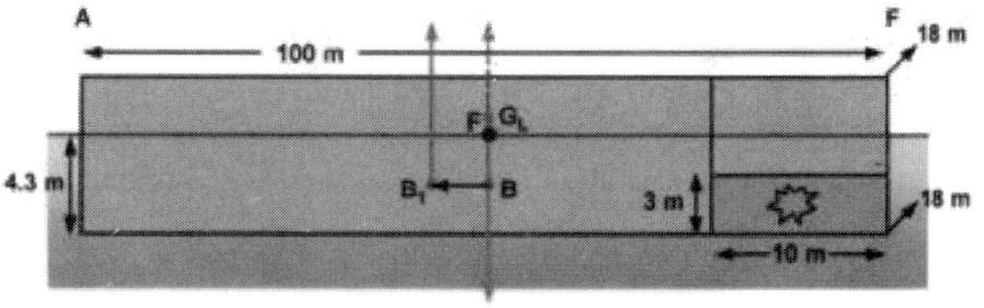

Fig. 22.19

It is necessary to take moments of volume about the AP to find the new LCB.

	Volume (m3)	lcb foap (m)	Moments (m4)
Total volume below final WL	(100 x 18 x 4.3)	50	387000
Volume of DB lost	-(10 x 18 x 3)	95	51300
Final	(100 x 18 x 4)	**46.625**	335700

LCB moves aft from a position 50 m foap to 46.625 m foap.

Trimming lever = 50 – 46.625 = 3.375 m

∴ *Trimming moment = (100 × 18 × 4 × 1.025) × 3.375 = **24907.5 t-m***
(Displacement remains constant!)

3. *Calculate MCTC* $MCTC = \frac{W \times GM_L}{100LBP}$

where $GM_L = KM_L - KG$

First calculate the KM_L *for the bilged condition.*

$KM_L = KB + BM_L$

At the final waterline $KB \neq \frac{Draught}{2}$

Consider the shape of the new intact underwater volume of the vessel in figure 22.19.
To calculate the KB for the bilged condition take 'moments of volume' about the keel.

In the bilged condition KB = 2.199 m

	Volume (m3)	KB (m)	Moments (m4)
Total volume below final WL	(100 x 18 x 4.3)	4.3/2	16641
Volume of DB lost	-(10 x 18 x 3)	3/2	810
Final	(100 x 18 x 4)	**2.199**	15831

$BM_L = \frac{BL^3}{12V}$

The water plane area afforded by the bilged compartment has remained intact due to the watertight flat, therefore:

$$BM_L = \frac{18 \times 100^3}{12 \times (100 \times 18 \times 4)} = 208.333 \text{ m}$$

Therefore: $KM_L = 2.199 + 208.333 = 210.532$ m

$GM_L = KM_L - KG$ $GM_L = 210.532 - 6.800 = 203.732$ m

(KG remains constant!)

$$MCTC = \frac{W \times GM_L}{100LBP}$$

$$MCTC = \frac{(100 \times 18 \times 4 \times 1.025) \times 203.732}{100 \times 100} = 150.354 \text{ t-m}$$

4. *Calculate the change of trim*

$COT \text{ (cms)} = \frac{\text{Trimming moment}}{MCTC} = \frac{24907.5}{150.354} = 165.7$ *cms by the head*

5. *Apportion the change of trim to the forward and aft draughts*

Because the water plane area has remained intact the position of the LCF remains unchanged at amidships.

Therefore, $Ta = Tf = \frac{165.7}{2} = 82.9$ *cms*

Apply Ta and Tf to the final mean draught of 4.300 m.

	Fwd	Aft
Final mean	4.300	4.300
Trim	0.829	0.829
FINAL	**5.129**	**3.471**

22.5 CALCULATING THE LIST WHEN AN AMIDSHIPS SIDE COMPARTMENT IS BILGED – PERMEABILITY 100%

22.5.1 Moment of inertia

We know that for a box-shaped vessel: $BM_{BOX} = \frac{LB^3}{12V}$ where: $\frac{LB^3}{12}$

is the moment of inertia of the water plane area, and V is the volume of displacement of the vessel.

The most influential factor affecting the BM is the size of the water plane area, but in particular, the breadth. Many students have difficulty understanding the value of the 'moment of inertia' (I) because it is difficult to picture. A way of thinking about the role that the moment of inertia plays is to consider that *the water plane area offers the ship resistance to rolling*. This is true because the greater the water plane area, and particularly the breadth; the greater will be BM, and consequently KM and GM, giving the ship greater initial stability.

The moment of inertia about an axis (of rotation) is equal to the product of an area and the square of its distance from that axis.

This will be looked at in more detail. The way to picture this is to consider that the ship stays upright and the water plane area rotates about a longitudinal axis of rotation that passes through the centre of flotation (instead of the ship rolling and the water line remaining horizontal).

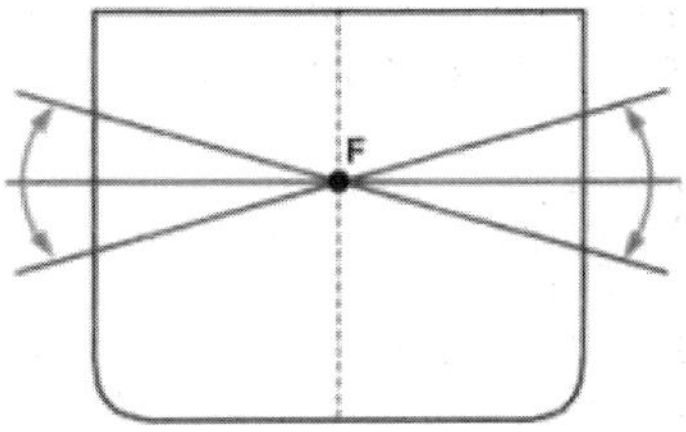

Fig. 22.20

22.5.2 Moments of inertia of rectangular water plane areas

The *smallest* values of moment of inertia for any rectangular water plane area occur when the axis of rotation (longitudinal or transverse) passes through the centroid of the water plane area concerned i.e. the axis of rotation passes through the centre of flotation (which is at the geometric centre of the water plane area).

The smallest *transverse* value of I is given by:

$$I_{II} = \frac{LB^3}{12}$$

The smallest *longitudinal* value of I is given by:

$$I_{LL} = \frac{BL^3}{12}$$

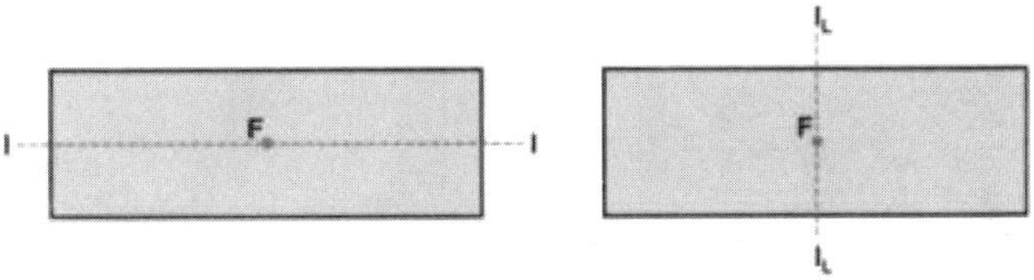

1.Smallest transverse value of I. 2.Smallest longitudinal value of I.

Fig. 22.21

The moment of inertia about an axis passing *along one edge* of the water plane area can also be found.

These values may be calculated as follows:

$$I_{XX} = \frac{LB^3}{3} \qquad I_{YY} = \frac{BL^3}{3}$$

The derivation of these formulae is not important, but use of them will allow the calculation of the moment of inertia of the water plane area when an amidships side compartment becomes bilged.

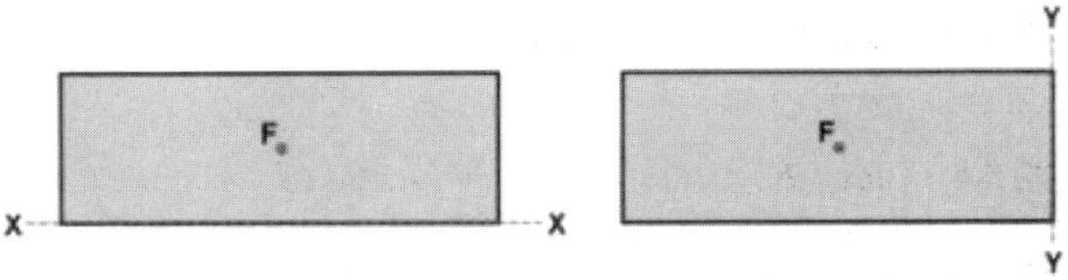

1. Transverse value of I about one edge. 2. Longitudinal value of I about one edge.

Fig. 22.22

22.5.3 The parallel axes theorem

This states that:

'the moment of inertia about any axis passing through the centroid of a water plane area is equal to the moment of inertia of the same water plane area about any parallel axis, minus the area of the water plane multiplied by the distance between the axes squared.'

Consider figure 22.23.

The moment of inertia about the axis **II** (which passes through the centre of flotation) is equal to the moment of inertia about the axis **XX** minus the product of the water plane area and the distance between the axes squared i.e.

$$\mathbf{I_{II} = I_{XX} - (A \times d^2)}$$

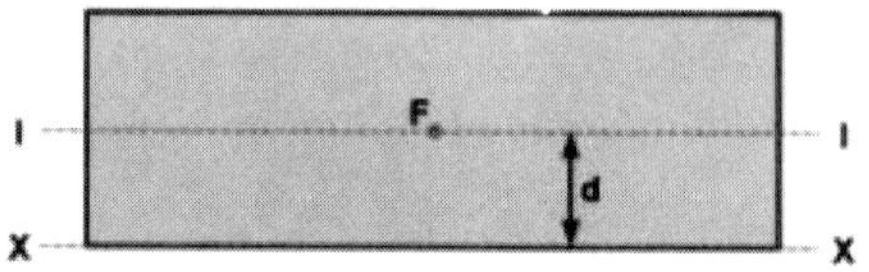

Fig. 22.23

For this formula to be true the two axes must be *parallel* and one of them must *pass through the centroid of the area* concerned.

Example 9

A box-shaped vessel has length 20 m and breadth 6 m.
Calculate:
- *(a) the moment of inertia for all the axis' of rotation shown;*
- *(b) the moment of inertia about the two axis' passing through the centre of flotation using the parallel axis' theorem.*

Solution (a)

$I_{II} = \dfrac{LB^3}{12} = \dfrac{20 \times 6^3}{12} = \mathbf{360\ m^4}$

$I_{LL} = \dfrac{BL^3}{12} = \dfrac{6 \times 20^3}{12} = \mathbf{4000\ m^4}$

$I_{XX} = \dfrac{LB^3}{3} = \dfrac{20 \times 6^3}{3} = \mathbf{1440\ m^4}$

$I_{YY} = \dfrac{BL^3}{3} = \dfrac{6 \times 20^3}{3} = \mathbf{16000\ m^4}$

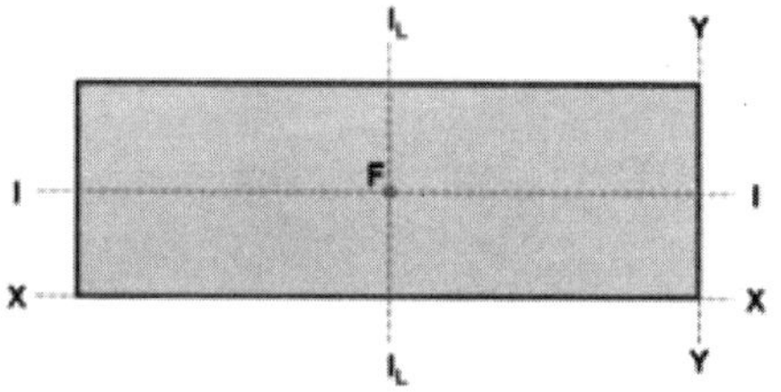

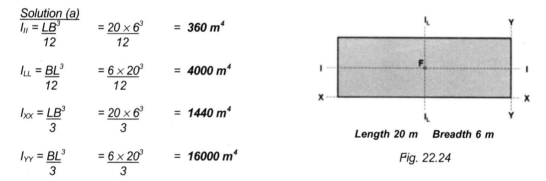

Length 20 m Breadth 6 m

Fig. 22.24

Solution (b)

Using the parallel axis theorem: $I_{II} = I_{XX} - (A \times d^2)$ *where d = 3 m:*
$I_{II} = 1440 - (20 \times 6 \times 3^2) = \mathbf{360\ m^4}$

Using the parallel axis theorem: $I_{LL} = I_{YY} - (A \times d^2)$ *where d = 10 m:*
$I_{LL} = 16000 - (20 \times 6 \times 10^2) = \mathbf{4000\ m^4}$

22.5.4 Calculating the moment of inertia of a water plane area of a box-shaped vessel with a bilged side compartment

The parallel axis theorem previously described will be used to calculate the moment of inertia of the water plane area of a box-shaped vessel where an amidships side compartment has become bilged. This will be necessary in order to find the KM, and hence GM of the vessel in the bilged condition.
Consider figure 22.25.

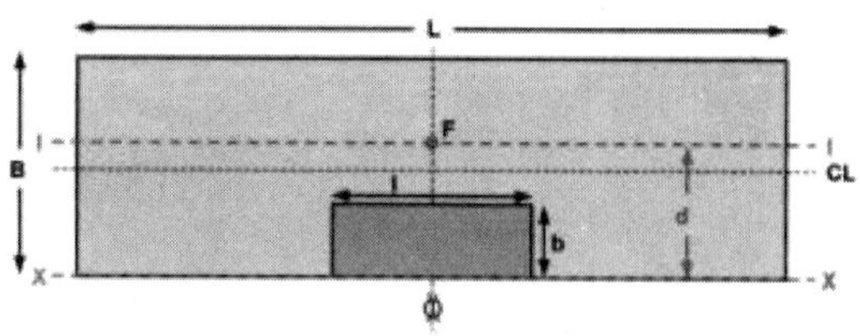

Fig. 22.25

When an amidships side compartment extending upwards the full depth of the vessel becomes bilged the centre of flotation (F) will move off the centre line, its new position with reference to side XX (axis XX) may be calculated by taking moments of area about one side. This will give the distance, **d**, between the two axes to be considered.

In order to calculate the BM in the bilged condition it will be necessary to calculate the new value of the transverse moment of inertia of the remaining intact water plane area about the new longitudinal axis of rotation passing through the new position of the centre of flotation (about axis II). This is achieved by using the parallel axis theorem whereby:

$$\mathbf{I_{II} = I_{XX} - (A \times d^2)}$$

where:

$$\mathbf{I_{XX} = \frac{LB^3}{3} - \frac{lb^3}{3}} \qquad \textbf{(1)}$$

and the intact water plane area is given by:

$$\mathbf{A = (LB) - (lb)} \qquad \textbf{(2)}$$

Combining formulae (1) and (2) above will allow the transverse moment of inertia of the damaged water plane area to be calculated:

$$\mathbf{I_{II} = \left(\frac{LB^3}{3} - \frac{lb^3}{3}\right) - \left((LB - lb) \times d^2\right)}$$

Once the value of I has been calculated, this is used to determine the BM in the bilged condition. Consider the next example.

<u>*Example 10*</u>

A box shaped vessel has length 96 m and breadth 18 m and floats at an even keel draught of 4.6 m in salt water. An amidships side compartment of length 24 m extending in from the side 6 m is bilged. Calculate:

(a) the initial BM value;

(b) the BM in the damaged condition.

<u>*Solution (a)*</u>

In the intact condition: $BM = \dfrac{LB^3}{12V}$

$$BM = \frac{96 \times 18^3}{12 \times (96 \times 18 \times 4.6)} = \mathbf{5.870m\ (Ans)}$$

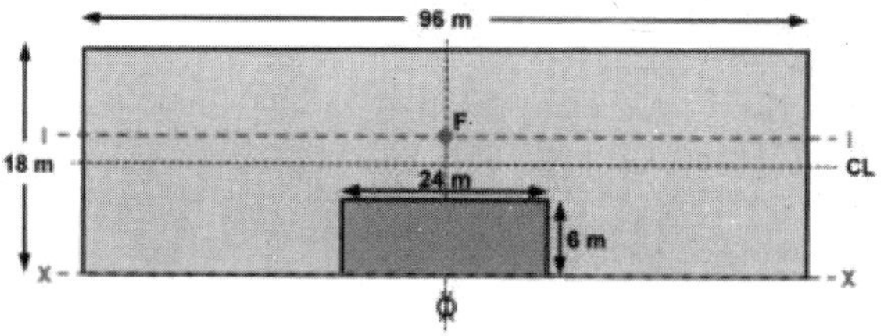

Fig. 22.26

<u>*Solution (b)*</u>

To calculate the BM in the damaged condition: $\mathbf{I_{II} = I_{XX} - (A \times d^2)}$

$$\mathbf{I_{II} = \left(\frac{LB^3}{3} - \frac{lb^3}{3}\right) - \left((LB - lb) \times d^2\right)}$$

1. Calculate the distance of the new LCF from one side of the WPA (XX in figure 22.26)

Take moments of area about side XX

	Area (m2)	Dist. From XX	Moments
Total Area	(96 x 18)	9	15552
Area bilged compartment	-(24 x 6)	3	432
Final	1584	**9.545**	15120

LCF is now 9.545 m from side XX.

2. *Calculate the transverse moment of inertia about the axis passing through the new position of the LCF*

$$I_{ll} = \left(\frac{LB^3}{3} - \frac{lb^3}{3}\right) - \left[(LB - lb) \times d^2 \right]$$

$$I_{ll} = \left(\frac{(96 \times 18^3)}{3} - \frac{(24 \times 6^3)}{3}\right) - \left(\left[(96 \times 18) - (24 \times 6)\right] \times 9.545^2\right)$$

$$I_{ll} = \left[186624 - 1728\right] - \left[(1728 - 144) \times 9.545^2\right]$$

$I_{ll} = 184896 - (1584 \times 9.545^2)$
$I_{ll} = 40582\ m^4$

3. *Calculate the BM for the bilged condition* $BM = \frac{I}{V}$

Using the lost buoyancy (constant displacement) method the volume of displacement remains constant, therefore: $BM = \frac{40582}{(96 \times 18 \times 4.6)}$ = ***5.105 m (Ans)***

22.5.5 Calculating the angle of list resulting from an amidships side compartment becoming bilged.

Consider a box-shaped vessel with side compartments amidships as in figure 22.27. **F** is the centre of flotation initially on the centre line. The vessel is floating upright on an even keel when a side compartment becomes bilged. The volume of buoyancy lost is shown.

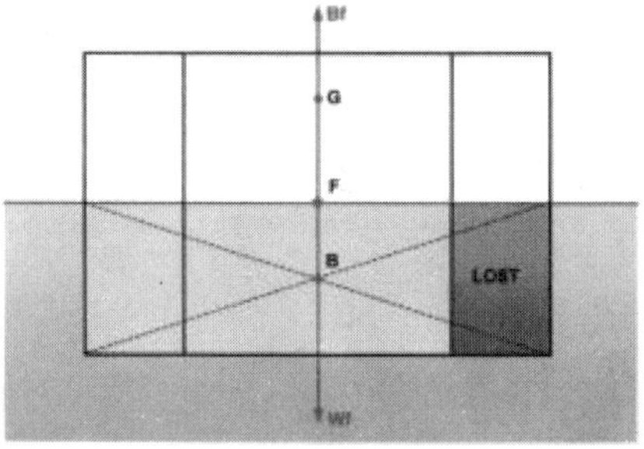

Fig. 22.27

The vessel will sink to regain the buoyancy lost. Figure 22.28 illustrates the shape of the buoyancy gained.

Because the water plane area has changed shape the centre of flotation moves off the centre line of the vessel (F to F_1). This causes the axis of rotation of the water plane area to move off the centre line as already discussed.

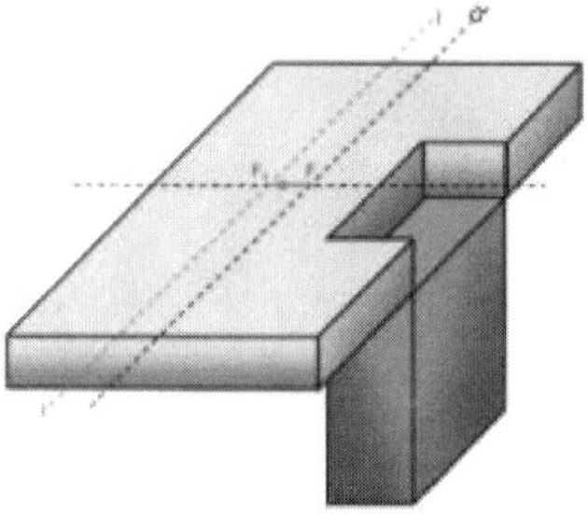

Fig. 22.28

Figure 22.29 shows the vessel after it has experienced sinkage but before it lists.

The transfer of the volume of buoyancy (**b** to $\mathbf{b_1}$) causes the centre of buoyancy, **B**, to move off the centre line (and upwards) to $\mathbf{B_1}$. The *horizontal* component of this shift creates the listing lever, which is equal to **GX**.

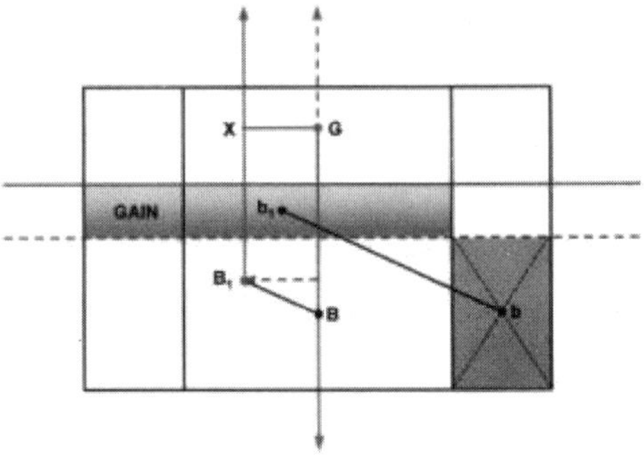

Fig. 22.29

The vessel will now list over to the bilged side (figure 22.30).

$\text{Tan } \theta_{LIST} = \frac{OPP}{ADJ} = \frac{GX}{XM} = \frac{BB_H}{XM}$

Where XM is the GM in the bilged condition.

Because of the symmetry of a box-shaped vessel BB_H is equal to the movement of the centre of flotation off the centre line (FF_1) that is found by taking moments of area of the water plane area about one edge (see example 10).

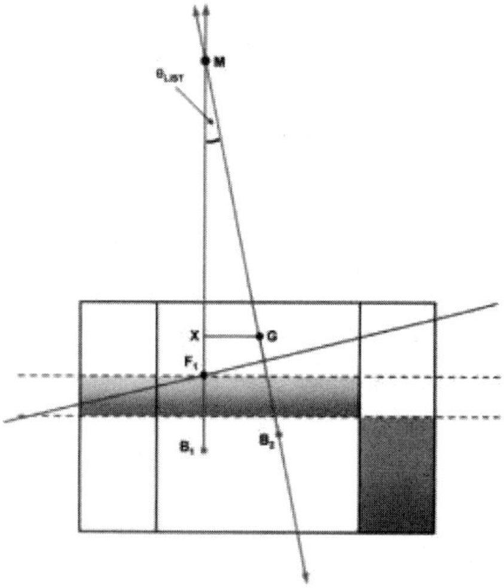

Fig. 22.30

Therefore:

$$\textbf{Tan } \theta_{LIST} = \frac{BB_H}{GM_{BILGED}}$$

Note

When calculating list arising from the loading, discharging or shifting of weights the formula:

$$\textbf{Tan } \theta_{LIST} = \frac{GG_H}{GM}$$ is used.

In this instance, GG_H is the cause of the list, which represents the distance that the *centre of gravity* of the ship is off the centre line at the time for which the list is being calculated.

When calculating the list caused by the bilging of a side compartment the formula:

$$\textbf{Tan } \theta_{LIST} = \frac{BB_H}{GM_{BILGED}}$$ is used.

Here the list is being caused by the *horizontal component of the movement of the centre of buoyancy* and the GM is that which applies to the vessel's damaged condition.

Example 11

A box-shaped vessel floating upright on an even keel in saltwater has the following particulars:

Length 120 m Breadth 25 m Draught 6.00 m KG 5.80 m

The vessel has a centre line watertight bulkhead with an empty amidships side compartment of 20m length.

Calculate the angle of list when this compartment becomes bilged.

Solution

By the lost buoyancy (constant displacement) method:

KG remains constant;

Displacement (and volume of displacement) remains constant.

Do a simple sketch.

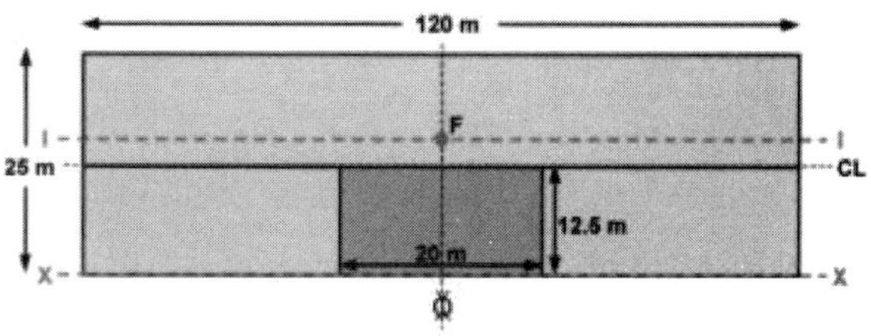

Fig. 22.31

1. *Calculate the sinkage and new upright draught.*

Consider the shapes of the volumes of buoyancy gained and lost.

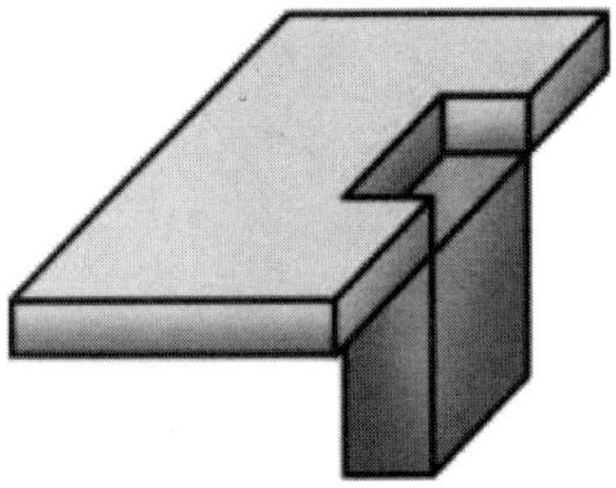

Fig. 22.32

VOLUME OF BUOYANCY LOST = VOLUME OF BUOYANCY GAINED

Let $\boldsymbol{x}$ *= sinkage* $\quad 20 \times 12.5 \times 6 = \left((120 \times 25) - (20 \times 12.5) \times\right) x$

$$1500 = 2750x$$

$$x = 0.545 \text{ m}$$

Therefore the mean draught in the bilged condition = 6.000 + 0.545 = ***6.545 m***

2. *Calculate the new position of the LCF from side XX (and hence BB_H)*

Take moments of area about side XX.

	Area (m2)	Dist. From XX	Moments
Total Area	(120 x 25)	12.5	37500
Area bilged compartment	-(20 x 12.5)	12.5/2	1562.5
Final	2750	**13.068**	35937.5

LCF is now 13.068 m from side XX.

Since the LCF has moved of the centre line by an amount equal to: 13.068 – 12.5 = 0.568m

BB_H is also equal to ***0.568 m.***

The distance between the axes to be used = ***13.068 m****.*

3. *Calculate the transverse moment of inertia about the axis passing through the new position of the LCF* $\quad \mathbf{I_{II} = I_{XX} - (A \times d^2)}$

$$I_{II} = \left(\frac{LB^3}{3} - \frac{lb^3}{3}\right) - \left((LB - lb) \times d^2\right)$$

$$I_{II} = \left(\frac{(120 \times 25^3)}{3} - \frac{(20 \times 12.5^3)}{3}\right) - \left(\left((120 \times 25) - (20 \times 12.5) \times\right) 13.068^2\right)$$

$$I_{II} = \left(625000 - 13021\right) - \left((3000 - 250) \times 13.068^2\right)$$

$$I_{II} = 611979 - 469625$$

$$I_{II} = \mathbf{142354\ m^4}$$

4. *Calculate BM for the bilged condition* $\quad BM = \dfrac{I}{V}$

Using the lost buoyancy (constant displacement) method the volume of displacement remains constant, therefore: $BM = \dfrac{142354}{(120 \times 25 \times 6)} = \mathbf{7.909\ m}$

5. *Calculate KB for the bilged condition*

$$KB = \frac{\text{draught}}{2} = \frac{6.545}{2} = 3.273 \text{ m}$$

6. *Calculate the GM in the bilged condition*

$KM = KB + BM$

Therefore: $KM = 3.273 + 7.909 = 11.182\ m$

$GM = KM - KG$

Therefore: $GM = 11.182 - 5.800 = 5.382\ m$

7. *Calculate the list*

$$\tan \theta_{LIST} = \frac{BB_H}{GM_{BILGED}}$$

$$\tan \theta_{LIST} = \frac{0.568}{5.382} = 0.10554$$

List = 6.02º (Ans)

22.6 REVIEW OF PRINCIPLES OF BILGING TO BE APPLIED TO CALCULATIONS

The accepted method of conducting bilging calculations is by using the *Lost Buoyancy (Constant Displacement)* method.

This assumes:

1. Whatever compartment is bilged, the volume of displacement (and displacement) does not change.

2. The KG of the vessel remains constant.

3. If the bilged compartment extends the full depth of the vessel, KB in the final condition will always be half the final draught.

4. If flooding of the compartment is restricted by a watertight flat below the final waterline final KB is not half the draught; it must be found by taking moments of volume about the keel. Doing a sketch for the final waterline condition will confirm this.

5. The centre of flotation is always at the centroid of the intact water plane area. If the bilged compartment is amidships the centre of flotation will always be amidships.
   If the bilged compartment is at the end of the vessel and there is no restricting watertight flat, then the LCF will be at half the length of the remaining intact water plane i.e. it will move a distance equal to half the length of the bilged compartment.
   If the bilged compartment is at the end of the vessel and there is a restricting watertight flat, then the LCF will remain at amidships since the water plane area will not be affected.

6. The position of B will be vertically below the centre of flotation if the bilged compartment extends the full depth of the vessel. In this instance any shift in B and F will be the same.

7. If the bilged compartment is at the end and flooding is restricted by a watertight flat B will not be in line with the LCF in the final condition i.e. LCF will remain amidships but B will move away from amidships (away from the position of the centroid of the bilged compartment). The LCB must be calculated by taking moments of volume about the aft perpendicular. Doing a sketch for the final waterline condition will confirm this.

8. $BM = \frac{I}{V}$ always, whether transversely or longitudinally.
   I is the *moment of inertia* of the *intact* water plane area taken about an axis passing through the centre of flotation.
   V is the *volume of displacement*. When using the constant displacement (lost buoyancy) method V remains constant so always use the original length, breadth and draught of the vessel.

9. *Side compartments:* In examinations the only scenario which is considered (usually) is where an amidships side compartment extending upwards the full depth of the vessel becomes bilged. In this case the movement of both the centre of flotation (FF_1) and the centre of buoyancy (BB_H) off the centre line will be the same, keeping them in the same vertical. The new positions of both B and F are found by taking moments of the water plane area about one side (XX in example 11).
   The KB in the bilged condition is taken to be *half the bilged draught*. This is not strictly true since this only applies when the centre of flotation is on the centre line (where the water plane area remains intact). The vessel will heel/list about a longitudinal axis that passes through the centre of flotation whereby the increase in draught on the heeled side will equal the decrease on draught on the high side. If the centre of flotation is off the centre line (F_1), as in the case considered, then there will be a greater increase of draught on the heeled side than decrease in draught on the high side. However, provided that the list is small, any error is assumed negligible so may be ignored.
   Finally, the list is calculated using: $\mathbf{Tan\,\theta_{LIST} = \frac{BB_H}{GM_{BILGED}}}$
   where the list is caused by the *movement of the centre of buoyancy* off the centre line and not the movement of a weight as in a normal list problem.

SECTION 23 – ANGLE OF HEEL WHEN TURNING

INTRODUCTION

When a ship has achieved a steady rate of turn it will heel in a direction *away* from the centre of the turning circle i.e. a turn to starboard will cause a heel to port. However, at the initial stages of the turn the direction of the heel is in fact opposite to this! This section identifies the forces that arise when a ship is undergoing a turn and explains the formula that can be used to determine the angle of heel that will occur.

Learning Objectives

On completion of this section the learner will achieve the following:

1. Understand the terms relating to a ship's turning circle.
2. Understand the forces that cause the ship to heel when turning.
3. Calculate the angle of heel when turning.
4. Calculate the increase in draught due to list or heel when turning.

23.1 TERMS RELATING TO A SHIP'S TURNING CIRCLE

Figure 23.1 shows the path traced out by the ship's centre of gravity during turning.

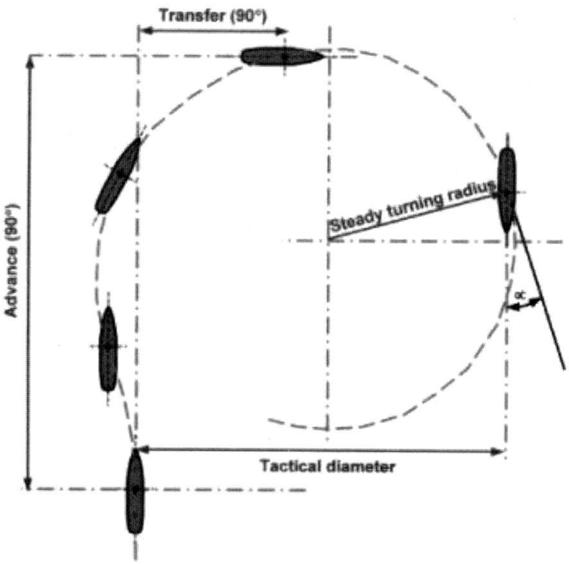

Fig. 23.1

23.1.1 Advance

This is the distance travelled by the ship's centre of gravity in a direction parallel to the ship's initial course. It is usually quoted for a 90° change of heading.

23.1.2 Transfer

This is the distance travelled by the ship's centre of gravity in a direction perpendicular to the ship's initial course. It is usually quoted for a 90° change of heading.

23.1.3 Tactical diameter

This is the distance travelled by the ship's centre of gravity in a direction perpendicular to the ship's initial course when the ship has altered its course by 180° and is on a reciprocal heading.

23.1.4 Steady turning circle radius

This is the steady radius of the turning circle when a steady rate of turn is achieved. This state is usually achieved by the time the ship has altered course between 90° and 180° however this will vary from ship to ship.

23.1.5 Yaw (∝)

This is the angle between the ship's fore and aft line and the direction of travel of the ship's centre of gravity at any instant during the turn.

23.2 FORCES THAT CAUSE THE SHIP TO HEEL DURING TURNING

Consider a ship turning to *starboard*. When the rudder is put over the thrust on the starboard face of the rudder has an athwartships component, **F**, which acts at the centre of pressure, **P**, of the rudder.

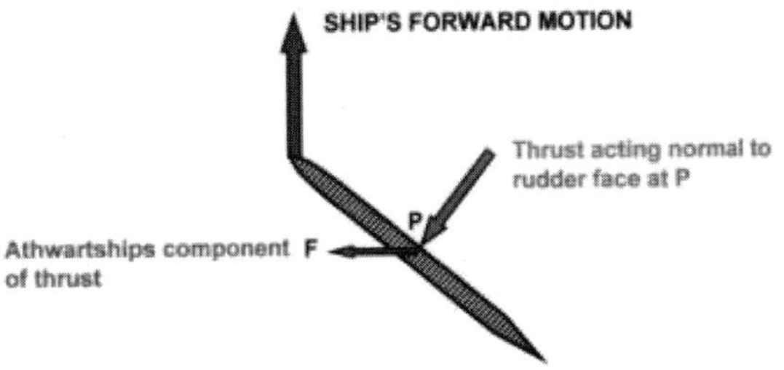

Fig. 23.2

An equal and opposite force, $\mathbf{F_1}$ arises, resisting the athwartships motion set up by the force on the rudder. This reaction acts on the port side at the *centre of lateral resistance* (**CLR**) and is located at the geometric centre of the underwater longitudinal area and is invariably higher than **P**.

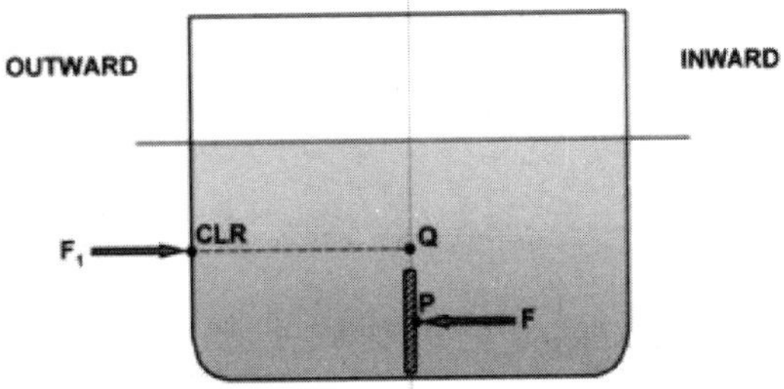

Fig. 23.3

The two forces, **F** at **P**, and $\mathbf{F_1}$ at the **CLR** set up an *inward* heeling couple for which the moment is given by: F × PQ

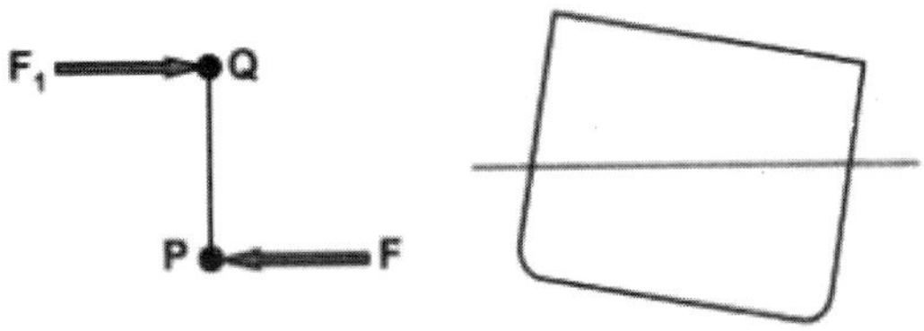

Initial inward heeling couple is created (for ship turning to starboard).

Fig. 23.4

Once the ship has achieved a steady rate of turn, the inward heel is overcome by the effect of the centrifugal force acting outwards through the ship's centre of gravity (G). This causes the characteristic *outward* heel to develop in the turn. The centrifugal force is given by:

$$\textbf{Centrifugal force (tonnes)} = \frac{WV^2}{gR}$$

where: ***'W'*** is the ship's displacement in tonnes;
'V' is the speed of the ship in metres per second;
'g' is the acceleration due to gravity (9.81 m/s^2), and;
'R' is the radius of the turning circle in metres.

The centrifugal force is opposed by the equal and opposite *centripetal force* acting through the CLR, where the CLR (for purpose of formula derivation) is assumed to be at the same height above the keel as the centre of buoyancy, B. Consider figure 23.5.

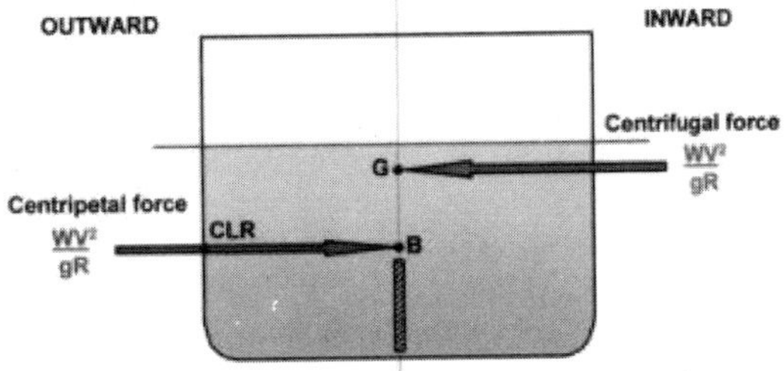

Fig. 23.5

The initial inward heeling moment is overcome by the outward heeling moment created by both the centrifugal and centripetal forces. If the initial inward heeling moment is ignored, the ship will heel outwards to an angle of steady heel (θ) when the outward heeling moment balances the normal righting moment for the angle of heel developed. At small angles of heel:

Righting moment (t-m) = GZ × Displacement

where: **GZ = GM × Sine θ**

Consideration of figure 23.6 will help to derive the formula for the angle of steady heel due to turning once the ship has achieved the steady rate of turn.

The formula is derived as follows: **B** and **B_1** are assumed to be at the same depth.

$$\text{Cos}\ \theta = \frac{\text{ADJ}}{\text{HYP}} = \frac{d}{BG}$$

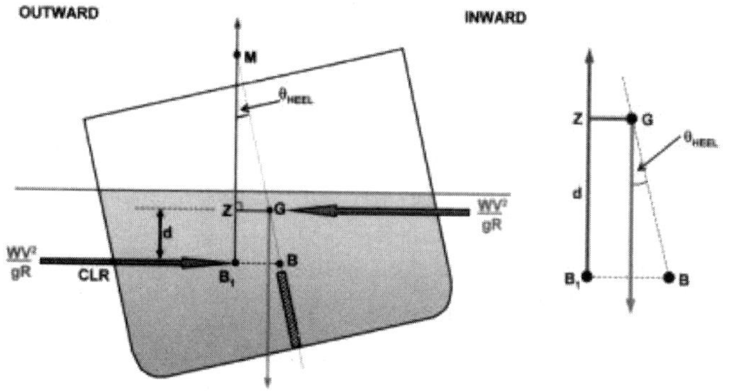

Fig. 23.6

Therefore: $d = BG \times \text{Cos}\ \theta$

At the *small* angle of heel shown: Righting moment = Heeling moment

∴ $$(W \times GZ) = \frac{WV^2}{gR} \times d$$

If: $d = BG \times \text{Cos}\theta$ and: $GZ = GM \times \text{Sin}\theta$

then: $$W \times GM \times \text{Sin}\theta = \frac{WV^2}{gR} \times BG \times \text{Cos}\theta$$

∴ $$gR \times W \times GM \times \text{Sin}\theta = WV^2 \times BG \times \text{Cos}\theta$$

Dividing both sides by Cosθ gives:

$$\frac{gR \times W \times GM \times \text{Sin}\theta}{\text{Cos}\theta} = WV^2 \times BG$$

∴ $$gR \times W \times GM \times \text{Tan}\theta = WV^2 \times BG$$

∴ $$\text{Tan}\theta = \frac{WV^2 \times BG}{gR \times W \times GM}$$

Thus: $$\mathbf{Tan\theta = \frac{V^2 \times BG}{g \times R \times GM}}$$

It should be noted that in practice the outward angle of heel developed in the turn will be slightly *less* than that given by the formula because of the small inward heeling moment set up by the athwartships component of thrust on the rudder.

However, the initial tendency for the ship to heel inward must never be overlooked. If, during a steady turn, the rudder is quickly returned to amidships, the outward heel will instantaneously increase. If the rudder is suddenly reversed i.e. put hard-a-port on a starboard turning circle, an even more serious outward angle of heel would arise (albeit temporarily) which could cause the ship to heel excessively.

23.3 CALCULATING THE ANGLE OF HEEL WHEN TURNING

The following examples will demonstrate the use of the formula. It should be noted that the speed (V) is in metres per second and not in knots. The following will help.

1 Knot = 1852 metres per hour

To convert metres per hour into metres per second divide by 3600; since there are 3600 seconds in an hour.

Thus, if a question states that a ship is doing a speed of 12 knots:

$$12 \text{ Knots} = \frac{(12 \times 1852)}{3600} = 6.173 \text{ m/sec.}$$

Example 1

Calculate the angle of heel developed when a ship doing 20 knots achieves a steady rate of turn to starboard and the radius of the turning circle is 300 m given that:

KM = 8.00 m KG = 6.00 m KB = 2.5 m

Solution

$$20 \text{ Knots} = \frac{(20 \times 1852)}{3600} = 10.289 \text{ m/sec.}$$

$GM = KM - KG \qquad GM = 8.00 - 6.00 = 2.00 \text{ m}$

$BG = KG - KBBG = 6.00 - 2.50 = 3.50 \text{ m}$

$$Tan\theta = \frac{V^2 \times BG}{g \times R \times GM} \qquad Tan\theta = \frac{10.289^2 \times 3.50}{9.81 \times 300 \times 2.00} = 0.06295$$

***θ* = 3.6° Port (Ans)**

Example 2

Calculate the maximum speed on a turning circle of diameter 620 m in order that the heel developed does not exceed 6° given that:

KM = 15.88 m KG = 14.26 m KB = 8.05 m

Solution

$GM = KM - KG \qquad GM = 15.88 - 14.26 \text{ m} = 1.62 \text{ m}$

$BG = KG - KBBG = 14.26 - 8.05 = 6.21 \text{ m}$

$$Tan\theta = \frac{V^2 \times BG}{g \times R \times GM} \qquad Tan\ 6^\circ = \frac{V^2 \times 6.21}{9.81 \times 310 \times 1.62}$$

$$Tan\ 6^\circ = \frac{6.21V^2}{4926.582} \qquad V^2 = \frac{Tan\ 6^\circ \times 4926.582}{6.21} = 83.382$$

$\therefore \qquad V = \sqrt{83.382} = 9.131 \text{ m/s}$

In knots: $\text{Speed} = \frac{9.131 \times 3600}{1852}$ = ***17.75 knots maximum (Ans)***

Note

Be careful not to use the diameter of the turning circle instead of the radius in the formula!

23.4 CALCULATING THE MAXIMUM DRAUGHT (INCREASE IN DRAUGHT) DUE TO LIST/HEEL

Obviously, as the ship heels when turning the draught increases on the low side. For passage planning purposes when under keel clearance might be limited it may be necessary to calculate the deepest draught in the turn. Consider figure 23.7.

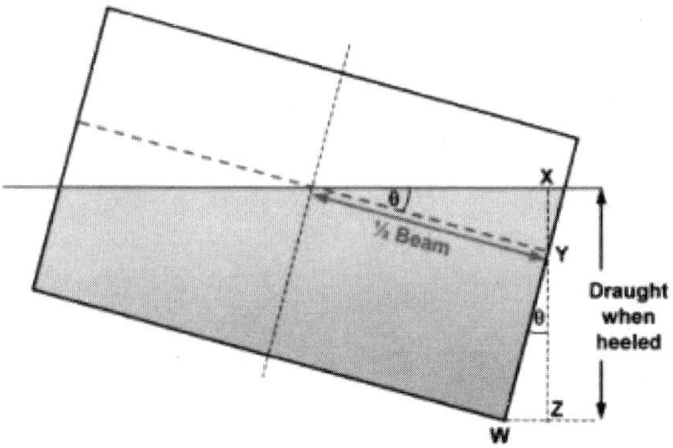

Fig. 23.7

The draught when heeled = XY + YZ

$$\text{Sin}\theta = \frac{\text{OPP}}{\text{HYP}} = \frac{\text{XY}}{\text{½ Beam}}$$

$\therefore$ **XY = ½ Beam × Sinθ (1)**

$$\text{Cos}\theta = \frac{\text{ADJ}}{\text{HYP}} = \frac{\text{YZ}}{\text{YW}} = \frac{\text{YZ}}{\text{Upright draught}}$$

$\therefore$ **YZ = Upright draught × Cosθ (2)**

Bringing together formulae (1) and (2) gives the formula for calculating the draught when heeled:

Draught when heeled = (½ Beam × Sinθ) + (Upright draught × Cosθ)

A margin of safety will be afforded by the turn of the bilge of the ship that is ignored when using this formula.

Example 3

A ship heels 5° as it makes a turn. If the draught when upright is 7.60 m calculate the draught when heeled given that the breadth is 18 m.

Solution

Draught when heeled = (½ Beam × Sinθ) + (Upright draught × Cosθ)
Draught when heeled = (½ × 18 × Sin 5°) + (7.60 × Cos 5°)
*= 0.784 + 7.571 = **8.355 m (Ans)***

SECTION 24 – WIND HEELING, ICE ACCRETION AND ROLLING

INTRODUCTION

At sea a ship will experience heeling due to the action of both wind and waves. In high latitudes ice accretion may occur resulting in an overall reduction in stability. This section considers these weather effects and describes minimum criteria that must be complied with.

Learning Objectives

On completion of this section the learner will achieve the following:

1. Understand the minimum criteria with respect to wind heeling as specified in the MCA publication *'Load Lines – Instructions for the Guidance of Surveyors'* and Chapter 3 of the *Code on Intact Stability for all Ships covered by IMO Instruments (IMO).*
2. Understand the method for making icing allowances as specified in the MCA publication *'Load Lines – Instructions for the Guidance of Surveyors'.*
3. Understand the term *still water rolling.*
4. Understand the factors that influence a ship's rolling motion in waves at sea.
5. Understand methods of minimising a ship's rolling motion at sea.

24.1 WIND HEELING

Minimum wind heeling criteria that applies to *all* ships is specified in Chapter 3 of the *Code on Intact Stability for all Ships covered by IMO Instruments (IMO).* Alternative requirements applicable to container ships are specified in the MCA publication *'Load Lines – Instructions for the Guidance of Surveyors'* and are *similar* to those specified in the IMO code.

The principal difference between the two sets of legislation arises mainly because of the difference in the units of pressure adopted for the purposes of calculation, IMO adopting the *Pascal* and the MCA using, incorrectly, Kg/m^2; these should be expressed as *Kilograms-force per square metre* (Kgf/m^2).

Because of the confusion often caused (even to the author) both versions of the wind heeling criteria are fully explained, however, the approach to be adopted in any particular case will depend upon the legislation applicable to any particular ship.

Because the MCA approach appears to many to be a little simpler, this will be discussed first, followed by the IMO approach.

24.1.1 Wind heeling considerations for container ships (MCA)

The MCA identifies two hazards associated with the carriage of containers on deck that might affect a ship's stability, they are:

(1) the possible failure of container securing arrangements causing a shift of the container cargo and consequent listing of the ship; and

(2) the large angles of heel caused by strong beam winds acting on the large lateral areas above the waterline afforded by the ship and containers.

With respect to (1) above, ship builders should take account of the probable ship motions likely to be experienced, including the acceleration forces to be experienced at distances away from the rolling axis that the securing arrangements must resist.

With respect to (2) above, *Part 8.2 of 'Load Lines – Instructions for the Guidance of Surveyors (MCA)* states the minimum requirements to be met by container ships likely to experience the adverse effects of wind heeling.

24.1.1.1 Wind heeling criteria for container ships (MCA)

Part 8.2 of 'Load Lines – Instructions for the Guidance of Surveyors (MCA) states the minimum criteria applicable to container ships as follows:

8.2.3 When the height of the lateral windage area measured from the load waterline to the top of the cargo containers situated on the weather deck is ***greater than 30% of the beam****, the shipbuilders should prepare a curve of statical stability for the ship in the worst service condition (taking into account the adverse effects of icing as appropriate). The windage area and its centre of gravity and lever to mid-draught should be stated.*

8.2.3.1 onwards describes the criteria that must be satisfied and is simplified in the rest of this sub-section.

Because the *righting moment* is a true measure of ship stability the GZ values for the aforementioned *worst anticipated service condition* are multiplied by the displacement value to give a curve of righting moments (t-m). This is plotted as shown in figure 24.1 to give both *Port* and *Starboard* values.

The angles of heel due to strong beam winds are found by first superimposing a wind heeling moment set up by a pressure of **48.5 Kgf/m²** assumed to be acting at the geometric centre of the lateral exposed area of the ship on one side. For the purpose of explanation the wind is assumed to be acting on the port side to cause the ship to heel to starboard.

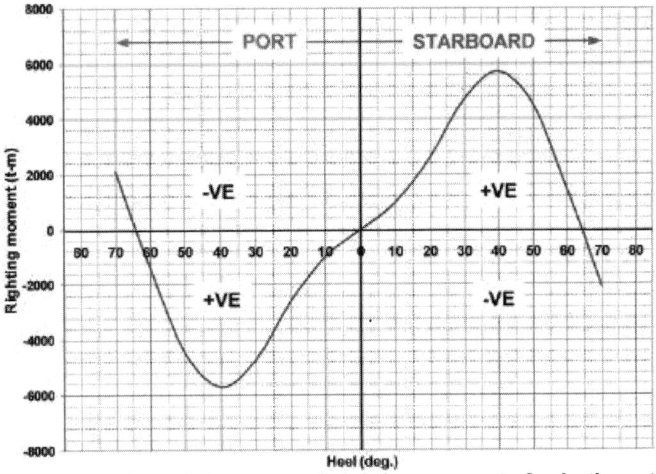

Representation of the curve of righting moments for both port and starboard angles of heel as adopted by the regulations.

Fig. 24.1

If the lateral exposed area on one side is ***A*** (m^2) then the force acting at **C** due to the steady wind is given by:

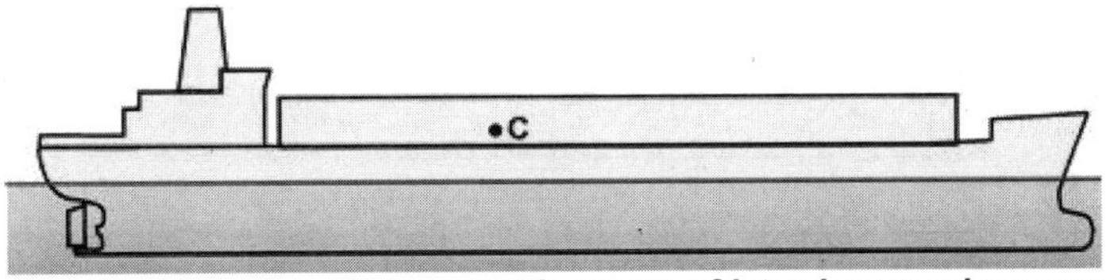

Wind assumed to act at geometric centre of lateral exposed area on one side above the load waterline (C).

Fig. 24.2

$$\textbf{Steady wind force (tonnes)} = \frac{(A \times 48.5)}{1000}$$

(Dividing by 1000 converts the steady wind force value from Kg's to tonnes!)

Consider figure 24.3.

The steady wind force of 48.5 Kgf/m² acting at C is resisted by an equal and opposite reaction at half draught depth which sets up a *steady wind heeling moment* given by:

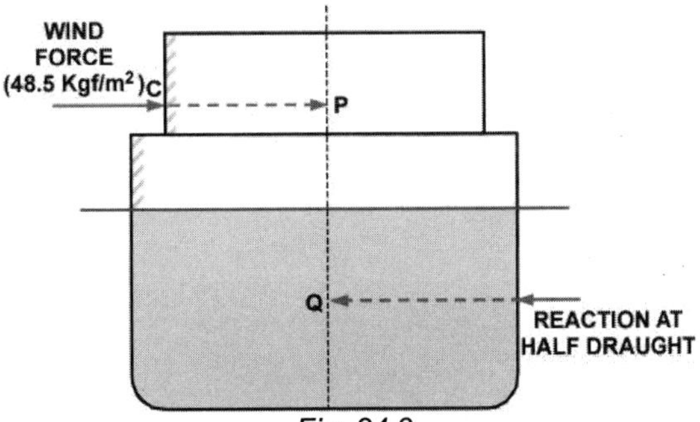

Fig. 24.3

$$\textbf{Steady wind heeling moment (t-m)} = \frac{(A \times 48.5)}{1000} \times PQ$$

This steady wind heeling moment is plotted as a horizontal heeling arm on the curve of righting moments. This is shown in figure 24.4, where it causes the ship to heel to *starboard*.

The *angle of steady heel* due to this steady wind is θ_1, where the ship's righting moments and wind heeling moment are equal. **θ_1 must not exceed $0.65 \times \theta_{DEI}$**

Because the ship is likely to be rolling due to the action of waves it is then assumed that the ship rolls 15° *into the wind* (to port) from the angle of steady wind heel to an angle θ_2.

At the instant the ship starts to recover a gusting wind is assumed to act, given by:

Gust wind heeling moment (t-m) = 1.5 × Steady wind heeling moment

The vessel will right itself but in so doing will initially heel over to θ_3, the *angle of dynamic heel*. This angle of dynamic heel is at a position such that the shaded area S_1 equals shaded area S_2. If it is borne in mind that *area under the righting moment curve* is a measure of *dynamical stability* (being the 'work required by the wind and waves to heel the ship to a particular angle of heel') then it will help in the understanding of why the ship would heel to θ_3 under the conditions assumed by these regulations.
The final requirement is that:

θ_3 – being the angle of dynamic heel, must not exceed the angle of heel at which progressive flooding would take place (θ_f).

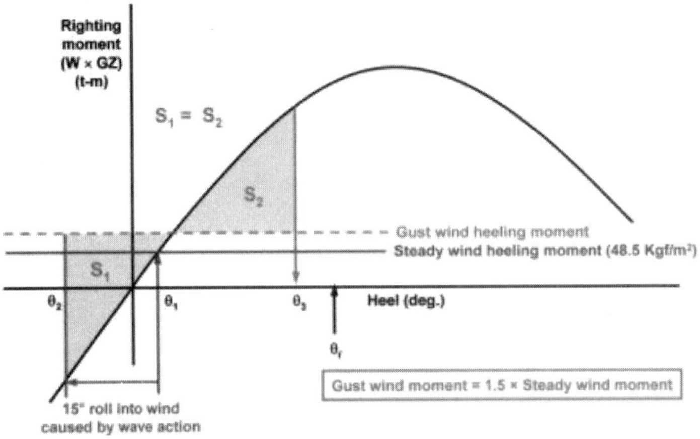

θ_1: angle of steady wind heel to not exceed $0.65\theta_{DEI}$.
θ_2: ship rolls 15° into steady wind as a result of wave action.
θ_3 : angle of heel to which ship will roll when acted upon by a gusting wind at the instant the ship starts to recover from θ_2 (θ_3 being the angle of dynamic heel).
θ_3: (angle of dynamic heel) to not exceed the angle of heel at which progressive down-flooding takes place (θ_f).

Fig. 24.4

24.1.1.2 Method to verify compliance with the regulations

In practice it would be difficult to calculate the value of the angle of dynamic heel (θ_3). Consider figure 24.5.

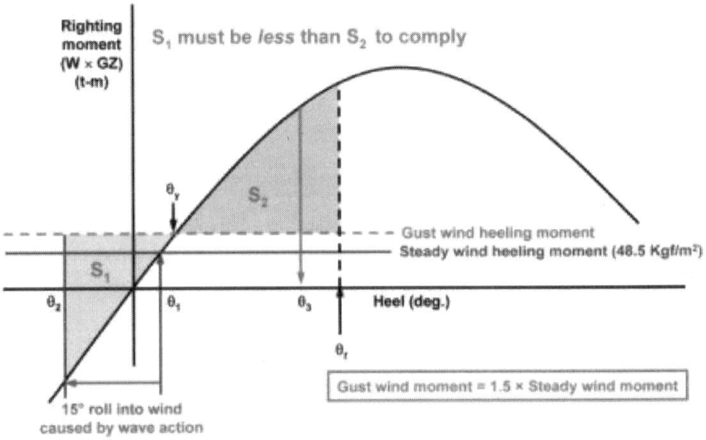

Fig. 24.5

The method to be adopted is as follows:

1. Calculate area S_1 using Simpson's rules.
2. From ship's data determine the angle of progressive flooding (θ_f) for the ship's loaded condition.
3. Calculate the area bounded by the *gust wind heeling moment arm* and the *righting moment curve* between θ_y and θ_f using Simpson's rules.
4. Provided that: **Area S_1 < Area S_2 (θ_y to θ_f)**, the ship will comply with the recommendations.

In many instances it will not be necessary to use Simpson's rules to verify compliance, since it will be obvious that the ship complies. Consider the following example.

Example 1

A container ship displacing 32000 tonnes has KG 9.80 m at a draught of 9.90 m and has a lateral windage area of 1400 m² where the geometric centre of the windage area is 16.2 m above the keel. KM is 10.15 m. The angle of deck edge immersion is 15° and the angle of progressive downflooding is 26°. Determine whether or not the stability is adequate in terms of the effects of strong beam winds if the righting levers (GZ) for the loaded condition are as follows:

θ	0°	10°	20°	30°
GZ (m)	0.00	0.06	0.14	0.24

Solution

1. *Calculate righting moment values*

Heel	GZ (m)	Displacement (t)	RM (t-m)
0	0.00	32000	0
10	0.06	32000	1920
20	0.14	32000	4480
30	0.24	32000	7680

2. *Calculate the steady wind and gusting wind heeling moment values*

Heeling lever PQ = Kg centroid of windage area – half draught

$$\text{Heeling lever PQ} = 16.20 - \frac{9.90}{2} = 11.25\text{ m}$$

$$\text{Steady wind heeling moment (t-m)} = \frac{(A \times 48.5)}{1000} \times PQ$$

$$\text{Steady wind heeling moment (t-m)} = \frac{(1400 \times 48.5)}{1000} \times 11.25 = 764\text{ t-m}$$

$$\text{Gust wind heeling moment (t-m)} = 1.5 \times 764 = 1146\text{ t-m}$$

3. *Plot the curve of righting moments for both sides of the upright condition and superimpose the wind heeling arms (Figure 24.6)*

From the figure the ***angle of steady wind heel is 4°.***

θ_2 is 11° on the other side of upright (being 15° into the wind from θ_1).

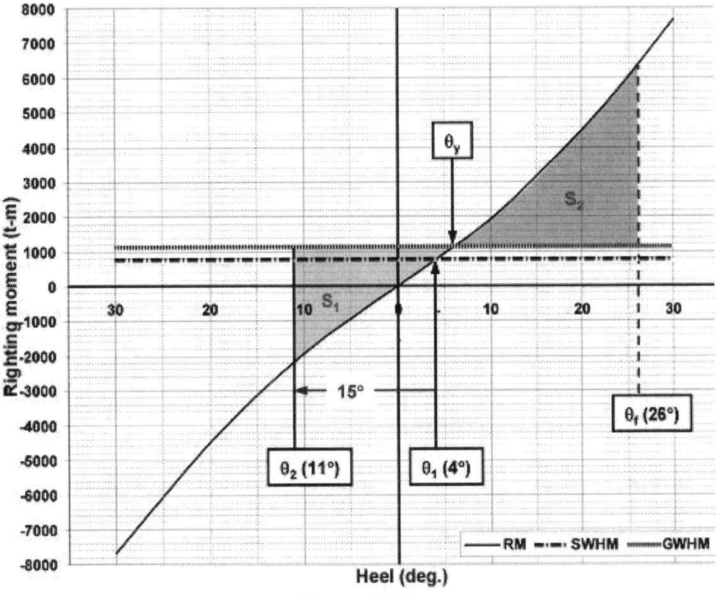

Figure 24.6

4. *Verify compliance by inspection (or Simpson's rules if required)*
It is evident from figure 24.6 that the ship complies since S_2 ***is greater than*** S_1.
i.e. ***Ship complies (Ans)***

Note It should be emphasised that the wind heeling criteria described here is applicable to UK registered container ships assigned freeboards in accordance with the *M.S. (Load Line) Regulations 1998* (as amended) only.

24.1.2 Wind heeling considerations for all ships (IMO)

Minimum wind heeling criteria that applies to *all* ships is specified in Chapter 3 of the *Code on Intact Stability for all Ships covered by IMO Instruments (IMO).* Specifically, regulation 3.2 supplements the general stability criteria laid down in regulation 3.1 of the Code and applies to all passenger and cargo ships of 24 m in length and over. The effects of rolling are also taken into account.

24.1.2.1 Units of wind pressure adopted by IMO

The MCA regulations (detailed in section 24.1.1) expressed the pressure exerted by the wind in terms of Kg/m^2 (Kilograms-force/m^2 to be correct) To many these units are readily understood in the context of the wind heeling moment formula used.

IMO adopts the use of the *Pascal (Pa)* for wind pressure and should therefore be defined so that a comparison of the MCA and IMO minimum criteria can be made.

The unit of force is the *Newton (N),* which is defined as being *the force required to cause a mass of 1 Kg to have an acceleration of 1 m/s^2.*

Weight is expressed in *Newtons* where: **Weight (N) = Mass (t) × Acceleration (m/s^2)**

Thus, a mass of 50 Kg will have a weight given by: Weight (N) = 50 Kg × 9.81 m/s^2 = **490.5 N**

where 9.81 m/s^2 is the acceleration at the earth's surface due to gravity. In other words, a mass of 50 Kg will exert a downward force of 490.5 N at the earth's surface.

The unit of pressure is the *Pascal (Pa)* where:

$$\textbf{PRESSURE (Pa)} = \frac{\textbf{FORCE (N)}}{\textbf{AREA (m}^2\textbf{)}}$$

The *steady wind force* assumed by the MCA regulations of 48.5 Kgf/m^2 expressed in Pascals would be: 48.5 Kgf/m^2 × 9.81 m/s^2 = **476 Pa**

The *gusting wind force* assumed by the MCA regulations expressed in *Pascals* would be:
1.5 × 476 = **714 Pa**

The IMO adopt slightly higher values than these, being 504 Pa and 756 Pa as will be seen.

24.1.2.2 Severe wind and rolling criterion (weather criterion) (IMO)

Regulation 3.2.2 of the Code details these requirements that apply to *all* passenger and cargo ships of 24 m in length and over.

IMO express the regulations in terms of the heeling arms (steady wind and gusting wind) being expressed in *metres* where these are superimposed on the curve of statical stability (GZ curve) in a similar format to that previously described. (The same method could be adopted for the MCA regulations if the calculated values of the steady wind heeling moment and gusting wind heeling moment where each divided by the displacement value to give a heeling arm in metres!)

The *steady wind heeling lever* in metres (l_{w1}) is calculated using:

$$l_{w1}\ (\text{m}) = \frac{PAZ}{1000g\Delta}$$

where: ***'P'*** is the wind pressure of 504 Pa;

'A' is the lateral area above the waterline afforded by the ship and deck cargo on one side;

'Z' is the vertical distance from the centre of A to the centre of the underwater lateral area or approximately to a point at one half the mean draught (m) (being the same as PQ – the heeling lever);

'Δ' is the displacement (t), and;

'g' is the acceleration due to gravity of 9.81 m/s^2.

The *gusting wind heeling lever* (l_{w2}) is given by:

$$l_{w2} = 1.5 \times l_{w1}$$

The wind heeling levers are then superimposed onto the curve of statical stability as illustrated in figure 24.7.

Area **b** should be *equal to or greater* than area **a**.

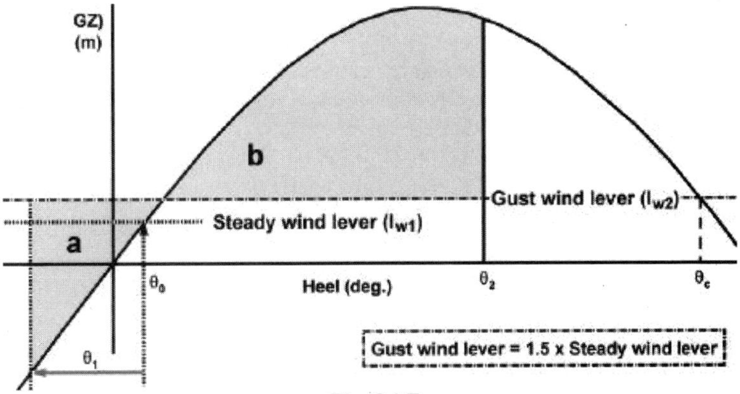

Fig. 24.7

The angles in figure 24.7 are defined as follows:

$\boldsymbol{\theta_0}$ is the angle of heel due to steady wind;

$\boldsymbol{\theta_1}$ is the angle of roll to windward due to wave action (* see note);

$\boldsymbol{\theta_2}$ is the angle of progressive downflooding **($\boldsymbol{\theta_f}$)** or **50°** or $\boldsymbol{\theta_c}$ whichever is *less*,

where: $\boldsymbol{\theta_f}$ is the angle of heel at which openings in the hull, superstructures or deck houses which cannot be closed weathertight immerse. In applying this criterion, small openings through which progressive flooding cannot take place need not be considered open.

$\boldsymbol{\theta_c}$ is the angle of heel of the second intercept between the gusting wind heeling lever (l_{w2}) and the GZ curve.

* Note: The angle of roll (θ_1) should be calculated as follows: $\boldsymbol{\theta_1 = 109kX_1X_2\sqrt{rs}}$ **(degrees)**

where: ***'X₁'*** is a factor which depends on the Breadth/draught ratio where the value of X_1 increases as the B/d ratio increases;

'X₂' is a factor that depends on the block coefficient of the ship where the value of X_2 increases as the C_B ratio increases;

'k' is a factor that depends on the roundness of the bilge and whether the ship has bilge keels fitted or not (the more rounded the bilge the easier the ship will roll and the greater will be the value of k (having a value between 0.70 and 1.00).

'r' is found by the formula: $\mathbf{r = 0.73 \pm (0.6 \times OG/d)}$ with:

'OG' being the distance between the centre of gravity of the ship and the waterline in metres (being + if the centre of gravity of the ship is above the waterline and – if below); ***'d'*** is the mean moulded draught of the ship in metres.

's' is a factor which depends on the rolling period of the ship where 's' reduces as the rolling period increases. The rolling period is given by:

$$\textbf{Rolling period (T secs)} = \frac{\mathbf{2CB}}{\sqrt{\mathbf{GM}}}$$

where: C = 0.373 + 0.023(B/d) – 0.043(L/100)

where: ***'B'*** is the moulded breadth of the ship (m);

'GM' is the metacentric height corrected for free surface effect (m).

Clearly, the tables in Chapter 3 of the Code must be consulted in order that the values for the various aforementioned factors can be ascertained.

24.2 ICING ALLOWANCES

With respect to icing regulation 8.28 of the MCA publication *'Load Lines – Instructions for the Guidance of Surveyors'* details the circumstances and method for making allowance for icing in the calculation of the ship's effective KG.

The stability information book of any ship, which may trade in an area where ice may form should contain information that indicates the effect of the formation of ice on exposed hull, superstructures, houses, deck cargo etc. This must be calculated as either a *full icing allowance* or a *half icing allowance.*

The *full icing allowance* should be applied:
(a) North of 66° 30' N between the Norwegian coast and 10° W.
(b) North of 63° N between 10° W and 28° W.
(c) North of 45° N between 28° W and the North American coast.
(d) North of the European, North American and Asian continents outside of the limits of longitude in (a), (b) and (c).
(e) The Sea of Okhotsk, Bering Sea and Gulf of Tartary.
(f) South of 60° S.

The *half icing allowance* should be applied:
(a) In the areas north of 61° N, between the Norwegian coast and 28° W, south of the areas to which the full allowance applies.
(b) Elsewhere in seasonal winter zones, as agreed by the MCA and the owners.

The icing allowances are as follows:

The *full allowance* assumes:
(a) That all exposed horizontal surfaces (decks, tops of houses and deck cargo) are carrying an ice weight of 30 kg/m^2.
(b) That vertical surfaces are carrying a weight equivalent to 15 kg/m^2 on the lateral area on ***one*** side of the ship (hull, houses, and deck cargo) above the waterline.

The *half icing allowance* should be taken as one half of these values.

The centre of gravity of each area of ice formation has to be estimated in order that the moment about the keel of each part of ice weight can be calculated.

Ice on booms, stays, rails etc. should be allowed for as *5% of the weight on vertical surfaces*, and the *vertical moment of this ice allowed for as 10% of the moment due to formation on vertical surfaces*.

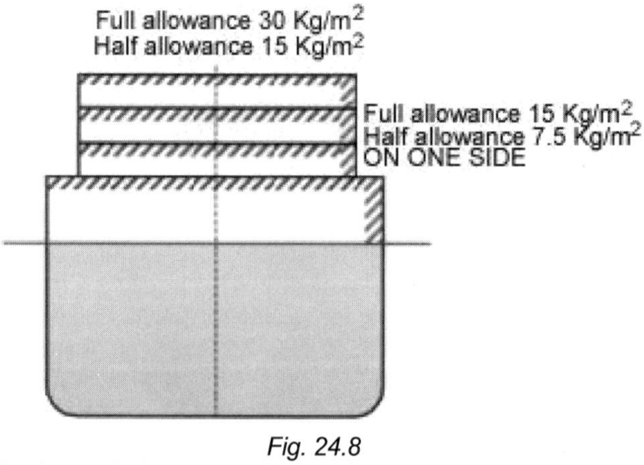

Fig. 24.8

Chapter 5 of the *Code on Intact Stability for all Ships covered by IMO Instruments (IMO)* gives similar details for icing but only one set of icing allowance figures are used, these being:

30 Kg/m^2 on exposed weather decks and gangways, and;
7.5 Kg/m^2 for the projected lateral area of *each* side of the ship above the waterline.

The geographical limits of areas in which the icing allowance has to be applied also differ a little and the Code should be consulted when compliance of these alternative criteria is a requirement.

Example 2
A ship displaces 31700 t and is loaded such that the solid KG is 9.12 m. KM is 9.46 m and total FSM's are estimated to be 2050 t-m at the worst anticipated stage of the voyage. The vessel is to enter an area where the full icing allowance applies.
Ship details are as follows:

Main deck 3100 m^2 at Kg 16.2 m;
2nd deck 60 m^2 at Kg 18.6 m;
3rd deck 42 m^2 at Kg 21.0 m;
Bridge deck 48 m^2 at Kg 23.4 m;
Funnel deck 56 m^2 at Kg 25.8 m;

Lateral exposed area above the waterline is 860 m^2 at a Kg of 13.64 m.
Calculate the effective GM and displacement that will allow for icing.

Solution

1. *Calculate weight of ice on decks using full icing allowance*

Main deck:	*$3100 \times 30 = 93000$ Kg = 93 tonnes at Kg 16.2 m*
2nd deck:	*$60 \times 30 = 1800$ Kg = 1.80 tonnes at Kg 18.6 m*
3rd deck:	*$42 \times 30 = 1260$ Kg = 1.26 tonnes at Kg 21.0 m*
Bridge deck:	*$48 \times 30 = 1440$ Kg = 1.44 tonnes at Kg 23.4 m*
Funnel deck:	*$56 \times 30 = 1680$ Kg = 1.68 tonnes at Kg 25.8 m*

2. *Calculate weight of ice on vertical surfaces on one side using full icing allowance*
$860 \times 15 = 12900$ Kg = 12.90 tonnes at Kg 13.64 m

3. *Calculate allowance for ice on booms, stays etc.*
Weight = 5% of the weight on vertical surfaces

Therefore: $\frac{12.90 \times 5}{100} = 0.65$ *tonnes*

Moment for ice on booms stays = 10% of the moment due to ice on vertical surfaces
Moment of ice on vertical surfaces = $12.90 \times 13.64 = 176$ t-m

10% = $\frac{176 \times 10}{100} = 18$ *t-m*

4. *Take moments about the keel to calculate effective KG and GM.*

	weight (t)	Kg (m)	moments (t-m)
Ship	31700.00	9.12	289104.00
FSM's			2050.00
Ice on main deck	93.00	16.20	1506.60
Ice on 2nd deck	1.80	18.60	33.48
Ice on 3rd deck	1.26	21.00	26.46
Ice on bridge deck	1.44	23.40	33.70
Ice on funnel deck	1.68	25.80	43.34
Ice on vertical surfaces	12.90	13.64	175.96
Ice on booms, stays etc.	0.65		18.00
FINAL	31812.73	**9.210**	292991.54

KM	9.460
KG	9.210
GM	**0.250**

Final effective GM allowing for icing = 0.250 m (Ans)

Finally, an examination question might be phrased as follows:
A ship operating in severe winter conditions may suffer from non-symmetrical ice accretion on decks and superstructure. Describe the effects on the overall stability of the ship, making particular reference to the ship's curve of statical stability.

When icing occurs as previously described the following may be expected to happen:

(1) Icing on horizontal decks and cargo surfaces will cause G to rise resulting in an increased KG/decreased GM.

(2) Icing on the lateral areas of the ship on one side above the waterline will cause the ship to list.

(3) Both (1) and (2) above will cause an increase in the ship's displacement resulting in a reduced freeboard (arguably the effects of this will be dependant on the ship's overall size in relation to the mass of ice accumulated).

Figure 24.9 illustrates the overall effects of icing on the curve of statical stability.

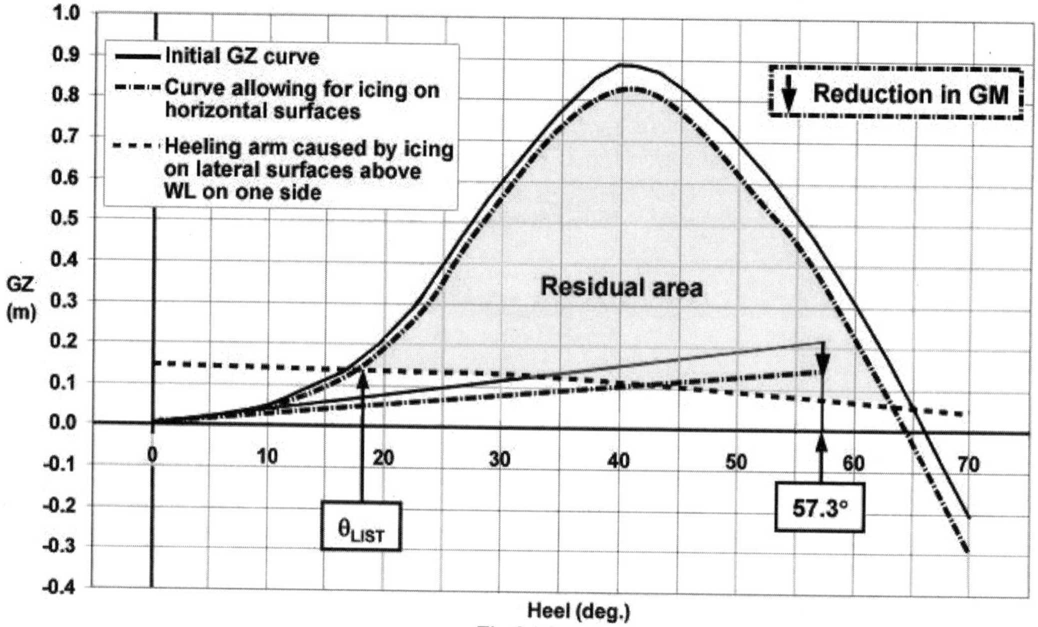

Fig 24.9

In summary, unsymmetrical icing will cause:

* *Initial GM to be reduced;*

* *All GZ values across the range of stability to be reduced;*

* *Dynamical stability (area under the curve) to be reduced making the ship less able to resist heeling by external forces;*

* *Range of stability to be reduced;* The angle at which deck edge immersion occurs (point of inflexion of the curve – not shown) to reduce a little as a result of the increased displacement.*

In effect, all aspects of stability will be worsened!

24.3 'STILL WATER' ROLLING

The rolling characteristics of a ship are governed by:

(1) the GM, and;

(2) the distribution of the weight components of the ship's structure and deadweight items with respect to the rolling axis, which is assumed to be at the centre of gravity of the ship (G).

The *roll period* (T) in seconds is the time taken for the ship to complete one complete oscillation i.e. the time it takes for the ship to roll from one side back through the upright to the extent of it's roll on the other side and back again.

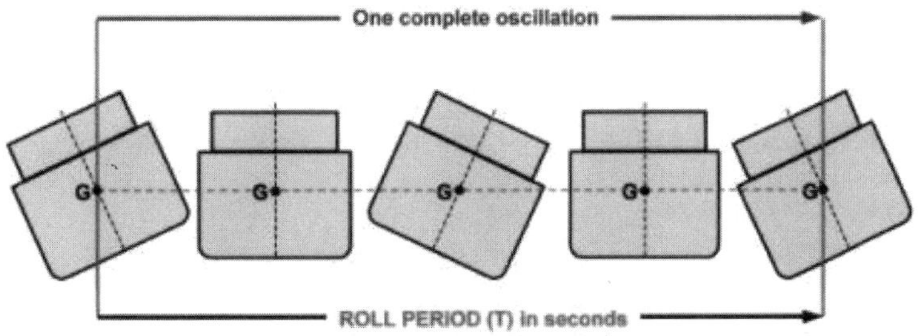

Fig. 24.10

The amplitude of the roll is defined as the extent of the roll in degrees.

24.3.1 Unrestricted rolling in still water

Unrestricted rolling is a hypothetical condition that assumes the ship is rolling in a 'frictionless' fluid such that the amplitude of the oscillations remains constant. In reality the amplitude of the roll decreases with each half-roll cycle until eventually the ship settles in the upright condition in still water (being due to water and air resistance).

The energy in this assumed *undamped* roll is totally potential energy at the limit of the roll, and; totally kinetic energy at the instant the ship passes through the upright position. At any intermediate position within the roll cycle the energy will be partly kinetic and partly potential; but the sum of these two quantities will remain constant. The ship will act in a similar manner to a pendulum under the same conditions.

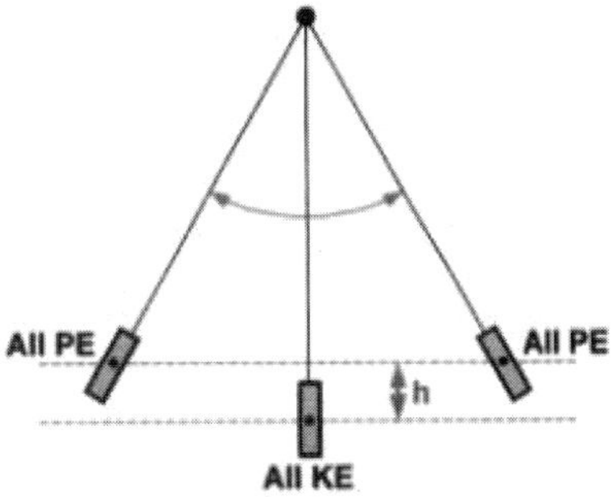

PE = mgh ***KE = ½mv²***

Fig. 24.11

At the extent of the roll, (1) and (3) in figure 24.12, the ship will possess all potential energy that will be equivalent to: PE at extent of roll to θ° = Area under righting moment curve from 0° to θ°

As the ship passes through the upright position, (2) in figure 24.11, the GZ and hence righting moment will be zero and potential energy at this point in the roll will be zero. However, the ship will possess all kinetic energy by virtue of its motion as it passes through the upright position.

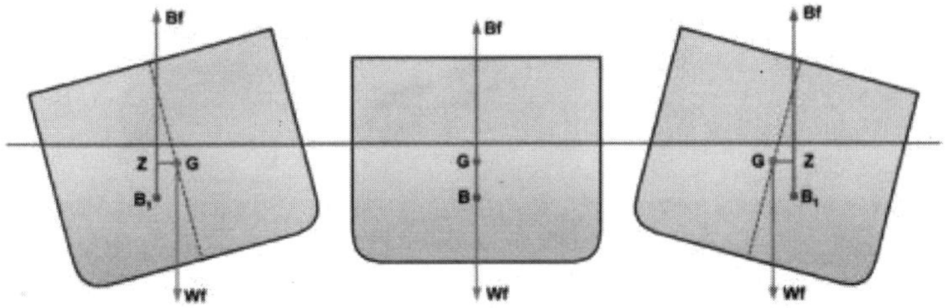

1. Extent of roll (all PE) ***2. Passing through the upright (all KE)*** ***3. Extent of roll (all PE)***

Fig. 24.12

Under the circumstances described the roll period (T) is approximated by the formula:

$$\mathbf{T\ (secs) = 2\pi \sqrt{\frac{I}{W \times g \times GM}}}$$

where: ***'I'*** is the moment of inertia of the ship's structure and all deadweight components about the rolling axis (G);
'W' is the ship's displacement in tonnes;
'g' is the acceleration due to gravity (9.81 m/s^2), and;
'GM' is the ship's effective metacentric height.

The value of I is found by: $\mathbf{I = \Sigma wr^2}$

where 'w' is the weight of each structural component of the ship and each item of deadweight and 'r' is the distance that each component is from the rolling axis, assumed to be at G.

The quantity $\mathbf{\Sigma wr^2}$ can be written as $\mathbf{Wk^2}$ where W is the ship's displacement and k is the *radius of gyration*.

24.3.2 Radius of gyration

The radius of gyration might be a difficult concept to understand but may be loosely defined as being for a ship *the distance from the centre of gravity (or rolling axis) at which the total weight (W) would have to be concentrated in order to give the ship the same moment of inertia as it actually has.*

For any particular ship the radius of gyration can be changed by altering the distribution of deadweight about the rolling axis as shown in figure 24.13.

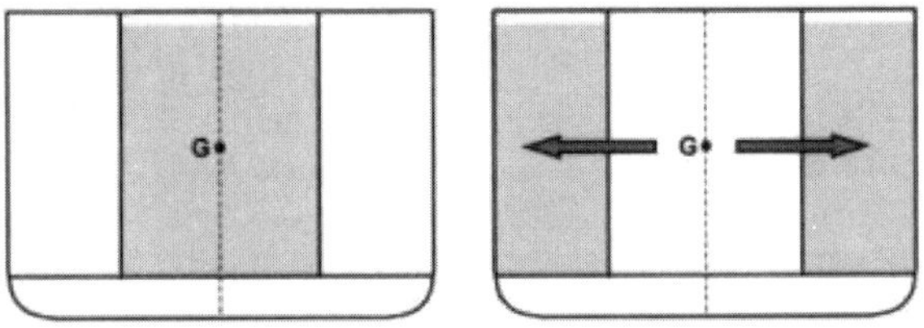

Moving weight to the sides of the ship away from the rolling axis (G) increases the radius of gyration (k) and increases the ship's rolling period.

Fig. 24.13

24.3.3 Formula for rolling period

Because $\mathbf{I = \Sigma wr^2}$, the formula for the still water rolling period becomes: $T\ (secs) = 2\pi \sqrt{\frac{Wk^2}{W \times g \times GM}}$

which simplifies to: $$\mathbf{T\ (secs) = \frac{2\pi k}{\sqrt{g \times GM}}}$$

This formula is substantially correct for small angles of heel where the formula $GZ = GM \times \sin\theta$ is valid.

The formula shows that for a constant value of I (or k) the rolling period is inversely proportional to the square root of the GM (so long as GM is positive) i.e.

As GM increases the rolling period reduces.

The formula also shows that the rolling period is directly proportional to the radius of gyration (k) i.e.

As k increases (by 'winging out' weights say), the rolling period increases.

An interesting analogy is when one considers the ability of a person to walk a tightrope! By using a *long pole* to increase the walker's radius of gyration, the 'roll period' of the person (as he wobbles to stay upright) is increased. Provided that the pole is long enough, the duration of each wobble that is experienced (as a result of periodic imbalance) becomes long enough for the person to be able to anticipate and correct for it. The longer the pole, the easier it is!

Any change in weight distribution that alters GM or k (and so alters I) will alter the rolling period. As a general rule a vertical movement of a given amount will have a greater effect on the rolling period than has an equal horizontal movement.

The long pole makes tightrope walking easy!
Fig. 24.14

24.3.4 Determining the GM by means of rolling period tests

Annex 3 of the *Code on Intact Stability for all Ships covered by IMO Instruments (IMO)* details the method of determining the light ship GM (and hence KG) by means of a rolling period test. This is permitted for ships up to 70 metres in length. It can be shown that the roll period is very much a function of the ship's beam and the formulae used for the rolling period test is:

$$\mathbf{T\ (secs) = \frac{f \times Beam}{\sqrt{GM}}}$$

where ***'f'*** is a factor for the rolling period known as the *rolling coefficient.* For coasters and fishing vessels the average values of ***f*** range between 0.60 and 0.88. Annex 3 of the Code should be consulted for more detail if required.

<u>Example 3</u>

Calculate the natural rolling period of a ship for which k is 4.0 m and GM is 1.20 m.

<u>Solution</u>

$$T\ (secs) = \frac{2\pi k}{\sqrt{g \times GM}} \qquad T\ (secs) = \frac{2\pi \times 4}{\sqrt{9.81 \times 1.20}} \qquad = \mathbf{7.3\ seconds\ (Ans)}$$

<u>Example 4</u>

A ship displaces 15000 tonnes, has GM 1.20 m and a roll period of 12 seconds. The ship loads 100 tonnes in position 6 metres above G. Calculate the new roll period.

<u>Solution</u>

$$T\ (secs) = \frac{2\pi k}{\sqrt{g \times GM}}$$

1. *Calculate the initial radius of gyration (k)*

$$k = \frac{T \times \sqrt{g \times GM}}{2\pi} \qquad k = \frac{12 \times \sqrt{9.81 \times 1.20}}{2\pi} \qquad = 6.553\ m$$

2. *Calculate the new value of I and new GM*

Original I = Wk² = 15000 × 6.553² =	*644127 m⁴*
I value of added weight = wx² = 100 × 6² =	*3600 m⁴*
Total	*647727 m⁴*

$$GG_v = \frac{w \times d}{W + w} = \frac{100 \times 6}{(15000 + 100)} \qquad = 0.0397\ m$$

Correction to I for shift of G = W × $(GG_v)^2$ = 15100 × 0.0397^2 = 24 m^4

Therefore: *Final value of I about the new G = 647727 – 24 = 647703 m^4*

New GM = 1.20 – 0.0397 = 1.1603 m

3. *Calculate new value of k*

$$I = Wk^2 \therefore \quad k^2 = \frac{I}{W} = \frac{647703}{15100} = 42.894$$

$$k = \sqrt{42.894} = 6.549\ m$$

4. *Calculate the new roll period*

$$T\ (secs) = \frac{2\pi k}{\sqrt{g \times GM}} \qquad T\ (secs) = \frac{2\pi \times 6.549}{\sqrt{9.81 \times 1.1603}} = \textbf{12.2 seconds (Ans)}$$

24.3.5 Resisted rolling in still water

When a ship is rolling in still water it will experience resistance caused by friction between the hull and the water; the water itself will be set in motion, this will also resist the rolling. The result is a damped oscillation, however the period given by the formula:

$$T\ (secs) = \frac{2\pi k}{\sqrt{g \times GM}}$$

remains substantially correct. The roll period of the ship is independent of the amplitude and as such the ship rolls *isochronously.* This means that if a given ship has a roll period of 10 seconds whilst rolling from 5° to port to 5° to starboard, the roll period will still be 10 seconds if the ship subsequently rolls from 20° to port to 20° to starboard. Obviously, the greater the amplitude of the rolling, the faster the ship's motion will be to maintain the constant roll period.

24.4 ROLLING IN WAVES

24.4.1 Wave theory

Very steep wind generated sea waveforms are essentially *trochoidal* in nature. A point marked on a bicycle tyre will appear to trace out a trochoidal curve as the bicycle is ridden past an observer, as illustrated in figure 24.15. Invert that pattern and you have the profile of a trochoidal water wave.

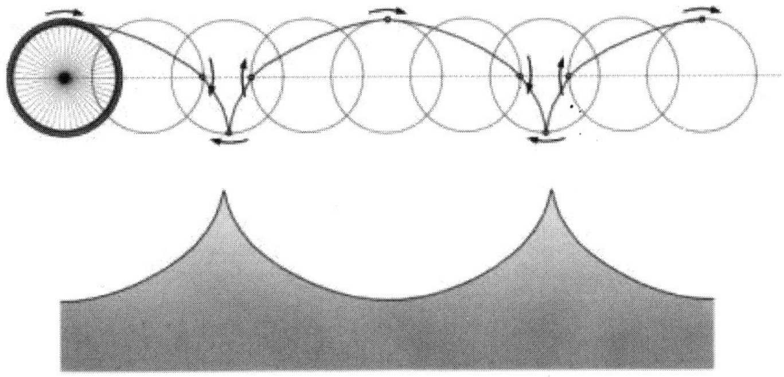

Fig. 24.15

When a wave passes in deep water there is virtually no actual displacement of water, the water particles move in an almost closed circular path. At the wave crests, the particles are moving in the same direction as wave propagation, whereas in the troughs they are moving in the opposite direction. At the surface the *orbital diameter* corresponds to wave height, but the diameters decrease exponentially with increasing depth, until at a depth roughly equal to half the wavelength, the orbital diameter is negligible, and there is virtually no displacement of the water particles This is why a submarine in deep water only has to submerge about 150 metres to avoid the effects of even the most severe storm at sea.

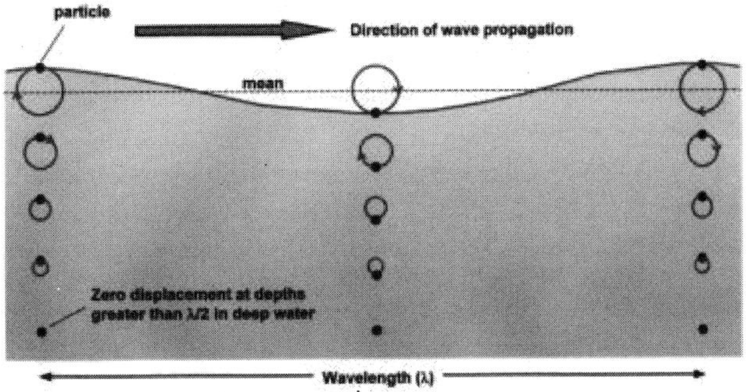

Fig. 24.16

The movement of a ship as a wave passes is also circular in fashion as it follows the orbital motion of the particles within the wave as shown in figure 24.17.

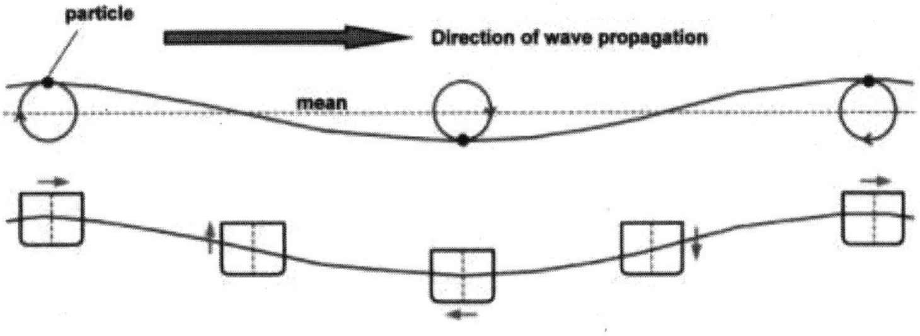

Fig. 24.17

When on the crest of the wave the ship will be moving in the same direction as wave travel, when in the trough the ship will be moving in the opposite direction to that of wave movement. In advance of the wave crest the ship will be being lifted and immediately after the wave crest has passed the ship will be dropping.

In open water: $\lambda = 0.17V^2 = 1.56T^2$

where: 'λ' is the wavelength in metres;

'*V*' is the wave speed in knots, and;

'*T*' is the wave period in seconds.

24.4.2 Ship rolling in waves

The ship's rolling motion in wave conditions is the resultant of:

(1) the oscillation due to the still water rolling period, and;

(2) the oscillation due to the wave period.

If the ship is acted upon by regular passing waves over a reasonable time period it will eventually roll with the same period as that of the wave (wave period being defined as the time interval in seconds between two successive peaks (or troughs) passing a fixed point). However, if the waves are of varying period, as is often the case, the ship will tend to revert to it's own natural rolling period. The amplitude of the ship's roll (in terms of maximum heel angle) will depend on the phasing of (1) and (2) above; and because the ship's still water rolling period is a function of both beam and GM it will depend on whether the ship is relatively broad and stable, or narrow and relatively unstable.

A wide, shallow vessel will tend to roll *away* from the wave crest (aligning the deck with the wave slope). This is because of the large heeling moment that will exist in the upright condition. Any broad vessel, or one with a large GM, consequently rolls heavily and this is a *characteristic of a ship that has a natural rolling period shorter than the wave period.* In such a condition the angular velocity of the roll will be excessive causing severe racking stresses.

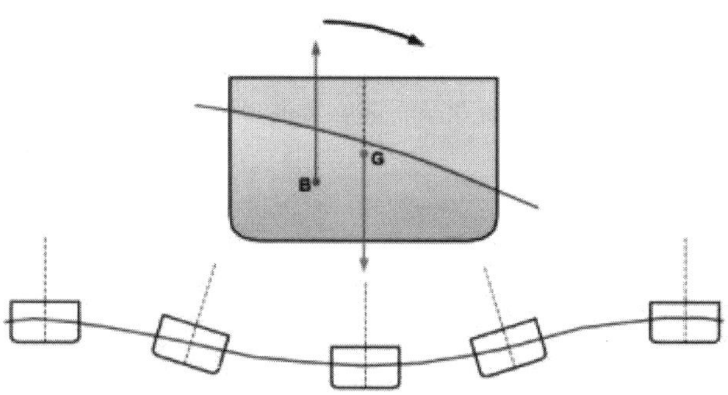

A broad vessel or one with a large GM will tend to roll away from the wave crest causing large angles of heel when rolling.

Fig. 24.18

The opposite is true for a vessel that is narrow in beam or one with a small GM, the effect here is for the vessel to tend to roll *into* the wave crest. This is a characteristic of any vessel which has a natural roll period longer than the wave period. The ship will roll to moderate angles of heel and will do so relatively slowly. Provided that there is adequate stability to ensure safety in heavy weather with breaking seas this will be the more desirable condition.

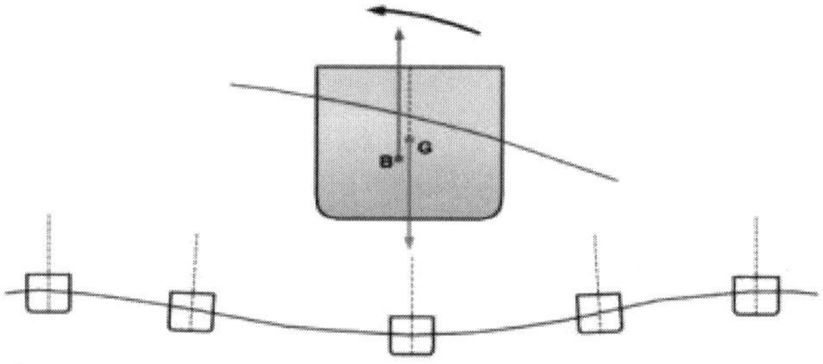

A narrow vessel with a small GM will tend to stay more upright on the wave slope, roll amplitude will be small (similar to a fishing float!).

Fig. 24.19

24.4.3 Synchronism

Synchronism is the name given to the condition that arises when the ship's natural rolling period equals the *period of encounter* of the waves. The natural 'still water' oscillation of the ship is added to by the forced oscillation of the waves and the amplitude of the roll increases by approximately ($\pi/2 \times$ wave slope) between successive wave crests and troughs. A wave slope of say 4°, causes each angle of roll to increase by about 6°, and the oscillation increases about 12° between successive wave crests (or troughs).

Synchronism is less likely, and if it does occur, is less dangerous when the ship has a long natural rolling period. The necessary long-period wave would have a comparatively low slope angle and the build up of the roll would be relatively slow.

Unless the GM is very large, the ship's natural rolling period can be expected to exceed the period of encounter of a *beam* sea. This is especially true if the wavelength does not exceed about 200 metres. In these circumstances synchronism is unlikely in a beam sea but may arise when the same waves are overtaking the ship on the quarter.

Capsizing due to the build up of rolling in synchronism conditions is unlikely because of the change in the ship's natural roll period when it is rolled to larger angles of inclination causing the synchronism effect to be arrested. However, the heavy rolling may cause a shift of cargo (especially deck cargo which is at greater distances from the rolling axis) or entry of water through deck openings. If this occurs, the ship will then roll in a fashion dictated by the shape of the curve of righting moments, heeling excessively to the listed side and further increasing the chances of subsequent cargo shift or flooding. There is always a risk of capsizing because of the lack of dynamical stability under these circumstances.

Synchronism can be remedied by:

(1) an alteration of course;

(2) an alteration of ship's speed (except when waves are on the beam);

(3) altering the ship's natural rolling period by:

  (a) changing the ship's GM, or:

  (b) changing the radius of gyration of the ship (such as by 'winging-out weights').

Synchronism is often, albeit temporarily, experienced when the ship is entering or leaving a port and is recognised by the ship rolling excessively and out of character with the actual sea conditions at the time. Breakwaters, natural coastline features and the shoaling effects created by sandbanks etc. in the vicinity of a port causes wave refraction to occur. This will be the cause of the ship encountering waves of widely differing directions and periods within relatively short periods of time, thus increasing the likelihood of encountering synchronism. Under such circumstances this type of rolling is often only a temporary condition.

24.5 METHODS ADOPTED TO MINIMISE A SHIP'S ROLLING MOTION AT SEA

Stabilising systems fall into two categories; being either *passive* or *active* systems and within each category the method adopted will be either by the fitting of 'fins' or tanks.

24.5.1 Passive systems

These include the fitting of bilge keels and tanks whereby the water has no positive means of transfer from side to side as the ship rolls.

24.5.1.1 Bilge keels

Bilge keels (or 'fin' type) stabilisers provide the best means of reduction in roll amplitude when a ship is operating at speed. Ideally, bilge keels should be fitted to all ships and be carefully sized to give optimum effect and aligned so as to give the least addition to frictional resistance. The effect of increased resistance will occur as the she ship actively rolls as the line of the bilge keel will no longer be in line with the flow of water along the hull and the more the ship rolls the greater will be the effect of the increased resistance.

Bilge keels should be fitted throughout the length of the parallel mid-body of the ship at the turn of the bilge. Roll amplitudes may be reduced by up to 35% and are therefore a very cost-effective means of limiting roll amplitude.

Bilge keels should always be fitted to ships having a large well-rounded bilge radius, whereas ships having a more square bilge shape will be more resistant to rolling.

24.5.1.2 Passive stabilising tanks

Passive stabilising tanks are those that reduce roll amplitudes by the movement of water from one side of the tank to the other as the ship rolls but where the effects of gravity alone cause the water transfer.

The 'flume' tank may simply be a single undivided and unobstructed rectangular tank. Often, it is a tank that is divided into three linked chambers as shown in figure 24.20. Other arrangements might include perforated longitudinal bulkheads (baffles) that restrict (but do not prevent) the flow of water from one side to the other.

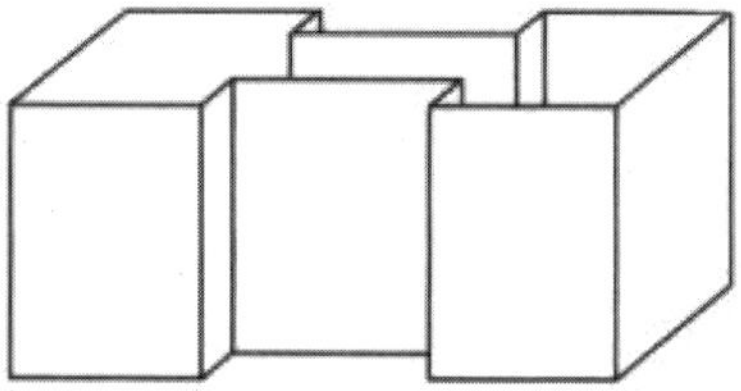

Flume tank
Fig. 24.20

The stabilising forces that are set up in these types of passive *free surface effect* tanks are a combination of the mass of liquid shifting and the horizontal acceleration forces generated as the liquid moves. The size of the stabilising moment due to the unsymmetrical distribution of liquid can be increased by a factor of three by the action of the wave moving across within the tank. An optimum fill level will ensure that the wave movement within the tank is 90° out of phase with that of the ship's rolling period. There should be a maximum difference in the quantities in the two sides of the tank when the ship is upright, and equal quantities in the two sides when the ship is at the limit of its roll (figure 24.21).

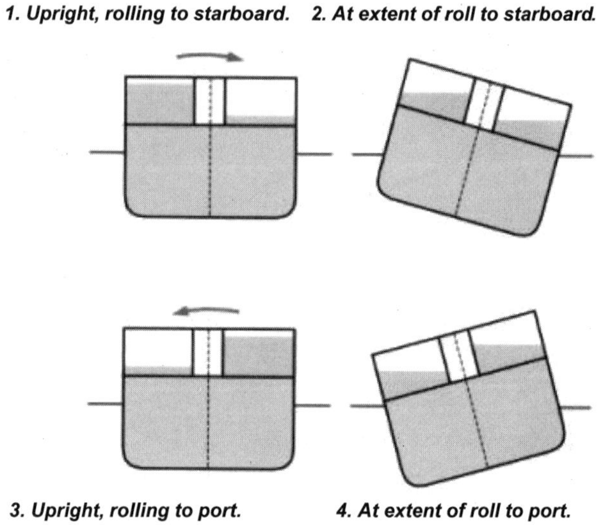

Fig. 24.21

The wave period of the tank may be varied to suit a particular ship at the design stage by changing the length of the centre chamber, or, by varying the openings in the longitudinal bulkheads (baffles). In service the optimum level to fill the tank will vary to allow adjustment for different GM conditions. The period of the wave within the tank should be equal to that of the ship's still water roll period, given by the formula:

$$T\ (\text{secs}) = \frac{2\pi k}{\sqrt{g \times GM}}$$

where GM is the metacentric height for the ship's condition at the time.

It is of particular importance that the free surface moments appropriate to the tank's condition when being used are accounted for when calculating the effective KG and, subsequently the GZ values.

Note Quite often these tanks are mistakenly referred to as being *stability* tanks rather than *stabilising* tanks. These tanks are aimed only at reducing the roll amplitude of the ship; they significantly *reduce* the ship's stability as a result of the high free surface moment values that are necessary to allow the effective operation of the tank.

24.5.2 Active systems

These include *active tank systems* and *stabilising fins*.

24.5.2.1 Active tanks

These tanks have a positive means of directing water to one side or the other. There are two tanks, one each side of the ship and the level of water is controlled by a pump or pumps acting in response to a gyro controlled roll sensing system. In the systems illustrated in figure 24.22, water is distributed so that the greatest quantity will be in the tank on the *high side* at the extent of the roll.

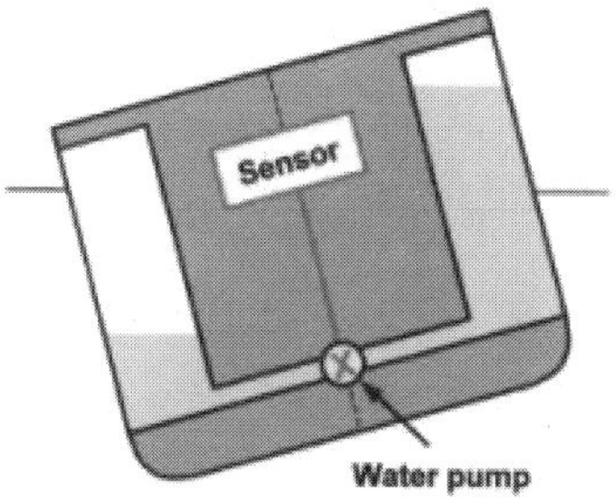

(a) Water is pumped from one tank to the other so as to keep the greater quantity in the higher tank.

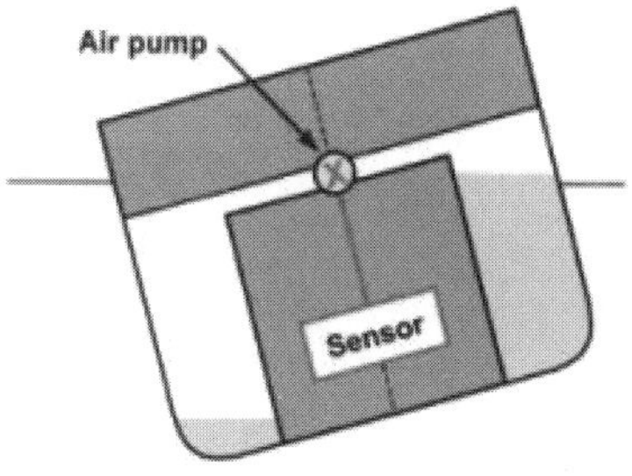

(b) Water level is controlled indirectly by means of air pressure above the water in each tank, the tanks are open to the sea at the bottom.

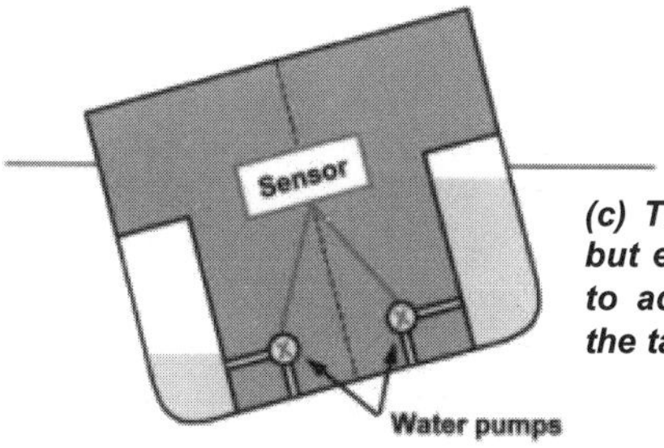

(c) This system is similar to (a) but each tank has its own pump to add and remove water from the tank as the ship rolls.

Fig. 24.22

24.5.2.2 *Active stabilising fins*

Active fins are fitted one each side near the top of turn of the bilge and are retractable. The fins are aerofoil is section and rotate around an athwartships axis. When the leading (forward) edge is tilted downwards the flow of water past the fin exerts a *downwards* force. At the same time the fin on the opposite side will have its leading edge tilted upwards to create an *upwards* force. This will create the stabilising moment that will counteract the rolling motion. An alternative arrangement is where the trailing edge of the fin is hinged and this moves up and down to cause the ship to counteract the rolling, as illustrated in figure 24.23.

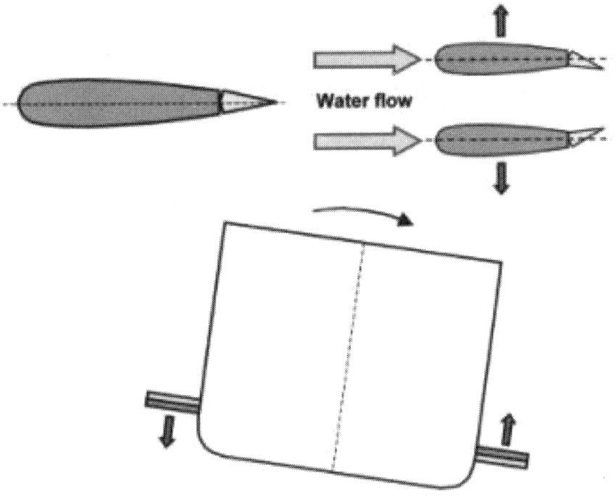

Fig. 24.23

The ship's rolling motion is sensed by an onboard gyro system that will operate the necessary electro-hydraulic actuating gear that will apply the optimum tilt of the fins to counteract the rolling motion. These systems are very effective on fast ships where they virtually eliminate all rolling effects, however they are less effective at slow speeds and are totally ineffective when the ship is stopped.

There are numerous types of stabilising systems available to ships, make sure that you understand whatever system is employed on your ship to gain the maximum benefit of having it fitted.

SECTION 25 – STABILITY PROBLEMS ASSOCIATED WITH SPECIFIC SHIP TYPES

INTRODUCTION

Ships are designed to fulfil a wide variety of operational roles ranging from the carriage of bulk solid and liquid cargoes, the carriage of containerised and roll-on roll-off cargoes and operations in offshore supply and the associated offshore service industries to name but a few. The many functions that a ship must satisfy dictate that there is an equally varied number of ship designs necessary to ensure that the appropriate operational requirements are met in each case. The varying designs of different ship type's means that certain ships will have stability characteristics unique to them and it is important that the various factors that influence such unique stability characteristics are understood by those who operate them.

Learning Objectives

On completion of this section the learner will achieve the following:

1. Understand the stability problems associated with the operation of *offshore supply vessels* and the meaning of the terms *'fixed'* and *'free trim'*.
2. Increase awareness of the stability problems associated with double hull tanker designs introduced as a measure to restrict the incidences of oil pollution.
3. Recognise the concerns and causes of the many bulk carrier losses with respect to structural integrity and the dangers of flooding of forward compartments highlighted by the loss of the *Derbyshire*; also to gain an understanding of the new structural requirements with respect to cargo density and damaged stability requirements.
4. Distinguish between *deterministic* and *probabilistic* approaches to damaged stability assessment and understand the deterministic requirements for passenger ship damaged stability.
5. Appreciate the major concerns of the operation and stability of ro-ro vessels and understand the basic concepts behind the recently enforced '*Stockholm Agreement*' aimed at improving the damaged stability and evacuation time available for crew and passengers after a ship has sustained damage.

25.1 OFFSHORE SUPPLY VESSELS

Special attention should be given to the loading, discharging, trim and stability of offshore supply vessels for the following reasons:

* *Both solid and liquid cargoes have to be loaded and discharged, often simultaneously, at sea.*

* *There is a risk of entrapment of water in a deck cargo of pipes.*

* *These vessels have a low freeboard in way of the cargo deck area aft but a large buoyant superstructure at the forward end.*

* *When heeled beyond the angle of after deck edge immersion severe loss of stability in terms of righting levers can occur as a result of the tendency of the vessel to trim further by the stern.*

* *These vessels often have stabiliser tanks.*

All of these factors must be considered during the compilation of the stability information for the vessel concerned and such information must include additional notes for the guidance of the master of any supply vessel.

25.1.1 Loading/discharging cargoes at sea

A supply vessel is called upon to perform complex cargo operations whilst at sea. This will include loading and discharging cargoes, both solid and liquid cargoes often simultaneously in addition to having to deal with personnel transfers also. It is essential that a high standard of awareness is maintained at all times by those involved to ensure crew safety and that adequate stability is maintained at all times.

The following points should be considered:

* Any trim limitation and minimum freeboard at the stern should be maintained. Ballasting should be carried out to counteract the effects of loading and discharging cargo.

* Cargo should always be discharged uppermost first i.e. discharge deck cargo prior to discharging from cargo tanks lower down in the vessel.

* When liquid cargo is to be discharged, as soon as pumping commences a full free surface of those tanks being pumped out should be allowed for.

* When a tank is to be ballasted at sea to counteract the removal of cargo from the vessel it should be noted that:

  (1) the tank should be assumed to have a full free surface as soon as ballasting commences, and;

  (2) the free surface will adversely affect the stability of the vessel before any benefit can be assumed from the weight of ballast water taken on board.

  Before ballasting commences it is important that a sufficient quantity of the highest deck cargo be unloaded to lower the centre of gravity of the vessel.

25.1.2 Allowances for entrapment of water in pipe cargoes

When pipes or casings are carried on deck an allowance must be made for the volume of entrapped water regardless of whether the pipes have wooden plugs or not. The *Code on Intact Stability for all Ships covered by IMO Instruments (IMO)* details the allowances that should be made as follows:

(Regulation 4.5.8.4) *Where pipes are carried on deck, a quantity of trapped water equal to a certain percentage of the net volume of the pipe deck cargo should be assumed in and around the pipes. The net volume should be taken as the internal volume of the pipes, plus the volume between the pipes. This percentage should be 30 if the freeboard amidships is equal to or less than 0.015L and 10 if the freeboard amidships is equal to or greater than 0.03L. For intermediate values of the freeboard amidships the percentage may be obtained by linear interpolation. In assessing the quantity of trapped water, the Administration may take into account positive or negative sheer aft, actual trim and area of operation.*

Instructions as to what allowance to be applied and how it should be applied must be included in the guidance notes for the master in the stability data book. It should be emphasised that the mass of this water is additional to the cargo deadweight permitted by the position of the appropriate load line mark.

25.1.3 Freeboard limitation aft

Excessive stern trim will always result in severely reduced freeboard aft. As such the position of deck cargo and tank contents should be arranged to minimise stern trim. Regulation 4.5.5.2 of the *Code on Intact Stability for all Ships covered by IMO Instruments (IMO)* states:

A minimum freeboard at the stern of at least 0.005L should be maintained in all operating conditions.

A statement as to the *maximum permissible trim* and the *minimum freeboard at the stern in mm* should be included in the guidance notes for the master in the stability data book.

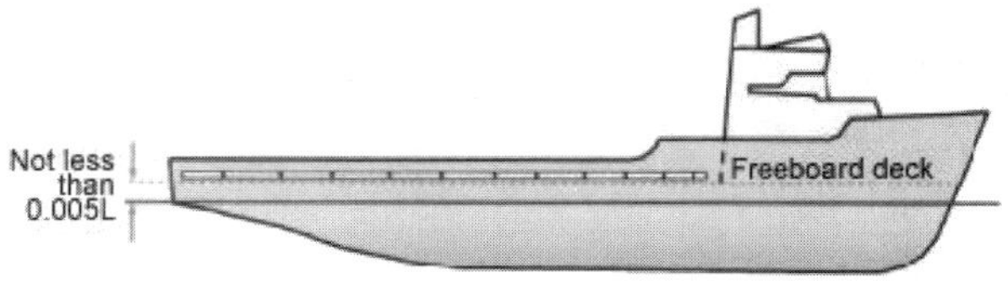

Fig. 25.1

25.1.4 The effect of stern trim and reserve forward buoyancy on stability

Supply vessels are characterised by a broad beam and shallow draught. The broad beam makes these vessels initially very stable but the low freeboard aft causes the deck edge to be submerged at small angles of heel. Beyond the angle of deck edge immersion any benefit of the broad beam is soon lost. All superstructure is in the forward quarter length of the vessel leaving the after three-quarters length available for cargo. This arrangement causes problems with respect to reserve buoyancy distribution as the ship is heeled as will be seen.

The effect of stern trim was introduced in section 17.6. A ship trimmed by the stern will have less overall stability than when on an even keel. Admittedly the GM and the stability at *small* angles of heel may be greater in the trimmed condition due to the greater water plane area increasing BM and the slightly greater KB; both leading to an improved KM initially.

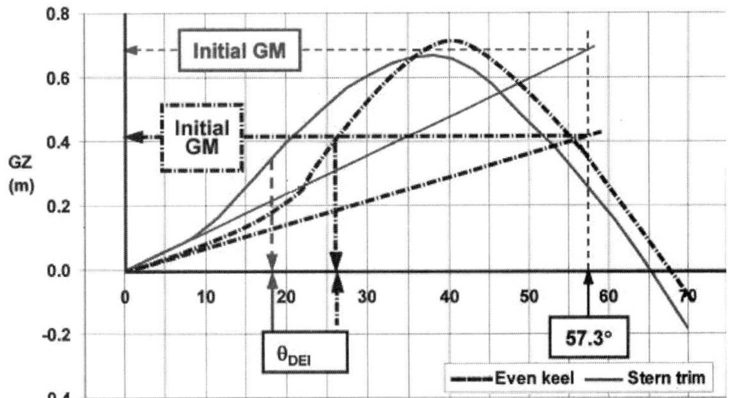

Fig. 25.2

However, the premature angle of heel at which the aft deck edge becomes immersed in the trimmed condition will result in an earlier deterioration of the GZ curve. The GZ curves for even keel and trimmed conditions are illustrated in figure 25.2.

When a supply boat is heeled beyond the angle of deck edge immersion aft sufficiently to cause the forward superstructure to displace water the effects can be quite dramatic as the ship will both *trim by the stern* and *suffer a loss of stability* even if the ship is on an even keel when upright. This is explained as follows:

Consider a typical supply boat on an even keel being progressively heeled to larger angles as shown in the following figures (25.3 to 25.5).

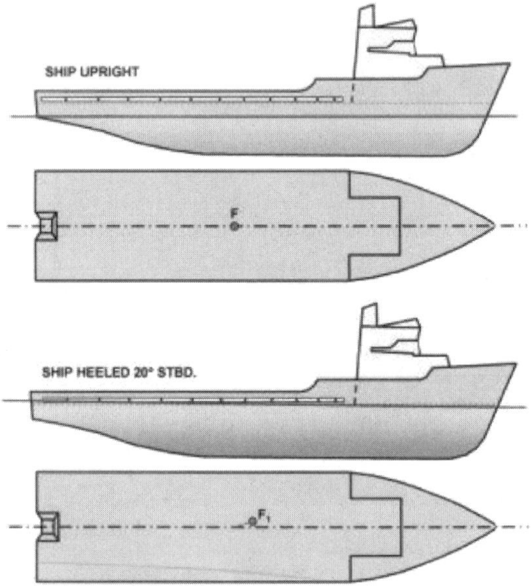

Fig. 25.3

represents the vessels intact water plane area;

represents the vessels intact underwater volume providing buoyancy force upthrust, and;

represents water shipped on deck after the aft deck has become immersed.

In the *upright condition* the ship is on an even keel. F is the longitudinal centre of flotation (located at the geometric centre of the water plane area) and is the point in the ship's length about which it will trim.

At *20° heel to starboard* the aft deck has become immersed, evidenced by the water on deck on the low side. Water plane area aft on the low side has been lost causing F to move forward. This is akin to moving the pivot point on a child's see-saw as shown in figure 25.4. *The ship starts to trim by the stern.*

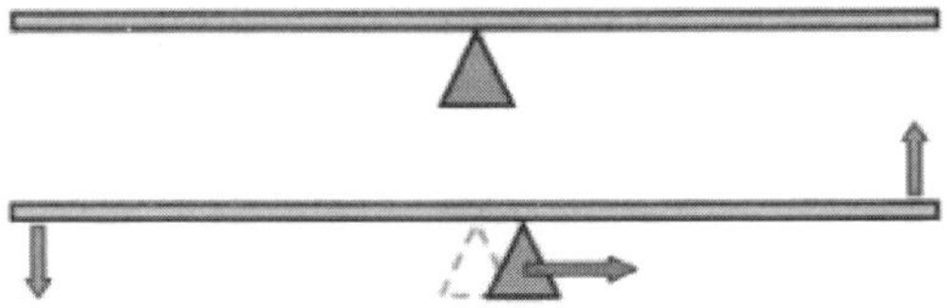
Fig. 25.4

The ship is now heeled progressively further.

At 30° heel the reserve buoyancy of the forward superstructure takes effect, volume of buoyancy being transferred from the high side aft where it is not being used to the low side forward on the heeled side. This causes the LCB to move forward creating a stern trimming couple. This, accompanied by the continuing forward movement of the centre of flotation causes the ship to trim significantly further by the stern as it continues to heel.

At 45° heel stern trim has increased causing the situation to become dangerous, whereby the after deck is becoming awash to such an extent that the angle of progressive flooding might soon be reached.

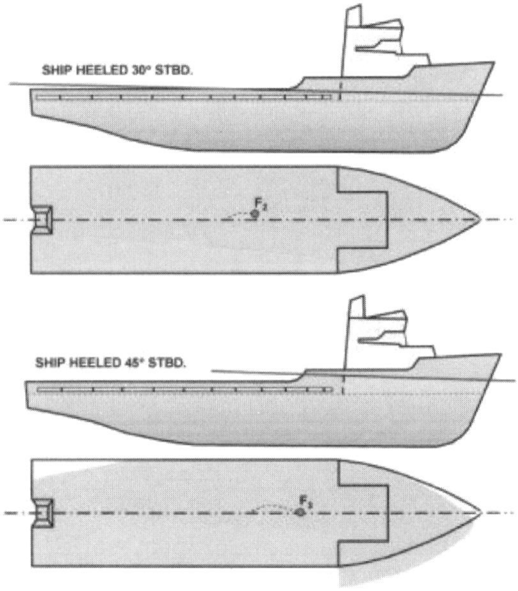

Fig. 25.5

Clearly, the effects on the ship being heeled to large angles of heel can have serious consequences with respect to reducing the angle of heel at which progressive downflooding takes place; but what of the effects of such ship behaviour on the curve of statical stability?

As the ship trims by the stern it loses buoyancy at the superstructure on the *low* side and gains buoyancy in way of the main hull on the *high* side. Figure 25.6 illustrates the loss of buoyancy forward due to the lift of the bow and gain of buoyancy aft due to sinkage. This redistribution of buoyancy (from forward bw side to aft high side) results in a shift of the centre of buoyancy towards the high side i.e. to a position B_1, closer to the centre line than B (figure 25.6). *Thus, righting lever (GZ) is reduced.*

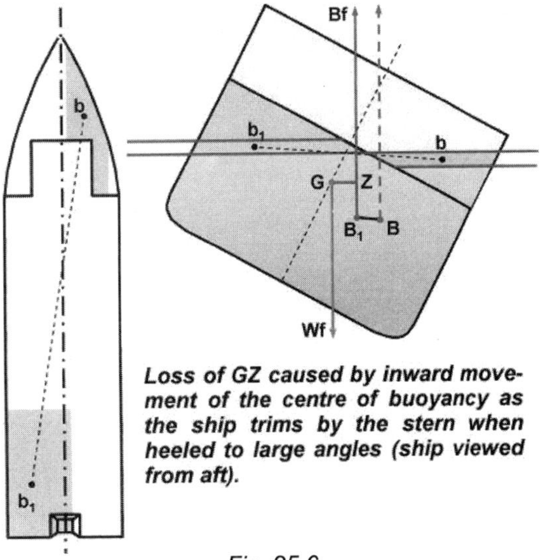

Loss of GZ caused by inward movement of the centre of buoyancy as the ship trims by the stern when heeled to large angles (ship viewed from aft).

Fig. 25.6

25.1.5 'Fixed trim' and 'free to trim' basis KN values

The KN values supplied for most ships are for an assumed condition of trim (usually even keel) and are calculated on a *'fixed trim'* basis. This means that any *inward* movement of the centre of buoyancy as the ship is heeled to large angles as depicted in figure 25.6 is ignored. If KN values for a supply vessel are calculated on a *'fixed trim'* basis this means that the values of GZ calculated for angles of heel where the reserve buoyancy of the forward superstructure takes effect will be greater than their actual value; the stability of the ship will be over estimated.

For supply vessels it is preferable that the KN values of the ship be derived on a *'free to trim'* basis. This means that the KN values are reduced to take account of the effect of the vessel trimming by the stern as it is heeled to larger angles where the reserve buoyancy of the forward superstructure takes effect, causing the reduction in GZ values.

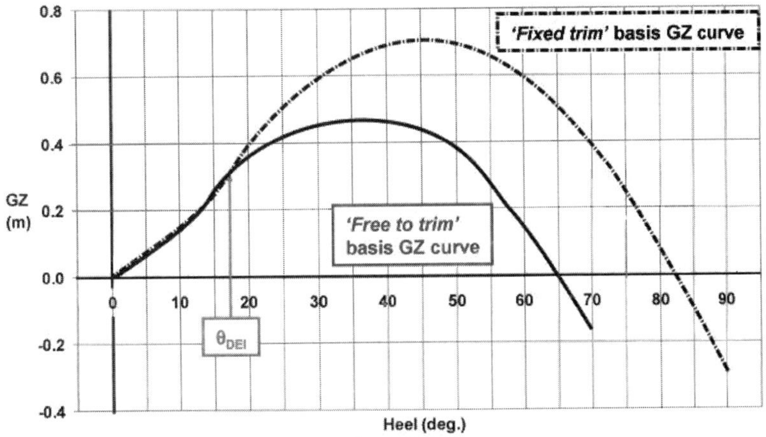

Fig. 25.7

When determining GZ values for such vessels always check the KN data. It should indicate the condition of trim assumed and whether the values are for an assumed *'fixed trim'* or *'free to trim'* basis. Remember that:

'Fixed trim' KN data will give greater GZ values than what the ship will actually have when heeled beyond the angle of deck edge immersion – stability will be overestimated!

The problems described are generally only relevant to vessels with large forward superstructures and low freeboards aft. On most cargo vessels that operate with only a small stern trim any such effects will generally be insignificant.

25.1.6 Intact stability criteria for supply vessels

Due to the hull form of supply vessels this alternative stability criteria may be substituted for that criteria laid down in regulation 3.1.2 of the *Code on Intact Stability for all Ships covered by IMO Instruments (IMO)* (for UK ships regulation 8.15 in *Load Line – Instructions for the Guidance of Surveyors (MCA)* allows the use of this alternative criteria).

* *The area under the curve of righting levers (GZ curve) should not be less than 0.070 metre-radian up to an angle of 15° when the maximum righting lever (GZ) occurs at 15° and 0.055 metre-radian up to an angle of 30° when the maximum righting lever (GZ) occurs at 30° or above. Where the maximum righting lever (GZ) occurs at angles of between 15° and 30°, the corresponding area under the righting lever curve should be:*

  $$0.055 + 0.001(30^\circ - \theta_{max}) \text{ metre-radian}$$

  (θ_{max} is the angle of heel at which maximum GZ occurs)

* *The area under the righting lever curve (GZ curve) between the angles of heel of 30° and 40°, or between 30° and the angle at which progressive downflooding takes place (θ_f), if this angle is less than 40°, should be not less than 0.03 metre-radian.*

* *The righting lever (GZ) should be at least 0.20 m at an angle of heel equal to or greater than 30°.*

* *The maximum righting lever (GZ) should occur at an angle of heel not less than 15°.*

* *The initial transverse metacentric height (GM) should not be less than 0.15 m.*

25.1.7 Stabiliser tanks

Most supply vessels are fitted with stabiliser tanks for the purpose of reducing roll amplitude during cargo load and discharge operations at sea. These were discussed in section 24.5. It is essential that they be filled to the correct level to provide optimum roll restriction. Guidance notes on the use of such tanks should be provided in the ship's stability data book. It must be recognised that the large free surface moments that these tanks cause will significantly reduce the ship's stability and this must always be allowed for.

25.2 DOUBLE HULL TANKERS

The traditional single skin design of tanker, where cargo tanks are subdivided into three by two longitudinal bulkheads and double bottom tanks where fitted in way of the engine room only where an inherently stable design of ship. Transverse subdivision was sufficient to limit the effects of free surfaces even when three, four or more cargo tanks where slack. The necessary high degree of subdivision of these vessels accompanied with only small, gasketed covers of steel provided a very strong structure despite being single skin. Reduced type 'A' freeboards where assigned to such ships because risk of sinking was considered low in the event of a compartment containing an oil cargo becoming damaged. Reasoning for this was explained in section 26.5.

Following the *Exon Valdez* disaster in Prince William Sound and the subsequent spillage of 11 million gallons of heavy crude oil along 1000 miles of the Alaskan coastline the United States introduced the requirement that all ships trading in their waters should have complete double hull protection of the oil cargo in an effort to minimise the risk of oil pollution (OPA 1990). The introduction of double hull designs caused by this increased legislation has caused a number of areas of concern.

25.2.1 Stability concerns

There are three main areas of concern:

* *Double bottoms result in a higher centre of gravity of the cargo and higher ship's KG when loaded.*

* *The strength characteristics of double hulls permit tank designs with greater free surfaces. Single hull tankers need longitudinal bulkheads which run throughout the length of the ship to provide the necessary longitudinal strength. The transverse spacing of these bulkheads was chosen to give tank sizes of approximate equal capacity and optimum bottom structure loads. The cellular nature of a double hull structure already provides the necessary longitudinal strength rendering further longitudinal bulkheads unnecessary for structural reasons. This permitted the single tank across arrangement (STA) to be adopted in many designs (recent changes to the MARPOL convention restrict this practice in new ships).*

* *Increased steel weight of double hull designs and reduced deadweight capacity increased the reluctance of operators to subdivide large centre cargo tanks. The resulting potential for loss of GM due to free surface effects is greatly increased.*

These concerns are warranted by the increased tanker lolling incidents that have occurred during load/discharge operations in double hull tankers of a single tank across (STA) design in the 35,000 to 150,000 DWT range. Below this range are mostly product carriers which have greater tank subdivision; above this range strength and tank size considerations preclude the use of the single tank across configuration.

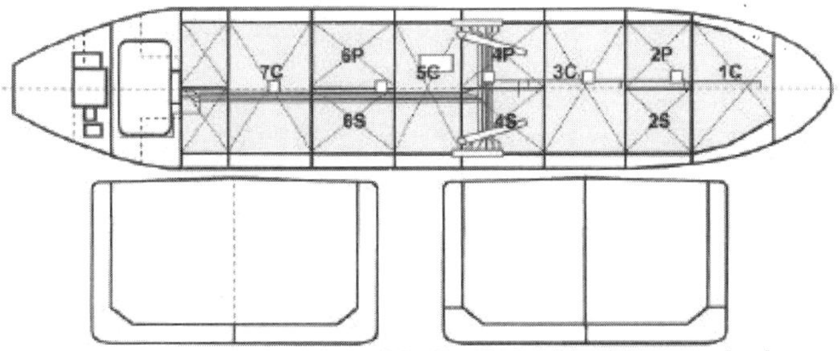

Suezmax tanker (136,055 dwt) built 1993 with altemate single tank across (STA) cargo tanks.

Fig. 25.8

A Suezmax tanker of 136,000 DWT built in 1993 is shown in figure 25.8 where cargo tanks 1, 3, 5 and 7 are single tank across (STA) arrangement. Note the alternate ballast tank arrangements within the double hull structure also.

The loss of GM that arises from a *single* STA cargo tank being slack is of the order of 0.75 m on such a ship. Such large losses in GM have led to the need for operational procedures to be in place to prevent such ships becoming unstable, particularly during simultaneous cargo and ballast handling operations. Such problems did not occur with traditional single hull design ships since these were inherently stable.

25.2.2 *Damaged stability considerations*

Owing to the intact stability problems so far discussed, compliance with damaged stability criteria is not so easy. Additional care is required with respect to cargo distribution to ensure that all envisaged damage scenarios as assumed by the regulations result in the ship meeting the required damaged stability criteria. If freeboard assignment is considered, the definition of a type 'A' ship includes assumptions with respect to damage and the final condition of equilibrium to be maintained. As a result of the stability problems associated with double hull tankers and the increased damaged stability requirements that must be met by type 'A' ships built after June 2000 it is unlikely that any new ships will qualify for the type 'A' tabular freeboard that may have been used in the calculation of the ship's summer freeboard.

If a double hull ship should suffer *low impact* grounding damage it is likely that the inner hull envelope containing the cargo will not be breached and oil spillage will not occur. In a smaller tanker the damaged space might be a 'U' shaped ballast tank which would allow free flooding right across the structure and up to the level of the waterline outside. The added weight of the floodwater (or lost buoyancy) would be considerable making it difficult to re-float the vessel. In a single hull tanker such damage would result in a loss of oil cargo, lightening the ship and making it easier to re-float. Had the damage been caused in a *minor impact* collision the loss of freeboard would be considerable in the double hull tanker whereas an increase in freeboard would take place in the single hull ship as oil spilled out.

In the case of a double hull tanker suffering *minor impact* damage to an 'L' shaped ballast tank on one side the ship would list considerably if still free-floating and this would have to be corrected by filling the opposite side tank with the overall result in substantial loss of freeboard. Another problem is that the introduced stresses might cause the design stress limits to be *exceeded*.

What is assumed by the regulations with respect to damage is arguably only applicable to *low impact* collisions or groundings. Many ship collisions in open water are relatively high impact collisions whereby the double hull boundary would be breached and oil loss would inevitably occur.

25.2.3 *Approaches to preventing double hull tanker lolling*

There are two approaches to preventing/minimising intact instability:

(1) Enforce by legislation the adoption of tanker designs that ensure 'intact stability' can be maintained during all possible simultaneous cargo and ballast operations (this being advocated by the *Oil Companies International Maritime Forum (OCIMF)*).

(2) Enforce by legislation a 'limited' design approach but allow the use of simple ship specific operating procedures and guidelines to be in place in conjunction with this to prevent lolling incidents (advocated by *IACS*).

The following table provides a comparison of the two approaches relative to tanker design and operations.

	DESIGN *Whereby lolling incidents are eliminated through inherently stable ship design*	***OPERATIONAL PROCEDURES*** *Whereby lolling incidents are prevented by the implementation of limited operational procedures*
Intact stability	Lolling not possible.	Lolling is possible if operational procedures are not followed.
Damaged stability	Additional subdivision of ballast and cargo tanks may be required to meet damaged stability requirements.	More tank arrangement options are available to improve damaged stability performance.
Capital costs	Increased costs if design requires the fitting of more cargo or ballast tanks and associated pipe work	No change from current construction costs.
Operational costs	Increased maintenance cost if design requires more cargo or ballast tanks.	Potential for more efficient pumping arrangements due to fewer tanks

Training	No additional training or procedures needed.	Requires continuous *ship-specific* based training.
Safety and pollution performance	Incidents due to lolling events are eliminated.	Overall safety and pollution prevention characteristics may be enhanced due to more tank arrangement options available.
Legislation compliance verification	One time verification at ship design stage.	Procedures to be continuously updated and verification of compliance at each cargo and/or ballast operation is necessary.

25.2.4 Maintenance

The likelihood of undetected corrosion is greatly increased since there is two to three times the steel work area of structure compared with a single hull tanker. The cellular nature of the double hull ballast spaces significantly increases the cost of inspection and repair of coating systems. Arguably, the structure in double hull spaces is such that access for close-up inspection is enhanced provided that side tanks are fitted with suitable stringers to serve as inspection platforms at reasonably spaced vertical intervals. The type and quality of tank coatings is now a very serious deciding factor in determining the economic trading life of a double hull ship.

It should be noted that SOLAS Chapter XI Regulation 2 requires that *enhanced surveys* be conducted on tankers. These specifically require that ultrasonic thickness measurements (UTM's) be conducted throughout the life of the ship as detailed in the ship's survey planning documentation.

25.3 BULK CARRIERS

A bulk carrier is essentially a single-decked ship with machinery aft. Many ships have single side skin construction as shown in figure 25.9.The block coefficient usually exceeds 0.80. Hopper shaped holds are formed by fitting corner tanks. These upper and lower wings may be termed *saddle* and *hopper* tanks respectively. The hold shape gives the bulk carrier a self-trimming property which minimises the likelihood of a dangerous shift of cargo. The shape ensures that during discharge the last of the cargo tends to run to a position below the hatchway. This facilitates the discharge by grabs. Hatchways are large and decks are clear. Salt water ballast can be carried in the upper and lower wing tanks as well as double bottoms and peaks. In most cases the total deadweight in ballast is very good (about 40% of the load deadweight) which gives a good bodily immersion.

Because of the high centre of gravity of the ballast in the top wing tanks, the ship is not unduly stiff in the ballast condition but still possesses adequate stability. The fact that a lot of the ballast is disposed towards the sides rather than the centreline also helps to give the ship a desirable relatively slow and easy rolling motion on a ballast passage. The distribution of ballast throughout the length of the ship should ensure relatively small bending moments and an absence of high shearing forces.

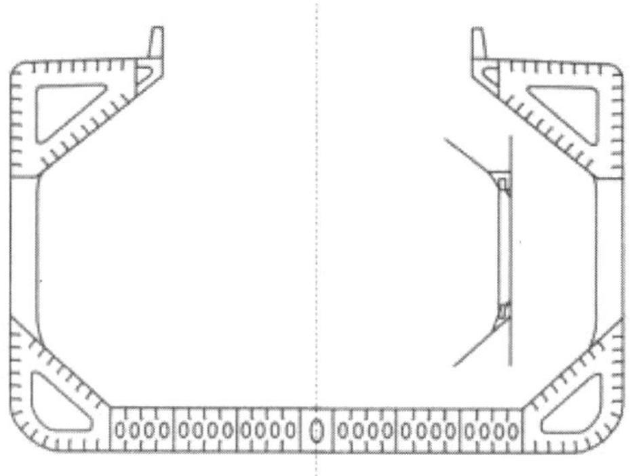

A typical single side skin bulk carrier configuration (combination framing system) showing web frame and side stiffener arrangements.

Fig. 25.9

Hold sizes are generally arranged to ensure adequate space for cargoes that stow at up to about 1.35 m^3/tonne. To make the ship more versatile and suitable for lighter cargoes, stowing at up to 1.5 - 1.6 m^3/tonne, the top wings can be constructed as dual purpose cargo/ballast spaces.

For cargo purposes they will be given small elliptical or oblong hatchways suitable for loading grain. Openings can be arranged in the lower part of the sloped tank plating to allow discharge via the lower hold. These openings will have either bolted watertight cover plates or hinged dogged covers and there is usually one such opening in each web space.

Loading a heavy cargo or an ore cargo in alternate holds, or in some other non-regular way, has several advantages. The increased height of stow achieved by alternate hatch loading gives a more reasonable height for the centre of gravity and avoids extreme stiffness. Furthermore there are fewer holds to suffer damage and to clean. However, the bending moments which are set up can be quite high and the shearing forces are bound to be much larger than in the ship which has been loaded more uniformly. The relative lengths of the various holds (some ships have alternate short and long holds) have a bearing on the resulting stresses but scantlings will always have to be increased to take account of the irregular loading pattern.

25.3.1 Bulk carrier concerns

The modern bulk carrier is often described as being the workhorse of the marine transport industry, but in the early 1990's bulk carrier losses generated doubts as to their structural integrity as many ships sank rapidly due to *catastrophic* and *sudden* structural failure often with the loss of all lives of those on board. Single side skin ships where of particular concern.

A study into bulk carrier survivability was carried out by the *International Association of Classification Societies (IACS)* at the request of IMO. IACS found that if a ship is flooded in the forward hold, the bulkhead between the two foremost holds may not be able to withstand the pressure that results from the sloshing mixture of cargo and water, especially if the ship is loaded in alternate holds with high density cargoes (such as iron ore). If the bulkhead between one hold and the next collapses, progressive flooding could rapidly occur throughout the length of the ship and the vessel would sink in a matter of minutes (figure 25.10).

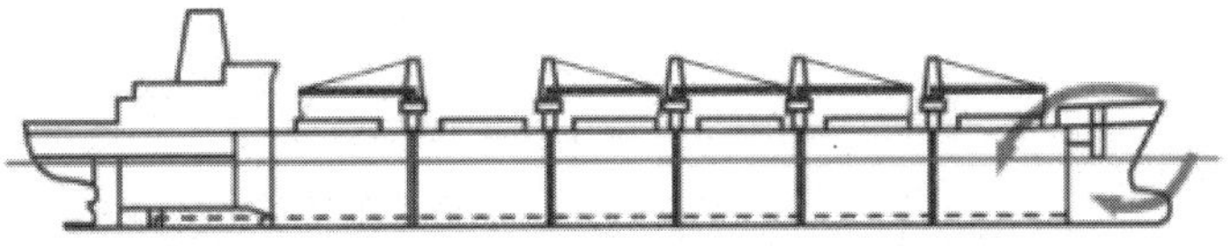

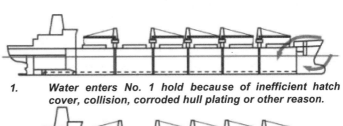

1. Water enters No. 1 hold because of inefficient hatch cover, collision, corroded hull plating or other reason.

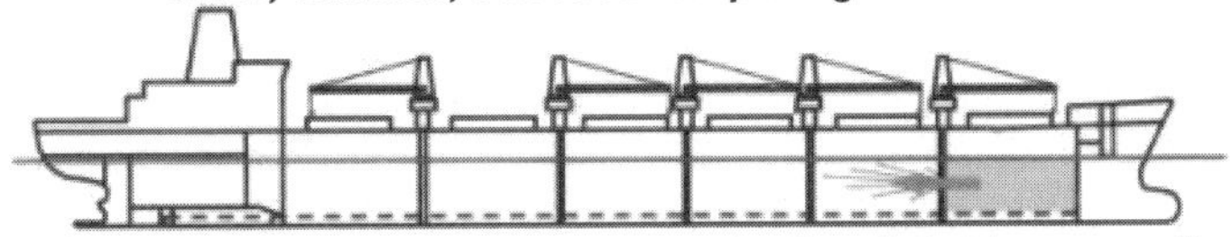

2. Weight of water and cargo in No. 1 hold causes the transverse watertight bulkhead to collapse.

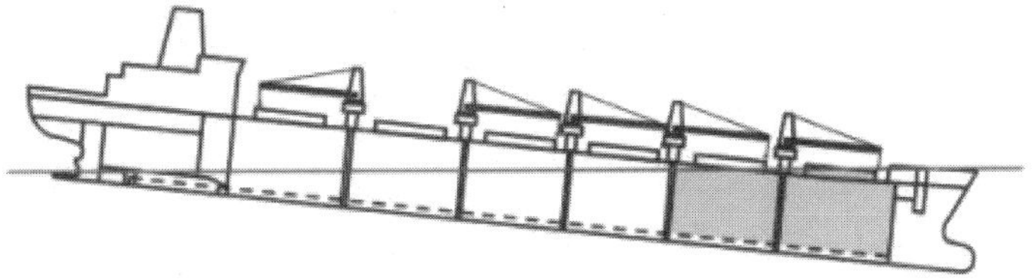

3. Hold No. 2 fills with water trimming the ship excessively by the head, ship sinks when holds 1 and 2 are flooded.

Fig. 25.10

IACS concluded that the most vulnerable areas are the bulkhead between numbers one and two holds at the forward end of the vessel and the double bottom of the ship at this location. During special surveys of ships, particular attention should be paid to these areas and, where necessary, reinforcements should be carried out.

The principle causes of structural failure are wastage due to corrosion and fatigue stresses when the ship is at sea. Poor maintenance regimes were a major contributory factor.

A further study into two-hold flooding by the U.S. Maritime Administration (MARAD) concluded that a midsize bulk carrier should survive all one-hold flooding scenarios provided that the ship was not suffering from steel corrosion wastage and undetected cracks but the flooding of any two adjacent holds would have disastrous consequences (figure 25.11).

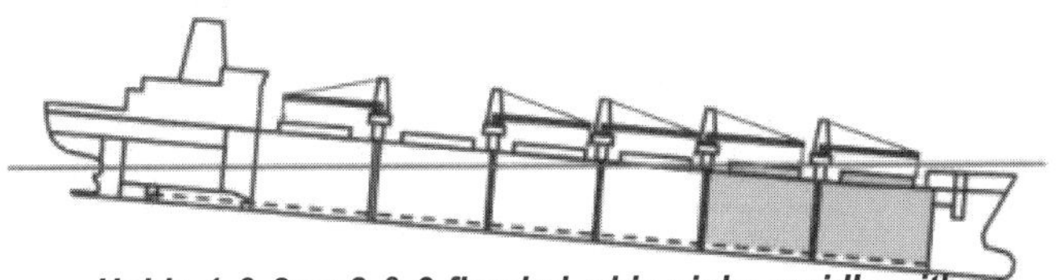

1. Holds 1 & 2 or 2 & 3 flooded, ship sinks rapidly with no time for crew to abandon.

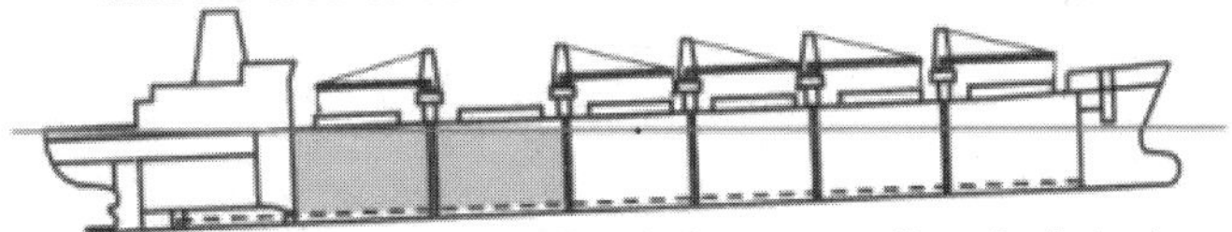

2. Both aftermost holds flooded causes after deck to be submerged and possible catastrophic down-flooding in the engine room.

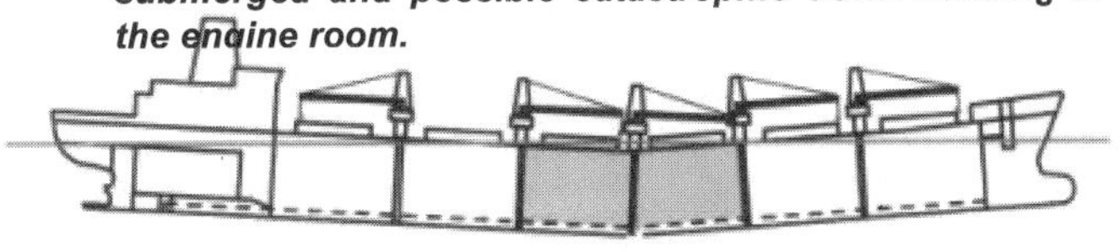

3. Flooding of any two remaining holds causes severe sagging stresses which could lead to sudden structural failure in a poorly maintained ship.

Fig. 25.11

25.3.2 New legislation aimed at improving bulk carrier safety

In November 1997 IMO adopted a new SOLAS Chapter XII – *Additional Safety Measures for Bulk Carriers* (for UK registered ships SI 1999 No.1644 *The Merchant Shipping (Additional Safety*

Measures for Bulk Carriers) Regulations 1999 came into force on 1st July 1999 which implements the new SOLAS regulations).

The regulations state that all new bulk carriers 150 metres or more in length of single side skin (built after 1st July 1999) carrying cargoes with a density of 1000 Kg/m³ and above should have sufficient strength to withstand the flooding of any one cargo hold, taking into account the dynamic effects resulting from the presence of water in the hold *(Regulation 5).*

For existing ships (built before 1st July 1999) carrying bulk cargoes with a density of 1780 Kg/m³ and above, the transverse watertight bulkhead between the two foremost cargo holds and the double bottom of the foremost cargo hold should have sufficient strength to withstand flooding and the related dynamic effects in the foremost cargo hold *(Regulation 6).*

Cargoes with a density of 1780 t/m³ and above (heavy cargoes) include iron ore, pig iron, steel, bauxite and cement. Lighter cargoes, but with a density of more than 1000 Kg/m³, include grains such as wheat and rice, and timber.

Under Chapter XII, surveyors can take into account restrictions on the cargo carried in considering the need for, and the extent of, strengthening of the transverse watertight bulkhead or double bottom. When restrictions on cargoes are imposed, the bulk carrier should be permanently marked with a solid equilateral triangle on the side shell amidships port and starboard with its apex 300 mm below the deck line. *(Regulation 8).*

The date of application of Chapter XII to existing bulk carriers depends on their age. Bulk carriers which are 20 years old and over on 1st July 1999 have to comply by the date of the first intermediate or periodic (special) survey after that date, whichever is earlier. Bulk carriers aged 15-20 years must comply by the first periodical (special) survey after 1st July 1999, but not later than 1st July 2002. Bulk carriers less than 15 years old must comply by the date of the first periodical (special) survey after the ship reaches 15 years of age, but not later than the date on which the ship reaches 17 years of age *(Regulation 3).*

Regulation 4 details the damaged stability requirements for bulk carriers. For bulk carriers of 150 metres in length and upwards of single side skin construction designed to carry solid bulk cargoes of 1000 Kg/m³ and above, constructed on or after 1st July 1999 when loaded to the summer load line, must be able to withstand the flooding of any one cargo hold in all loading conditions and remain afloat in a *satisfactory condition of equilibrium* as that prescribed in the definition of a type 'A' ship in Part 3 of the IMO publication *'Load Lines – 2002 Edition' Regulation 27 (See section 26.4.1).*

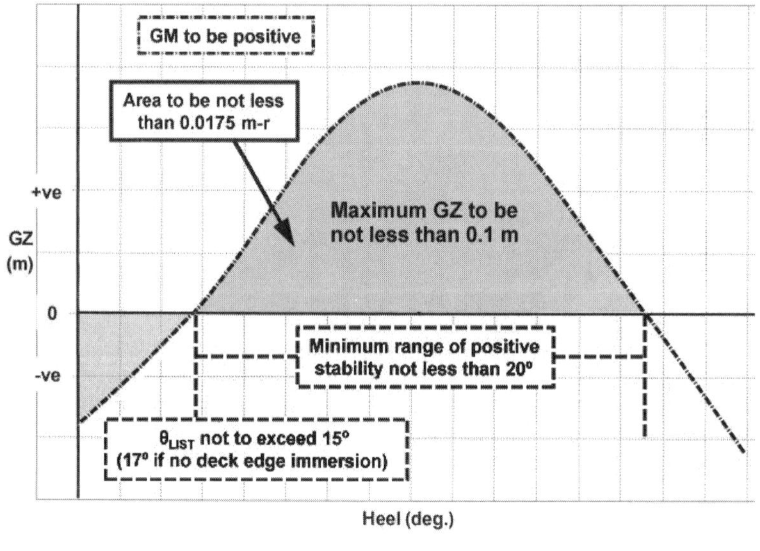

Damaged stability criteria for single side skin bulk carriers 150 m and over carrying solid bulk cargoes 1000 Kg/m³ and above constructed on or after 1st July 1999 after flooding any one cargo hold (IMO and MCA).

Fig. 25.12

It is also required that bulk carriers undergo the enhanced survey programme of inspections as required by regulation XI/2. Regulation 11 requires that all bulk carriers of 150 metres in length and upwards be fitted with a loading instrument capable of providing information on hull girder shear forces and bending moments.

In November 1997 IMO adopted the *BLU Code (Code of Practice for the Safe Loading and Unloading of Bulk Carriers) (IMO)* and reference should also be made to these regulations as appropriate.

25.3.3 December 2002 SOLAS amendments

Following the 1998 publication of the report into the sinking of the bulk carrier *Derbyshire* the Maritime Safety Committee (MSC) initiated a further review of bulk carrier safety, involving the use of Formal Safety Assessment (FSA) studies to help assess what further changes in the regulations might be needed. This resulted in the MSC adopting amendments to Chapter XII to further improve bulk carrier safety. These amendments include:

- *the fitting of high level alarms and level monitoring systems in order to detect water ingress;*
- *the availability and access for operation of pumping systems to allow the draining and pumping dry space bilges and ballast tanks located forward of the collision bulkhead;*
- *requirements for access in cargo areas of oil tankers and bulk carriers to ensure that vessels can be properly surveyed, this is to be taken into account at the building stage.*

Future changes yet to be adopted will include the need for all bulk carriers 150 metres in length and upwards to be fitted with double side hulls, improved coating systems, the fitting of a forecastle and many others all aimed at further improving bulk carrier safety.

25.4 PASSENGER SHIP SUBDIVISION AND DAMAGED STABILITY REQUIREMENTS

Examination candidates are often questioned on the current passenger ship damaged stability criteria and the damage assumptions on which this criteria is based. In order to more fully understand the requirements the methods of subdivision calculation must first be introduced.

25.4.1 Approaches to subdivision in general

Subdivision refers to the position and number of transverse and longitudinal bulkheads required to subdivide the ship in such a way that it can withstand an acceptable amount of damage; whereby water will flood into the ship causing loss of freeboard, change of trim and listing.

There have been international rules for the subdivision of *passenger ships* (carrying more than 12 passengers) since the 1929 International Conference on Safety of Life at Sea. The standard of subdivision required has been modified little over the years but the method of calculation has however changed with the advent of computers which make calculations easy and has ended the use of the 'floodable curves method'. The requirements of these rules were set out in a *deterministic* format. New rules for *passenger ro-ro* ships detailed in IMO Resolution A.265(VIII) employ a *probabilistic* approach (A/A_{max}).

Until recently, the only subdivision requirements for *cargo ships* were for those with reduced tabular freeboards (B-60 and B-100 ships) and a classification society's requirement for a minimum number of bulkheads based on ship length. This changed with the adoption by IMO in 1990 of Resolution MSC 19(58) which added a new Part B-1 to the 1974 SOLAS requirements. Cargo ships built on or after 1st February 1992 now have subdivision requirements based on the *probabilistic* approach as detailed in the new Part B-1 regulations. It is envisaged that in the near future a probabilistic approach to the subdivision of *all* passenger ships (and not just passenger ro-ro ships as at present) will be adopted similar to that of the cargo ship method.

25.4.2 Probabilistic approach to subdivision

The probabilistic approach addresses the probability of damage occurring at *any* particular location throughout the ship. It considers the likelihood of damage resulting in the flooding of one, two or any number of adjacent compartments and of the damage penetrating or not penetrating longitudinal bulkheads and watertight decks or flats.

Since the location and size of the damage is random, it is not possible to state precisely which part of the ship becomes flooded, however, the probability of flooding a space can be determined if the probability of occurrence of certain types of damages is known. The probability of flooding a space is equal to the probability of occurrence of all such damages which just open the considered space. A space is deemed to be a part of the volume of the ship which is bounded by undamaged watertight structural divisions.

Next, it is then assumed that a particular space(s) is flooded. The various factors which will influence whether the ship can survive such flooding to be taken into account include the initial draught and GM, the permeability of the space and the weather conditions, all of which are random at the time when the ship is damaged. Provided that the limiting combinations of the aforementioned variables and the probability of their occurrence are known, the probability that the ship will not capsize or sink, with the considered space(s) flooded can be determined.

The probability of survival in each case of damage is assessed and the summation of all positive probabilities gives an *'Attained Subdivision Index (A)'* which must be greater than a *'Required Subdivision Index (R)'* which is based on ship's length and complement for passenger ships and on ship's length only for cargo ships.

The ratio A/R allows a percentage of compliance to be calculated for the ship. In terms of the new rules for *passenger ro-ro* ships detailed in IMO Resolution A.265(VIII) the ratio A/A_{max} is considered, whereby deadline dates for compliance are related to the percentage value obtained for a particular ship.

25.4.3 *Deterministic approach to subdivision*

In the deterministic rules the maximum extent of damage and the permeability of flooded compartments are precisely defined. For example, on a passenger ship the assumed maximum *transverse* extent of damage is set at one fifth of the breadth of the ship (B/5) measured inboard from the ship's side. This makes the precise positioning of a longitudinal watertight bulkhead critical (figure 25.13): if it is inboard of the B/5 limit by only a few millimetres the space inboard of it becomes 'intact buoyancy' for the purpose of considering compliance with the prescribed damaged stability criteria and may also be used to increase the permissible length of the compartment assumed to be damaged; if it is outboard of the B/5 limit then from a subdivision point of view it does not exist, although the rules require that damaged stability calculations be done on the assumption it is not breached if this results in a more onerous situation.

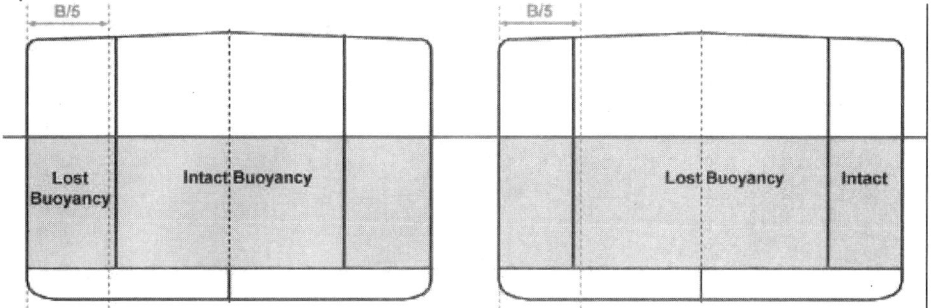

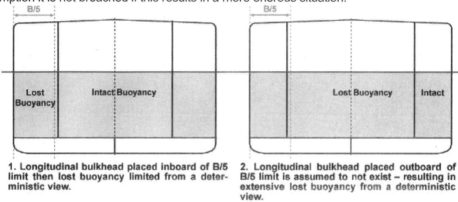

1. Longitudinal bulkhead placed inboard of B/5 limit then lost buoyancy limited from a deterministic view.

2. Longitudinal bulkhead placed outboard of B/5 limit is assumed to not exist – resulting in extensive lost buoyancy from a deterministic view.

Fig. 25.13

25.4.4 *Comparison of the two approaches to ship subdivision*

Under the probabilistic based regulations the precise positioning of subdivisions does not matter and damage calculations are made with and without the bulkheads being breached. The probabilistic approach takes a similar approach with respect to the watertightness of decks. The probabilistic method takes into account *safety against capsize* and *safety against flooding*.

The deterministic method only considers the safety against flooding. Having decided on the required level of subdivision for a ship based on the 'floodable length curves' method *each* damaged condition scenario (being based on the predefined damage assumptions) must be investigated to verify that the minimum damaged stability criteria is met. It is possible that the ship could pass the subdivision rules but fail on damaged stability. Under the probabilistic method the ship will satisfy the damaged stability criteria as well as it is taken into account in the subdivision calculations.

The arguments clearly favour the rational of the probabilistic rules and it is envisaged that the deterministic rules will eventually be phased out.

Objections to the probabilistic rules are:

* *the complexity of the large amount of calculations required despite the use of modern computing programmes to conduct them, and;*

* *the guidance that the deterministic rules gave to the designer with respect to location of structural subdivisions, since the damage assumptions are known at the outset.*

25.4.5 *Deterministic rules for passenger ship*

These are detailed in Chapter II-1 Part B of the SOLAS regulations. (For UK registered ships the calculation procedure for subdivision is to be found in Schedule 2 of MSN 1698 (M)). This section aims only to provide a summary of the procedure for the calculation of the maximum length of watertight compartments; reference should also be made to the relevant regulations in Chapter II/1 Part B of the regulations.

When a passenger ship suffers damage, loss of the ship is initially accepted to occur when the *bulkhead deck* becomes immersed below the damaged waterline at any point in the ship's length. However, a margin of safety is desirable so the limit is taken to be when the *margin line* becomes submerged.

Bulkhead deck
This is the uppermost deck up to which transverse watertight bulkheads are carried.

Margin line
This is a line drawn at least 76 mm below the upper surface of the bulkhead deck at the side of a subdivided ship. If the margin line should become submerged in the event of damage then the ship is deemed to be lost.

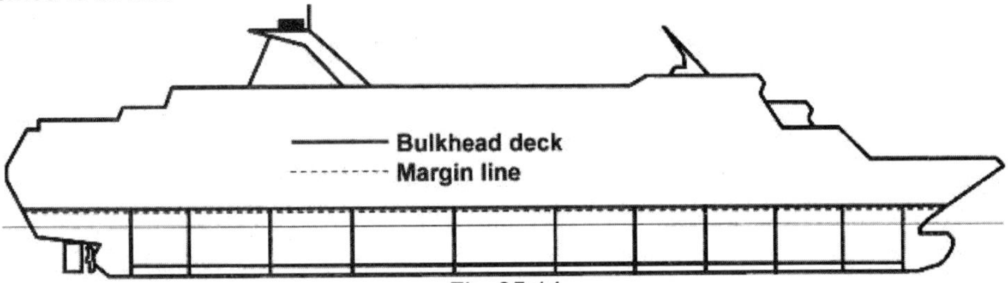

Fig. 25.14

The subdivision of a passenger ship is dependent on various features such as the ship's length, draught, freeboard, block coefficient and sheer and on the relative amounts and locations of space put to different uses, such as for accommodation, machinery, cargo and stores. These features are taken into account in a particular way.

1. The extent to which the spaces above and below the margin line are devoted to accommodation (for passengers and crew), the number of passengers, and the spaces devoted to cargo and machinery below the margin line determine the *Criterion of Service numeral* (C_S).

2. The *length* of the ship and the *Criterion of Service* numeral determine the *Factor of Subdivision (F)*.

3. The *form* of the ship and the *length* of the ship determine the *Floodable Lengths* of the compartments.

4. The *Floodable Lengths* and the *Factor of Subdivision* are used to determine the *Permissible Lengths* of the compartments since:

Permissible length = Floodable length × Factor of subdivision

Criterion of Service numeral (C_S)
The Criterion of Service numeral is a measure of the ship's passenger service. It is calculated from one of several alternative formulae, to take into account such things as the total number of passengers, the volume occupied by them above the margin line, the total space devoted to accommodation below the margin line and the relative amounts of machinery and cargo space. One of the formulae which may be used to determine the criterion of service numeral is:

$$C_S = 72 \frac{(M + 2P)}{V}$$

where: *M* is the volume of the machinery space below the margin line (m^3);
P is the volume of passenger spaces below the margin line, and;
V is the whole volume of the ship below the margin line (m^3).

The value of C_S obtained by the formula lies generally between 23, in a predominantly cargo ship, and 123 in a predominantly passenger ship; these two values, 23 and 123, are deemed to be the extreme values for later stages of the subdivision calculation.

Factor of Subdivision (F)

The Factor of Subdivision is determined from the values of the Criterion of Service Numeral (Cs) and length (L) by one of several formulae. An increase of either C_S or length decreases the Factor of Subdivision and leads to a closer spacing of the bulkheads i.e. the *'Permissible Lengths'* of the compartments is reduced.

Compartment standard

The reciprocal of the factor of subdivision is called the *Compartment Standard.* When F = ½ (0.5) the ship's compartment standard is 2 and when F = ? (0.33) the standard is 3. To say that a ship has a 'two compartment' standard implies that in that ship any two adjacent compartments have a combined length equal to that of one compartment in a 'one compartment' standard ship of the same length. This means that a 'two compartment standard' ship must be able to withstand the flooding of any two adjacent compartments within its length; a 'three compartment standard' ship must be able to withstand the flooding of any three adjacent compartments.

In most cases the values of C_S and L give a factor of subdivision which results in a 'compartment standard' which is not a whole number. For example, if F = 0.65 the compartment standard would be 1.54 (being the reciprocal). The ship would therefore be classed as being a '1 compartment standard' ship and must be capable of withstanding the flooding of any single compartment. If F = 0.42 the compartment standard would be 2.38; the ship would be classed as being a '2 compartment standard' and must be capable of withstanding the flooding of any two adjacent compartments. (figure 25.15). The value of F can never be greater than 1.00.

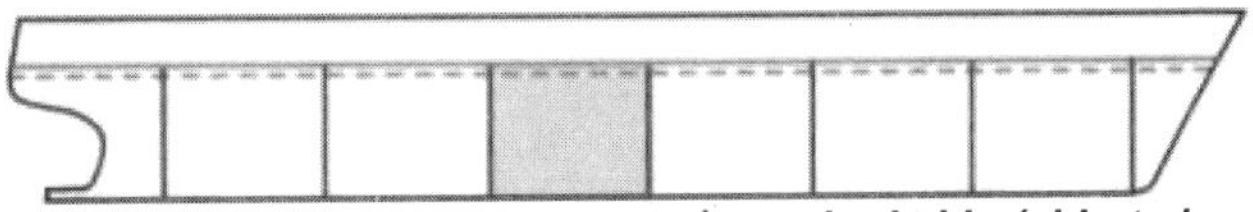

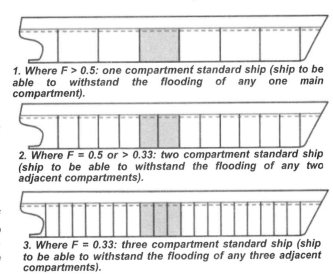

1. Where F > 0.5: one compartment standard ship (ship to be able to withstand the flooding of any one main compartment).

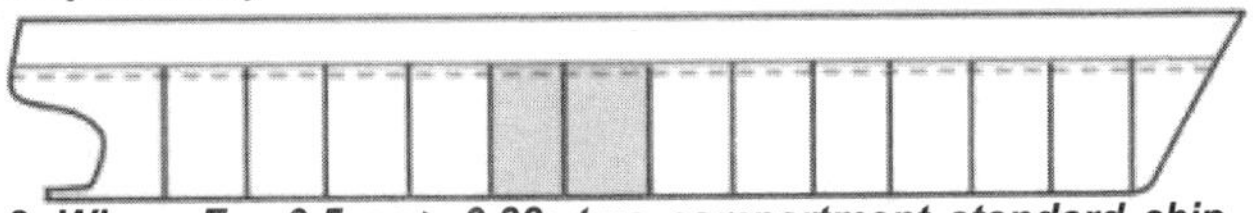

2. Where F = 0.5 or > 0.33: two compartment standard ship (ship to be able to withstand the flooding of any two adjacent compartments).

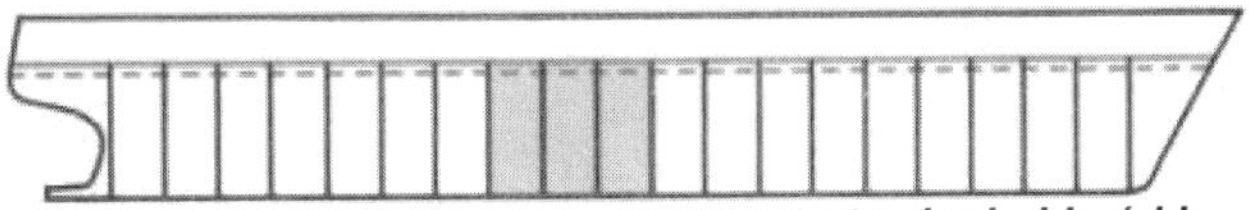

3. Where F = 0.33: three compartment standard ship (ship to be able to withstand the flooding of any three adjacent compartments).

Fig. 25.15

Permissible lengths of compartments

The factor of subdivision (F) is used to determine permissible lengths of compartments when multiplied by their respective floodable lengths i.e.

Permissible length = Floodable length × Factor of subdivision

The features of the ship that are considered in determining the *floodable lengths* for the purpose of subdivision calculation include:

1. Block coefficient (C_B);
2. Freeboard ratio (given by: $\dfrac{\text{Freeboard amidships measured to the margin line}}{\text{Subdivision draught}}$
3. Sheer ratio; two ratios are used: Forward sheer ratio = $\dfrac{\text{Sheer forward}}{\text{Subdivision draught}}$,and;

   Aft sheer ratio = $\dfrac{\text{Sheer aft}}{\text{Subdivision draught}}$
4. Compartment permeability.

The above factors and the ship's length govern the *Floodable Lengths* of the compartments.

Floodable Length

The floodable length, at any point in the ship's length, is the maximum length of compartment having its centre at that point, which can be flooded without submerging the margin line. It is expressed as a percentage of the ship's length. The floodable length at any position depends on the position of the compartment and the form of the ship.

Twenty four diagrams of floodable length are published, twelve assuming a compartment permeability of 100% and twelve assuming 60% compartment permeability. Each of the diagrams in a series of twelve is for a different position in the length of the ship (the position being expressed as a fraction or percentage of the ship's length in order that the diagrams are suitable for *ships* of all lengths). The diagrams incorporate the form variables, *block coefficient, freeboard ratio* and *sheer ratio* (forward or aft depending on the position of the compartment concerned). One such diagram, in simplified form is shown in figure 25.16. This particular diagram is for a position 20%L forward of the aft perpendicular (aft terminal), with permeability of 60%.

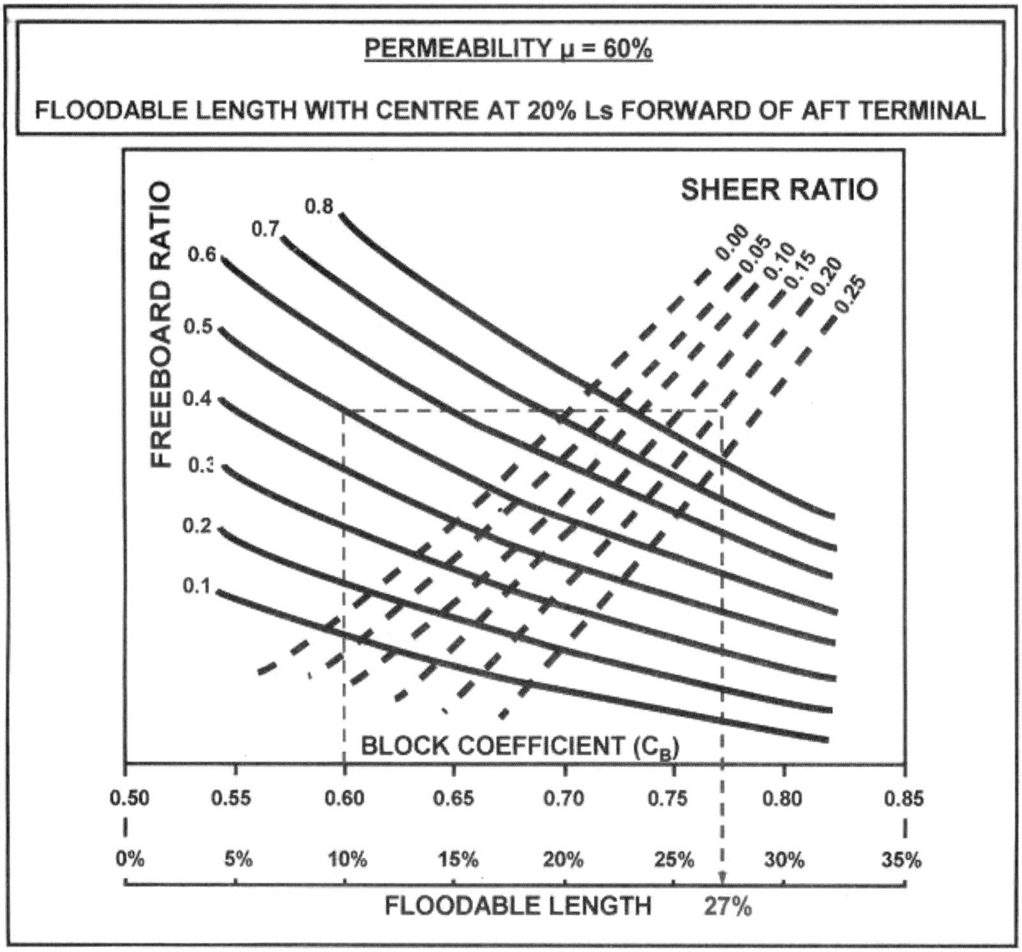

Fig. 25.16

The diagram shows that if the ship had a block coefficient of 0.60, freeboard ratio of 0.50 and a sheer ratio aft of 0.20 the floodable length is 27%. This is to say that 27% of the ship's length centred at a point 20% of the ship's length from aft, could be flooded (with permeability of 60%) without submerging the margin line (assuming a factor of subdivision of 1.00). If the length of the ship was 100 m say, the floodable length of a compartment centred at a position 20% of the ship's length from aft would be 27 metres.

If reference is then made to the other eleven diagrams of the series, each for a different position in the ship, using the same 'form' (block coefficient, freeboard ratio and sheer ratio) another eleven floodable length values are obtained, each expressed as a percentage of the ship's length. The twelve floodable length values can then be used to draw a *curve of floodable lengths*. The X axis for this curve represents the ship's length, marked off in percentages of length (from aft). The Y axis, drawn to the same scale, shows the floodable length for each position in the length of the ship.

A curve of floodable lengths for the same ship form, derived from the series of twelve diagrams assuming 100% permeability would give a curve of the same nature as that shown but having much smaller ordinates; the floodable lengths become smaller when the permeability is increased (figure 25.17).

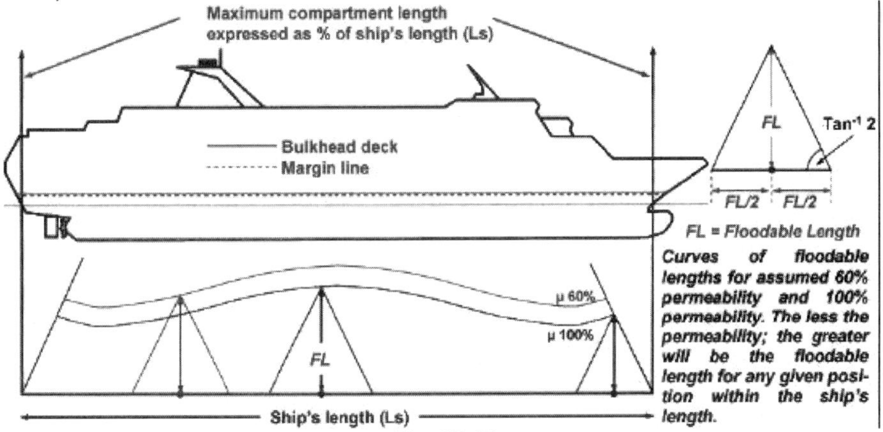

Fig. 25.17

The curve of floodable lengths for a given permeability throughout the ship has a characteristic 'W' shape as shown. It has maximum ordinates at about amidships where the flooding of an amidships compartment would cause bodily sinkage but little change of trim so these compartments can be comparatively long. The ordinates reduce on either side of amidships; because of the increased trimming effect when such spaces are flooded they must be shorter. The ordinates then increase again towards the very ends of the ship; the finer lines (and increased sheer in many cases which raises the margin line) allow a greater length to be flooded near the extreme ends of the ship.

When the floodable lengths are known for both 60% and 100% permeabilities, an interpolation formula is used to obtain the correct floodable lengths for intermediate permeability values. For *small* differences in permeability the floodable length ordinates can be taken to vary inversely as the permeability values.

The permeability must vary throughout the length of any given ship according to the way in which different spaces are allocated to different purposes.

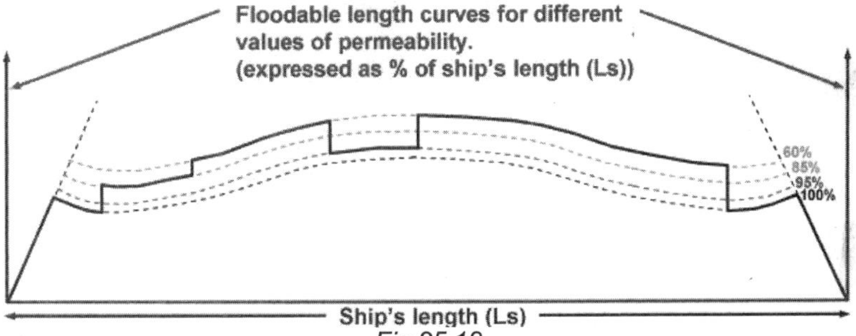

Fig.25.18

Uniform permeability values are determined by various formulae for the machinery space and the spaces forward and aft of the machinery space. Reference should be made to *Regulation 5.*
Once the permeability values are calculated curves of floodable lengths may be plotted to account for the different permeability values (figure 25.18).

This curve of floodable lengths could be used to determine suitable bulkhead positions if the factor of subdivision for the ship is one. When the factor of subdivision is less than one, the ordinates of the curve must be multiplied by this factor to obtain (smaller) ordinates for the *Curve of Permissible Lengths.*

Permissible length = Floodable length × Factor of subdivision

The permissible length curve has the same general form as the floodable length curve but is reduced in height.

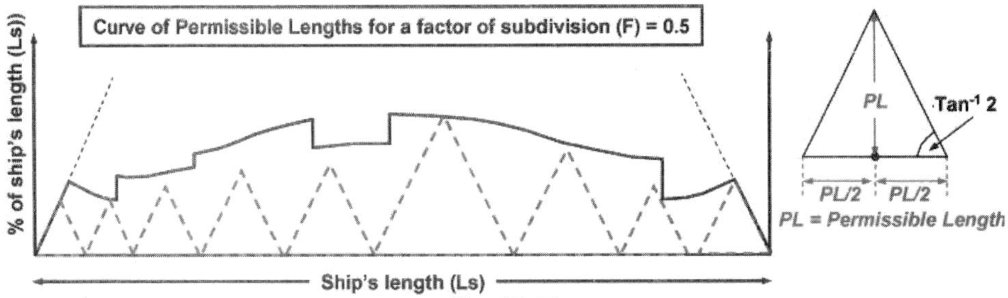

Fig. 25.19

At each proposed bulkhead position a line is drawn at an angle to the base line the tangent of which is 2. These lines must have points of intersection on or below the permissible length curve for the proposed bulkhead position to be acceptable – because the base of the triangle (the distance between the bulkheads) is equal to the point of intersection this must be less than (or equal to) the permissible length of the compartment. If any point of intersection is above the permissible length curve the distance between the proposed bulkheads is too great and one or more bulkheads will have to be relocated or an additional bulkhead may need to be fitted.

Note The collision bulkhead which should also be watertight up to the bulkhead deck shall be fitted at a distance from the ship's forward perpendicular not less than 5% of the length of the ship and not more than 3.0 metres plus 5% of such length.

Although the description of the calculation of the spacing of watertight bulkheads described the use of floodable length curves (which is still valid) much of the calculation will be conducted using computer programmes specifically designed for the purpose of subdivision calculations.

25.4.6 Subdivision load lines for passenger ships

Some passenger ships have flexible operating schedules whereby the ratio of cargo to passenger carriage can vary from one passage to the next. Certain spaces may be used for cargo or passenger accommodation alternatively which will change the criterion of service numeral (C_S). This leads to a change in the factor of subdivision (F) and consequently would lead to changes in the permissible lengths of compartments within the ship. To allow for the changes in passenger ship utilisation additional subdivision load lines may be assigned.

Subdivision load lines are additional to the ordinary load lines and are applicable when in a passenger condition i.e. when a ship is carrying more than 12 passengers. When spaces can be adapted for the accommodation of passengers and the carriage of cargo alternatively, more than one subdivision load line will be assigned, to take care of the varying circumstances. The various subdivision load lines are identified by C_1 at the deepest draught and C_2, C_3 etc. when there are alternative conditions (Ships of Classes other than I and II have a subdivision mark C or, when there is more than one mark, C_A, C_B, C_C etc., C_A being for the deepest draught condition). The marks are cut in, or welded, and painted in the usual way.

No subdivision load line can be above the deepest *salt water* load line as assigned under the Load Line Rules.

In no case can a ship be so loaded that in *salt water* the subdivision load line (appropriate to the particular voyage and condition of service, as stated on the Passenger Certificate) is submerged. Regardless of the position of the subdivision load line the ship must not of course be overloaded in respect of the 'ordinary' load line applicable to the season and zone.

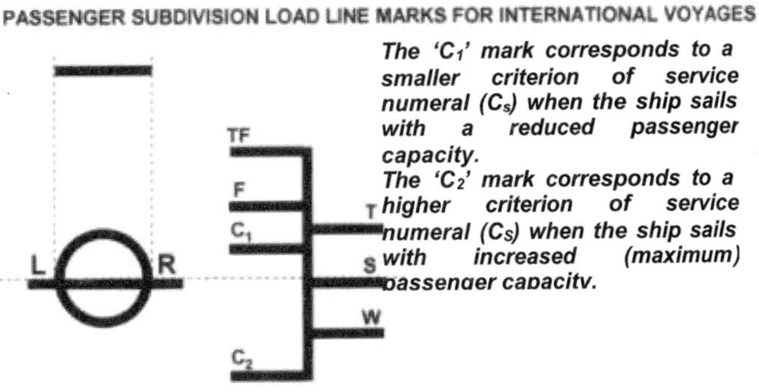

PASSENGER SUBDIVISION LOAD LINE MARKS FOR INTERNATIONAL VOYAGES
The 'C1' mark corresponds to a smaller criterion of service numeral (Cs) when the ship sails with a reduced passenger capacity.
The 'C2' mark corresponds to a higher criterion of service numeral (Cs) when the ship sails with increased (maximum) passenger capacity.
L
R
TF
F
C1
T
S
W
C2

Fig. 25.20

<u>Note</u> When a space which may be used for cargo or accommodation is converted to accommodation for passengers there will be an increase in the Criterion of Service numeral (C_S) and, consequently, a reduction in the Factor of Subdivision (F). This in turn should lead to a reduction of the permissible lengths of compartments. If the bulkhead arrangement has been chosen to suit the less onerous 'cargo' condition the spacing will be too great for the 'passenger' condition. The ship will have to be assigned a greater freeboard in the 'passenger' condition. The increased freeboard leads to an increase in the floodable lengths and consequently to an increase in the permissible lengths of compartments. The freeboard is increased sufficiently to ensure that the increase in permissible lengths matches the actual distance between bulkheads. The alternative (C_2) load line for the higher service condition must therefore be marked at a lower position than C_1.

When the subdivision load line C_1 is lower than the tropical load line T, the inference is that even in the least onerous passenger condition the ship is not sufficiently well subdivided to load to the draught permitted by the Load Line Rules.

25.4.7 Passenger ship stability in the damaged condition

Details are contained in Chapter II-1 Part B Regulation 8 of the SOLAS regulations (for UK registered ships the damaged stability requirements are to be found in Schedule 3 of MSN 1698 (M)). The requirements of *MSN 1698 (M) Schedule 3*, which are essentially the same as Regulation 8 of the SOLAS regulations, are summarised as follows:

<u>*Assumptions on which the calculations are based*</u>

Sufficiency of intact stability of every ship following damage and flooding shall assume the following:

1. *The ship to be in assumed worst service condition;*

2. *Volume and surface permeabilities shall be assumed as follows:*

Space	***Permeability***
Occupied by vehicular cargo	*90%*
Occupied by other cargo or stores	*60%*
Appropriated as accommodation for passengers and crew	*95%*
Appropriated for machinery	*85%*
Appropriated for liquids	*0 or 95%**
(whichever results in the more onerous requirements.)*	

Higher surface permeabilities shall be assumed in respect of spaces which, in the vicinity of the damaged water plane, contain no substantial quantity of accommodation or machinery and spaces which are not generally occupied by any substantial quantity of cargo or stores.

3. *The extent of damage shall be assumed as follows:*
   (a) *longitudinal extent: 3 m plus 3% of the length of the ship, or 11 m, whichever is less. Where the required factor of subdivision (F) is 0.33 or less, the assumed longitudinal extent of damage shall be increased as necessary so as to include any two consecutive main transverse watertight bulkheads (i.e. the ship must be able to withstand the flooding of any three adjacent compartments);*

   (b) *transverse extent: 20% of the breadth of the ship, measured inboard from the ship's side at right angles to the centreline at the level of the deepest subdivision load waterline taken parallel to the keel;*

   (c) *vertical extent: from the base line upwards without limit.*

   (d) *If any damage of lesser extent than that indicated above would result in a more severe condition regarding heel or loss of metacentric height, such damage shall be assumed for the purpose of the calculation.*

Sufficiency of stability in the damaged condition (ships constructed on or after 29th April 1990)
The intact stability of the ship shall be deemed to be sufficient if the calculations show that, after the assumed damage, the condition of the ship is as follows:-

(1) *In the final stage after damage, and after equalisation where provided:*
   (a) *the positive residual righting lever curve has a range of at least 15 degrees beyond the angle of equilibrium; this range may be reduced to a minimum of 10 degrees in the case where the area under the righting lever curve is that specified in subparagraph (b) is increased by the ratio 15/Range, where Range is expressed in degrees;*

   (b) *the area under the righting lever curve is at least 0.015 metre-radians, measured from the angle of equilibrium to the lesser of:*
      (i) *the angle at which progressive flooding occurs; or*
      (ii) *22 degrees (measured from the upright) in the case of one compartment flooding, or 27 degrees (measured from the upright) in the case of simultaneous flooding of two or more adjacent compartments;*

   (c) *a residual righting lever (GZ) value, is to be obtained within the range specified in subparagraph (1)(a), when determined by the formula:*

$$GZ\ (m) = \frac{\text{heeling moment (t.m)}}{\text{displacement (t)}} + 0.04$$

   where the heeling moment is to be taken as the greatest value resulting from any one of the following effects:
      (i) *the crowding of all passengers towards one side of the ship;*
      (ii) *the launching of all fully-loaded davit-launched survival craft on one side of the ship; or*
      (iii) *the pressure of the wind on one side of the ship;*

   where in no case shall the GZ value so determined be less than 0.10 metres;

   (d) *for the purpose of calculating the heeling moments in subparagraph (1)(c), the following assumptions shall be made*
      (i) *moments due to crowding of passengers:*
         (aa) *4 persons per square metre;*
         (bb) *a mass of 75 kilograms for each passenger; and*
         (cc) *passengers shall be distributed on available deck areas towards one side of the ship on the decks where muster stations are located and in such a way that they produce the most adverse heeling moment;*

(ii) moments due to launching of all fully loaded davit-launched survival craft on one side:

(aa) all lifeboats and rescue boats fitted on the side to which the ship has heeled after having sustained damage shall be assumed to be swung out fully loaded and ready for lowering;

(bb) for lifeboats which are arranged to be launched fully loaded from the stowed position, the maximum heeling moment during launching should be taken;

(cc) a fully loaded davit-launched lifecraft attached to each davit on the side to which the ship has heeled after having sustained damage shall be assumed to he swung out ready for lowering;

(dd) persons not in the life-saving appliances which are swung out shall not provide either additional heeling or righting moment;

(ee) life-saving appliances on the side of the ship opposite to the side to which the ship has heeled shall be assumed to be in a stowed position;

(iii) moments due to wind pressure:-

(aa) a wind pressure of 120N/m^2 to be applied;

(bb) the area applicable shall be the projected lateral area of the ship above the waterline corresponding to the intact condition; and

(cc) the moment arm shall be the vertical distance from a point at one half of the mean draught corresponding to the intact condition to the centre of gravity of the lateral area;

(e) in intermediate stages of flooding, or during equalisation where applicable the maximum righting lever shall be at least 0.05 metres and the range of positive righting levers shall be at least 7 degrees. In all cases only one breach in the hull and only one free surface need to be assumed;

(2) The final condition of the ship after damage and, in the case of asymmetrical flooding, after equalisation measures have been taken shall be as follows:

(a) in the case of symmetrical flooding there shall be a positive residual metacentric height of at least 50 millimetres as calculated by the constant displacement method;

(b) in the case of asymmetrical flooding the angle of heel for one-compartment flooding shall not exceed 7 degrees. For the simultaneous flooding of two or more adjacent compartments a heel of 12 degrees may be permitted; and

(c) in no case shall the margin line be submerged in the final stage of flooding.

At intermediate stages of flooding the margin line is not to be submerged unless partial subdivision above the margin line (such as partial bulkheads or webs) which sufficiently restricts the flow of water along the bulkhead deck and results in an angle of heel not exceeding 15 degrees. In the case of ships carrying vehicles on the bulkhead deck, the angle of heel at intermediate stages of flooding shall not be greater than that which will submerge the margin line;

(3) For the purpose of the requirements in this section:

(a) when major progressive flooding occurs, that is when it causes rapid reduction in the righting lever of 0.04 metres or more, the righting lever curve is to be considered as terminated at the angle at which the progressive flooding occurs, and the range and area referred to in subparagraphs (1)(a) and (b) should be measured to that angle; and

(b) in cases where the progressive flooding is of a limited nature that does not continue unabated and causes an acceptable slow reduction in righting lever of less than 0.04 metres, the remainder of this curve shall be partially truncated by assuming that the progressively flooded space is so flooded from the beginning.

Figure 25.21 provides a summary of the damaged stability requirements.

SUFFICIENCY OF STABILITY IN THE DAMAGED CONDITION FOR PASSENGER SHIPS CONSTRUCTED ON OR AFTER 29TH APRIL 1990 (UK *MCA* requirements)

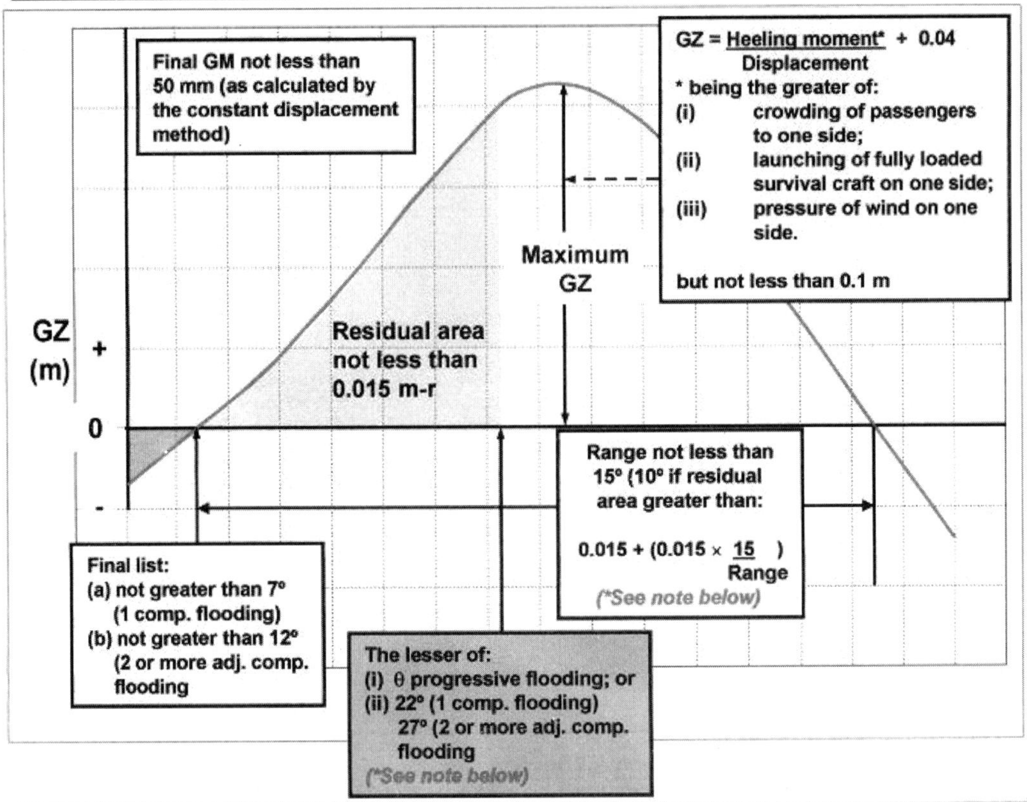
Final GM not less than 50 mm (as calculated by the constant displacement method)
GZ = Heeling moment* + 0.04
Displacement
* being the greater of:
(i) crowding of passengers to one side;
(ii) launching of fully loaded survival craft on one side;
(iii) pressure of wind on one side.
but not less than 0.1 m
Maximum GZ
GZ (m)
+
0
-
Residual area not less than 0.015 m-r
Range not less than 15° (10° if residual area greater than:
0.015 + (0.015 × 15 / Range)
(*See note below)
Final list:
(a) not greater than 7° (1 comp. flooding)
(b) not greater than 12° (2 or more adj. comp. flooding
The lesser of:
(i) θ progressive flooding; or
(ii) 22° (1 comp. flooding)
27° (2 or more adj. comp. flooding
(*See note below)

* *When major progressive flooding occurs that causes rapid reduction in the righting lever of 0.04 metres or more, the righting lever curve is to be considered as terminated at the angle at which the progressive flooding occurs, and the range and area should be measured to that angle.*

Fig. 25.21

Some passenger ships may require cross flooding arrangements to meet the damaged stability requirements and should preferably be self activating; if not the operating arrangements must be accessible from a position above the bulkhead deck. Cross flooding must be effective to reduce the list to an acceptable degree within 15 minutes.

Presentation of limiting stability information

The master of the ship shall be supplied with the data necessary to maintain sufficient intact stability under the service conditions to enable the ship to withstand the critical damage.

In the case of ships requiring cross-flooding the master of the ship shall be informed of the conditions of stability on which the calculations of heel are based and be warned that excessive heeling might result should the ship sustain damage when in a less favourable condition.

The data referred to above to enable the master to maintain sufficient stability shall include information which indicates the maximum permissible height of the ship's centre of gravity above keel (KG), or alternatively the minimum permissible metacentric height (GM), for a range of draughts or displacements sufficient to include all service conditions. The information shall show the influence of various trims taking into account the operational limits.

25.5 RO-RO PASSENGER SHIPS

Ro-Ro ships are often considered by the travelling public and many in the maritime profession as being the most unsafe ships in operation (due to the potential for loss of life which is much greater than that of other ship types such as bulk carriers), however, more onerous legislation that has been recently introduced and further recommendations for the future are aimed to address the serious safety issues concerning these ships.

These ships are designed to carry vehicular cargo on the bulkhead deck and other higher vehicle decks within the ship. Watertight doors are fitted at the bow and/or stern to allow the vehicles to drive on and off. An essential design requirement is that vehicles can be loaded and discharged very rapidly, this being of particular importance for ships engaged on regular short sea passages where strict schedules must be met and port congestion be limited. These demanding operational requirements severely restrict design flexibility for such ships. Additionally, ferries often operate in high traffic density areas where risk of collision is greatly increased, particularly when the routes involve crossing busy shipping lanes.

25.5.1 Stability problems associated with the design and operation of Ro-Ro passenger ships

These can be summarised as follows:

(1) *Lack of sub-division of vehicle decks*
The large open vehicle decks of ro-ro vessels make them particularly vulnerable to stability loss. Even when only modest amounts of water are admitted a considerable loss of GM results from the introduced free surface effect; considerable listing will also occur as the water accumulates on one side of the vessel.

(2) *High permeability of compartments*
When vehicle decks are fully laden there is still great potential for flooding due to the high permeability of the spaces allowing large volumes of water to be admitted in damage situations.

(3) *The requirement for bow and stern doors*
These are essential for quick turn around times, particularly on ships engaged on short sea passages where tight schedules have to be met. Watertight integrity of the bow and stern doors is of the utmost importance, however, maintaining their effectiveness is a cause for concern. Bow doors (visors) are subjected to considerable wave impact forces when the ship is at sea, particularly due to the high speeds at which these vessels operate at. Large bow flare increases receptiveness to high impact pressures on the bow. When encountering quartering seas the transverse forces can cause excessive loads on lock pins and hinge arrangements principally designed to resist loads in a longitudinal direction. Transverse loadings will be increased when the ship heels. Particular attention must be paid to bow door design and regular watertight integrity checks as they are likely to distort in service making it unlikely that they will remain watertight over an extended period of time. Ro-ro vessels will also be equipped with the widest possible stern ramp or with a slewing ramp. This results in a very fiat and wide transom and consequently severe slamming can be experienced aft even in moderate seas.
Loss of the *Herald of Free Enterprise* was not due to bow door failure, it was due the vessel proceeding to sea with the bow door open as a result of crew incompetence, as the ship increased speed on leaving the harbour, the combination of squat and the bow wave allowed water to enter the lower vehicle deck through the open bow doors which caused rapid flooding and capsize. Fortunately the vessel settled on a sandbank on its side which undoubtedly limited the loss of life.

The loss of the *Estonia* was caused by breach of the bow door causing substantial flooding and listing, it was the transverse forces of the waves on the bow visor as the ship listed to starboard that caused the bow visor to come away which exacerbated the situation causing the ultimate loss of the ship.

(4) *Potential for cargo shift of vehicular cargoes*

The very nature of ro-ro cargoes present securing problems, particularly as there is a wide range of vehicle types, lengths, widths and heights which means that individual ro-ro cargoes have unique individual securing requirements. Many vehicles carry loads themselves which need to be adequately secured. If a ro-ro unit or its cargo were to break loose, subsequent impact with adjacent units can lead to extensive damage to the ship's structure in addition to causing list. Spillage of liquid cargoes and fuel make cargo decks slippery increasing the ease with which cargoes could shift, not to mention the associated hazards of any cargoes spilled.

(5) *Wind heeling*

Assigned freeboard on ro-ro ships is usually quite small, being measured from the bulkhead deck or some other designated deck, this being the result of the reduction of freeboard allowed when considering the correction for superstructure when freeboard is assigned. However, ro-ro ships are of considerable height above the load water line and the large exposed lateral areas can cause wind heeling to be considerable. This should be considered from a stability point of view.

(6) *Large angle of heel when turning*

A sharp turn on a ferry moving at high speed is liable to produce a large heel angle and, if the vehicle cargo shifts, the ship may not return to the upright. Such turns may be necessary to avoid other ships in close quarter situations in congested waters.

(7) *Flooding of vehicle decks during fire fighting operations*

The presence of many vehicles with their petrol tanks in large enclosed vehicle decks is a hazard against which even the best fire detection and extinguishing systems cannot provide infallible protection. Fires on vehicle decks will activate water spray systems. The water on deck itself will pose a hazard to the ship's stability, but scuppers on deck should provide sufficient drainage to lower spaces where it can be pumped overboard. However, scuppers may become blocked by rubbish or debris from burning vehicles and their cargoes. A small heel may result, but sudden capsize will be unlikely unless the ship's initial stability was marginal.

(8) *Estimation of ro-ro vehicle weights*

For the purpose of stability calculation accurate figures with respect to vehicle weights and their centre of gravity is essential, however there will be instances when the weight of some ro-ro cargoes and heights of centre of gravity have to be estimated. For UK ships legislation is in place requiring the weighing of goods vehicles and other cargoes for Class II and Class II(A) ro-ro passenger ship operations (SI 1988 No. 1275). Certain allowance should be made with respect to the accuracy of stability calculations as appropriate.

(9) *Potential for substantial loss of water plane area after suffering damage*

When a ro-ro ship suffers damage whereby the margin line submerges and the bulkhead deck becomes flooded due to sinkage and change of trim, perhaps by the head as a result of breach of the bow door, considerable loss of water plane area might result. The subsequent reduction in KM, as a result of the reduced BM can significantly reduce GM to an unacceptable value resulting in negative stability. Capsize might be rapid and it is essential that loss of the ship be delayed as much as possible to increase evacuation time.

(10) *Passenger and crew evacuation*

It has been stated that many ro-ro vessel casualties involve very rapid sinking of the ship with little time for the evacuation of passengers whose numbers might run into thousands. Current research is focused on improving ro-ro safety overall, but it is also addressing methods by where sinking of the ship can be delayed to extend evacuation times.

25.5.2 Methods of improving ro-ro ship stability

It might be considered that the large loss of GM that results from water on vehicle decks can be anticipated for when considering the damaged stability requirements by enforcing the need for a very high GM for intact stability purposes. However, an excessively stiff condition can cause uncomfortable sea keeping characteristics and may lead to dangerous situations for those on board. Vehicular cargoes by their very nature have a high potential for shifting and if they were caused to break loose as a result of the rapid acceleration forces caused by the ship's short roll period, ship damage could result. Increased safety by enforcing a high 'intact' GM is therefore partly nullified by reduced safety related to possible cargo shift and sea keeping.

Approaches to improving ro-ro design include:

Perforated vehicle decks

Vehicle decks should be perforated to allow automatic down-flooding of accumulated water. The drainage systems must be capable of allowing very large quantities of water to drain directly into a lower tank where water can build up safely as the vessel floats in a stable and upright condition. This will have the effect of maximising the damaged GM by both restricting the free surface effect and lowering the ship's centre of gravity. Accumulated water in the lower tank can be pumped out to regain freeboard.

Limited longitudinal and transverse subdivisions on vehicle decks

Clearly this will have some impact on the efficiency of loading and discharge but these disadvantages can be limited. On one ship longitudinal bulkheads were added to each side of the vehicle deck along three-quarters of the ship's length, closed at each end by watertight doors. These bulkheads and doors formed enclosed lanes wide enough for freight vehicle stowage. Watertight doors were top-hinged so that minimum stowage space was wasted and when opened in port vehicles could drive straight through.

Inner bow door

To limit the effect of water ingress via a damaged bow door an extra inner door can be installed behind the bow door or visor to act as a second line of defence against flooding. More stringent maintenance regimes should be adopted for all watertight openings in the hull.

Improved damaged stability by the fitting of side sponsons

Increasing the effective water plane area improves intact stability but more importantly improves the damaged stability characteristics of the ship also. Retrospective fitting of side sponson tanks improves damaged stability for existing ships to ensure compliance with more recent legislation.

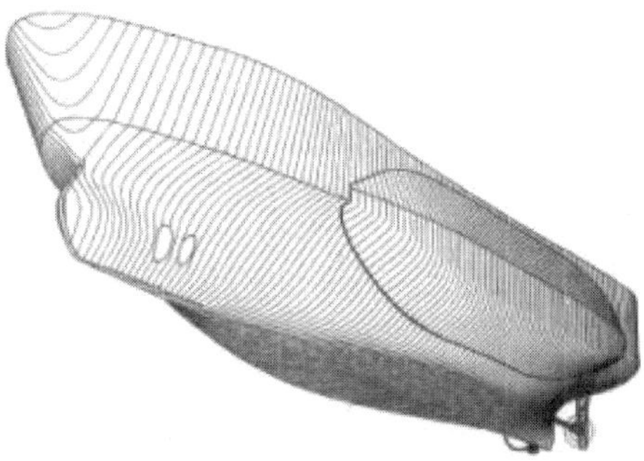

Side sponson tanks may be fitted to improve A/A_{max} ratio for compliance with Stockholm Agreement legislation.

Fig. 25.22

There are many innovative designs being currently developed and an internet search will reap much more information on improvements in ro-ro safety.

25.5.3 Damaged stability requirements for ro-ro passenger ships

Standards for ro-ro ship configuration, construction and operation have come under close scrutiny since the tragic losses of the *Herald of Free Enterprise* and more recently the *Estonia* amongst others. In many cases loss of a ro-ro ship is the result of accumulation of water on open cargo decks but of major concern is the rapid sinking after flooding or damage and the lack of time for vessel abandonment which ultimately leads to extensive of loss of life.

The loss of the *Estonia* in particular warranted concerted action by IMO to address the water on deck problem and to find means of ensuring that ro-ro ships stay afloat longer after an accident to allow greater time for vessel abandonment.

The *Stockholm Agreement* as it is known assesses the standard of ro-ro survivability in terms of the probability that the vessel will survive after the vessel has suffered damage with water ingress, damage being based on the probability that it will take place in different parts of the ship. The total probability of survival depends on two factors: the probability that a compartment is being flooded and the probability that the vessel will survive flooding of that compartment. MSC/Circ. 574 details the simplified calculation procedure to assess the survivability characteristics based on Resolution A.265(VIII). The regulations require the calculation of an A/Amax value, 'A' being the attained subdivision index and 'Amax' being the maximum value of survivability for the ship in question. The A/Amax ratio is expressed as a percentage for the purpose of implementation of the regulations.

The principle probabilistic elements in the A/Amax calculation are:

'a' a factor which estimates the probability of damage occurring at a position in the ship's length;

'p' a factor which estimates the probability of the longitudinal extent of damage;

'r' a factor which estimates the probability of the degree of penetration in from the ship's side, and;

's' a factor which is a measure of survival probability.

In addition to the above the stability standard the *Stockholm Agreement* requires the effects of a hypothetical amount of sea water which is assumed to have accumulated on the first deck above the designed waterline to be taken into account. It also takes account of the significant wave heights in certain geographical locations to be used when determining the height of water accumulated on decks.

It is not my intention to go into detail the requirements for ro-ro ships, but the regulations in Part B of SOLAS should be consulted with respect to set dates of compliance for existing ships which range from 1st October 1998 to 1st October 2010, these dates depending on the A/Amax value of the ship, the number of persons carried and the age of the ship. Such regulations and calculation procedures are complicated and would not be examined upon unless studying for a qualification at a higher level than this publication is based, however, a basic understanding of the principles previously described should suffice. After all, this publication is orientated towards people who operate ships and not those men in 'white coats' who design them!

Finally, as many ships have unique characteristics with respect to strength and stability, the guidance notes in the stability data book should always be consulted. Always seek advice from those people who have served on the ship concerned as they will have much more knowledge on the ship's unique characteristics which they will have gained from experience.

SECTION 26 – CALCULATION AND ASSIGNMENT OF FREEBOARD

INTRODUCTION

All ships (with certain exceptions) are required to be surveyed and marked with permanent load line markings in accordance with the *International Convention on Load Lines, 1966 as modified 1988*. The principle purpose of load line assignment is to ensure that the ship always has sufficient reserve buoyancy and intact stability when proceeding to sea. Reference is made to Part 3 of the IMO publication *'Load Lines – 2002 Edition'* that details the procedure for the calculation and assignment of freeboards. *It will be necessary to refer to this publication as much of the detail of the regulations is not included in this text.*

For UK registered ships reference should be made to the following publications:

The Merchant Shipping (Load Line) Regulations 1998 (S.I. 1998 No. 2241)

The Merchant Shipping (Load Line) (Amendment) Regulations 2000 (S.I. 2000 No. 1335)

MSN 1752 (M)

Load Line – Instructions for the Guidance of Surveyors (MCA)

For the purpose of this section the requirements detailed will be those as stipulated under the 1966 Load Line Convention that has been modified by the 1988 Protocol (as found in **Part 3 – Annex B – Annex I – Chapters I-IV of the IMO publication *'Load Lines – 2002 Edition'*)**. Where the MCA requirements differ significantly, applicable to UK registered ships only, then such differences will be emphasised.

The following ships are not required to have load lines assigned:

- warships;
- new ships of less than 24 metres in length;
- existing ships of less than 150 tons gross;
- pleasure yachts not engaged in trade, and;
- fishing vessels.

(Annex A – Article 5)

The principal conditions that must be satisfied before freeboard may be assigned to any ship take account of the following:

- *structural strength of the ship;*
- *preservation of reserve buoyancy;*
- *physical means of preventing entry of water into the hull;*
- *safety of the crew on the weather deck;*
- *potential wetness of the weather deck;*
- *stability in the normal loaded condition (intact stability);*
- *degree of subdivision and stability after suffering prescribed damage.*

The seasonal zones, areas and periods that determine the appropriate load line in a particular sea area at a given time of year are set out in *Annex II* and are shown by way of the chart attached to this annex. The *Tropical, Summer* and *Winter* freeboard zones are based upon the following weather criteria:

Summer Zones – Regions where not more than 10% of wind speeds exceed force 8 Beaufort (34 knots).

Tropical Zones – Regions where not more than 1% of wind speeds exceed force 8 Beaufort (34 knots) and not more than one tropical storm in a ten-year period occurs in an area of 5° latitude/longitude square in any one separate calendar month.

Winter Zones – Are all other regions.

It is a criminal offence for the Master and/or shipowner to allow a vessel to be operated in a zone, when in the upright condition, the relevant amidships zone load line would be below the still load waterline. Such an action would immediately invalidate all Classification Society and Load Line certification and will lead to criminal prosecution.

Learning Objectives

On completion of this section the learner will achieve the following:

1. Understand the appropriate terms and definitions associated with the calculation and assignment of freeboard.
2. Recognise the ship's side markings relating to freeboard assignment.
3. Understand the conditions of assignment applicable to all ships.
4. Understand the additional conditions of assignment for type 'A' ships (tankers).
5. Understand the distinction between type 'A' and type 'B' ships.
6. Understand the conditions necessary for certain type 'B' vessels to be awarded reduced tabular freeboards.
7. Understand the calculation procedure for the assignment of a type 'A' freeboard.
8. Understand the calculation procedure for the assignment of a type 'B' freeboard.
9. Understand the conditions of assignment of timber freeboards.
10. Know the required load line surveys that a ship must undergo and the preparations necessary for such surveys.

26.1 DEFINITIONS

The following definitions for the purpose of freeboard calculation are detailed in *Regulation 3*.

26.1.1 Length (L)

This is taken as 96% of the total length on a waterline at 85% of the least moulded depth, or, as the length from the fore side of the stem to the axis of the rudder stock on that waterline, if greater.

26.1.2 Perpendiculars (FP, AP)

The forward and after perpendiculars are taken as being at the forward and after ends of the length (L). The forward perpendicular shall coincide with the foreside of the stem on the waterline on which the length (L) is measured.

26.1.3 Amidships

Amidships is at the middle of the length (L).

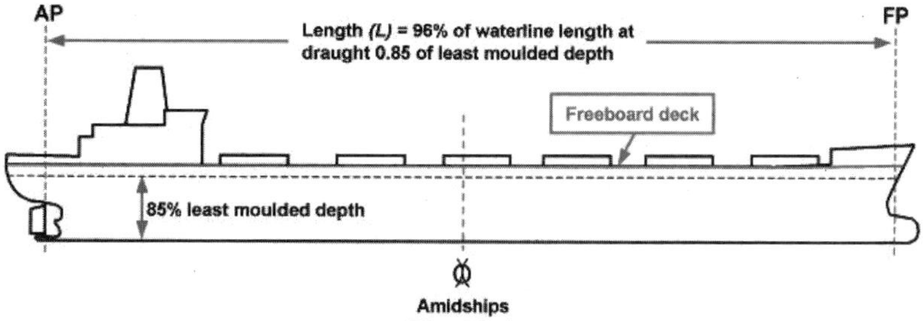

Fig. 26.1

26.1.4 Breadth (B)

Unless expressly provided otherwise, the breadth (B) is the maximum breadth of the ship, measured amidships to the moulded line of the frame in a ship with a metal shell and to the outer surface of the hull in a ship with a shell of any other material.

26.1.5 Moulded depth

This is the vertical distance measured from the top of the keel to the top of the freeboard deck beam at side.

In ships having rounded gunwales, the moulded depth shall be measured at the point of intersection of the moulded lines of the deck and side shell plating, the lines extending as though the gunwale were of angular design.

Where the freeboard deck is stepped and the raised part of the deck extends over the point at which the moulded depth is to be determined, the moulded depth shall be measured to a line of reference extending from the lower part of the deck along a line parallel with the raised part.

26.1.6 Depth for freeboard (D)

This is the moulded depth amidships, plus the thickness of the freeboard deck stringer plate, where fitted, plus $\frac{T(L-S)}{L}$ if the exposed freeboard deck is sheathed, where:

T is the mean thickness of the exposed sheathing clear of deck openings, and
S is the total length of superstructures.

The depth for freeboard (D) in a ship having a rounded gunwale with a radius greater than 4% of the breadth (B) or having topsides of unusual form is the depth for freeboard of a ship having a midship section with vertical topsides and with the same round of beam and area of topside section equal to that provided by the actual midship section.

26.1.7 Block Coefficient (C_b)

Is given by: $$C_b = \frac{\text{Volume of displacement at draught } 0.85D}{\text{Length}^* \times \text{Breadth}^* \times \text{draught (at 85\% of least moulded depth)}}$$

(* as previously defined) (in no case shall the block coefficient (C_b) be taken to be less than 0.68.)

26.1.8 Freeboard

The freeboard assigned is the distance measured vertically downwards amidships from the *upper edge* of the deck line to the *upper edge* of the related load line.

26.1.9 Freeboard Deck

This is normally the uppermost continuous deck exposed to weather and sea, which has permanent means of closing all openings in the weather part thereof, and below which all openings in the sides of the ship are fitted with permanent means of watertight closing (figure 26.1). In a ship having a discontinuous freeboard deck, the lowest line of the exposed deck and the continuation of that line parallel to the upper part of the deck is taken as the freeboard deck (figure 26.2).

The owner may opt to designate a lower deck as the freeboard deck provided that it is a complete and permanent deck in a fore and aft direction at least between the machinery space and peak bulkheads and continuous athwartships (this is typical for a Ro-Ro vessel). In such cases that part of the hull that extends above the freeboard deck may be treated as superstructure for the purposes of calculation of freeboard (figure 26.2).

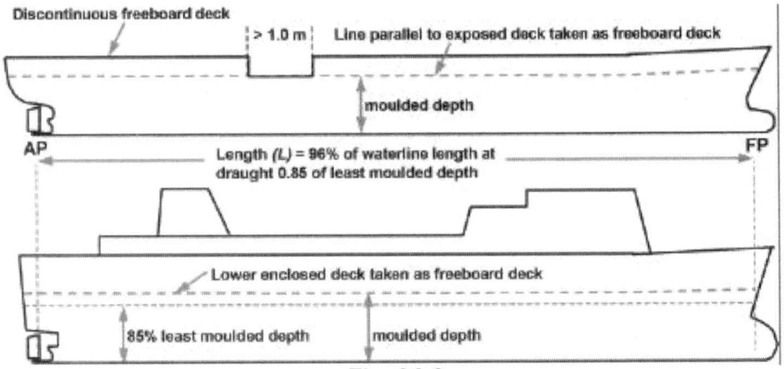

Fig. 26.2

26.1.10 Superstructure

A superstructure is a decked structure on the freeboard deck, extending from side to side of the ship or with the side plating not being inboard of the shell plating more than 4% of the breadth (B). A *raised quarter-deck* is regarded as a superstructure. (*Raised quarter-decks* are often associated with smaller ships. With the machinery space sited aft and being proportionally larger in smaller ships there is a tendency for the ship to be trimmed by the head when fully loaded. To prevent this, the height of the aftermost holds may be increased to increase deadweight aft; this is achieved by means of a raised quarter-deck.)

An *enclosed superstructure* is a superstructure with:

(a) enclosing bulkheads of efficient construction;

(b) access openings, if any, in these bulkheads fitted with doors complying with the requirements of regulation 12 (see 26.3.3).

(c) all other openings in sides or ends of the superstructure fitted with efficient weathertight means of closing.

A bridge or poop shall not be regarded as enclosed unless access is provided for the crew to reach machinery and other working spaces inside these superstructures by alternative means which are available at all times when bulkhead openings are closed.

The height of a superstructure is the least vertical height measured at side from the top of the superstructure deck beams to the top of the freeboard deck beams.

The length of a superstructure is the mean length of the part of the superstructure which lies within the length (L).

Superstructure

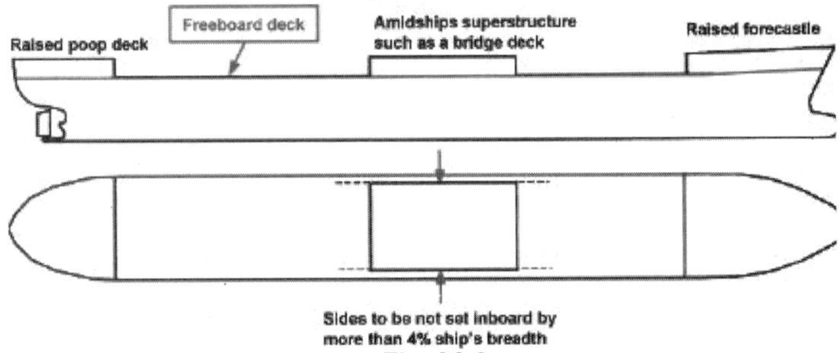

Fig. 26.3

26.1.11 Flush deck ship

Is one that has no superstructure on the freeboard deck.

26.1.12 Weathertight

Means that in any sea conditions water will not penetrate into the ship.

26.2 SHIP'S SIDE MARKINGS

26.2.1 Deck line (Regulation 4)

The deck line is a horizontal line marked amidships on each side of the ship. Its upper edge shall normally pass through the point where the continuation outwards of the upper surface of the freeboard deck intersects the outer surface of the shell plating.

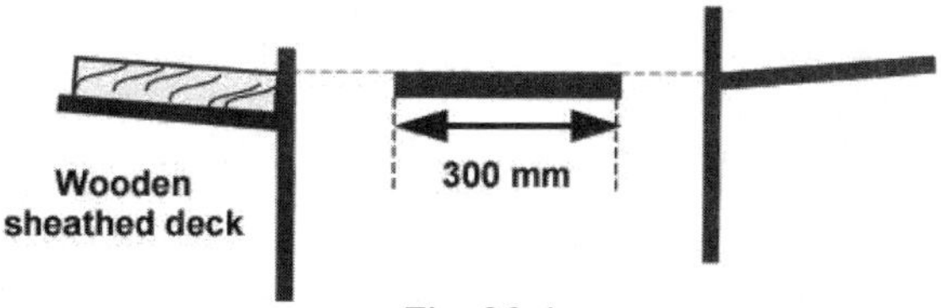

Fig. 26.4

However, the deck line may be placed with reference to another fixed point on the ship on condition that the freeboard is correspondingly corrected and that the reference point location and the identification of the freeboard deck is clearly indicated on the International Load Line Certificate. This is typical in the case of a ship having a radiused sheerstrake (rounded gunwale) (figure 26.5).

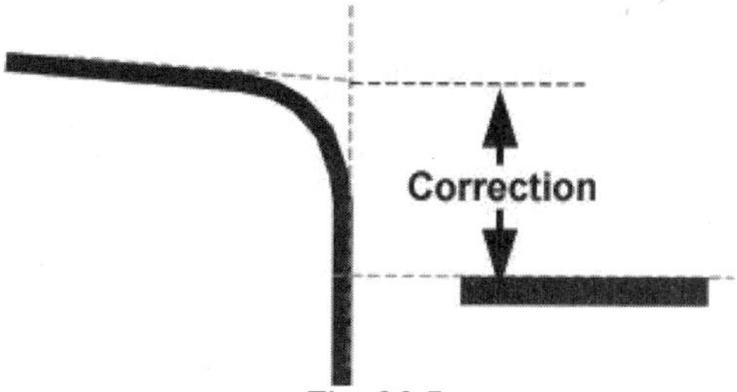

Fig. 26.5

26.2.2 Load line mark and accompanying load lines (Regulations 5 to 8)

The Load Line Mark consists of a ring 300 mm in outside diameter and 25 mm thick which is intersected by a horizontal line 450 mm in length and 25 mm thick, the *upper edge* of which passes through the *centre* of the ring. The centre of the ring is placed amidships and at a distance equal to the assigned summer freeboard measured vertically below the *upper edge* of the deck line. These are indicated in figure 26.6 and were also discussed in Section 4.

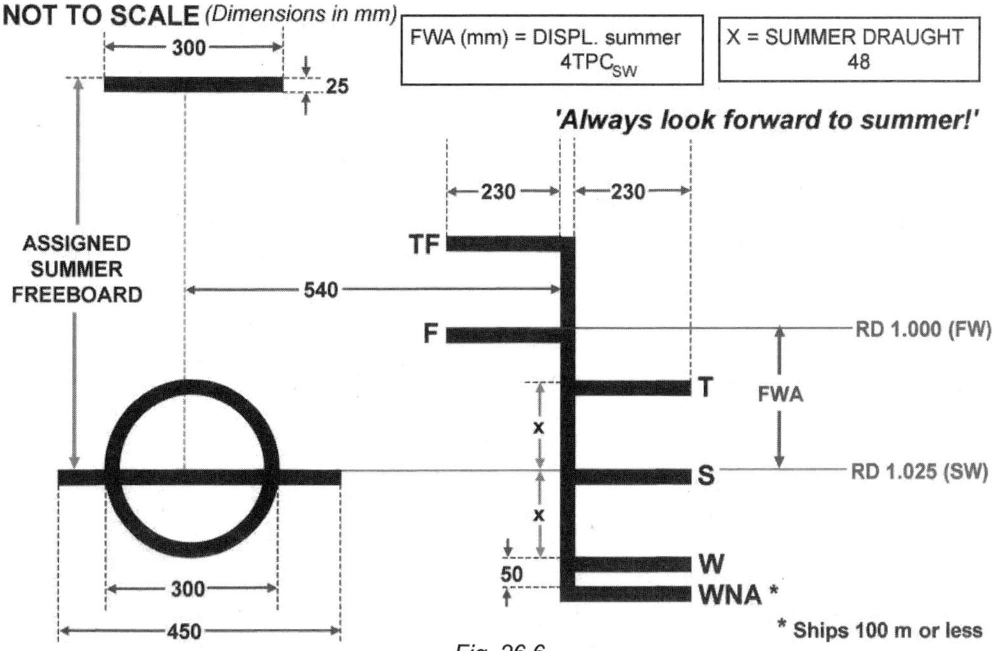

Fig. 26.6

If timber freeboards are assigned the timber load lines are marked in addition to the ordinary load lines as shown in figure 26.7.

TIMBER LOAD LINE MARKS - STARBOARD SIDE

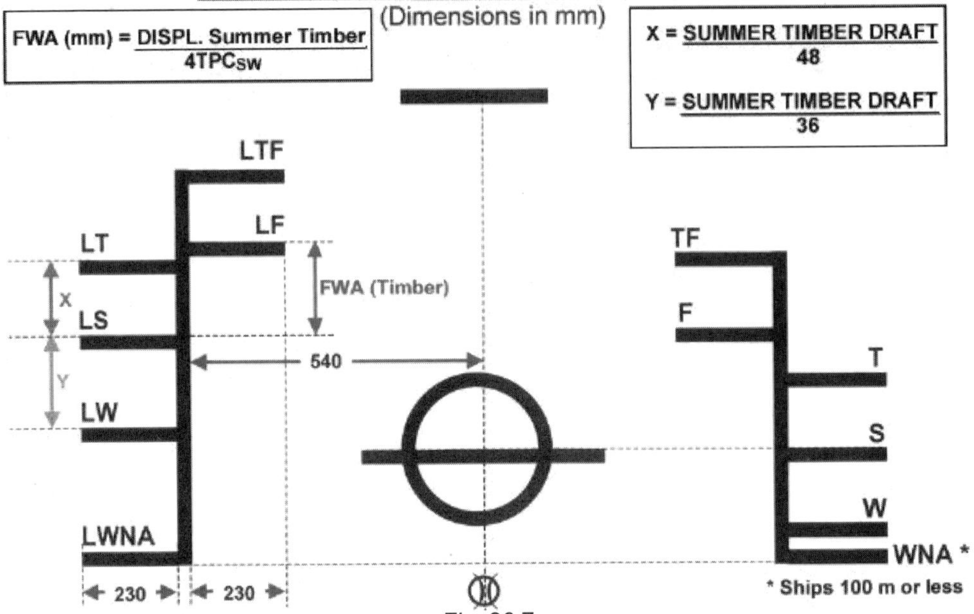

Fig. 26.7

Where a ship is assigned a *greater than minimum* freeboard so that the load line mark is marked at a position corresponding to, or lower than, the lowest seasonal load line assigned at a minimum freeboard in accordance with the calculation procedure, only the *Fresh Water Load Line* need be marked. Such load lines are termed *'All Seasons Load Lines'* and are illustrated in figure 26.8.

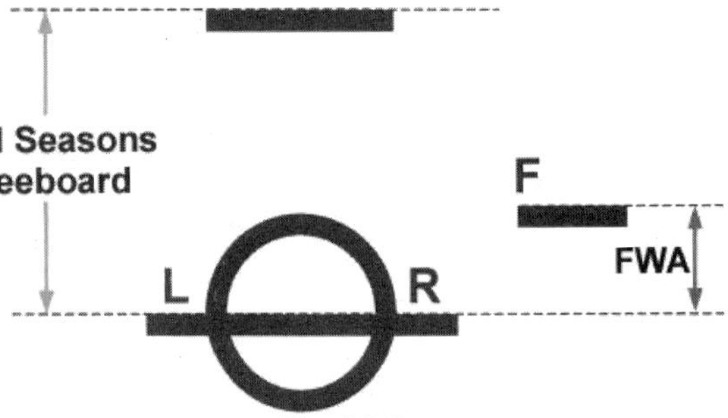

Fig. 26.8

Sailing ships are only required to have the Fresh Water (F) and Winter North Atlantic (WNA) load lines marked.

In addition to the load line markings the initials of the Assigning authority must be marked above the load line mark to identify the Authority's name as shown in figure 26.8 (Lloyds Register). No more than four letters are permitted and each initial must measure approximately 115 mm in height and 75 mm in width.

All markings must be *clearly* and *permanently* marked, being white or yellow on a dark background or in black on a light background. Permanent marking is achieved by the marks being centre-punched onto the ship's side or being welded onto the ship's side. They must also be clearly visible. The marks must be verified as being in place by an approved surveyor before the International Load Line Certificate is issued.

26.3 CONDITIONS OF ASSIGNMENT OF FREEBOARD APPLICABLE TO ALL SHIPS

26.3.1 Structural strength
It is recognised that ships *'built and maintained in conformity with the requirements of a classification society recognised by the Administration'* may be considered to possess the necessary structural strength for freeboards to be assigned (*Regulation 1*).

26.3.2 Information to be supplied to the master
Regulation 10 states:

(1) The master of every new ship shall be supplied with sufficient information, in an approved form, to enable him to arrange for the loading and ballasting of his ship in such a way as to avoid the creation of any unacceptable stresses in the ship's structure, provided that this requirement need not apply to any particular length, design or class of ship where the Administration considers it to be unnecessary.

(2) Every ship which is not required under the International Convention for Safety of Life at Sea in force to undergo an inclining test upon its completion shall:
- *(a) be so inclined and the actual displacement and position of the centre of gravity shall be determined for the light ship condition;*
- *(b) have supplied for the use of its master such reliable information in an approved form as is necessary to enable him by rapid and simple processes to obtain accurate guidance as to the stability of the ship under all conditions likely to be encountered in normal service;*
- *(c) carry on board at all times its approved stability information together with evidence that the information has been approved by the Administration;*
- *(d) if the Administration so approves, have its inclining test on completion dispensed with, provided basic stability data are available from the inclining test of a sister ship and it is shown to the satisfaction of the Administration that reliable stability information for the ship can be obtained from such basic data.*

Chapter 2 of the *Code on Intact Stability for all Types of Ships Covered by IMO Instruments (IMO)* details more specifically the information that must be provided to the master of all ships in order that stability calculations may be accurately conducted to ensure the ship's safe operation. The current MCA requirements are found in Schedule 6 of MSN 1752(M). Refer to *Section 19 – Inclining Experiment*.

26.3.3 Structural conditions of assignment
The conditions of assignment specified in regulations 11 to 26 should be studied but may be summarised as follows:

Bulkheads at the exposed ends of superstructures shall be of efficient construction (*Regulation 11*).

All access openings in bulkheads at the ends of enclosed superstructures shall be fitted with steel weathertight doors that will provide equivalent bulkhead strength when closed. They must be sealed by gaskets and clamping devices, be capable of being operated from both sides and have sills of at least 380 mm above the level of the deck (*Regulation 12*).

Two positions of hatchways, doorways and ventilators are defined as follows:

<u>Position 1</u> *Upon exposed freeboard and raised quarter-decks, and upon exposed superstructure decks situated forward of a point located a quarter of the ship's length from the forward perpendicular.*

<u>Position 2</u> *Upon exposed superstructure decks situated abaft a quarter of the ship's length from the forward perpendicular. (Regulation 13)*

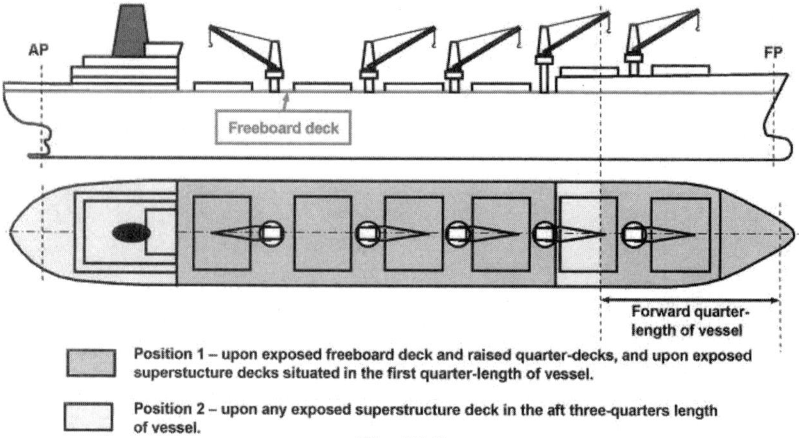
AP
FP
Freeboard deck
Forward quarter-length of vessel
Position 1 – upon exposed freeboard deck and raised quarter-decks, and upon exposed superstructure decks situated in the first quarter-length of vessel.
Position 2 – upon any exposed superstructure deck in the aft three-quarters length of vessel.

Fig. 26.9

Regulation 15 details the requirements for hatchways closed by portable wooden hatch covers that are secured weathertight by tarpaulins and battening devices. Most modern ships are now fitted with steel hatch covers so regulation 16 is more relevant.

For ships fitted with steel weathertight covers the principal requirements are:

* Hatchway coamings in position 1 are to be at least 600 mm above the deck; in position 2 they are to be at least 450 mm above the deck. (If these are of equivalent superstructure height and strength and have an average width of at least 60% of the ship's breadth at their point of location then they will be regarded as being a trunk and the additional reserve buoyancy that is afforded by them will be taken into account in the calculation of freeboard, which is usually the case.)

* Covers are to be of mild steel and be able to sustain the following loads:
In position 1 – not less than 1.75 t/m^3;
In position 2 – not less than 1.30 t/m^3.

* The means for securing of the hatch covers shall be such as to ensure weathertightness in any sea conditions and the hatch covers will be subjected to tests at the initial (and subsequent) surveys to ensure the effectiveness of the arrangements. (*Regulation 16*)

Machinery space openings in positions 1 and 2 shall be properly framed and efficiently enclosed by steel casings, if the casings themselves are not protected by other structures there strength will be specially considered (it is usual on most ships to gain access to the engine room from inside a protecting superstructure). *(Regulation 17)*

Miscellaneous openings in freeboard and superstructure decks such as manholes and flush scuttles in position 1 or 2 or within superstructures other than enclosed superstructures shall be closed by substantial covers capable of being made watertight. Unless secured by closely spaced bolts, the covers shall be permanently attached. Openings in freeboard decks other than hatchways, machinery space openings, manholes and flush scuttles shall be protected by an enclosed superstructure, or by a deckhouse or companionway of equivalent strength and weathertightness. In position 1 the height above the deck of sills to the doorways in companionways shall be at least 600 mm. In position 2 it shall be at least 380 mm. *(Regulation 18)*

Ventilators in position 1 or 2 to spaces below freeboard or superstructure decks shall have steel coamings of at least 900 mm and 760 mm respectively above the deck. Ventilator openings shall be provided with weathertight closing appliances, if the ship is not more than 100 m in length they must be permanently attached. If the coamings extend to more than 4.5 m above the deck in position 1, and 2.3 m in position 2, they need not be fitted with closing arrangements unless specifically required by the Administration. *(Regulation 19)*

Where air pipes to ballast or other tanks extend above the freeboard or superstructure decks they should be of substantial construction and extend upwards to a height above the deck at least 760 mm on the freeboard deck and 450 mm on the superstructure deck. They shall be fitted with a permanently attached means of closing.*(Regulation 20)*

Cargo ports and other similar openings in the ship's sides below the freeboard deck shall be kept to a minimum number compatible with the design and proper working of the ship. Doors must be designed to ensure structural integrity and watertightness. The lower edge of such openings shall not be below a line drawn parallel to the freeboard deck at side, which has its lowest point level with the upper edge of the uppermost load line.*(Regulation 21)*

Discharges shall be fitted with efficient and accessible means for preventing water from passing inboard. Normally each separate discharge shall have one automatic non-return valve with a positive means of closing it from a position above the freeboard deck. Where, however, the vertical distance from the summer load waterline to the inboard end of the discharge pipe exceeds 0.01L, the discharge may have two automatic non-return valves without positive means of closing, provided that the inboard valve is always accessible for examination under service conditions; where that vertical distance exceeds 0.02L, a single automatic non-return valve may be accepted subject to the approval of the Administration.

Scuppers and discharge pipes originating at any level and penetrating the shell either more than 450 mm below the freeboard deck or less than 600 mm above the summer load waterline shall be provided with a non-return valve at the shell (the valve may be omitted if the piping is of substantial thickness).

All shell fittings and valves required by regulation 12 shall be of steel, bronze or other approved ductile material. All pipes are to be of steel or other approved equivalent material. *(Regulation 22)*

Side scuttles to spaces below the freeboard deck or to spaces within enclosed superstructures shall be fitted with efficient hinged inside deadlights arranged so that they can be effectively closed and secured watertight. *(Regulation 23)*

Freeing ports shall be provided in bulwarks to allow for rapid freeing of water from decks. Required freeing port area is specified in terms of a number formulae detailed in regulation 24. *(Regulation 24)*

Protection of crew is to be ensured by the provision of efficient guard rails or bulwarks which are to be fitted to all exposed freeboard and superstructure decks. These should be at least 1 metre in height from the deck. In the case of guard rails, the opening below the lowest course of the guard rails shall not exceed 230 mm. The other rails shall not be more than 380 mm apart. Special provision, including lifelines, shall be made as necessary for allowing the crew safe access to all parts of the ship during the normal operation of the ship, this will include access in way of deck cargoes also. *(Regulation 25)*

26.4 TYPE 'A' SHIPS AND THEIR ADDITIONAL SPECIAL CONDITIONS OF ASSIGNMENT

A type 'A' ship is any ship designed to carry liquid cargoes in bulk such as tankers, chemical carriers, LPG and LNG carriers. However, the regulations give a much more precise definition.

26.4.1 Type 'A' ship – definition (Regulation 27)

For the purpose of assigning freeboards a type 'A' ship is one which:

(a) *is designed to carry only liquid cargoes in bulk;*

(b) *has a high integrity of the exposed deck with only small access openings to cargo compartments, closed by watertight gasketed covers of steel or equivalent material, and;*

(c) *has a low permeability of loaded cargo compartments.*

A type 'A' ship if over 150 m in length to which a freeboard less than type 'B' has been assigned, when loaded in accordance with the assumed initial condition of loading, shall be able to withstand the flooding of any compartment or compartments, with an assumed permeability of 0.95, consequent upon the damage assumptions specified, and shall remain afloat in a satisfactory condition of equilibrium. In such a ship the machinery space shall be treated as a floodable compartment, but with a permeability of 0.85.

In the above paragraph:
The *initial condition of loading* before flooding shall be determined as follows:

(a) The ship is loaded to its summer load waterline on an imaginary even keel.

(b) When calculating the vertical centre of gravity, the following principles apply:

(i) Homogeneous cargo is carried.
(ii) All cargo compartments, except those referred to under (iii), but including compartments intended to be partially filled, shall be considered fully loaded except that in the case of fluid cargoes each compartment shall be treated as 98% full.
(iii) If the ship is intended to operate at its summer load waterline with empty compartments, such compartments shall be considered empty provided the height of the centre of gravity so calculated is not less than as calculated under (ii).
(iv) 50% of the individual total capacity of all tanks and spaces fitted to contain consumable liquids and stores is allowed for. It shall be assumed that for each type of liquid, at least one transverse pair or a single centreline tank has maximum free surface, and the tank or combination of tanks to be taken into account shall be those where the effect of free surfaces is the greatest; in each tank the centre of gravity of the contents shall be taken at the centre of volume of the tank. The remaining tanks shall be assumed either completely empty or completely filled, and the distribution of consumable liquids between these tanks shall be effected so as to obtain the greatest possible height above the keel for the centre of gravity.
(v) At an angle of heel of not more than 5° in each compartment containing liquids, as prescribed in (ii) except that in the case of compartments containing consumable fluids, as prescribed in (iv), the maximum free surface effect shall be taken into account.
Alternatively, the actual free surface effects may be used, provided the methods of calculation are acceptable to the Administration.
(vi) Weights shall be calculated on the basis of the following values for specific gravities:

salt water	1.025
fresh water	1.000
oil fuel	0.950
diesel oil	0.900
lubricating oil	0.900

The *damage assumptions* are as follows:

(a) The vertical extent of damage in all cases is assumed to be from the base line upwards without limit.

(b) The transverse extent of damage is equal to B/5 or 11.5 m, whichever is the lesser, measured inboard from the side of the ship perpendicularly to the centreline at the level of the summer load waterline.

(c) If damage of a lesser extent than specified in sub-paragraphs (a) and (b) results in a more severe condition, such lesser extent shall be assumed.

(d) Except where otherwise required by paragraph (10)(a) ***(which relates to B-100 vessels)*** the flooding shall be confined to a single compartment between adjacent transverse bulkheads provided the inner longitudinal boundary of the compartment is not in a position within the transverse extent of assumed damage. Transverse boundary bulkheads of wing tanks which do not extend over the full breadth of the ship shall be assumed not to be damaged, provided they extend beyond the transverse extent of assumed damage prescribed in sub-paragraph (b).

If in a transverse bulkhead there are steps or recesses of not more than 3 m in length located within the transverse extent of assumed damage as defined in subparagraph (b), such transverse bulkhead may be considered intact and the adjacent compartment may be floodable singly. If, however, within the transverse extent of assumed damage there is a step or recess of more than 3 m in length in a transverse bulkhead, the two compartments adjacent to this bulkhead shall be considered as flooded. The step formed by the afterpeak bulkhead and the afterpeak tank top shall not be regarded as a step for the purpose of this regulation.

(e) Where a main transverse bulkhead is located within the transverse extent of assumed damage and is stepped in way of a double bottom or side tank by more than 3 m, the double bottom or side tanks adjacent to the stepped portion of the main transverse bulkhead shall be considered as flooded simultaneously. If this side tank has openings, into one or several holds, such as grain feeding holes, such hold or holds shall be considered as flooded simultaneously. Similarly in a ship designed for the carriage of fluid cargoes, if a side tank has openings into adjacent compartments, such adjacent compartments shall be considered as empty and as being flooded simultaneously. This provision is applicable even where such openings are fitted with closing appliances, except in the case of sluice valves fitted in bulkheads between tanks and where the valves are controlled from the deck. Manhole covers with closely spaced bolts are considered equivalent to the unpierced bulkhead except in the case of openings in topside tanks making the topside tanks common to the holds.

(f) Where the flooding of any two adjacent fore and aft compartments is envisaged, main transverse watertight bulkheads shall be spaced at least ? $L^{2/3}$ or 14.5 m, whichever is the lesser, in order to be considered effective. Where transverse bulkheads are spaced at a lesser distance, one or more of these bulkheads shall be assumed as non-existent in order to achieve the minimum spacing between bulkheads.

The *condition of equilibrium* after flooding shall be considered as satisfactory provided that:

(a) The final waterline after flooding, taking into account sinkage, heel and trim, is below the lower edge of any opening through which progressive downflooding may take place. Such openings shall include air pipes, ventilators and openings which are closed by means of weathertight doors or hatch covers, and may exclude those openings closed by means of manhole covers and flush scuttles (which comply with regulation 18), cargo hatch covers of the type described in regulation 27(2) ***(referring to the small, watertight and gasketed*** *covers of steel as required for type 'A' ships)*, remotely operated sliding watertight doors, and side scuttles of the non-opening type (which comply with regulation 23). However, in the case of doors separating a main machinery space from a steering gear compartment, watertight doors may be of a hinged, quick-acting type kept closed at sea, whilst not in use, provided also that the lower sill of such doors is above the summer load waterline

(b) If pipes, ducts or tunnels are situated within the assumed extent of damage penetration as defined in paragraph (12)(b) *(being the transverse extent of damage)*, arrangements shall be made so that progressive flooding cannot thereby extend to compartments other than those assumed to be floodable in the calculation for each case of damage.

(c) The angle of heel due to unsymmetrical flooding does not exceed 15°. If no part of the deck is immersed, an angle of heel of up to 17° may be accepted.

(d) The metacentric height in the flooded condition is positive.

(a) When any part of the deck outside the compartment assumed flooded in a particular case of damage is immersed, or in any case where the margin of stability in the flooded condition may be considered doubtful, the residual stability is to be investigated. It may be regarded as sufficient if the righting lever curve has a minimum range of 20° beyond the position of equilibrium with a maximum righting lever of at least 0.1 m within this range. The area under the righting lever curve within this range shall be not less than 0.0175 metre-radians. The Administration shall give consideration to the potential hazard presented by protected or unprotected openings which may become temporarily immersed within the range of residual stability.

(f) The Administration is satisfied that the stability is sufficient during intermediate stages of flooding.

<u>Note</u> MCA requires that the GM must be at least 50 mm.

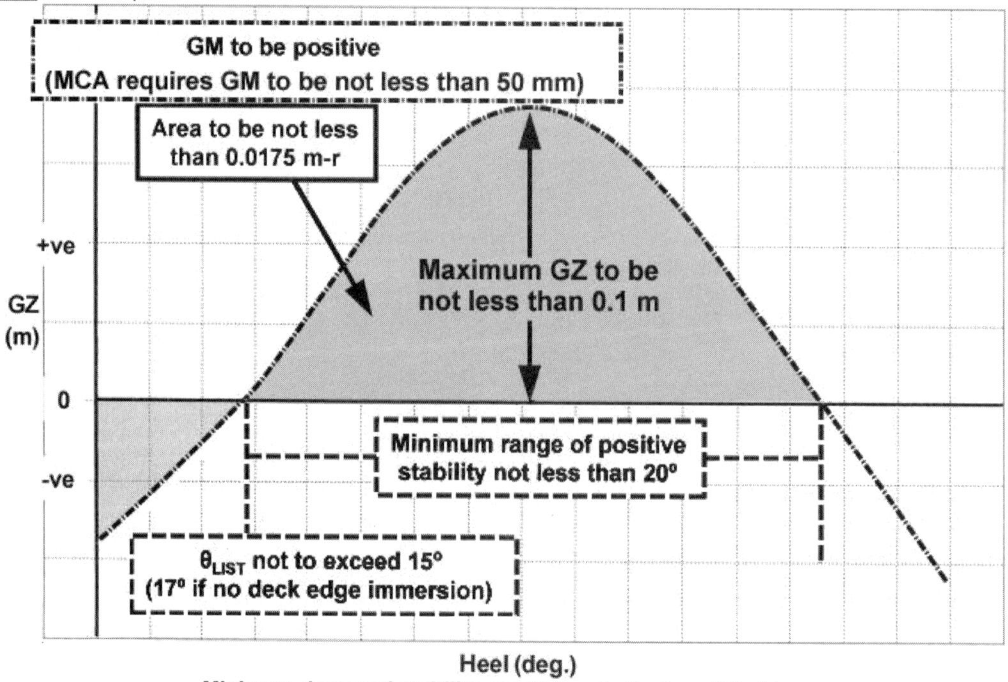

Minimum damaged stability requirements for type 'A' ships.
Fig. 26.10

26.4.2 Special structural conditions of assignment for type 'A' ships (Regulation 26)

(1) Machinery casings on type 'A' ships, as defined in regulation 27, shall be protected by an enclosed poop or bridge of at least standard height, or by a deckhouse of equal height and equivalent strength, provided that machinery casings may be exposed if there are no openings giving direct access from the freeboard deck to the machinery space. A door complying with the requirements of regulation 12 may, however, be permitted in the machinery casing, provided that it leads to a space or passageway which is as strongly constructed as the casing and is separated from the stairway to the engine-room by a second weathertight door of steel or other equivalent material.

(2) An efficiently constructed fore and aft permanent gangway of sufficient strength shall be fitted on type 'A' ships at the level of the superstructure deck between the poop and the midship bridge or deckhouse where fitted or equivalent means of access shall be provided to carry out the purpose of the gangway, such as passages below deck. Elsewhere, and on type 'A' ships without a midship bridge, arrangements to the satisfaction of the Administration shall be provided to safeguard the crew in reaching all parts used in the necessary work of the ship.

(3) Safe and satisfactory access from the gangway level shall be available between separate crew accommodations and also between crew accommodations and the machinery space.

(4) Exposed hatchways on the freeboard and forecastle decks or on the tops of expansion trunks on type 'A' ships shall be provided with efficient watertight covers of steel or other equivalent material.

(5) Type 'A' ships with bulwarks shall have open rails fitted for at least half the length of the exposed parts of the weather deck or other effective freeing arrangements. The upper edge of the sheer strake shall be kept as low as practicable.

(6) Where superstructures are connected by trunks, open rails shall be fitted for the whole length of the exposed parts of the freeboard deck.

26.5 THE DISTINCTION BETWEEN TYPE 'A' SHIPS AND TYPE 'B' SHIPS EXPLAINED

A type 'B' ship is any ship other than a type 'A' ship.

When assigning freeboards to ships the first part of the calculation procedure is to firstly ascertain the *tabular freeboard* from the appropriate table in regulation 28. Type 'A' tabular freeboards are smaller than type 'B' tabular freeboards for ships of equivalent length because of the structural layout and types of cargo carried.

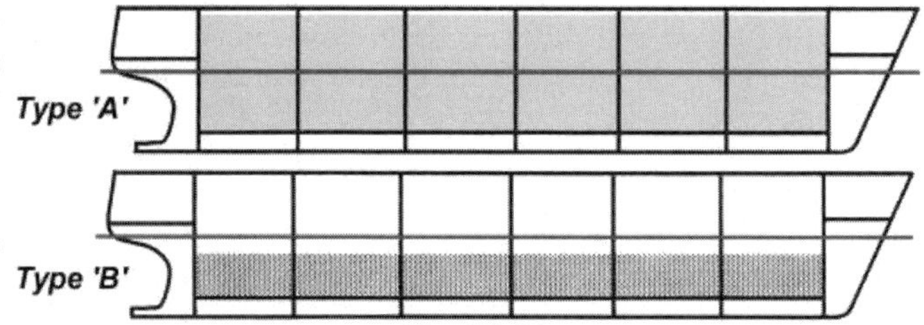

Fig. 26.11

Consider two ship hulls, one designed to carry oil cargoes (type 'A') and another designed to carry a bulk cargo of iron ore say (type 'B').

Consider what will happen if a loaded amidships compartment becomes bilged in each ship.

In the case of the type 'A' ship the cargo oil will run out of the damaged compartment, resulting in a reduction in displacement and an increase in the freeboard.

In the case of the type 'B' ship the seawater will run into the damaged compartment, resulting in an increase in displacement and a reduction in the freeboard.

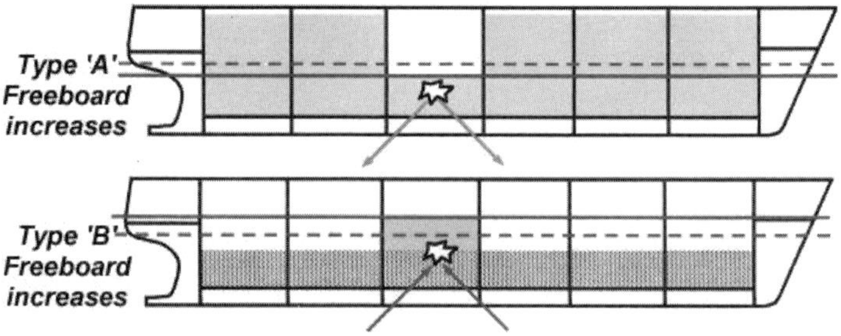

Fig. 26.12

The general *advantages* of a Type 'A' ship can be summarised as follows:

* *High watertight integrity of the exposed freeboard deck as cargo tanks have small access openings closed by watertight and gasketed covers of steel.*

* *Loaded cargo tanks have a low permeability.*

* *Because of the large free surface effects possible with liquid cargoes, type 'A' ships must have a high degree of subdivision, both longitudinally and transversely. This subdivision limits the volume of lost buoyancy when a compartment becomes bilged, unlike the relatively large hold of a cargo vessel (type 'B' ship).*

* *The greater degree of subdivision improves the stability characteristics in the damaged condition when damage is in way of a transverse bulkhead causing the flooding of two adjacent loaded compartments.*

* *Greater subdivision also reduces the effect of trim when near end compartments become bilged.*

* *Cargo pumps provide efficient means of maintaining a level of flood water in a damaged cargo compartment, especially if the damaged compartment was empty.*

In contrast type 'B' ships have comparatively large hatchways which can only be made *weathertight*. Depending on the nature of the cargo, permeability of loaded holds can be high (as with dense cargoes). If a type 'B' ship exceeds 100 metres in length, is fitted with steel hatch covers and has sufficient subdivision to meet certain damage stability criteria they may be allowed a reduction in freeboard (B-60 and B-100 vessels).

26.6 B-60 AND B-100 TABULAR FREEBOARDS

26.6.1 B-60 and B-100 tabular freeboards explained

If a type 'B' ship can satisfy certain additional conditions of assignment with respect to structure and damaged stability it will qualify for a reduction in its tabular freeboard. This reduction may be 60% the difference between the tabular A and tabular B freeboard, and in some cases be 100% the difference; hence the terms 'B-60' and 'B-100'.

Consider the extracts from the freeboard tables in regulation 28 below:

TABLE A		TABLE B	
Length of ship (metres)	**Freeboard (millimetres)**	**Length of ship (metres)**	**Freeboard (millimetres)**
140	1803	140	2109
141	1820	141	2130
142	1837	142	2131
143	1853	143	2171

For a given length of ship the tabular freeboard is less for a Type 'A' ship than a Type 'B' ship.

If the ship to which freeboard is to be assigned were 140 m in length the tabular freeboards would be:

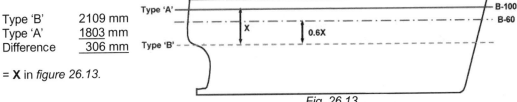

Type 'B'	2109 mm
Type 'A'	1803 mm
Difference	306 mm

= **X** in *figure 26.13.*

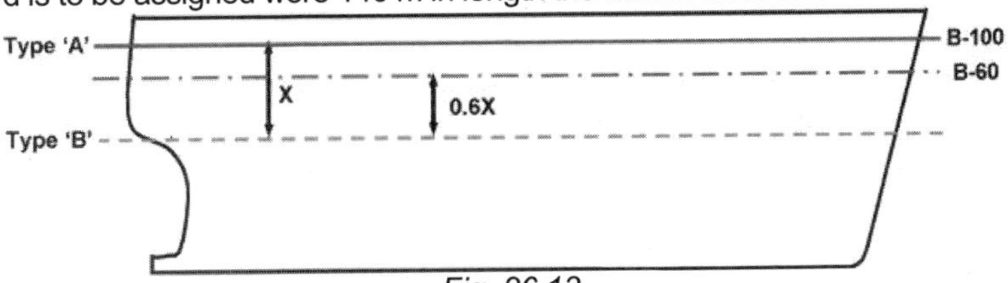

Fig. 26.13

If a type 'B' ship has a certain improved standard of subdivision and steel hatch covers it may qualify for a reduction in the tabular freeboard of 60% the difference between the type 'A' and type 'B' freeboards, hence, the term 'B-60'.
Tabular Freeboard assigned = 2109 - (0.6 × 306) = 1925 mm.

Further improvement in design might qualify the type 'B' ship a reduction of the full amount of the difference - 'B-100'.
Tabular Freeboard assigned = 2109 - (1 × 306) = 1803 mm.
(It can be seen that type 'A' and type 'B-100' tabular freeboards are the same!)

26.6.2 Additional conditions of assignment for type 'B-60' freeboard (Regulation 27)

The following additional conditions must be satisfied:

(1) Ship must be over 100 m in length.

(2) measures must be provided for the protection of the crew on exposed decks must be adequate (such as the fitting of a raised catwalk or underdeck walkways along each side of the hull).

(3) arrangements for freeing water off the deck must be adequate (railings instead of bulwarks may have to be fitted).

(4) hatch covers in positions 1 and 2 must be of steel and have adequate strength, special care being given to their sealing and securing arrangements.

(5) the ship, when loaded in accordance with the *initial condition of loading*, shall be able to withstand the flooding of any compartment or compartments, with an assumed permeability of 0.95, consequent upon the *damage assumptions* specified and shall remain afloat in a satisfactory *condition of equilibrium*.

If the ship is over 150 m in length, the machinery space may be treated as a floodable compartment with a permeability of 0.85.

(The *initial condition of loading*, *damage assumptions* and *condition of equilibrium* are the same as those applicable in the definition of a type 'A' ship – *section 26.4.1.*)

26.6.3 Additional conditions of assignment for type 'B-100' freeboard (Regulation 27)

The following additional conditions must be satisfied:

(1) All the special conditions of assignment applicable to type 'A' ships (as per *section 26.4.2*);

(2) All the additional conditions applicable to the assignment of 'B-60' freeboards in the previous *sub-section - 26.6.2.*

(3) the ship, when loaded in accordance with the *initial condition of loading*, shall be able to withstand the simultaneous flooding of any *two adjacent* fore and aft compartments (not including the machinery space) with an assumed permeability of 0.95, consequent upon the *damage assumptions* specified and shall remain afloat in a satisfactory *condition of equilibrium*.

If the ship is over 150 m in length, the machinery space may be treated as one of the floodable compartments with a permeability of 0.85.

(The *initial condition of loading*, *damage assumptions* and *condition of equilibrium* are the same as those applicable in the definition of a type 'A' ship – *section 26.4.1.*)

26.7 CALCULATION PROCEDURE FOR THE ASSIGNMENT OF A TYPE 'A' FREEBOARD

This section details the calculation procedure for the assignment of summer freeboard for a type 'A' ship to which corrections will be applied to determine the seasonal zone load lines.

It must be emphasised that the calculation procedure is only summarised in this section as it is the reasoning behind each of the corrections that will be questioned on in examinations and not the full detail of an actual freeboard assignment calculation. Chapter III – Freeboards (Regulations 27 to 40) should be consulted for more detail if required.
The expressions in this schedule are those as defined in the definitions given in section 26.1. Freeboard is determined as follows:

26.7.1 Obtain the tabular freeboard (Regulation 28)
From *Table A* ascertain the ship's tabular freeboard for the ship's length (L).
The *tabular freeboard* is the freeboard that would be assigned to a *standard ship* built to the highest recognised standard and having five specific characteristics as follows:

* a block coefficient of 0.68;
* a length to depth ratio of 15 i.e. L/D = 15;
* no superstructure;
* a parabolic sheer of the freeboard deck attaining a particular height at the forward and after perpendiculars as prescribed by formulae (depending on the length of the ship);
* a minimum bow height above the load waterline as prescribed by formulae (depending on C_b and length of ship).

It is how each of the above characteristics for the ship in question differs from the standard ship that will determine whether the corrections to the tabular freeboard are *added* or *subtracted.*

26.7.2 Correction for block coefficient (Regulation 30)
The *standard ship* has a block coefficient of 0.68. If C_b is *greater* than this the freeboard must be *increased*. This is achieved by: Tabular Freeboard $\times \dfrac{C_b + 0.68}{1.36}$

Reasoning for this is as follows:

A larger C_b causes an increase in the underwater volume, so freeboard must be increased in order that the reserve buoyancy amounts to the same percentage of the greater displaced volume as it would have been had C_b been 0.68. This is illustrated in figure 26.14.

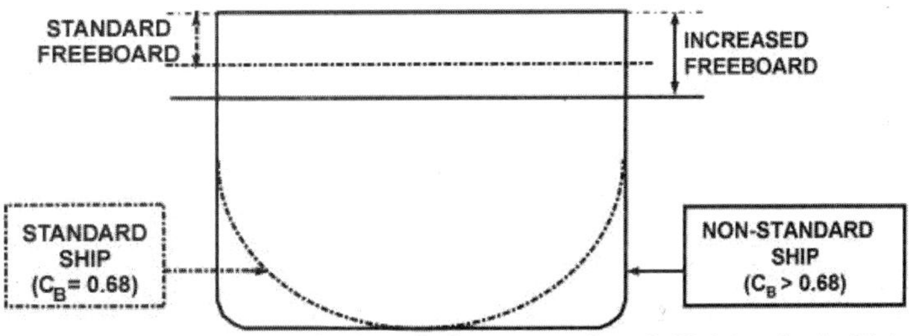

Freeboard is increased when C_b is greater than 0.68 (standard ship) to ensure that the same percentage of reserve buoyancy is maintained.

Fig. 26.14

The tabular freeboard having been corrected for block coefficient is termed *Basic Freeboard* under the *M.S. (Load Line) Regulations 1998 (MSN 1752(M).*

26.7.3 Correction for depth (Regulation 31)
The *standard ship* has a L/D ratio of 15. If the L/D ratio is *less than 15*, which is usually the case, the *freeboard is increased.*

If the L/D ratio is *greater than 15* then the *freeboard may be decreased* provided that the ship has an enclosed superstructure covering at least 0.6L amidships, a complete trunk or a combination of detached enclosed superstructures and trunks which extend all fore and aft.

Reasoning for this is as follows. Consider the two vessels shown.

If the ships in *figure 26.15* are considered where an amidships compartment extending the full depth of the hull were flooded due to damage, *Ship 1* would experience greater sinkage and loss of freeboard than *Ship 2*, since in each case, the volume of buoyancy that has been lost must be regained by the remaining intact parts of the hull.

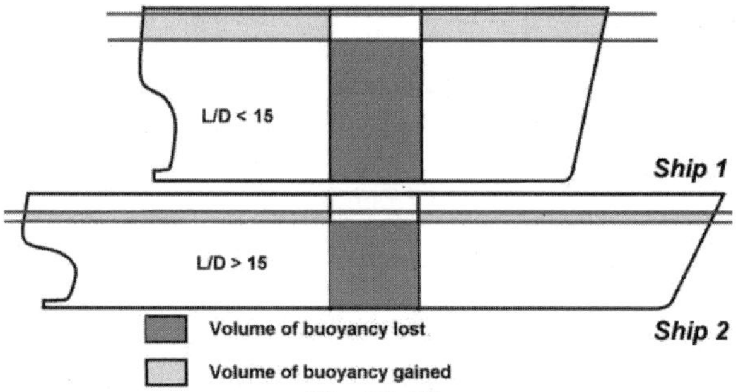

Fig. 26.15

26.7.4 Correction for position of deck line (Regulation 32)

If the actual depth to the upper edge of the deck line is greater or less than the depth for freeboard (D), the difference if greater, shall be added to, or if less shall be deducted from, the freeboard.

Figure 26.16 illustrates the example of a rounded sheer strake.

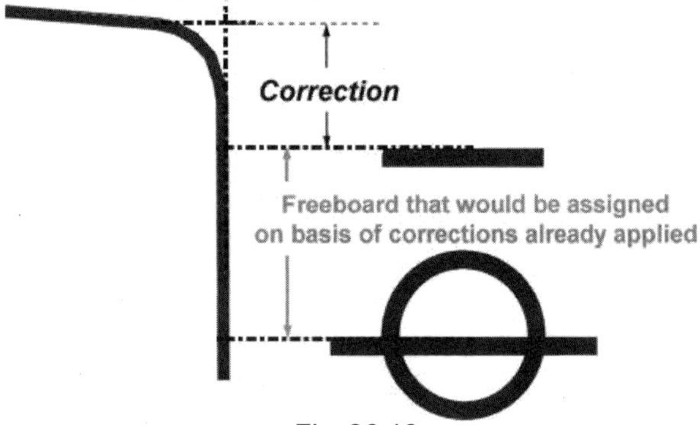

Fig. 26.16

26.7.5 Correction for superstructure and trunks (Regulations 33 to 37)

The *standard ship* has no superstructure. Enclosed superstructures of a significant height are important in providing reserve buoyancy above the freeboard deck. Freeboard *deductions* are allowed for effective enclosed superstructure length as a proportion of the ship's freeboard length. The deduction in freeboard allowed is determined by a number of formulae and tables.

Regulation 33 defines the standard height of superstructure as given in the following table:

Standard heights for intermediate lengths are obtained by interpolation.

	Standard height (m)	
***L* (m)**	***Raised quarter-deck***	***All other superstructures***
30 or less	0.90	1.80
75	1.20	1.80
125 or more	1.80	2.30

Regulation 36 allows the reserve buoyancy of trunks to be taken into consideration also. Although not precisely defined in the regulations a trunk may be regarded as *a structure having equivalent bulkhead strength as that of a superstructure that opens directly into the space below the freeboard deck and having an average width of at least 60% of the ship at the position in which they are situated.* Hatch coamings that have heights equivalent to that of the standard height of the superstructure as determined by the above table may be considered as trunks that provide additional reserve buoyancy for the ship.

Regulation 37 details the deduction of freeboard that will be permitted for effective length of superstructures and trunks. It is always a *deduction* in freeboard since the standard ship has no superstructure.

26.7.6 Correction for sheer profile (Regulation 38)

Sheer is defined as being the curvature of the freeboard deck in a fore and aft direction.

Benefits of sheer include:

* Greater reserve buoyancy at the ends of the ship, particularly forward, ensuring good lift in a head/following sea;
* Reduces water shipped on deck;
* Reduces risk of foredeck being submerged after collision thus improving survivability in the damaged condition and helps to maintain an acceptable angle of heel at which progressive downflooding takes place.

The tabular freeboards are based upon a standard sheer profile (standard ship), measured at seven equally spaced stations along the hull. A process based on Simpson's 1331 Rule of area estimation is applied separately to the sheer measurements from the aft perpendicular to amidships and the forward perpendicular to amidships to produce measures of effective sheer aft and forward respectively.

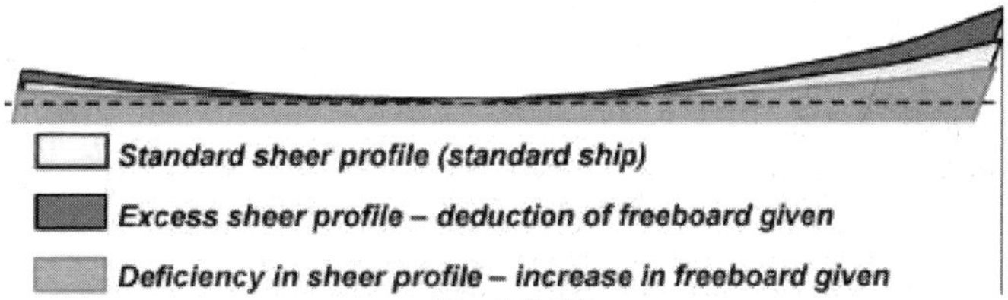

Fig. 26.17

Any deficiency in sheer will result in an *increase* in freeboard.

Excess sheer will result in a *deduction* in freeboard.

The amount of the deduction or increase in freeboard is determined by formulae in regulation 38.

26.7.7 Correction for bow height (Regulation 39)

A minimum allowable bow height must be maintained when the vessel is floating to the summer load line at its design trim. The assigned Summer Freeboard for a vessel must be *increased*, if necessary, to ensure that the minimum bow height requirements are met.

The minimum bow height (H_B) in millimetres measured at the forward perpendicular at the summer waterline is given by the following formulae:

$$H_B = 56L\left(1 - \frac{L}{500}\right) \times \frac{1.36}{C_B + 0.68} \quad \text{if freeboard length (L)} < 250 \text{ m} \quad \text{or}$$

$$H_B = 7000 \times \frac{1.36}{C_B + 0.68} \quad \text{if freeboard length (L)} \geq 250 \text{ m}$$

(C_b shall not be less than 0.68)

If the freeboard as calculated from considering the previous corrections is less than the bow height minimum, then the bow height formula minimum will be assigned as the Summer Freeboard.

The required bow height may be achieved by:

* including sheer provided sheer extends over at least 0.15L from the forward perpendicular; or

* fitting a raised forecastle provided that such a forecastle extends over at least 0.07L from the forward perpendicular.

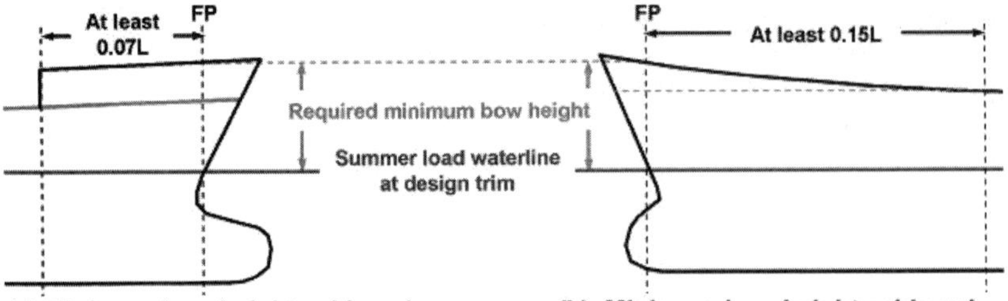

(a) Minimum bow height achieved by fitting superstructure.

(b) Minimum bow height achieved by increased sheer.

Fig. 26.18

The freeboard as calculated applies to the ship when in salt water and is assigned to the ship as its *Summer* freeboard. The summer freeboard shall not be less than 50 mm; if the ship has hatches in position 1 that are not made of steel then the summer freeboard shall not be less than 150 mm (ignoring the correction for the position of the deck line).

The Tropical (T), Winter (W), Winter North Atlantic (WNA) and Fresh water (F) freeboards are then calculated as illustrated in figure 26.6 (section 26.2.2).

26.8 CALCULATION PROCEDURE FOR THE ASSIGNMENT OF A TYPE 'B' FREEBOARD

Freeboard is determined as follows:

26.8.1 Obtain the tabular freeboard (Regulation 28)

From *Table B* ascertain the ship's tabular freeboard for the ship's length (L).

If the ship qualifies for the reduction in tabular freeboard, either 60% or 100% (B-60 or B-100) then this is applied as previously discussed in section 26.6.

26.8.2 Correction to tabular freeboard for type 'B' ships having wooden hatch covers (Regulation 27)

If the ship has hatchways in Position 1, the covers of which are not made of steel but are made of wood with tarpaulin covers then the tabular freeboard obtained from Table B will be *increased* by an amount dependant on the length of ship (Regulation 27(6)).

26.8.3 Correction to tabular freeboard for type 'B' ships under 100 metres in length (Regulation 29)

If any Type 'B' ship is not more than 100 m in length and has enclosed superstructures the total effective length (E) of which does not exceed 35% of the ship's length (L) the freeboard will be *increased* by the following amount: $7.5(100 - L)(0.35 - \frac{E}{L})$ mm.

A shorter vessel is likely to pitch more as it makes way through the water and as such the presence of superstructure forward and aft becomes more important in minimising the amount of water shipped. Longer ships (over 100 m) tend to pass through the waveform and thus will pitch less.

The tabular freeboard thus so far corrected (type 'B' Basic Freeboard) now has the same corrections as described in section 26.7 previously for the type 'A' ship applied to obtain the assigned summer freeboard.

26.9 TIMBER FREEBOARDS (Chapter IV)

Ships regularly carrying timber can be assigned reduced 'timber freeboards' that allow for an increase in the maximum draught when the vessel is carrying a deck cargo of timber. The regulations consider a deck cargo of wood to be additional reserve buoyancy, provided that it is well secured and covers the entire length of the ship's cargo deck up to at least standard superstructure height. The timber deck cargo will also offer a greater degree of protection for the hatches against the sea.

The term *'timber deck cargo'* means a cargo of timber carried on an uncovered part of a freeboard or superstructure deck.

The timber (lumber) load lines and the special timber minimum stability criteria only apply to the vessel when it is loaded with timber on deck that meets the timber conditions of assignment. The normal load line marks limit the drafts for any other loaded condition of the ship.

It is the responsibility of the shipowner to decide whether or not to have the ship built that meets all the special timber conditions of assignment and many will choose not to, in which case, the ship's draft will be restricted by the normal load lines, even when it is loaded with timber on deck.

26.9.1 Special construction requirements applicable to ships assigned timber freeboards (Regulation 43)

These are summarised below:

Superstructures: The ship must have a forecastle of at least standard height not less in length than 0.07L. Additionally, if the ship is less than 100 m in length it shall be fitted aft with either:

* a poop of not less than standard height ;or
* a raised quarterdeck having either a deckhouse or a strong steel hood, so that the total height is not less than the standard height of an enclosed superstructure.

Double bottom tanks: Double bottom tanks within the midship half-length of the ship are to have satisfactory watertight longitudinal subdivision in order to minimise the loss of stability due to the free surface effects of slack tanks.

Bulwarks: The ship is to be fitted with permanent bulwarks at least one metre in height, specially stiffened on the upper edge and supported by strong bulwark stays attached to the deck and provided with necessary freeing ports, or, efficient guardrails and stanchions of at least one metre in height of especially strong construction.

26.9.2 Stowage requirements (Regulation 44)

In addition to the requirements stated below the *Code of Safe Practice for Ships Carrying Timber Deck Cargoes (IMO)* should also be consulted. For UK registered ships this code is enforced by *SI 1999 No. 336 Merchant Shipping (Carriage of Cargoes) Regulations*.

The general requirements are as follows:

Openings in the weather deck over which the timber cargo is stowed should be securely closed and battened down.

Ventilators and air pipes should be efficiently protected against damage resulting from a shift of the cargo.

The timber stow should extend over the entire available length of the weather deck in the well or wells between superstructures. Where there is no limiting superstructure at the after end, the timber should extend at least to the after end of the aftermost hatchway. This ensures that the reserve buoyancy afforded by the stow and superstructures is evenly distributed along the ship's length and there is no trimming effect due to the immersion of a partial stow, either near the bow or stern, occurring at the furthest extent of a roll.

The timber deck cargo should extend athwartships as close as possible to the ship's side, allowance being given for obstructions such as guard rails, bulwark stays, uprights etc. provided that any gap thus created at the side of the ship does not exceed 4% of the ship's breadth.

The timber should be stowed as solidly as possible to at least the standard height of a superstructure other than any raised quarter deck.

When within a Winter seasonal zone during the period specified as being a Winter season the timber will be stowed so that at no point throughout its length does the height of the deck cargo above the level of the weather deck at side exceed one third of the extreme breadth of the ship.

The deck cargo should not interfere with the ship's safe operation and navigation, including access to ship's steering arrangements.

Uprights, when required by the nature of the timber, should be of adequate strength considering the breadth of the ship; the strength of the uprights should not exceed the strength of the bulwark and the spacing should be suitable for the length and character of timber carried, but should not exceed 3 metres. Strong angles or metal sockets or equally efficient means should be provided for securing the uprights.

The timber deck cargo should be efficiently secured throughout its length by independent overall lashings. The spacing of the lashings should be determined by the maximum height of the cargo above the weather deck in the vicinity of the lashing:

* for a height of 4 m and below the spacing should be not more than 3 m;
* for a height of 6 m and above the spacing should be not more than 1.5 m;
* at intermediate heights the spacing is obtained by linear interpolation of the above figures.

When timber is in lengths of less than 3.6 m, the spacing of the lashings should be reduced or other suitable provisions made to suit the length of timber. The lashings should be capable of withstanding an ultimate tensile load of not less than 13600 Kg. They should be fitted with sliphooks and turnbuckles which should be accessible to allow adjustment of the lashings during the passage. Wire rope lashings should have a short length of long link chain to permit the length of the lashings to be regulated. Shackles, stretching devices and all other ancillary lashing components incorporated into a chain or wire rope lashing and its securings should have a minimum ultimate load of 14100 Kg. Each component should be proof loaded to 5600 Kg.

The timber deck cargo is to be distributed so as to:

* avoid excessive loading with respect to the strength of the deck and supporting structure;
* to ensure that the ship will retain adequate stability with respect to:
  - vertical distribution;
  - effects of wind heeling;
  - losses of weight low down in the ship due to fuel/stores consumption;
  - increases of timber weight caused by water absorption and icing.

The crew should have safe access across the deck stow by means of a walkway fitted over the timber deck cargo. Guard rails or lifelines not more than 330 mm apart vertically should be provided on each side of the cargo deck to a height of at least 1 metre above the cargo.

26.9.3 Calculation of the Summer timber freeboard (Regulation 45)

The Summer Timber freeboard is calculated as for the ordinary Assigned Summer freeboard but an alternative percentage of 'Superstructure Deduction' is applied in the freeboard calculation. The table in regulation 37 is modified by substituting the percentages for those given in the table in regulation 45. It is this alternative correction that causes the difference between the Assigned

Summer freeboard and the Summer Timber freeboard whereby benefit is given for the timber deck cargo being additional effective superstructure.

Corrections to the Summer Timber freeboard to give the other seasonal freeboards are as shown in figure 26.7 in section 26.2.2.

26.9.4 Minimum IMO stability criteria for ships carrying timber deck cargoes

Chapter 4 Regulation 4.1 of the *Code on Intact Stability for all Types of Ships Covered by IMO Instruments (IMO)*, hereafter referred to as the Code, details the minimum intact stability requirements for cargo ships 24 metres in length and over engaged in the carriage of timber deck cargoes.

Ships that are provided with and make use of their timber load line should also comply with the following requirements:

* *The area under the righting lever curve (GZ curve) should not be less than 0.08 metre-radians up to 40° heel or the angle of downflooding if this angle is less than 40°.*

* *The maximum value of the righting lever (GZ) should be at least 0.25 m.*

* *At all times during the voyage, the metacentric height (GM) should not be less than 0.10 m after correction for the free surface effects of liquid in tanks and, where appropriate, the absorption of water by the deck cargo and /or ice accretion on the exposed surfaces. (Details regarding ice accretion are given in Chapter 5 of the Code)*

* *When determining the ability of the ship to withstand the combined effects of beam wind and rolling (Regulation 3.2 of the Code; section 24.1.2.2 of this text) the 16° limiting angle of heel under the action of steady wind should be complied with, but the additional criterion of 80% of the angle of deck edge immersion may be ignored.*

The Code requires that comprehensive stability information be provided which takes into account the timber deck cargo to include guidance as to the stability of the ship under varying conditions of service. This assumes permeability of the cargo of 25% (by volume), if permeability is likely to be significantly different from this value then additional information as appropriate must be provided.

The stability of the ship must be positive at all times and should be calculated having regard to:

* the increased weight of the timber deck cargo due to:
  (1) absorption of water, and;
  (2) ice accretion if applicable;

* variations in consumables (such as fuel consumption from tanks low down in the ship);

* the free surface effects of liquids in tanks, and;

* weight of water trapped in broken spaces within the timber deck cargo and especially logs.

Ships carrying timber deck cargoes should operate, as far as possible, with a margin of safety with respect to metacentric height (GM), however the metacentric height should preferably *not* exceed 3% of the breadth of the ship in order to prevent excessive accelerations in rolling that would cause large racking stresses and high stresses on cargo lashings which might result in cargo loss or shift.

The Administration may allow the buoyancy of the timber deck cargo to be taken in to account in the derivation of the KN curves, assuming a permeability of 25% of the volume of the timber (this is allowed under the MCA criteria and is explained fully in section 26.9.5.

In the arrival condition it should be assumed that the weight of the timber deck cargo has increased by 10% due to water absorption.

Finally, the stowage of the timber deck cargo must be in accordance with the requirements of Chapter 3 of the *Code of Safe Practice for Ships Carrying Timber Deck Cargoes 1991 (IMO).*

26.9.5 Minimum MCA (UK ships) stability criteria for ships carrying timber deck cargoes
The MCA requirements (as detailed in the *M. S. (Load Line) Regulations 1998* and *MSN 1752(M)*) differ to the IMO requirements.

* *The area under the curve of righting levers (GZ curve) shall not be less than:*
(i) 0.055 metre-radians up to an angle of 30°;
(ii) 0.09 metre-radians up to an angle of 40° or the angle at which the lower edge of any openings in the hull, superstructures or deckhouses which cannot be closed weathertight, are immersed if that angle is less; and
(iii) 0.03 metre-radians between the angles of heel of 30° and 40° or such lesser angle as referred to in subparagraph (ii) above.

* *The righting lever (GZ) shall be at least 0.20 m at an angle of heel equal to or greater than 30°.*

* *The maximum righting lever shall occur at an angle of heel not less than 30°.*

* *The initial transverse metacentric height shall not be less than 0.15 m. In the case of a ship carrying a timber deck cargo that complies with the area requirements above by taking into account the volume of timber deck cargo, the initial transverse metacentric height shall not be less than 0.05 m.*

Schedule 6 – 5(2) of MSN 1752(M) states that the calculation of effective KG must allow for 15% increase in the weight of the deck timber due to water absorption during the voyage. Consideration must also be given to the effects of wind heeling and ice accretion as appropriate (MCA requirements) and consumptions of fuel and stores during the voyage as previously described. Stability data must include alternative KN curves/tables to account for the specified heights of timber deck cargo stows. In the derivation of the additional KN values to be supplied ***only 75% of the timber volume must be considered as reserve buoyancy as 25% of the volume must be allowed for water absorption.***

The principle of the inclusion of the timber as reserve buoyancy in the derivation of the alternative KN data is illustrated in figure 26.19.

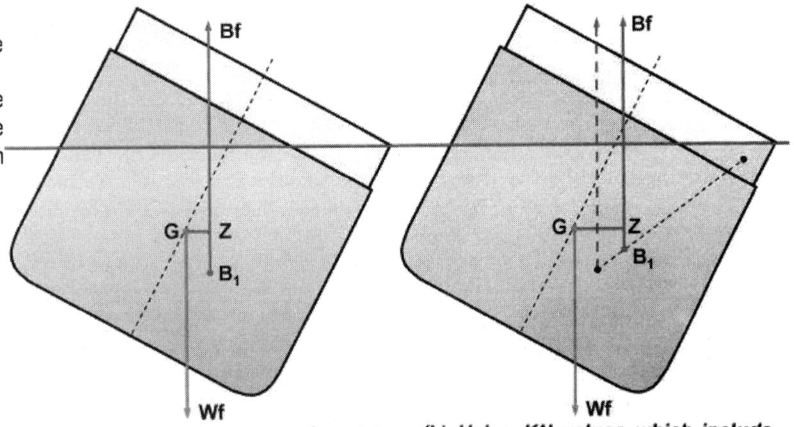

(a) When heeled beyond θ_{DEI} GZ values are small when the reserve buoyancy of the timber is not included (GZ values derived from ship's ordinary KN values).

(b) Using KN values which include 75% of the volume of the immersed timber as reserve buoyancy causes an outward movement of B which increases the GZ values.

Fig. 26.19

26.10 LOAD LINE CERTIFICATION AND SURVEYS

All ships must be issued with a load line certificate. The form of the certificate will depend upon the Assigning Authority as follows:

* If the certificate is an *International Load Line Certificate* it shall be in the form prescribed by the 1966 Convention which is detailed in the IMO publication *'Load Lines – 2002 Edition'.*
* If the certificate is a *United Kingdom Load Line Certificate* (applicable to UK registered ships that must comply with the *M. S. (Load Line) Regulations 1998*) it shall be in the form prescribed in Schedule 8 of MSN 1752(M).

26.10.1 Surveys

A ship will be subject to the following surveys:

* *Initial survey* before the ship is put into service;
* *Renewal survey* at intervals not exceeding five years;
* *Annual survey* within 3 months either way of the anniversary date of the load line certificate. The surveyor will endorse the load line certificate on satisfactory completion of the annual survey.

The period of validity of the load line certificate may be extended for a period not exceeding 3 months for the purpose of allowing the ship to complete its voyage to the port in which it is to be surveyed.

26.10.2 Load line survey preparation

The preparation for a load line survey will involve ensuring that the hull is watertight below the freeboard deck and weathertight above it (cargo tank lids on tankers must be watertight).

Reference should be made to the *Form of record of conditions of assignment of load lines* as specified in Part 6 of *'Load Lines – 2002* Edition' (*Record of particulars* as detailed in MSN 1752(M) for UK ships).

The following checks should be conducted prior to survey:

(1) Check that all access openings at the ends of enclosed superstructures are in good condition. All dogs, clamps and hinges should be free and greased. Gaskets and other sealing arrangements should not show signs of perishing (cracked rubbers). Ensure that doors can be opened from both sides. Ensure that door labels such as '*To be kept closed at sea'* are in place.

(2) Check all cargo hatches and accesses to holds for weathertightness. Securing devices such as clamps, cleats and wedges are to be all in place, well greased and adjusted to provide optimum sealing between the hatch cover and compression bar on the coaming. Replace perished rubber seals as necessary. Hose test hatches to verify weathertightness.

(3) Check the efficiency and securing of portable beams.

(4) For wooden hatches, ensure that the hatch boards are in good condition and that the steel binding bands are well secured. A minimum of at least two tarpaulins should be provided at each hatch which must be in good condition, waterproof and of a strong approved material. Locking bars and side wedges must be in place and be in good order.

(5) Inspect all machinery space openings on exposed decks.

(6) Check that manhole covers on the freeboard deck are capable of being made watertight.

(7) Check that all ventilator openings are provided with efficient weathertight closing appliances.

(8) All air pipes must be provided with permanently attached means of closing.

(9) Inspect cargo ports below the freeboard deck and ensure that they are watertight.

(10) Ensure that all non-return valves on overboard discharges are effective.

(11) Side scuttles below the freeboard deck or to spaces within enclosed superstructures must have efficient internal watertight deadlights. Inspect deadlight rubber seals and securing arrangements.

(12) Check all freeing ports, ensure shutters are not jammed, hinges are free and that pins are of non-corroding type (gun metal).

(13) Check bulwarks and guardrails are in good condition.

(14) Rig life lines (if required) and ensure they are in good order.

(15) De-rust and repaint deck line, load line mark, load lines and draught marks.

On the day of the survey ensure that the International Load Line certificate and associated documentation are available for inspection. Sufficient manpower should be made available for the operation of hatch covers and the rigging of staging and ladders to allow the surveyor to view the load line and draught marks. The ship's stability data book should also be on hand for inspection.

SECTION 27 – SHEAR FORCES AND BENDING MOMENTS IN SHIPS

INTRODUCTION

When a ship is floating in still water conditions the hull will experience longitudinal deflections created by the uneven distribution of weight forces and buoyancy forces along its length. These stresses will always exist no matter how the ship is loaded and will never be totally eliminated. At sea, longitudinal stresses will be increased and decreased in a cyclical manner as waves pass along the ship's length. It is the responsibility of those loading the ship to ensure that the longitudinal stresses likely to be experienced are maintained within acceptable limits. Although it is not a requirement that manual shear force and bending moment calculations be conducted on board, it is essential that those responsible for loading the ship have an understanding of the causes of such stresses and that they can correctly interpret the graphical data presented on modern loading calculating programs.

Learning Objectives

On completion of this section the learner will achieve the following:

1. Understand how *shear forces* and *bending moments* arise in a vessel floating in still water.
2. Produce simple *shear force* and *bending moment* diagrams for box-shaped vessels floating on an even keel in still water.
3. Understand sea wave bending and the assumptions that might be made with respect to wave profiles causing maximum longitudinal bending.
4. Understand how stress data may be represented on modern stress loading programs.

27.1 SHEAR FORCES AND BENDING MOMENTS IN STILL WATER CONDITIONS

In still water a ship will experience shearing forces and bending moments as a consequence of uneven distribution of weight forces and buoyancy forces acting along its length.

Consider a box-shaped vessel of uniform construction having three holds of equal length. The light displacement of the vessel is 9000 tonnes and it is floating on an even keel.

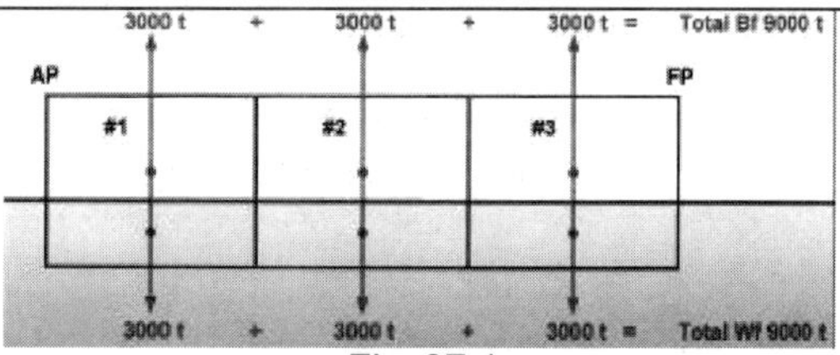

Fig. 27.1

The vessel will displace a mass of water equal to the displacement of the vessel in the light condition. The total weight force (Wf) acting downwards equals the total buoyancy force (Bf) acting upwards.

Since each of the holds are the same length, the weight force attributable to each hold will be the same, being 3000 tonnes for each. The volume (and hence mass) of water displaced by each hold will also be the same, 3000 tonnes. It can be seen that the distribution of weight force and buoyancy force exactly matches throughout the length of the vessel and in this condition the vessel's structure will experience no stress.

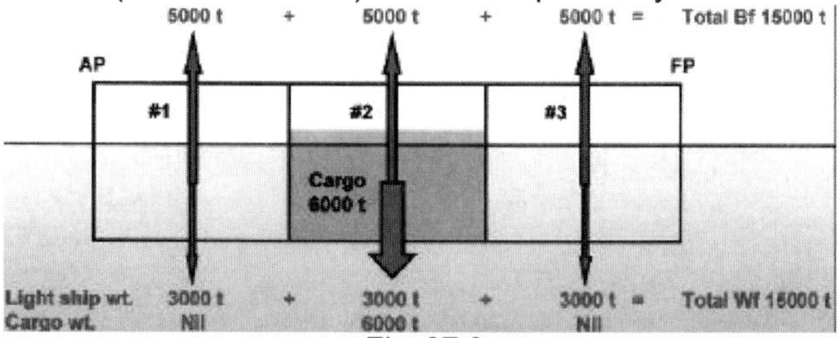

Fig. 27.2

6000 tonnes of bulk cargo is now loaded into No. 2 hold and is trimmed level (figure 27.2).

The buoyancy force is evenly distributed along the length of the vessel, since 5000 tonnes of water is displaced by each hold, however, the distribution of the weight force is not the same as can be seen.

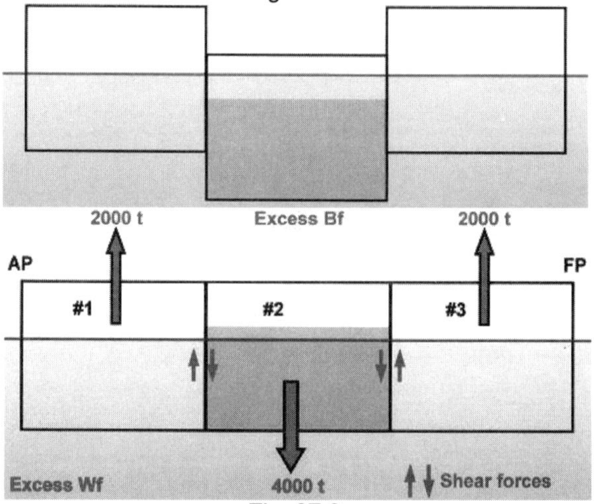

Fig. 27.3

n numbers 1 and 3 holds there is an excess of buoyancy force of 2000 tonnes, whereas in number 2 hold there is an excess of weight force of 4000 tonnes. These *excesses* of weight forces and buoyancy forces create the *shearing forces*. The shearing forces are the *vertical forces that tend to cause the ship to be sliced into different parts.* Consider what would happen to the vessel in figure 27.2 if each hold could float independently of the others.

It would be hoped that the vessel would not shear at the bulkheads as illustrated; the ship would experience bending moments that in this instant would cause the vessel to be *sagged* (figure 27.4). The opposite situation arises when a vessel is loaded at the ends and less in the amidships section, causing the vessel to be *hogged*.

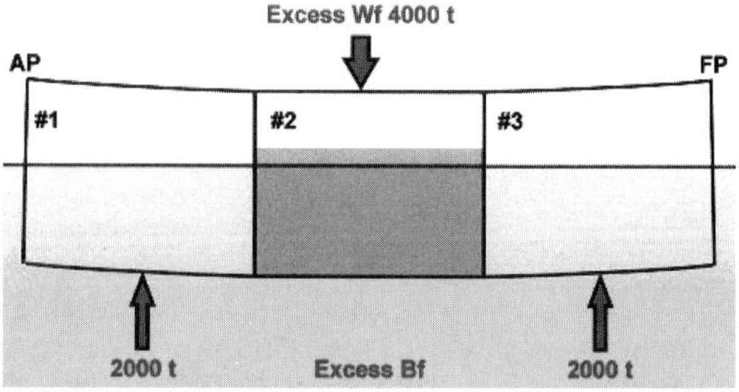

Sagging caused by loading the amidships hold only.

Fig. 27.4

27.2 SIMPLE SHEAR FORCE AND BENDING MOMENT DIAGRAMS FOR BOX-SHAPED VESSELS

The values of shear force and bending moment can be easily calculated for any position within the box-shaped vessel's length. However, it should be evident that the maximum values of shear force will occur at the bulkhead positions. Follow example 1 which details a method of calculating the values of *loads*, *shear forces* and *bending moments*.

Example 1

In the light condition a box-shaped vessel is 45 m in length, 8 m in breadth and floats at a draught of 3.0 m in fresh water. The vessel has three holds each 15 m in length. 90 tonnes of bulk cargo is loaded into number 2 hold and is trimmed level. For the loaded condition construct the following:

(a) load curve;
(b) curve of shear forces,
(c) curve of bending moments.
(d) Identify the positions where the maximum shearing forces and bending moments occur.

Values of shear forces and bending moments are to be calculated at 5 metre intervals starting from the after perpendicular (AP) and at amidships (22.5 m foap).

27.2.1 Producing the curve of loads

Solution (a)

1. *Calculate the distribution of the lightweight displacement of the vessel.*
   Light displacement = (L × B × d) × density
   Light displacement = (45 × 8 × 3.0) × 1.000 = 1080 tonnes
   Being a box-shaped vessel of uniform construction the lightweight displacement evenly distributed = $\frac{1080\ t}{45\ m}$ = **24 t/m**
2. *Calculate the distribution of all deadweight items (cargo).*
   Cargo evenly distributed in No. 2 hold = $\frac{90\ t}{15\ m}$ = **6 t/m**
3. *Calculate the load displacement and distribution of the buoyancy force.*
   Load displacement = Light displacement + Deadweight
   Load displacement = 1080 + 90 = 1170 tonnes
   Being a box-shaped vessel of uniform construction the buoyancy force evenly distributed = $\frac{1170\ t}{45\ m}$ = **26 t/m**
4. *Calculate the loads in each hold and plot the 'load curve'.*

Hold No.	Lightweight (t/m)	Deadweight (t/m)	Total Wf (t/m)	Bf (t/m)	LOAD (t/m)
3	24	0	24	26	2 up
2	24	6	30	26	4 down
1	24	0	24	26	2 up

The load in tonnes per metre represents the excess of buoyancy force or weight force in each hold. The load curve is shown in figure 27.5.

Note: Because total weight force equals total buoyancy force, it follows that the excesses of buoyancy force (represented by the area above the base line) and the excesses of weight force (represented by the area below the base line) must also be equal. This is always the case. Note also that the unit of load is tonnes/metre.

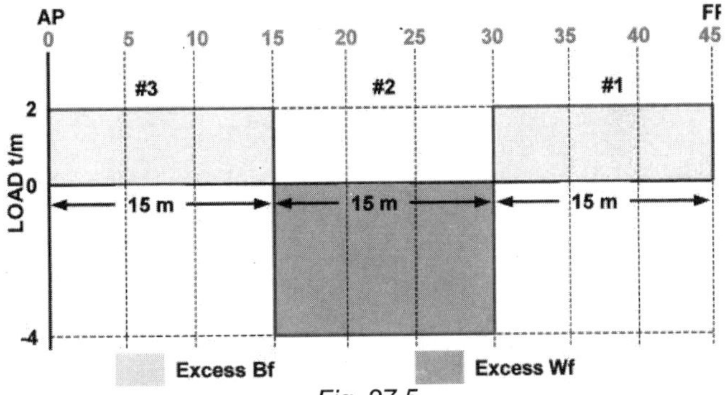

Fig. 27.5

27.2.2 Producing the curve of shear forces

The shear force at any position is defined as being *the algebraic sum of the loads acting to the left (or right) of the position in question and is measured in tonnes*.

Integrating the load curve will produce the curve of shear forces but don't panic; there is an easy way to do this!

The *maximum* shear force values will arise at the positions where the loads change direction, being at the bulkhead positions.

Consider the aforementioned definition of *shear force*. For our purposes this definition of *shear force* can be modified to read as being the *area under the load curve to the left of the point in question.*

Therefore: *SF at AP = 0 tonnes (since there is no area to the left of the AP under the curve!)*

Placing a sheet of paper over the curve and moving it to the right at 5 metre intervals, calculate the net area to the left of the edge of the sheet for each point in question (figure 27.6).

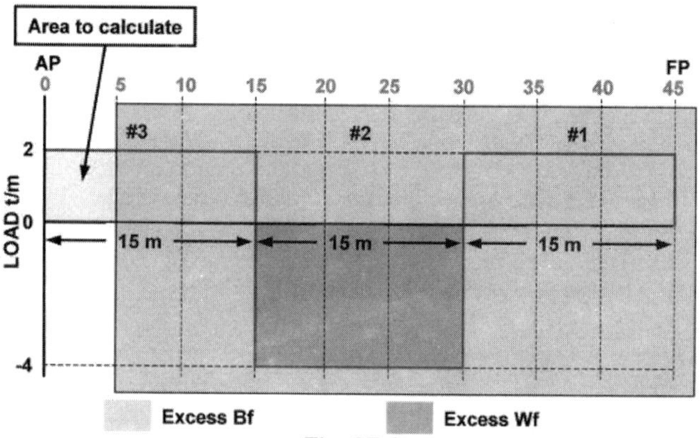

Fig. 27.6

SF at 5 m foap = 2 t/m × 5 m
= 10 tonnes.

Now calculate the SF value at 10 m foap (by moving the paper further to the right and revealing more of the curve to the left.

SF at 10 m foap = 2 t/m × 10 m
= 20 tonnes.

SF at 15 m foap (Bulkhead 3/2) = 2 t/m × 15 m = 30 tonnes.

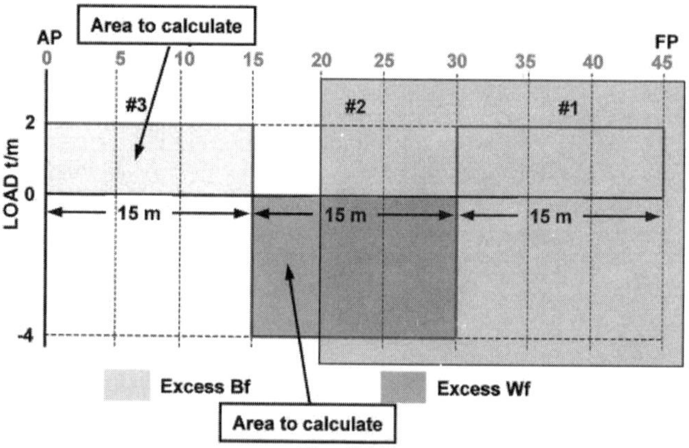

Fig. 27.7

At 20 m foap there is area revealed *above* and *below* the baseline and this is treated as *positive* and *negative* as per the load scale.

SF at 20 m foap = (2 t/m × 15 m) + (-4 t/m × 5 m) = 10 tonnes.

Continuing with this method gives:

SF at amidships (22.5 m foap) = (2 t/m × 15 m) + (-4 t/m × 7.5 m) = 0 tonnes

SF at 25 m foap = (2 t/m × 15 m) + (-4 t/m × 10 m) = -10 tonnes.

SF at 30 m foap (bulkhead 2/1) = (2 t/m × 15 m) + (-4 t/m × 15 m) = -30 tonnes

SF at 35 m foap = (2 t/m × 15 m) + (-4 t/m × 15 m) + (2 t/m × 5 m) = -20 tonnes

SF at 40 m foap = (2 t/m × 15 m) + (-4 t/m × 15 m) + (2 t/m × 10 m) = -10 tonnes

SF at 45 m foap = (2 t/m × 15 m) + (-4 t/m × 15 m) + (2 t/m × 15 m) = 0 tonnes

(Obviously the SF at the FP is 0 tonnes.)

In summary, the values of shear force are as follows:

SF at AP =	*0 tonnes*
SF 5 m foap =	*10 tonnes*
SF 10 m foap =	*20 tonnes*
SF 15 m foap = (bulkhead 2/1)	*30 tonnes*
SF 20 m foap =	*10 tonnes*
SF 22.5 foap = (amidships)	*0 tonnes*
SF 25 m foap = (bulkhead 2/1)	*-10 tonnes*
SF 30 m foap =	*-30 tonnes*
SF 35 m foap =	*-20 tonnes*
SF 40 m foap =	*-10 tonnes*
SF at 45 m foap = (FP)	*0 tonnes*

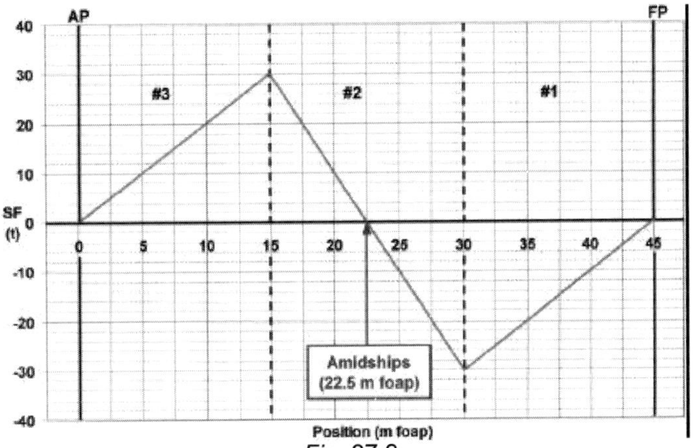

Fig. 27.8

Careful study of this method will lead to a more simplified approach with practice. The curve of shear forces can now be plotted as shown in figure 27.8.

27.2.3 Producing the curve of bending moments

The bending moment values are calculated in exactly the same way as the shear force values, by considering the *areas under the shear force* curve to the left of the position in question.

The area of a triangle is given by: **Area = ½ Base × Perpendicular height**

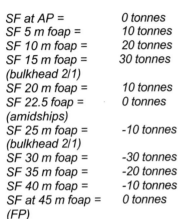

The area of a trapezium as shown is given by: $\textbf{Area} = \frac{(a + b)}{2} \times \textbf{base}$

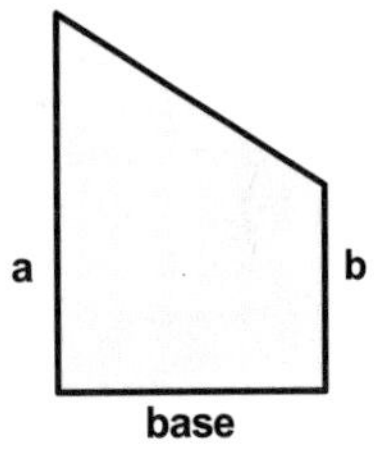

The bending moment values are calculated as follows:

BM at AP = 0 tonnes (since there is no area to the left of the AP under the SF curve!)

Placing a sheet of paper over the curve and moving to the right as far as the first bulkhead position (Bulkhead 3/2), calculate the areas as before (figure 27.9).

BM 5m foap = ½ × 5m × 10 t = 25 t-m

BM 10m foap = ½ × 10m × 2 t = 100 t-m

BM 15m foap (bulkhead 3/2)
= ½ × 15 m × 30 t = 225 t-m

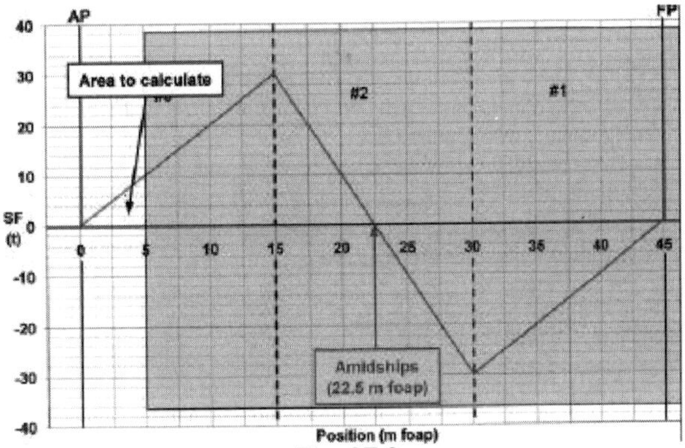

Fig. 27.9

Once past bulkhead 3/2 it is necessary to consider the area of a trapezium formed by the area under the shear force curve to the right of the bulkhead as seen in figure 27.10.

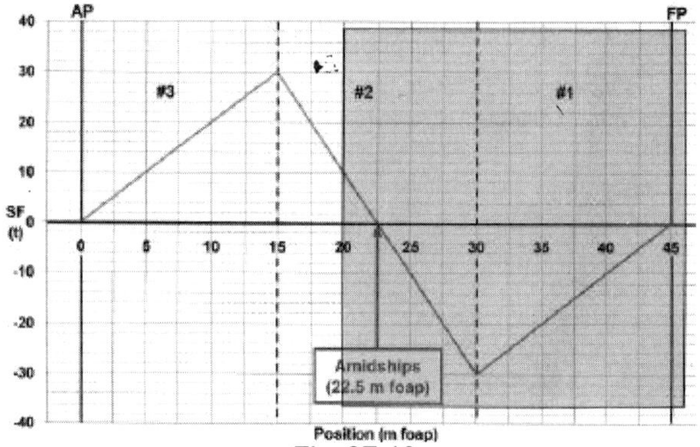

Fig. 27.10

BM 20 m foap
=(½×15m×30 t)+((30t+10t)×5m)/2=325 t-m

BM at amidships (22.5 m foap)
= ½ × 22.5 × 30 = 337.5 t-m

BM at 25 m foap
= 337.5 t-m + (½ × 2.5 m × -10 t) = 325 t-m
(Since we know the area from 0 to 22.5 m foap, being 337.5 t-m!)

BM at 30 m foap (bulkhead 2/1) = 337.5 + (½ × 7.5 m × -30 t) = 225 t-m

BM at 35 m foap = 225 + ((-30 t + -20 t)/2 × 5 m) = 100 t-m
(Since we know the area from 0 to 30m foap, being 225 t-m!)

BM at 40 m foap = 225 + ((-30 t + -10 t)/2 × 10 m) = 25 t-m

BM at FP = 0 t-m

In summary, the values of bending moment are as follows:

BM at AP =	*0 t-m*
BM at 5 m foap =	*25 t-m*
BM at 10 m foap =	*100 t-m*
BM 15 m foap (bulkhead 2/1) =	*225 t-m*
BM at 20 m foap =	*325 t-m*
BM at 22.5 foap (amidships) =	*337.5 t-m*
BM at 25 m foap (bulkhead 2/1) =	*325 t-m*
BM at 30 m foap =	*225 t-m*
BM at 35 m foap =	*100 t-m*
BM at 40 m foap =	*25 t-m*
BM at 45 m foap (FP) =	*0 t-m*

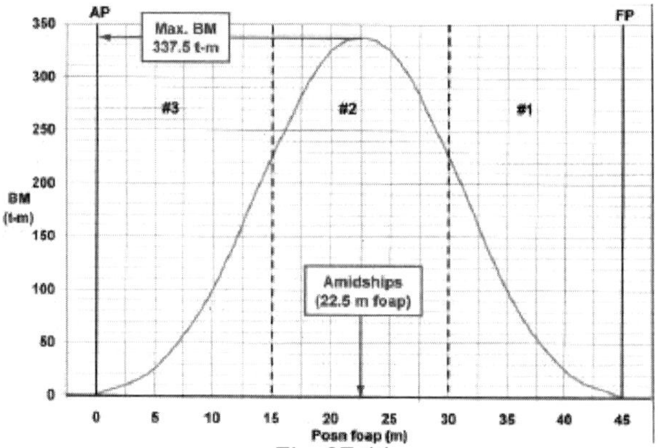

Fig. 27.11

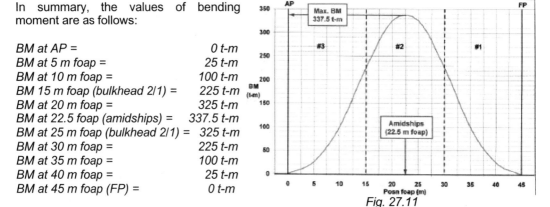

Figure 27.11 shows the plotted bending moment curve.

<u>*Summary*</u>
The maximum shear force values occur at the positions where the direction of the loads change direction; at the bulkheads being:
30 tonnes at 15 m foap (in line with bulkhead 3/2), and;
-30 tonnes at 30 m foap (in line with bulkhead 2/1)
The maximum bending moment value of (337.5 t-m) occurs at amidships (22.5 m foap), where the shear force value is zero.
It should be noted that a point of inflexion of the bending moment curve will occur in any position where there is a shear force maximum (being at the bulkhead positions in this example).
In this first example the vessel was sagged. Consider example 2 where the ship is in a hogged condition.

27.2.4 A harder example illustrating key points of interest

Example 2

A box shaped vessel has length 80 m and breadth 10 m and is floating in the light condition at a draught of 3.0 m in water RD 1.010. It is divided into four holds of equal length. Cargo is loaded as follows:

follows:	*No. 1*	*120 tonnes,*
	No. 2	*120 tonnes,*
	No. 3	*empty,*
	No.4	*160 tonnes.*

Construct the curves of shear force and bending moment, calculating the maximum values and stating the positions where they occur.

Solution

Producing the load curve

1. *Calculate the distribution of the lightweight displacement of the vessel.*
   Light displacement = (L × B × d) × density
   Light displacement = (80 × 10 × 3.0) × 1.010 = 2424 tonnes

   Being a box-shaped vessel of uniform construction the lightweight displacement evenly distributed = $\frac{2424\ t}{80\ m}$ *=* ***30.3 t/m***

2. *Calculate the distribution of all deadweight items (cargo).*
   Cargo evenly distributed in No. 1 hold = $\frac{120\ t}{20\ m}$ *=* ***6 t/m***

   Cargo evenly distributed in No.2 hold is also ***6 t/m***
   Cargo evenly distributed in No. 4 hold = $\frac{160\ t}{20\ m}$ *=* ***8 t/m***

3. *Calculate the load displacement and distribution of the buoyancy force.*
   Load displacement = Light displacement + Deadweight
   Load displacement = 2424 + 120 + 120 + 160 = 2824 tonnes
   Being a box-shaped vessel of uniform construction the buoyancy force evenly distributed = $\frac{2824\ t}{80\ m}$ *=* ***35.3 t/m***

4. *Calculate the loads in each hold and plot the 'load curve'.*

Hold No.	Lightweight (t/m)	Deadweight (t/m)	Total Wf (t/m)	Bf (t/m)	LOAD (t/m)
4	30.3	8	38.3	35.3	3 down
3	30.3	0	30.3	35.3	5 up
2	30.3	6	36.3	35.3	1 down
1	30.3	6	36.3	35.3	1 down

The load in tonnes per metre represents the excess of buoyancy force or weight force in each hold.

The load curve is shown in figure 27.12.

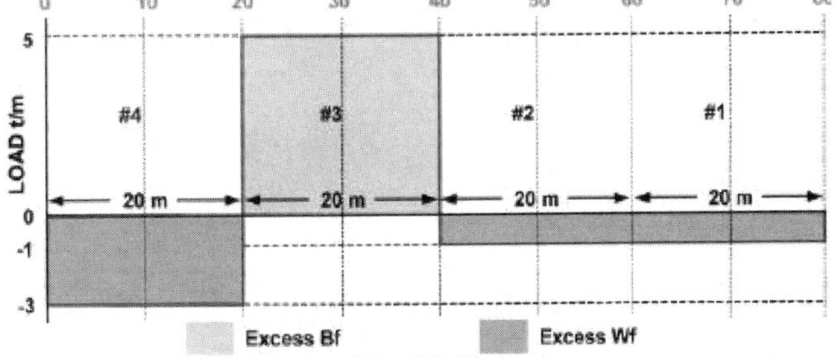

Fig. 27.12

Producing the shear force curve

Calculate values at 10 metre intervals using the procedure previously described.

SF at AP = 0 tonnes
SF at 10 m foap = (-3 t/m × 10 m) = -30 tonnes
SF at 20 m foap (bulkhead 4/3) = (-3 t/m × 20 m) = -60 tonnes
SF at 30 m foap = -60 t + (5 t/m × 10 m) = -10 tonnes
SF at 40 m foap (bulkhead 3/2 and amidships) = -60 t + (5 t/m × 20 m) = 40 tonnes
SF at 50 m foap = 40 t + (-1t/m × 10 m) = 30 tonnes
SF at 60 m foap (bulkhead 2/1) = 40 t + (-1 t/m × 20 m) = 20 tonnes
SF at 70 m foap = 20 t + (-1 t/m × 10 m) = 10 tonnes
SF at 80 m foap (FP) = 20 t + (-1 t/m × 20 m) = 0 tonnes

Figure 27.13 shows the shear force curve.

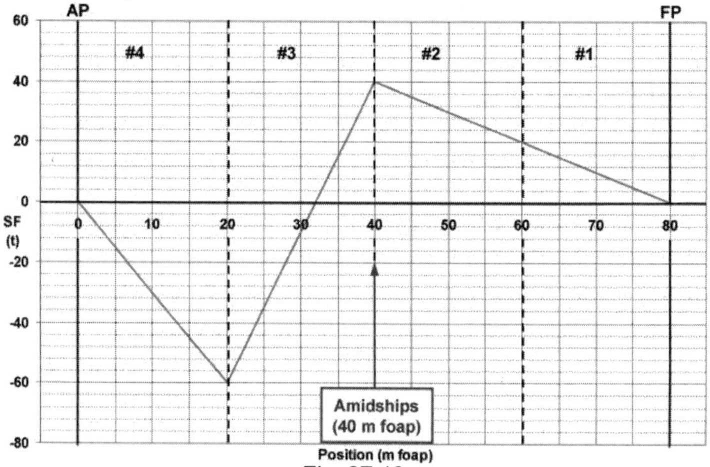

Fig. 27.13

It can be seen that the position of zero shear force lies in hold no. 3 and the value of the bending moment must be calculated for this position as it will be a maximum value. The position of this maximum value could be estimated from the shear force curve (about 32 m foap) but it is more accurate to calculate it by using the similar triangles created by the shear force values for the bulkhead positions 4/3 and 3/2 as shown in figure 27.14.

Let the position be 'x' metres from bulkhead 4/3 where the total hold length is 20 metres.

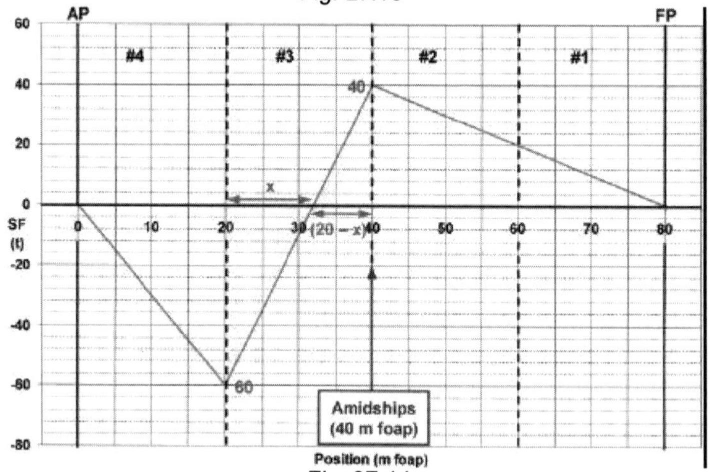

Fig. 27.14

In the similar triangles:

$\frac{x}{60} = \frac{(20 - x)}{40}$ *Therefore:* $40x = 60(20 - x)$

$\therefore \quad 40x = 1200 - 60x \quad \therefore \quad 40x + 60x = 1200$

$\therefore \quad 100x = 1200 \quad \therefore \quad x = 12$ *metres*

The position of zero shear force is at 32 m foap.

It is essential for examination purposes that this method be used to calculate this position.

Producing the bending moment curve
Calculate values at 10 metre intervals including that for 32 m foap using the procedure previously described.

BM at AP = 0 t-m
BM 10 m foap $= \frac{1}{2} \times 10\text{ m} \times -30\text{ t} = -150\text{ t-m}$
BM 20 m foap (Bulkhead 4/3) $= \frac{1}{2} \times 20\text{ m} \times -60\text{ t} = -600\text{ t-m}$
BM at 30 m foap = -600 t-m + Area trapezium 20 m to 30 m foap
$$= -600\text{ t-m} + \frac{(-60\text{ t} + -10\text{ t})}{2} \times 10\text{ m} = -950\text{ t-m}$$

BM at 32 m foap (zero SF) $= -600\text{ t-m} + (\frac{1}{2} \times 12\text{ m} \times -60\text{ t}) = -960\text{ t-m}$
BM at 40 m foap (Bulkhead 3/2) $= -960 + (\frac{1}{2} \times 8\text{ m} \times 40\text{ t}) = -800\text{ t-m}$
(Amidships)
BM at 50 m foap = -800 t-m + Area trapezium 40 m to 50 m foap
$$= -800\text{ t-m} + \frac{(40\text{ t} + 30\text{ t})}{2} \times 10\text{ m} = -450\text{ t-m}$$

BM at 60 m foap (Bulkhead 2/1) = -800 t-m + Area trapezium 40 m to 60 m foap
$$= -800\text{ t-m} + \frac{(40\text{ t} + 20\text{ t})}{2} \times 20\text{ m} = -200\text{ t-m}$$

BM at 70 m foap = -200 t-m + Area trapezium 60 m to 70 m foap
$$= -200\text{ t-m} + \frac{(20\text{ t} + 10\text{ t})}{2} \times 10\text{ m} = -100\text{ t-m}$$

BM at 80 m foap (FP) $= -200\text{ t-m} + (\frac{1}{2} \times 20\text{ m} \times 20\text{ t}) = 0\text{ t-m}$

Calculating these values is tedious and a large-scale graph of the shear force curve will make life a lot easier. Remember that it is just a matter of calculating the area to the *left* of the position in question each time.

The bending moment curve is shown in figure 27.15.

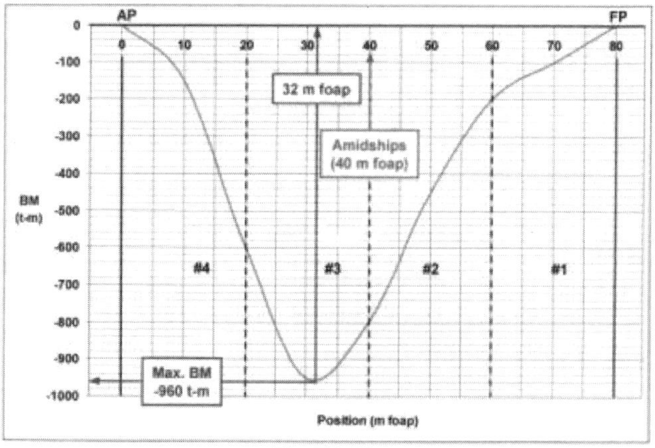

Fig.27.15

<u>*Summary*</u>
The maximum shear force values are as follows:

-60 tonnes at 20 m foap (in line with bulkhead 4/3), and;
40 tonnes at 40 m foap (in line with bulkhead 3/2)

The maximum bending moment value of –960 t-m occurs at 32 m foap, where the shear force value is zero.

27.3 SEA WAVE BENDING

So far only the causes of longitudinal bending in *still water* (or the *harbour condition*) have been discussed. A well-loaded ship subjected to minimal stress in still water will encounter cyclical longitudinal bending when encountering waves at sea. The extreme case scenario occurs at sea when the ship encounters waves where the wavelength is equal to the ship's length and either of the following occurs:

- the ship is caused to *sag* when the trough is amidships and the wave crests are at the ends, or;

- the ship is caused to *hog* when the wave crest is amidships and the troughs are at the ends.

Design staff will make assumptions about the wave profile to be encountered by the ship that will create the worst possible longitudinal bending moments.

Typical assumptions might be:

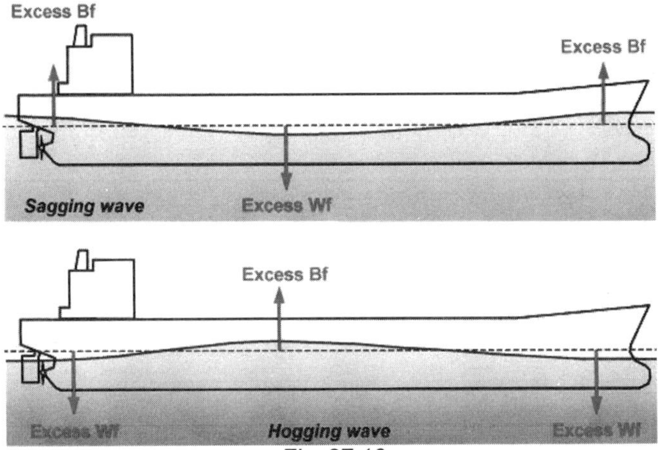

Fig. 27.16

(1) the wave is trochoidal in form.

(2) the wave length is equal to the ship's length between perpendiculars.

(3) the wave height is equivalent to that given by: $\mathbf{0.617\sqrt{L}}$ (metres) where L is the ship's LBP.

Unlike bending in still water, the bending due to waves alone will alternate in direction as the wave passes along the length of the ship. The absolute worst case scenarios assumed by loading programme manufacturers by necessity must be one of the following depending on how the ship is loaded at the time the loading programme is being used for stress calculations:

- an initially *sagged* ship in still water encountering a *'sagging wave'* at sea, or;

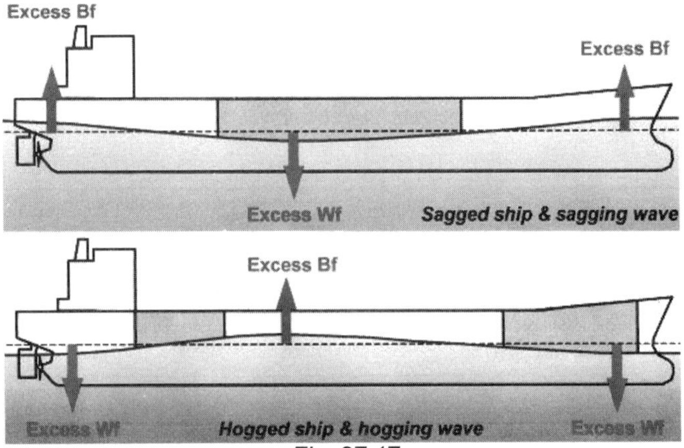

Fig. 27.17

- an initially *hogged* ship in still water encountering a *'hogging wave'* at sea.

27.4 STRESS LOADING PROGRAMME REPRESENTATIONS

27.4.1 Calculation conventions

When calculating the values of shear force and bending moments in the previous examples the convention followed was:

(1) The ship profile considered is always for the starboard side (this is the accepted convention for all ship's plans);

(2) Shear force and bending moment values where calculated starting from the after perpendicular (AP) working forward.

For the simple sagged and hogged conditions considered this gave shear force and bending moment curves as depicted in figure 27.18.

The convention used allows the condition of the ship, whether it be sagged or hogged, to be easily recognised. Quite often loading programme manufacturers might adopt this convention, however it is not crucial.

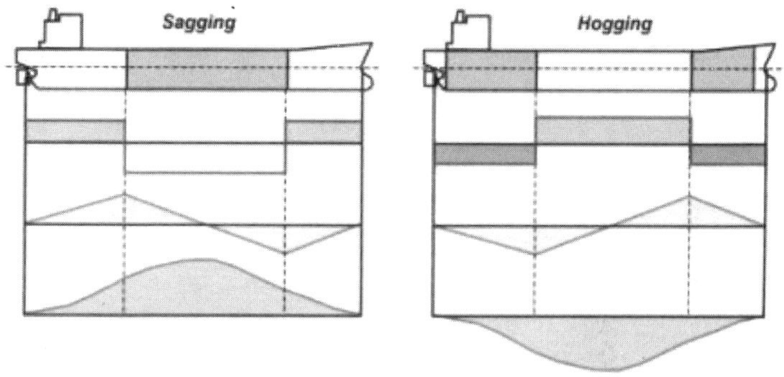

Fig. 27.18

Had the shear force and bending moment values been calculated from the forward perpendicular working aft, then the same values would have been obtained, but the signs would be reversed to give a 'mirror' image of the curves using the convention that we have adopted.

27.4.2 Stress calculating programs – system requirements and data representation

Generally, ships over 150 metres in length and other ships that are likely to be subjected to excessive longitudinal stresses must be provided with a loading calculator to allow the values of shearing forces and bending moments to be calculated for any condition of loading. This will usually be in the form of a computer programme that has been approved by the classification society whereby a Certificate of Approval will be issued. There are strict guidelines on the use and testing of such programmes and compliance with the appropriate classification society regulations regarding such programmes will be subject to verification during periodical classification society surveys.

The loading program should be capable of calculating the following hull girder shear forces and bending moments according to the appropriate classification society regulations:

(1) Still water shear forces.

(2) Still water bending moments.

(3) Still water torsion moments, where applicable (mostly a requirement for container ships).

(4) Sea-going condition shear forces.

(5) Sea-going condition bending moments.

(6) Sea-going condition torsion moments where applicable.

Although the actual values of shear forces (in tonnes) and bending moments (in tonnes-metres) for positions along the vessels length will be given these often have little relevance to the operator. It is the *visual representation* of the shear force and bending moment *curves* displayed along with the curves representing the *maximum permissible* values for both the harbour (still water) and sea-going conditions that will convey the true state of loading of the ship to the user.

A typical representation is illustrated in figure 27.19.

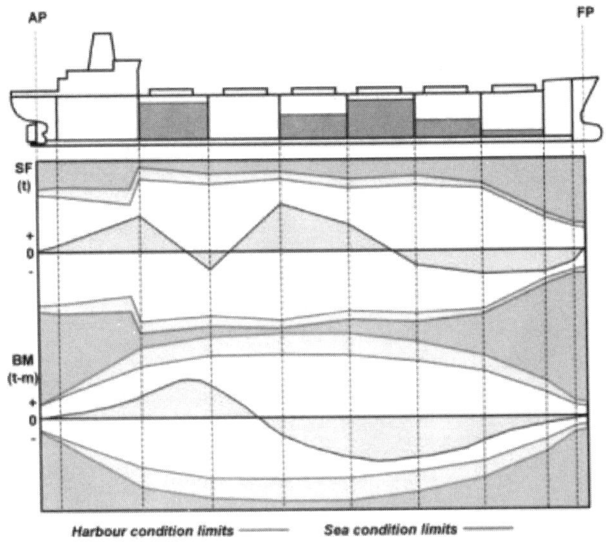

Fig. 27.19

This is a common form of representation adopted by many loading program manufacturers. It can be seen that the harbour (still water) limits are *higher* than those for when the ship is at sea. This allows more leeway when planning a loading schedule, whereby the program will be used to calculate the stress values at intermediate stages during loading in port. Provided that the shear force and bending moment curves do not extend into the red area then the ship will not suffer excessive stress *in harbour*. Once loading is complete it should be verified that the curves do not extend into the yellow area, representing the acceptable stress limits for when the ship is at sea. The limit settings will be determined by the classification society that will be such that they are at some acceptable percentage of absolute maximum that the structure can withstand, perhaps 80% say. It should be noted that as the ship ages and the effects of corrosion start to take effect to weaken the structure, the maximum permissible shear forces and bending moments can be expected to reduce and this will require the program data to be modified to reflect this.

It will also be noted that a ship may experience both sagging and hogging at the same time in different parts in the length. This is particularly true at intermediate stages in a loading procedure and when alternate hold loading is required in the case of dense bulk cargoes. A typical fully loaded general cargo ship will invariably be sagged, whereby the aft and fore peak tanks will be empty (along with the excess of buoyancy force that will occur in the vicinity of the engine room) and cargo is in holds extending forward and aft of the amidships region.

Finally, most loading programs include the ability to calculate the ship's stability also. However, it must be emphasised that the program must be classification society approved, and if provided it must be periodically checked by manual calculations. Testing procedures will be stipulated and must be followed. Obviously, any program will only be effective if the person using it inputs the correct data!

SECTION 28 – PRACTICAL SHIP LOADING PROBLEMS

INTRODUCTION

The purpose of this section is to bring together all that has been studied in the previous sections and to complete a full ship loading problem using the stability data book for *M.V. Almar.* Ideally the PC on which this programme is run should be connected to a printer as it will be necessary to print copies of the worksheets provided in this section for practice purposes.

Before starting this section the learner should be familiar with the content of the stability data book for *M.V. Almar*.

Learning Objectives

On completion of this section the learner will achieve the following:

1. Perform a full ship load calculation in order to determine:
   - final displacement;
   - final fluid KG;
   - final fluid GM;
   - final draughts;
   - GZ values for the loaded condition;
   - compliance with minimum intact stability criteria (IMO).
   - that the ship is not overloaded with respect to the permissible seasonal freeboard.

28.1 INTRODUCTION TO LOADING SHEET DATA

The way in which information is presented for a ship's loading calculation depends on the preferences of the person doing the calculation and the needs of a particular shipping company, since they will probably want duplicate copies of all calculations made with respect to the loaded condition of the ship.

For the purpose of this program there are three worksheets to be completed in a full ship load problem.

1. Hold cargo information;
2. Tank sounding sheet;
3. Loading sheet.

Let us consider each worksheet.

28.1.1 Hold cargo information sheet

This details the cargo that is loaded in the holds. Since *M.V. Almar* is a bulk carrier the following format has been adopted.

HOLD CARGO

HOLD	Ullage (m)	Volume (Cu. mtrs)	SF (Cu. mtrs/t)	Weight (t)	VCG (m)
1					
2					
3					
4					
5					
6					

When loading a bulk cargo efforts should be made to trim the cargo as level as possible.

In order to calculate the weight of cargo loaded the Stowage Factor (SF) must be known.

Stowage Factor may be defined as being *the volume occupied by 1 tonne of cargo.*

The weight of cargo in a hold is found by the formula:

$$\textbf{Weight (t)} = \frac{\textbf{Volume (m}^3\textbf{)}}{\textbf{SF (m}^3\textbf{/t)}}$$

Thus; if No. 4 Hold was filled to an ullage of 7.00 m with a bulk cargo having a stowage factor of 1.324 m^3/t, the weight of cargo in the hold is found by:

$$\text{Weight} = \frac{\text{Volume}}{\text{SF}}; \qquad \text{Weight} = \frac{3250}{1.324} = \textbf{\textit{2455 tonnes}}$$

The volume of cargo was taken from the data sheet for *Cargo Hold No. 4.*

The value for stowage factor will be given in the cargo documentation at the port of loading.

28.1.2 Tank sounding sheet

This details the tank status for the condition of loading. For *M.V. Almar* the following format has been adopted.

TANK SOUNDING SHEET

TANK	Sounding (cms)	Tabulated weight (t)	RD	Actual weight (t)	LCG (m foap)	VCG (m)	Tabulated FSM's (tm)	Assumed RD	Actual FSM's (tm)
HEAVY OIL									
Deep wing tank No. 7P								1.000	
Deep wing tank No. 7S								1.000	
Service tank P (Heavy oil)								1.000	
DB tank No. 1P								1.025	
DB tank No. 1S								1.025	
DB tank No. 2C								1.025	
DB tank No. 3C								1.025	
DB tank No. 4C								1.025	
DB tank No. 5C								1.025	
LIGHT OIL									
DB tank No. 7P								1.000	
DB tank No. 7S								1.000	
Service tank P (Light oil)								1.000	
FRESH WATER									
Tween deck tank aft P								1.000	
Tween deck tank aft S								1.000	
Stern tank								1.000	
DB tank No. 8								1.000	
Aft peak tank (FW)								1.000	
BALLAST WATER									
Fore peak tank								1.025	
No. 1 Top wing tank P								1.025	
No. 1 Top wing tank S								1.025	
No. 2 Top wing tank P								1.025	
No.2 Top wing tank S								1.025	
No. 3+4 Top wing tank P								1.025	
No. 3+4 Top wing tank S								1.025	
No. 5 Top wing tank P								1.025	
No. 5 Top wing tank S								1.025	
No. 6 Top wing tank P								1.025	
No. 6 Top wing tank S								1.025	
Upper cross tank								1.025	
Lower cross tank								1.025	
DB tank No. 2P								1.025	
DB tank No. 2S								1.025	
DB tank No. 3P								1.025	
DB tank No. 3S								1.025	
DB tank No. 4P								1.025	
DB tank No. 4S								1.025	
DB tank No. 5P								1.025	
DB tank No. 5S								1.025	
DB tank No. 6P								1.025	
DB tank No. 6S								1.025	
DB tank No. 6C								1.025	
DB tank No. 1P								1.025	
DB tank No. 1S								1.025	
DB tank No. 2C								1.025	
DB tank No. 3C								1.025	
DB tank No. 4C								1.025	
DB tank No. 5C								1.025	
Aft peak tank (SW)								1.000	

The contents of each column are as follows;

TANK
Indicates the tank space for which the row of figures applies to.

Sounding (cms)
Gives the sounding of the tank contents (in centimetres) as actually dipped and/or anticipated for the condition of loading under consideration.

Tabulated weight (t)
Is the weight of the liquid in the tank *as tabulated for the density assumed by the tank sounding table.* See bottom of tank sounding table for the density assumed or the value in the *'Assumed RD'* column.

RD
Is the *actual Relative Density* of the liquid in the tank as observed by hydrometer reading or, in the case of fuel oil, documentation received when bunkering. For salt water ballast the relative density may be assumed as being 1.025.

Actual weight (t)
Is the *actual weight of the liquid in the tank,* whereby the weight as tabulated in the tank sounding table has been corrected for the *actual RD of the liquid.*

LCG (m foap)
Is the tabulated longitudinal centre of gravity (LCG) of the volume of the liquid in the tank expressed in metres forward of the aft perpendicular (foap) for the appropriate tank sounding.

VCG (m)
Is the tabulated Kg of the liquid in the tank expressed in metres for the appropriate tank sounding.

Tabulated FSM's
Are the free surface moments in tonnes-metres of the liquid surface in the tank *as tabulated for the density assumed by the tank sounding table.* See bottom of tank sounding table for the density assumed or the value in the *'Assumed RD'* column.

Assumed RD
Is the relative density assumed by the tank sounding table.

Actual FSM's
Are the free surface moments in tonnes-metres of the liquid surface in the tank *having been corrected for the actual RD of the liquid.*

28.1.3 Loading sheet

This tabulated loading sheet is used to calculate the final solid and fluid KG and final LCG (by moments) to allow the GZ values and final trim to be calculated.

The lightship data has already been included on the sheet and is as follows:

Light Displacement	*6675 t*
Lightship VCG (KG)	*9.000 m*
Lightship vertical moments	*60075 t-m*
Lightship LCG foap	*70.500 m*
Lightship longitudinal moments about AP	*470588 t-m*
LBP	*167.87 m*

LOADING SHEET

ITEMS OF DEADWEIGHT	WEIGHT t	VCG m	V.MOMENTS tm	LCG m	L.MOMENTS tm	FSM's tm
Deep wing tank No. 7P						
Deep wing tank No. 7S						
Service tank P (Heavy oil)						
DB tank No. 1P						
DB tank No. 1S						
DB tank No. 2C						
DB tank No. 3C						
DB tank No. 4C						
DB tank No. 5C						
TOTAL HEAVY OIL						
DB tank No. 7P						
DB tank No. 7S						
Service tank P (Light oil)						
TOTAL LIGHT OIL						
Tween deck tank aft P						
Tween deck tank aft S						
Stern tank						
DB tank No. 8						
Aft peak tank (FW)						
TOTAL FRESH WATER						
Fore peak tank						
No. 1 Top wing tank P						
No. 1 Top wing tank S						
No. 2 Top wing tank P						
No.2 Top wing tank S						
No. 3+4 Top wing tank P						
No. 3+4 Top wing tank S						
No. 5 Top wing tank P						
No. 5 Top wing tank S						
No. 6 Top wing tank P						
No. 6 Top wing tank S						
Upper cross tank						
Lower cross tank						
DB tank No. 2P						
DB tank No. 2S						
DB tank No. 3P						
DB tank No. 3S						
DB tank No. 4P						
DB tank No. 4S						
DB tank No. 5P						
DB tank No. 5S						
DB tank No. 6P						
DB tank No. 6S						
DB tank No. 6C						
DB tank No. 1P						
DB tank No. 1S						
DB tank No. 2C						
DB tank No. 3C						
DB tank No. 4C						
DB tank No. 5C						
Aft peak tank (SW)						
TOTAL BALLAST WATER						
STORES AND CREW						
Hold No. 1						
Hold No. 2						
Hold No. 3						
Hold No. 4						
Hold No. 5						
Hold No. 6						
Cargo on deck						
Water absorbtion						
TOTAL CARGO						
TOTAL DEADWEIGHT						**TOTAL FSM's**
LIGHT SHIP	6675	9.000	60075	70.500	470588	
DISPLACEMENT						

28.2 PRACTICAL SHIP LOAD PROBLEMS

Using the data sheets previously detailed two examples of typical ship load problems are demonstrated. Simply follow the procedure.

Example 1

M.V. Almar loads bulk cargo in all holds as detailed in the cargo hold information shown.

HOLD CARGO

HOLD	Ullage (m)	Volume (Cu. mtrs)	SF (Cu. mtrs/t)	Weight (t)	VCG (m)
1	0.0		1.253		
2	8.0		1.253		
3	0.0		1.253		
4	0.0		1.253		
5	0.0		1.253		
6	0.0		1.253		

The soundings of all tanks for the proposed sailing condition are as indicated in the Tank Sounding Sheet.

Stores and crew shall be assumed to be: 125 t VCG 14.500 m LCG 45.000 m foap

PART 1

By completion of the Loading Sheet calculate:

(a) *the final displacement;*

(b) *the final solid KG;*

(c) *the final fluid KG and GM;*

(d) *the sailing draughts in salt water (RD 1.025).*

PART 2

(e) *By constructing the curve of statical stability for the loaded condition, verify that the ship complies with the minimum IMO intact stability criteria.*

(f) *Does the ship have adequate freeboard for the Summer Zone?*

EXAMPLE 1 *TANK SOUNDING SHEET*

TANK	Sounding (cms)	Tabulated weight (t)	RD	Actual weight (t)	LCG (m foap)	VCG (m)	Tabulated FSM's (tm)	Assumed RD	Actual FSM's (tm)
HEAVY OIL									
Deep wing tank No. 7P	1080		0.990					1.000	
Deep wing tank No. 7S	900		0.990					1.000	
Service tank P (Heavy oil)	320		0.990					1.000	
DB tank No. 1P	140		0.990					1.025	
DB tank No. 1S	140		0.990					1.025	
DB tank No. 2C	140		0.990					1.025	
DB tank No. 3C	140		0.990					1.025	
DB tank No. 4C	135		0.990					1.025	
DB tank No. 5C	140		0.990					1.025	
LIGHT OIL									
DB tank No. 7P	135		0.850					1.000	
DB tank No. 7S	135		0.850					1.000	
Service tank P (Light oil)	340		0.850					1.000	
FRESH WATER									
Tween deck tank aft P	FULL		1.000					1.000	
Tween deck tank aft S	FULL		1.000					1.000	
Stern tank	FULL		1.000					1.000	
DB tank No. 8	FULL		1.000					1.000	
Aft peak tank (FW)								1.000	
BALLAST WATER									
Fore peak tank								1.025	
No. 1 Top wing tank P								1.025	
No. 1 Top wing tank S								1.025	
No. 2 Top wing tank P								1.025	
No.2 Top wing tank S								1.025	
No. 3+4 Top wing tank P								1.025	
No. 3+4 Top wing tank S								1.025	
No. 5 Top wing tank P								1.025	
No. 5 Top wing tank S								1.025	
No. 6 Top wing tank P								1.025	
No. 6 Top wing tank S								1.025	
Upper cross tank								1.025	
Lower cross tank								1.025	
DB tank No. 2P								1.025	
DB tank No. 2S								1.025	
DB tank No. 3P								1.025	
DB tank No. 3S								1.025	
DB tank No. 4P								1.025	
DB tank No. 4S								1.025	
DB tank No. 5P								1.025	
DB tank No. 5S								1.025	
DB tank No. 6P								1.025	
DB tank No. 6S								1.025	
DB tank No. 6C								1.025	
DB tank No. 1P								1.025	
DB tank No. 1S								1.025	
DB tank No. 2C								1.025	
DB tank No. 3C								1.025	
DB tank No. 4C								1.025	
DB tank No. 5C								1.025	
Aft peak tank (SW)	210		1.025					1.000	

Solution (PART 1)

Complete the *Hold Cargo* data sheet by obtaining the values of volume and then calculating the actual weight in each hold. Enter also the VCG values for transfer to the loading sheet later.

HOLD	Ullage (m)	Volume (Cu. mtrs)	SF (Cu. mtrs/t)	Weight (t)	VCG (m)
1	0.0	5010	1.253	3998	8.220
2	8.0	3070	1.253	2450	4.880
3	0.0	5350	1.253	4270	7.650
4	0.0	5000	1.253	3990	7.650
5	0.0	4840	1.253	3863	7.650
6	0.0	5680	1.253	4533	7.740

Note that if the ullage in a hold is 0.0 m then the hold is full!

Complete the *Tank Sounding* sheet. Consider the data given for *DB tank No. 1P* as an example (Page 45).

We are given the sounding of 140 cms and RD of the fuel oil in the tank as being 0.990.
Enter sounding tables with sounding of 140 cms.
Weight 226.7 t LCG 144.48 m foap VCG 0.736 m
FSM's 965 t-m.

The values of weight and FSM's are for an assumed density of 1.025. These must be adjusted for the actual RD of the fuel oil which is 0.990.

Actual weight $= 226.7 \times \dfrac{0.990}{1.025} = 219.0$ *tonnes*

Actual FSM's $= 965 \times \dfrac{0.990}{1.025} = 932$ *t-m*

The following values are entered into the sheet:

Actual weight 219.0 tonnes;
LCG 144.48 m;
VCG 0.736 m;
Actual FSM's 932 t-m.

The same is done for all the tanks that have soundings tabulated. The completed sheet is as shown.

EXAMPLE 1 ***TANK SOUNDING SHEET***

TANK	Sounding (cms)	Tabulated weight (t)	RD	Actual weight (t)	LCG (m foap)	VCG (m)	Tabulated FSM's (tm)	Assumed RD	Actual FSM's (tm)
HEAVY OIL									
Deep wing tank No. 7P	1080	194.4	0.990	192.5	28.220	6.902	6.0	1.000	5.9
Deep wing tank No. 7S	900	239.4	0.990	237.0	28.220	8.950	76.0	1.000	75.2
Service tank P (Heavy oil)	320	12.2	0.990	12.1	26.300	10.692	1.0	1.000	1.0
DB tank No. 1P	140	226.7	0.990	219.0	144.480	0.736	965.0	1.025	932.0
DB tank No. 1S	140	226.7	0.990	219.0	144.480	0.736	965.0	1.025	932.0
DB tank No. 2C	140	285.3	0.990	275.6	124.280	0.736	1163.0	1.025	1123.3
DB tank No. 3C	140	297.2	0.990	287.1	103.960	0.736	1232.0	1.025	1189.9
DB tank No. 4C	135	252.2	0.990	243.6	84.340	0.711	1850.0	1.025	1786.8
DB tank No. 5C	140	321.0	0.990	310.0	63.880	0.736	1116.0	1.025	1077.9
LIGHT OIL									
DB tank No. 7P	135	103.6	0.850	88.1	23.290	0.711	144.0	1.000	122.4
DB tank No. 7S	135	103.6	0.850	88.1	23.290	0.711	144.0	1.000	122.4
Service tank P (Light oil)	340	23.8	0.850	20.2	29.100	10.795	48.0	1.000	40.8
FRESH WATER									
Tween deck tank aft P	FULL	108.0	1.000	108.0	6.440	12.580	0.0	1.000	0.0
Tween deck tank aft S	FULL	108.0	1.000	108.0	6.440	12.580	0.0	1.000	0.0
Stern tank	FULL	90.0	1.000	90.0	-0.440	9.860	0.0	1.000	0.0
DB tank No. 8	FULL	38.9	1.000	38.9	9.850	1.390	0.0	1.000	0.0
Aft peak tank (FW)								1.000	
BALLAST WATER									
Fore peak tank								1.025	
No. 1 Top wing tank P								1.025	
No. 1 Top wing tank S								1.025	
No. 2 Top wing tank P								1.025	
No.2 Top wing tank S								1.025	
No. 3+4 Top wing tank P								1.025	
No. 3+4 Top wing tank S								1.025	
No. 5 Top wing tank P								1.025	
No. 5 Top wing tank S								1.025	
No. 6 Top wing tank P								1.025	
No. 6 Top wing tank S								1.025	
Upper cross tank								1.025	
Lower cross tank								1.025	
DB tank No. 2P								1.025	
DB tank No. 2S								1.025	
DB tank No. 3P								1.025	
DB tank No. 3S								1.025	
DB tank No. 4P								1.025	
DB tank No. 4S								1.025	
DB tank No. 5P								1.025	
DB tank No. 5S								1.025	
DB tank No. 6P								1.025	
DB tank No. 6S								1.025	
DB tank No. 6C								1.025	
DB tank No. 1P								1.025	
DB tank No. 1S								1.025	
DB tank No. 2C								1.025	
DB tank No. 3C								1.025	
DB tank No. 4C								1.025	
DB tank No. 5C								1.025	
Aft peak tank (SW)	210	15.5	1.025	15.9	4.860	1.613	30.0	1.000	30.8

All the weights that are in the *Hold Cargo* sheet and the completed *Tank Sounding data sheet* may now be transferred onto the *loading sheet*. The vertical and longitudinal moments are then calculated and summed to allow calculation of the final *solid KG* and *LCG*.

To make the calculation a little easier sub-totals of various items such as Total Heavy Oil, Total Light Oil etc. are used to break the calculation up into manageable parts.

The Light ship figures are included as the last weight.

The completed loading sheet is as follows.

(Note that weights and moments values are expressed as whole numbers, any errors as a result of rounding the figures up will be negligible.)

Example 1 **LOADING SHEET**

ITEMS OF DEADWEIGHT	WEIGHT t	VCG m	V.MOMENTS tm	LCG m	L.MOMENTS tm	FSM's tm
Deep wing tank No. 7P	193	6.902	1332	28.220	5446	6
Deep wing tank No. 7S	237	8.950	2121	28.220	6688	75
Service tank P (Heavy oil)	12	10.692	128	26.300	316	1
DB tank No. 1P	219	0.736	161	144.480	31641	932
DB tank No. 1S	219	0.736	161	144.480	31641	932
DB tank No. 2C	276	0.736	203	124.280	34301	1123
DB tank No. 3C	287	0.736	211	103.960	29837	1190
DB tank No. 4C	244	0.711	173	84.340	20579	1787
DB tank No. 5C	310	0.736	228	63.880	19803	1078
TOTAL HEAVY OIL	**1997**		**4720**		**180252**	**7124**
DB tank No. 7P	88	0.711	63	23.290	2050	122
DB tank No. 7S	88	0.711	63	23.290	2050	122
Service tank P (Light oil)	20	10.795	216	29.100	582	41
TOTAL LIGHT OIL	**196**		**341**		**4681**	**285**
Tween deck tank aft P	108	12.580	1359	6.440	696	0
Tween deck tank aft S	108	12.580	1359	6.440	696	0
Stern tank	90	9.860	887	-0.440	-40	0
DB tank No. 8	39	1.390	54	9.850	384	0
Aft peak tank (FW)						0
TOTAL FRESH WATER	**345**		**3659**		**1736**	**0**
Fore peak tank						
No. 1 Top wing tank P						
No. 1 Top wing tank S						
No. 2 Top wing tank P						
No.2 Top wing tank S						
No. 3+4 Top wing tank P						
No. 3+4 Top wing tank S						
No. 5 Top wing tank P						
No. 5 Top wing tank S						
No. 6 Top wing tank P						
No. 6 Top wing tank S						
Upper cross tank						
Lower cross tank						
DB tank No. 2P						
DB tank No. 2S						
DB tank No. 3P						
DB tank No. 3S						
DB tank No. 4P						
DB tank No. 4S						
DB tank No. 5P						
DB tank No. 5S						
DB tank No. 6P						
DB tank No. 6S						
DB tank No. 6C						
DB tank No. 1P						
DB tank No. 1S						
DB tank No. 2C						
DB tank No. 3C						
DB tank No. 4C						
DB tank No. 5C						
Aft peak tank (SW)	16	1.613	26	4.860	78	31
TOTAL BALLAST WATER	**16**		**26**		**78**	**31**
STORES AND CREW	**125**	**14.50**	**1813**	**45.000**	**5625**	
Hold No. 1	3998	8.220	32864	144.94	579470	
Hold No. 2	2450	4.880	11956	124.38	304731	
Hold No. 3	4270	7.650	32666	103.94	443824	
Hold No. 4	3990	7.650	30524	84.46	336995	
Hold No. 5	3863	7.650	29552	62.05	239699	
Hold No. 6	4533	7.740	35085	42.31	191791	
Cargo on deck						
Water absorbtion						
TOTAL CARGO	**23104**		**172646**		**2096511**	**0.0**
TOTAL DEADWEIGHT	**25783**		**183204**		**2288882**	**TOTAL**
LIGHT SHIP	**6675**	**9.000**	**60075**	**70.500**	**470588**	**FSM's**
DISPLACEMENT	**32458**	**7.495**	**243279**	**85.017**	**2759470**	**7440**

From the loading sheet the results are:

(a) *Final Displacement **32458 tonnes***

(b) *Final solid **KG 7.495 m***

To calculate the fluid KG and GM

Entering the hydrostatic particulars with a displacement of 32458 tonnes gives a value for KM = 9.488 m

$$\text{Correction to GM for FSE (m)} = \frac{\text{Total FSM's (t-m)}}{\text{Displacement (t)}}$$

$$\text{Correction to GM for FSE (m)} = \frac{7440}{32458} = 0.229 \text{ m}$$

KM	9.488
KG SOLID	7.495
GM SOLID	1.993
FS CORR'N	0.229
GM FLUID	**1.764**

(c) To calculate the sailing draughts

Enter data with final displacement and obtain TMD, MCTC, LCB and LCF positions.

$$\text{Final TMD} = 10.10 + \left(0.1 \times \frac{318}{350}\right) = 10.191 \text{ m}$$

$$\text{MCTC} = 409 + \left(2 \times \frac{318}{350}\right) = 411 \text{ t-m}$$

$$\text{LCB} = 85.86 + \left(-0.04 \times \frac{318}{350}\right) = 85.82 \text{ m foap}$$

$$\text{LCF} = 82.41 + \left(-0.09 \times \frac{318}{350}\right) = 82.33 \text{ m foap}$$

Calculate the change of trim from even keel for the final condition.

Final LCG = 85.017 m; use 85.02 since LCB is only tabulated to two decimal places.

$$COT_{\text{FROM EVEN KEEL}} = \frac{W \times (LCB \sim LCG)}{MCTC}$$

$$COT_{\text{FROM EVEN KEEL}} = \frac{32458 \times (85.82 - 85.02)}{411} = 63.2 \text{ cms}$$

A simple sketch will indicate whether the COT is by the head or by the stern.

Apportion the change of trim from even keel to the forward and aft draughts, applying Ta and Tf to the final even keel draught (TMD).

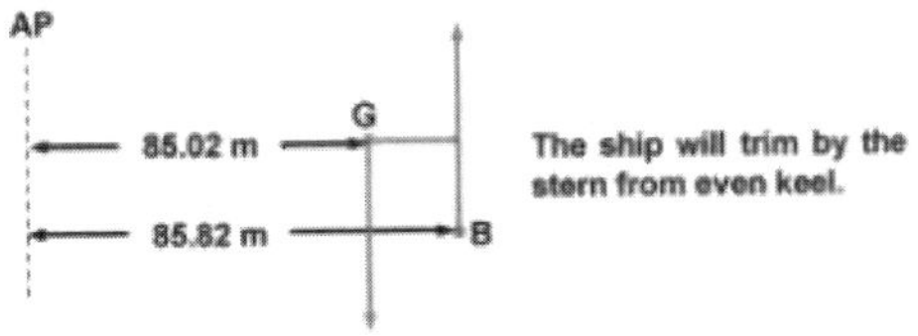

Fig.28.1

$$Ta = COT \times \frac{a}{LBP} = 63.2 \times \frac{82.33}{167.87} = 31.0 \text{ cms} = 0.310 \text{ m}$$

$$Tf = COT - Ta \quad Tf = 63.2 - 31.0 = 32.2 \text{ cms} = 0.322 \text{ m}$$

	Fwd	Aft
Final TMD	10.191	10.191
Trim (by stern)	0.322	0.310
Final draughts	**9.869**	**10.501**

Apply Ta and Tf to the final TMD to obtain final draughts.

Solution (PART II)

KG SOLID	7.495
FS CORR'N	0.229
KG FLUID	**7.724**

Heel	**10**	**20**	**30**	**40**	**60**	**80**
KN	1.66	3.35	4.78	6.03	7.66	8.00
KG*Sin Heel	1.34	2.64	3.86	4.96	6.69	7.61
GZ	**0.32**	**0.71**	**0.92**	**1.07**	**0.97**	**0.39**

Using KN values calculate the values of GZ for the loaded condition (interpolation for KN values not shown)

Plot the curve of statical stability.

Using Simpson's Rules calculate the areas under the curve.

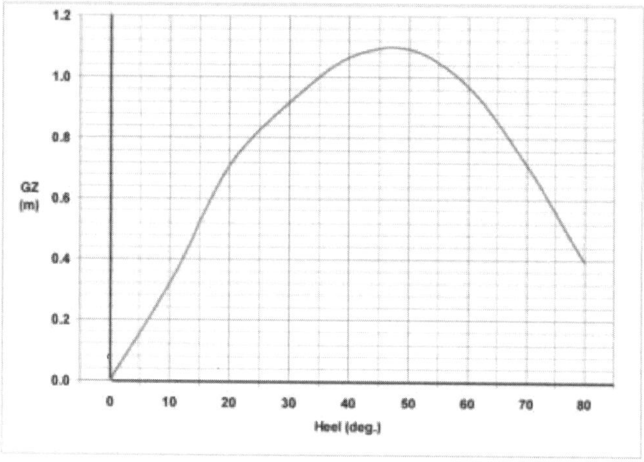

Fig. 28.2

Area 0° to 30°

Heel	GZ	SM	Area Fn.
0	0.00	1	0.00
10	0.32	3	0.96
20	0.71	3	2.13
30	0.92	1	0.92
		SUM	**4.01**

$$Area = \frac{3}{8} \times \frac{10}{57.3} \times 4.01$$

Area = 0.262 m-r

Area 0° to 40°

Heel	GZ	SM	Area Fn.
0	0.00	1	0.00
10	0.32	4	1.28
20	0.71	2	1.42
30	0.92	4	3.68
40	1.07	1	1.07
		SUM	**7.45**

$$Area = \frac{1}{3} \times \frac{10}{57.3} \times 7.45$$

Area = 0.433 m-r

Area 30° to 40°

Take the difference between the two areas calculated.
Area = 0.433 – 0.262 = ***0.171 m-r***

Consideration of the GZ curve and the calculated areas gives the following answer:

	IMO Criteria (Minimum)	**Actual**	**Complies**
GM	Not less than 0.15 m	**1.764**	**YES**
Area 0 to 30	Not less than 0.055 m-r	**0.262**	**YES**
Area 0 to 40 (X)	Not less than 0.09 m-r	**0.433**	**YES**
Area 30-40 (X)	Not less than 0.03 m-r	**0.171**	**YES**
Max GZ	At least 0.2 m	**1.10**	**YES**
Heel max GZ	At least 30 deg.	**47 deg.**	**YES**

The ship complies with all the criteria.
Final true mean draught = 10.191 m
Summer Load Draught = 10.200 m

Therefore the ship has adequate freeboard for the Summer Zone.

Note Because the ship is close to the maximum draught for the Summer Zone the draughts should be carefully monitored near completion of cargo to ensure that the ship does not complete overloaded.

It should be noted that the draughts on completion of loading *as observed* will invariably differ from those *calculated*. There will always be some weights on board that have not been accounted for. If the observed and calculated draughts are significantly different then it is possible to calculate a *constant*. A constant is a correction defined in terms of a single weight and LCG position that will account for any errors for weights not included and may be included on the loading sheet. Because the lightship data changes as the ship increases in age it follows that the constant will have to be recalculated every so often.

Example 2

M.V. Almar loads a cargo of timber (SF 1.67 m^3/t) in the holds and on deck as detailed below. The ship is not assigned timber freeboards and the limiting draught is that which corresponds to the Summer zone. An allowance of 15% of the weight of timber on deck is to be allowed for water absorption.

Quantity of timber on deck is 4020 tonnes, Kg 16.660 m and Lcg 89.13 m foap.

HOLD CARGO

HOLD	Ullage (m)	Volume (Cu. mtrs)	SF (Cu. mtrs/t)	Weight (t)	VCG (m)
1	0.0		1.67		
2	0.0		1.67		
3	0.0		1.67		
4	0.0		1.67		
5	0.0		1.67		
6	0.0		1.67		

The soundings of all tanks for the proposed sailing condition are as indicated in the Tank Sounding Sheet.

Stores and crew shall be assumed to be:
125 t   VCG 14.500 m   LCG 45.000 m foap

PART 1

By completion of the Loading Sheet calculate:

(a) the final displacement;
(b) the final solid KG;
(c) the final fluid KG and GM;
(d) the sailing draughts in salt water (RD 1.025).

PART 2

(e) By constructing the curve of statical stability for the loaded condition, verify that the ship complies with the minimum IMO intact stability criteria.
(f) Does the ship have adequate freeboard for the Summer Zone?

EXAMPLE 2 *TANK SOUNDING SHEET*

TANK	Sounding (cms)	Tabulated weight (t)	RD	Actual weight (t)	LCG (m foap)	VCG (m)	Tabulated FSM's (tm)	Assumed RD	Actual FSM's (tm)
HEAVY OIL									
Deep wing tank No. 7P	840		0.970					1.000	
Deep wing tank No. 7S	600		0.970					1.000	
Service tank P (Heavy oil)	340		0.970					1.000	
DB tank No. 1P								1.025	
DB tank No. 1S								1.025	
DB tank No. 2C								1.025	
DB tank No. 3C								1.025	
DB tank No. 4C								1.025	
DB tank No. 5C	85		0.970					1.025	
LIGHT OIL									
DB tank No. 7P	40		0.850					1.000	
DB tank No. 7S	40		0.850					1.000	
Service tank P (Light oil)	320		0.850					1.000	
FRESH WATER									
Tween deck tank aft P	160		1.000					1.000	
Tween deck tank aft S	160		1.000					1.000	
Stern tank								1.000	
DB tank No. 8	135		1.000					1.000	
Aft peak tank (FW)								1.000	
BALLAST WATER									
Fore peak tank								1.025	
No. 1 Top wing tank P								1.025	
No. 1 Top wing tank S								1.025	
No. 2 Top wing tank P								1.025	
No.2 Top wing tank S								1.025	
No. 3+4 Top wing tank P								1.025	
No. 3+4 Top wing tank S								1.025	
No. 5 Top wing tank P								1.025	
No. 5 Top wing tank S								1.025	
No. 6 Top wing tank P								1.025	
No. 6 Top wing tank S								1.025	
Upper cross tank								1.025	
Lower cross tank								1.025	
DB tank No. 2P	310		1.025					1.025	
DB tank No. 2S	310		1.025					1.025	
DB tank No. 3P								1.025	
DB tank No. 3S								1.025	
DB tank No. 4P								1.025	
DB tank No. 4S								1.025	
DB tank No. 5P								1.025	
DB tank No. 5S								1.025	
DB tank No. 6P	FULL		1.025					1.025	
DB tank No. 6S	FULL		1.025					1.025	
DB tank No. 6C								1.025	
DB tank No. 1P								1.025	
DB tank No. 1S								1.025	
DB tank No. 2C								1.025	
DB tank No. 3C								1.025	
DB tank No. 4C								1.025	
DB tank No. 5C	100		1.025					1.025	
Aft peak tank (SW)	FULL		1.025					1.000	

Solution (PART 1)

Complete the *Hold Cargo* data sheet by obtaining the values of volume and then calculating the actual weight of timber in each hold. Enter also the VCG values for transfer to the loading sheet later. Also calculate the 15% allowance for the timber cargo on deck.

Timber on deck = 4020 tonnes, Kg 16.660 m and Lcg 89.13 m foap

Allowance for water absorption = $\frac{4020}{100} \times 15 = 603$ *t*

HOLD CARGO

HOLD	Ullage (m)	Volume (Cu. mtrs)	SF (Cu. mtrs/t)	Weight (t)	VCG (m)
1	0.0	5010	1.67	3000	8.220
2	0.0	5460	1.67	3269	7.650
3	0.0	5350	1.67	3204	7.650
4	0.0	5000	1.67	2994	7.650
5	0.0	4840	1.67	2898	7.650
6	0.0	5680	1.67	3401	7.740

Complete the *Tank Sounding* sheet.

EXAMPLE 2 ***TANK SOUNDING SHEET***

TANK	Sounding (cms)	Tabulated weight (t)	RD	Actual weight (t)	LCG (m foap)	VCG (m)	Tabulated FSM's (tm)	Assumed RD	Actual FSM's (tm)
HEAVY OIL									
Deep wing tank No. 7P	840	151.2	0.970	146.7	28.220	5.710	6.0	1.000	5.8
Deep wing tank No. 7S	600	159.6	0.970	154.8	28.220	6.920	76.0	1.000	73.7
Service tank P (Heavy oil)	340	12.9	0.970	12.5	26.300	10.795	1.0	1.000	1.0
DB tank No. 1P								1.025	
DB tank No. 1S								1.025	
DB tank No. 2C								1.025	
DB tank No. 3C								1.025	
DB tank No. 4C								1.025	
DB tank No. 5C	85	194.9	0.970	184.4	63.880	0.461	2270.0	1.025	2148.2
LIGHT OIL									
DB tank No. 7P	40	28.8	0.850	24.5	23.290	0.236	100.0	1.000	85.0
DB tank No. 7S	40	28.8	0.850	24.5	23.290	0.236	100.0	1.000	85.0
Service tank P (Light oil)	320	22.4	0.850	19.0	29.100	10.692	48.0	1.000	40.8
FRESH WATER									
Tween deck tank aft P	160	57.6	1.000	57.6	6.440	11.880	120.0	1.000	120.0
Tween deck tank aft S	160	57.6	1.000	57.6	6.440	11.880	120.0	1.000	120.0
Stern tank								1.000	
DB tank No. 8	135	18.9	1.000	18.9	9.850	0.694	49.0	1.000	49.0
Aft peak tank (FW)								1.000	
BALLAST WATER									
Fore peak tank								1.025	
No. 1 Top wing tank P								1.025	
No. 1 Top wing tank S								1.025	
No. 2 Top wing tank P								1.025	
No.2 Top wing tank S								1.025	
No. 3+4 Top wing tank P								1.025	
No. 3+4 Top wing tank S								1.025	
No. 5 Top wing tank P								1.025	
No. 5 Top wing tank S								1.025	
No. 6 Top wing tank P								1.025	
No. 6 Top wing tank S								1.025	
Upper cross tank								1.025	
Lower cross tank								1.025	
DB tank No. 2P	310	254.8	1.025	254.8	124.270	1.115	5.0	1.025	5.0
DB tank No. 2S	310	254.8	1.025	254.8	124.270	1.115	5.0	1.025	5.0
DB tank No. 3P								1.025	
DB tank No. 3S								1.025	
DB tank No. 4P								1.025	
DB tank No. 4S								1.025	
DB tank No. 5P								1.025	
DB tank No. 5S								1.025	
DB tank No. 6P	FULL	261.2	1.025	261.2	42.190	1.300	0.0	1.025	0.0
DB tank No. 6S	FULL	261.2	1.025	261.2	42.190	1.300	0.0	1.025	0.0
DB tank No. 6C								1.025	
DB tank No. 1P								1.025	
DB tank No. 1S								1.025	
DB tank No. 2C								1.025	
DB tank No. 3C								1.025	
DB tank No. 4C								1.025	
DB tank No. 5C	100	229.3	1.025	229.3	63.880	0.536	2270.0	1.025	2270.0
Aft peak tank (SW)	FULL	178.4	1.025	182.9	4.660	8.820	0.0	1.000	0.0

All the weights that are in the *Hold Cargo* sheet and the completed *Tank Sounding data sheet* may now be transferred onto the *loading sheet*. The vertical and longitudinal moments are then calculated and summed to allow calculation of the final *solid KG* and *LCG*.

Remember to include the allowance for water absorption of the timber deck cargo.

The completed loading sheet is as follows.

Example 2 **_LOADING SHEET_**

ITEMS OF DEADWEIGHT	WEIGHT t	VCG m	V.MOMENTS tm	LCG m	L.MOMENTS tm	FSM's tm
Deep wing tank No. 7P	147	5.710	839	28.220	4148	6
Deep wing tank No. 7S	155	6.920	1073	28.220	4374	74
Service tank P (Heavy oil)	13	10.795	140	26.300	342	1
DB tank No. 1P						
DB tank No. 1S						
DB tank No. 2C						
DB tank No. 3C						
DB tank No. 4C						
DB tank No. 5C	184	0.461	85	63.880	11754	2148
TOTAL HEAVY OIL	**499**		**2137**		**20618**	**2229**
DB tank No. 7P	25	0.236	6	23.290	582	85
DB tank No. 7S	25	0.236	6	23.290	582	85
Service tank P (Light oil)	19	10.692	203	29.100	553	41
TOTAL LIGHT OIL	**69**		**215**		**1717**	**211**
Tween deck tank aft P	58	11.880	689	6.440	374	120
Tween deck tank aft S	58	11.880	689	6.440	374	120
Stern tank						
DB tank No. 8	19	0.694	13	9.850	187	49
Aft peak tank (FW)						
TOTAL FRESH WATER	**135**		**1391**		**934**	**289**
Fore peak tank						
No. 1 Top wing tank P						
No. 1 Top wing tank S						
No. 2 Top wing tank P						
No.2 Top wing tank S						
No. 3+4 Top wing tank P						
No. 3+4 Top wing tank S						
No. 5 Top wing tank P						
No. 5 Top wing tank S						
No. 6 Top wing tank P						
No. 6 Top wing tank S						
Upper cross tank						
Lower cross tank						
DB tank No. 2P	255	1.115	284	124.270	31689	5
DB tank No. 2S	255	1.115	284	124.270	31689	5
DB tank No. 3P						
DB tank No. 3S						
DB tank No. 4P						
DB tank No. 4S						
DB tank No. 5P						
DB tank No. 5S						
DB tank No. 6P	261	1.300	339	42.190	11012	0
DB tank No. 6S	261	1.300	339	42.190	11012	0
DB tank No. 6C						
DB tank No. 1P						
DB tank No. 1S						
DB tank No. 2C						
DB tank No. 3C						
DB tank No. 4C						
DB tank No. 5C	229	0.536	123	63.880	14629	2270
Aft peak tank (SW)	183	8.820	1614	4.660	853	0
TOTAL BALLAST WATER	**1444**		**2984**		**100882**	**2280**
STORES AND CREW	**125**	**14.50**	**1813**	**45.000**	**5625**	
Hold No. 1	3000	8.220	24660	144.94	434820	
Hold No. 2	3269	7.650	25008	124.38	406598	
Hold No. 3	3204	7.650	24511	103.94	333024	
Hold No. 4	2994	7.650	22904	84.46	252873	
Hold No. 5	2898	7.650	22170	62.05	179821	
Hold No. 6	3401	7.740	26324	42.31	143896	
Cargo on deck	4020	16.660	66973	89.13	358303	
Water absorbtion	603	16.660	10046	89.13	53745	
TOTAL CARGO	**23389**		**222595**		**2163080**	0
TOTAL DEADWEIGHT	**25661**		**231135**		**2292857**	**TOTAL**
LIGHT SHIP	**6675**	**9.000**	**60075**	**70.500**	**470588**	**FSM's**
DISPLACEMENT	**32336**	**9.006**	**291210**	**85.460**	**2763445**	**5009**

From the loading sheet the results are:

(a) *Final Displacement **32336 tonnes***
(b) *Final solid **KG 9.006 m***
To calculate the fluid KG and GM

Entering the hydrostatic particulars with a displacement of 32458 tonnes gives a value for KM = 9.481 m

$$\text{Correction to GM for FSE (m)} = \frac{\text{Total FSM's (t-m)}}{\text{Displacement (t)}}$$

$$\text{Correction to GM for FSE (m)} = \frac{5009}{32336} = 0.155\ m$$

KM	9.481
KG SOLID	9.006
GM SOLID	0.475
FS CORR'N	0.155
GM FLUID	**0.320**

(c) To calculate the sailing draughts

Enter data with final displacement and obtain TMD, MCTC, LCB and LCF positions.

$$\text{Final TMD} = 10.10 + \left(0.1 \times \frac{196}{350}\right) = 10.156\ m$$

$$MCTC = 409 + \left(2 \times \frac{196}{350}\right) = 410\ t\text{-}m$$

$$LCB = 85.86 + \left(-0.04 \times \frac{196}{350}\right) = 85.84\ m\ foap$$

$$LCF = 82.41 + \left(-0.09 \times \frac{196}{350}\right) = 82.36\ m\ foap$$

Calculate the change of trim from even keel for the final condition.

Final LCG = 85.46 m.

$$COT_{FROM\ EVEN\ KEEL} = \frac{W \times (LCB \sim LCG)}{MCTC}$$

$$COT_{FROM\ EVEN\ KEEL} = \frac{32336 \times (85.84 - 85.46)}{410} = 29.97\ cms\ (30.0\ cms)$$

A simple sketch will indicate whether the COT is by the head or by the stern.

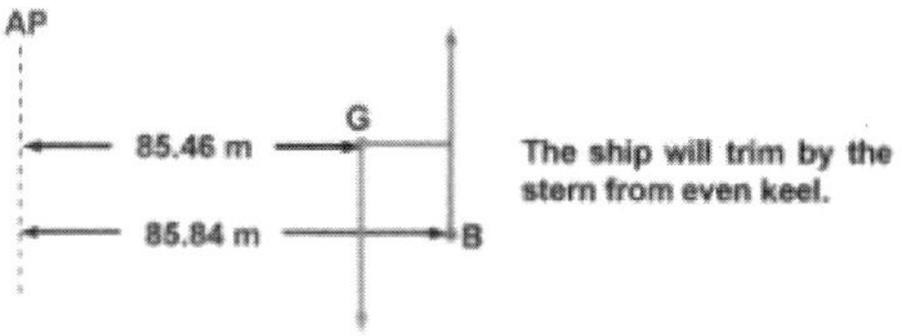

Fig.28.3

Apportion the change of trim from even keel to the forward and aft draughts, applying Ta and Tf to the final even keel draught (TMD).

$$Ta = COT \times \frac{a}{LBP} = 30.0 \times \frac{82.36}{167.87} = 14.7 cms = 0.147m$$

$$Tf = COT - Ta \quad Tf = 30.0 - 14.7 = 15.3\ cms = 0.153\ m$$

Apply Ta and Tf to the final TMD to obtain final draughts.

	Fwd	Aft
Final TMD	10.156	10.156
Trim (by stern)	0.153	0.147
Final draughts	**10.003**	**10.303**

Solution (PART II)

Using KN values calculate the values of GZ for the loaded condition (interpolation for KN values not shown)

KG SOLID	9.006
FS CORR'N	0.155
KG FLUID	**9.161**

Heel	**10**	**20**	**30**	**40**	**60**	**80**
KN	1.66	3.35	4.78	6.04	7.67	8.00
KG*Sin Heel	1.59	3.13	4.58	5.89	7.93	9.02
GZ	**0.07**	**0.22**	**0.20**	**0.15**	**-0.26**	**-1.02**

Plot the curve of statical stability.

Using Simpson's Rules calculate the areas under the curve.

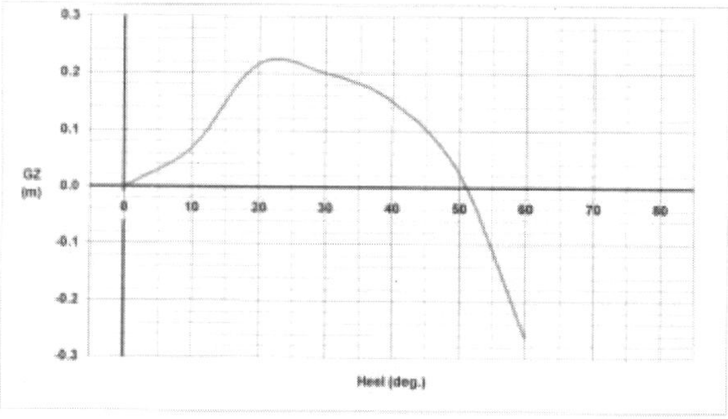

Fig. 28.4

Area 0° to 30°

Area $= \frac{3}{8} \times \frac{10}{57.3} \times 1.07$

Area = 0.070 m-r

Heel	GZ	SM	Area Fn.
0	0.00	1	0.00
10	0.07	3	0.21
20	0.22	3	0.66
30	0.20	1	0.20
		SUM	**1.07**

Area 0° to 40°

Area $= \frac{1}{3} \times \frac{10}{57.3} \times 1.67$

Area = 0.097 m-r

Area 30° to 40°

Heel	GZ	SM	Area Fn.
0	0.00	1	0.00
10	0.07	4	0.28
20	0.22	2	0.44
30	0.20	4	0.80
40	0.15	1	0.15
		SUM	**1.67**

Take the difference between the two areas calculated.
Area = 0.097 – 0.070 = ***0.027 m-r***

Consideration of the GZ curve and the calculated areas gives the following answer:

	IMO Criteria (Minimum)	**Actual**	**Complies**
GM	Not less than 0.15 m	**0.320**	**YES**
Area 0 to 30	Not less than 0.055 m-r	**0.070**	**YES**
Area 0 to 40 (X)	Not less than 0.09 m-r	**0.097**	**YES**
Area 30-40 (X)	Not less than 0.03 m-r	**0.027**	**NO**
Max GZ	At least 0.2 m	**0.22**	**YES**
Heel max GZ	At least 30 deg.	**23 deg.**	**NO**

The ship does not comply with all the criteria

Final true mean draught = 10.156 m *Summer Load Draught = 10.200 m*

Therefore the ship has adequate freeboard for the Summer Zone.

Had the ship been assigned timber freeboards the optional set of KN data that would have been available would have been derived using the volume of the timber on deck as additional reserve buoyancy and the ship would probably have complied with he Load Line criteria. In order to improve the situation an alternative ballast arrangement should be considered to remove some of the free surface moments of the slack tanks and lowering the ship's centre of gravity. Alternatively, because the ship is close to the maximum permitted displacement for the summer zone the amount of deck cargo might have to be reduced.

BIBLIOGRAPHY

IMO SOLAS CONSOLIDATED EDITION 2001 International Maritime Organization London, 2001

IMO LOAD LINES 'International Convention on Load Lines, 1996 and Protocol of 1988 CONSOLIDATED EDITION, 2002 International Maritime Organization London, 2002

IMO CODE ON INTACT STABILITY FOR ALL TYPES OF SHIPS COVERED BY IMO INSTRUMENTS 2002 Edition International Maritime Organization London, 2002

THE MARITIME AND COASTGUARD AGENCY Load line – Amendment 3 - Instructions for the Guidance of Surveyors 2001 Edition HMSO

IMO BC CODE Code of Safe Practice for Solid Bulk Cargoes 2001 Edition International Maritime Organization London, 2001

IMO International Code for the Safe Carriage of Grain in Bulk (International Grain Code) 2000 Edition International Maritime Organization London, 2001

D.G.M WATSON PRACTICAL SHIP DESIGN 1998 Edition ELSEVIER

THE ROYAL INSTITUTE OF NAVAL ARCHITECTS SIGNIFICANT SHIPS OF 1992 Warwick Printing Co. Ltd. London

THE ROYAL INSTITUTE OF NAVAL ARCHITECTS SIGNIFICANT SHIPS OF 1993 Warwick Printing Co. Ltd. London

PROF. DRACOS VASSALOS & PROF. APOSTOLOS PAPANIKOLAOU Stockholm Agreement – Past, Present & Future (Part I) February 2001 SU-SSRC/NTUA-SDL

IMO MSC/Circ.574 THE CALCULATION PROCEDURE TO ASSESS THE SURVIVANILITY CHARACTERISTICS OF EXISTING RO-RO PASSENGER SHIPS WHEN USING A SIMPLIFIED METHOF BASED UPON RESOLUTION A.265(VIII) International Maritime Organization London, 1991

STATUTORY INSTRUMENTS (HMSO)

1999 No. 336	Merchant Shipping (Carriage of Cargoes) Regulations
1998 No. 2241	Merchant Shipping (Load Line) Regulations
2000 No. 1335	Merchant Shipping (Load Line) (Amendment) Regulations
1988 No. 1275	Merchant Shipping (Weighing of Goods Vehicles and Other Cargo) Regulations
1989 No. 270	Merchant Shipping (Weighing of Goods Vehicles and Other Cargo) (Amendment) Regulations
1995 No. 1210	Merchant Shipping (Survey and Certification) Regulations
1996 No. 2418	Merchant Shipping (Survey and Certification) (Amendment) Regulations
1997 No. 647	Merchant Shipping (Ro-Ro Passenger Ship Survivability) Regulations
1997 No. 1509	Merchant Shipping (Cargo Ship Construction) Regulations
1998 No. 2514	Merchant Shipping (Passenger Ship Construction: Ships of Classes I, II and II(A)) Regulations
1998 No. 2515	Merchant Shipping (Passenger Ship Construction: Ships of Classes III to VI(A)) Regulations

1999 No.643	Merchant Shipping (Cargo Ship Construction) (Amendment) Regulations
1999 No. 1644	Merchant Shipping (Additional Safety Measures for Bulk Carriers) Regulations
2000 No. 1334	Merchant Shipping (Survey and Certification) (Amendment) Regulations
2001 No. 152	Merchant Shipping (Mandatory Surveys for Ro-Ro Ferry and High Speed Passenger Craft) Regulations

MGN's & MSN's (Maritime and Coastguard Agency)

MGN 60(M)	Code of Safe Practice for Solid Bulk Cargoes (BC Code): 1996 Amendment. Carriage of Coal Cargoes
MGN 107 (M)	Merchant Shipping (Carriage of Cargoes) Regulations 1999
MGN 108 (M)	Hull stress monitoring systems
MGN 144(M)	The Merchant Shipping (Additional Safety Measures for Bulk Carriers) Regulations 1999 (SI 1999/1644)
MGN 210(M)	Advice on the Dangers of Flooding of Forward Compartments
MGN 245(M)	Inspection of Shell Loading Doors on Ro-Ro Ferries
M1084	M.S. (Cargo Ship Construction and Survey) Regulations 1981
M1231	Safe cargo-handling operations in offshore supply vessels
M1393	Weighing of goods vehicles and other cargo for Class II and Class II(A) Ro/Ro passenger ship operations
M1445	Roll-on/roll-off (Ro-Ro) ships: stowage and securing of vehicles - Code of Practice
M1458	Offshore support vessels
M1613	The Merchant Shipping (Survey and Certification) Regulations 1995 – arbitration procedure
MSN 1671 (M)	Merchant Shipping (Cargo Ship Construction) Regulations 1997: Schedules
MSN 1671 (M)	Amendment No. 1
MSN 1671 (M)	Amendment No. 2
MSN 1673 (M)	Agreement concerning specific stability requirements for Ro-Ro passenger ships undertaking regular scheduled international voyages between or to or from designated ports in North West Europe and the Baltic Sea
MSN 1698 (M)	Merchant Shipping (Passenger Ship Construction: Ships of Classes I to II(A)) Regulations 1998
MSN 1699(M)	Merchant Shipping (Passenger Ship Construction: Ships of Classes III to VI(A)) Regulations 1998
MSN 1715(M)	Subdivision and damage stability of cargo ships of 80 m in length and over
MSN 1715(M)	Amendment No. 1
MSN 1752(M)	The Merchant Shipping (Load Line) Regulations 1998, as amended by the Merchant Shipping (Load Line) (Amendment) Regulations 2000

INDEX